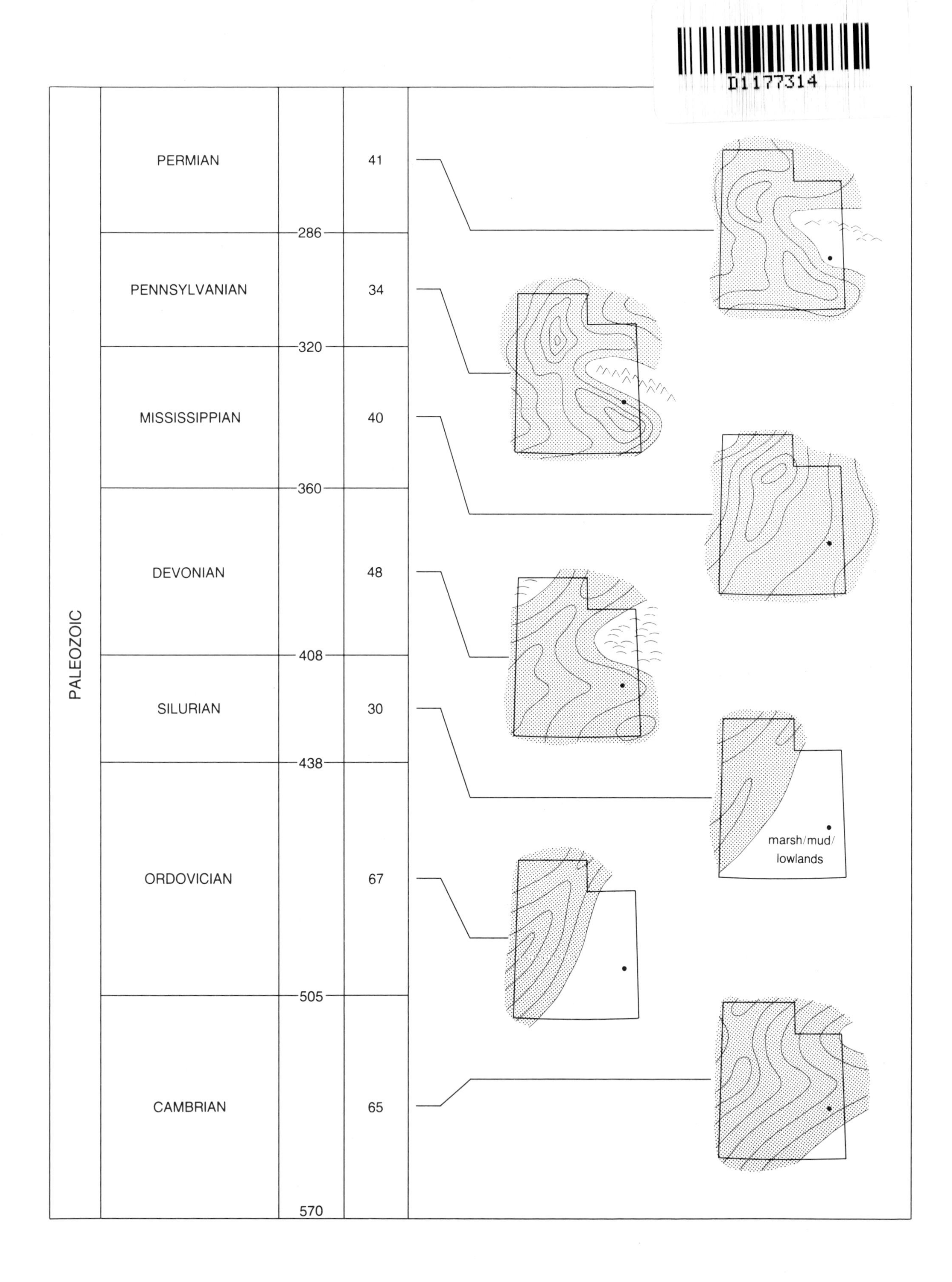
PALEOZOIC
PERMIAN
41
286
PENNSYLVANIAN
34
320
MISSISSIPPIAN
40
360
DEVONIAN
48
408
SILURIAN
30
438
ORDOVICIAN
67
505
CAMBRIAN
65
570
marsh/mud/
lowlands

Rod Millar's cover photograph shows the Gooseneck of the Colorado River from the viewpoint at Utah's Dead Horse Point State Park; the image is 360° and virtually free of optical distortion. For years Rod Millar has utilized various methodologies and technical innovations to capture the essence of Utah scenery; the special 360° continuous-image camera comes close to fulfilling his quest.

William Lee Stokes provided invaluable information to Mr. Millar on the unique attributes of the Colorado Plateau to further a proposal which identified sixty-seven separate areas. It is hoped that these areas, which combine to illustrate a geologic theme, will be designated a Thematic World Heritage Site by the United Nations. That proposal is presently being reviewed by the U.S. Department of the Interior.

Type design by
Keith Montague of
Bailey-Montague Associates

Cover design by
Leigh MacManus

Geology of Utah

WILLIAM LEE STOKES

DEDICATION

To my sister *Marion*
whose gifts helped make
this book a reality.

Geology of Utah

WILLIAM LEE STOKES

PUBLISHED BY

UTAH MUSEUM
OF
NATURAL HISTORY

UTAH GEOLOGICAL
AND
MINERAL SURVEY

Salt Lake City, Utah

Library of Congress Catalog Card Number 81-51918
ISBN - 0-940378-05-1

Printed in the United States of America

First printing - 1987
Second printing - 1988

OCCASIONAL PAPER NUMBER 6
of the
Utah Museum of Natural History

INTRODUCTION

Over the last fifty years, William Lee Stokes has been a steady contributor to the mapping and interpretation of Utah geology. This book is a late dividend of a long professional career that has been almost exclusively invested in Utah and its neighboring states. Born in 1915 in the coal mining town of Hiawatha, Utah and raised in dinosaur country, Emery County, young Stokes had a natural affinity for the rocks, fossils, and landscape of his immediate environs. At college and graduate school, he built on his youthful interests to produce a master's thesis and doctor's dissertation on the stratigraphy, dinosaurs, and uranium resources of the Morrison Formation and the history of the Colorado Plateau. When he settled into teaching at the University of Utah, his professional interests expanded to include the geologic history and processes of essentially all of Utah. He admits to having traversed most of Utah's canyons and mountains and it is obvious that he remembers it all with the familiarity that many people reserve for their friends. Dr. Stokes' intimacy with rocks is literally familial - eight fossil species have been named for him, including, of course, a dinosaur, Stokesosaurus. And he has named thirteen formations in or partly within the state.

For twenty-three years Dr. Stokes taught an extraordinarily popular course, Geology and Scenery of Utah, at the University of Utah. This book is an important by-product of those approximately 1000 classroom sessions, and its content reflects the intent of those presentations to share a respect of Utah's geology and to indicate the physical relationship of the rock units to each other, to their environments of formation, and to the creatures that are fossilized within them. No less important is the relationship of the present scenery to the geologic past. It is hoped that readers, without too much effort, will better understand their own relationship to the land on which they live.

Utahns have a unique opportunity to appreciate their geologic heritage. An unusually large segment of earth's history is recorded in over 250 formations that crop out in different areas of the state and virtually every geologic influence that shaped the earth — lakes, glaciers, wind, igneous action, tectonic forces, and erosion have left unmistakable impressions. Utah's economy is more closely linked to geology than most other states. In the past, the state relied upon the mining and energy industries and now tourism, based mainly on geologic attractions, is a major source of income. National and state parks related to geology and rocks have been set aside in many areas of the state. Also, the design and construction of nearly every major structure in Utah should consider geology because few other states have Utah's vulnerability to the geologic hazards associated with earthquakes, landslides, rockfalls, unstable soil conditions, high ground water, floods, liquefaction, and shifting lakes.

So this book is chiefly about understanding and appreciating Utah's geology. Dr. Stokes has devoted his career to these objectives. In addition to his professional work as a geologist, his teaching career, and prolific writings, Dr. Stokes contributed to both the organizations that are now publishing this work. He founded and directed the precursor to the Museum of Natural History (the Earth Science Museum) and developed the Cleveland-Lloyd Quarry, an abundant source for exhibits throughout the world. He has consistently supported the Utah Geological and Mineral Survey, contributing his time and knowledge to many guidebooks and technical publications. Therefore, it was with pleasure and a sense of gratitude that the Utah Museum of Natural History and the Utah Geological and Mineral Survey undertook the publication of this work. It represents work sponsored by neither of these organizations. It is published essentially as prepared by Dr. Stokes and has not been edited to conform with current editorial policies of the Utah Geological and Mineral Survey. It is directed to the intelligent and curious reader, professional as well as novice. For this reason, it deliberately risks annoying not only those who know too much by explaining the elementary but also those who know too little by elaborating on technical details. We hope that readers will simply skip sections of little interest to them. This book also reflects the belief that geology is to be seen, not merely imagined. The profuse illustrations and photos are as important as the text in clarifying the relationship of geology to scenery and human activity.

It is hoped that this book, which presents Dr. Stokes' understanding and knowledge of Utah's geology and his experience in relating his subject to university students, will benefit readers, encourage public respect, and increase the appreciation of Utah's geologic heritage.

Genevieve Atwood, UGMS
Don Hague, Utah Museum of Natural History

AUTHOR'S PREFACE

Utah, the Beehive State, might also be called the Bedrock State. Probably no area of similar size in the nation displays more of the raw, unobscured rock formations than does Utah. The scarcity of soil must be counted as unfavorable to agriculture and grazing but the exposed bedrock that appears abundantly over such vast areas creates unusual opportunities for the geologist and prospector. Not only do the formations appear with unobscured clarity, they occur also in great variety. Over 500 formations have already been recognized within the boundaries of the State. Included are igneous, metamorphic, and sedimentary units of all types.

The range in age is from ancient Precambrian, over two billion years old, to the sand dunes that are creeping today across the desert landscape. Every system of the well-known geologic column is represented, some almost completely. Furthermore, each system contains diagnostic fossils and distinctive rock types. Few other states can make this claim.

The structure likewise ranges from simple to complex. The Colorado Plateaus display the world's best "layer-cake" geology with the formations mostly in their original level attitudes. On the other hand, the Great Basin is known for complex faulting and folding that challenges the skill of the geologist to unravel. Several great episodes of volcanic action have created both surface and subsurface igneous bodies of diverse form and composition. Finally, the last finishing touches on the landscape came with the glaciers and extensive lakes of the ice-age.

Utah is rightfully called a geologist's paradise, but there is much more to it than a source of illustration for textbooks or a place to conduct summer training camps for geology students Two important benefits that have resulted from the long series of past events should be stressed whenever geology is considered. These are mineral resources and scenery.

Utah has yielded about 500 mineral species; of these about 55 are native, having been discovered here for the first time. The important ore minerals are concentrated in ore bodies which in turn make up the deposits of world famous camps such as Bingham, Tintic, and Park City. The metals are associated chiefly with igneous activity. By contrast are the valuable nonmetalic deposits such as coal, oil shale, and salt produced by sedimentary processes. Utah is regarded as an indispensable storehouse of fossil fuels and again there are types and varieties that are rare elsewhere. Utah is said to be the only state that produces the three primary mineral fertilizers nitrogen, phosphate, and potash.

It may be that the other natural resource, geologic scenery, will in the end be more valuable than the mines and quarries. Scenic areas are everywhere. Five great National Parks, two extensive National Recreation Areas, six of the seven National Monuments, and about 18 of the 34 State Parks have been established because of geologic features. A seemingly endless stream of tourists visit Utah chiefly to look at the geologic scenery. As of 1986, mining (including the extraction of all mineral products) ranks 10th as a producer of wealth in Utah and tourism ranks 5th. The many essential and aesthetic values that spring from the unique geology of Utah are not fully appreciated or understood by the average citizen. In the past, in far too many instances, it has been outsiders who have pointed out and developed the scenic spots or have opened the mines to profitable exploitation.

For over twenty years, I have taught a college level course on the Geology of Utah. The challenge to disseminate the basic essentials of the subject has grown with the years. At the same time, there has been the frustrated urge to write a textbook. As long as I taught the class, my students compiled their own texts, good or bad, in the form of journals. It is my hope that this book might find a place in the curriculum of Utah colleges and universities to provide a uniform understanding of the landscape that surrounds us.

For what more should a writer hope than that his work will answer some questions, or provide new insights, or add to the enjoyment of others who are interested in his subject. The rocks and scenery of Utah are my subject. They were a long time in the making and will endure a long time to come. To share the fascination of learning about them and understanding them to some degree is the purpose of this book.

William Lee Stokes

ACKNOWLEDGMENTS

Literally hundreds of investigators have contributed to my understanding of the geology of Utah. Obviously I cannot acknowledge all of these individually but I have tried in the bibliography to properly credit my major sources. A second substantial group which I greatly appreciate consists of my many students who kept alive an incentive to teach and explain. I hope to have sensed what it is the average citizen wants to know and can understand about the earth he or she lives on. And special thanks to those who have encouraged me time and time again, over the past ten years, to finish my book.

As to the book itself, I must acknowledge the efforts of an unusually lengthy succession of editors: Genevieve Atwood, James R. Stringfellow, Gloria J. Kerns, Carolyn M. Olsen, Martha R. Smith, David E. Scardena, and Klaus D. Gurgel. Genevieve Atwood read the manuscript with great thoroughness and in many ways improved the organization and clarity; Carolyn M. Olsen worked page by page and illustration by illustration to unify the entire book, Hellmut H. Doelling reviewed the first paste-up.

For ten years a succession of typists and compositors worked on the manuscript. Initially, the clerical staff of the Department of Geology and Geophysics transcribed the hand-written manuscript and compiled the bibliography and the lists of formations.

Gloria J. Kerns compiled the glossary; final photo-ready graphics and paste-up were done by Leigh MacManus; half-tones by Kent D. Brown.

From the first, my plans included liberal use of illustrations. Geology, possibly more than any other science, depends on accurate diagrams, maps, and sections, as well as well-captioned photographs. I have gathered illustrations from many sources, mostly from colleagues, state and federal agencies, and files of professional and amateur photographers. Those whom I have paid for special photographs or illustrations include Arthur C. King, James Howell III, Ward Roylance, and Philip L. Howland. Colleagues who went to special pains to supply photographs include John A. Burger, Robert Q. Oaks, Harold J. Bissell, Clyde T. Hardy, Donald Preston, Hellmut H. Doelling, M. Dane Picard, and Glen Ungerman.

For the several line drawings, I am indebted to several gifted artists. John K. Balsley sketched the twelve plates of selected Utah Guide fossils, Jeffrey B. Hulen put the paleogeography of the time-scale intervals in graphic form, and Tricia Bizuk compiled the outcrop maps and location maps of the physiographic sections. UGMS draftspersons Brent R. Jones, Sandra R. Stewart, and Donald E. Powers converted my rough stratigraphic data into the graphic columns. It is impossible to overestimate the value of these illustrations and I am truly appreciative.

This book has been expensive and time consuming to all concerned. In 1975, the University of Utah awarded me a D.P. Gardner Research Fellowship which released me from teaching duties so I could commence work on the manuscript. Of course, I didn't start from scratch. I had been teaching a course in Utah geology for over 20 years and had accumulated many first-hand observations; stacks of papers, notes, and clippings; and many photographs and slides. For financial help in purchasing other illustrations and employing artists, I am indebted to a generous grant from the University of Utah Mineral Lease Fund of the School of Mines and Mineral Industries. Incidentally, these funds came, not unfittingly, from money alloted to the educational system from the leasing of public lands.

My sister Marion E. Jensen provided a substantial grant through the University of Utah Development Fund which was the real "seed money" that ensured the eventual production of the book. Paul Q. Callister also gave me a helpful cash contribution. Needless to say, the greatest expense, that of printing and manufacturing the book, has been borne by the Utah Geological and Mineral Survey with taxpayers' money. Representing as it does a contribution intended for the general public, I hope that Utah citizens will find the book a worthwhile investment.

TABLE OF CONTENTS

1 THE GEOLOGY OF UTAH

Figure 1-1. View across Canyonlands National Park looking southwest from Dead Horse Point. Colorado River below with successive Permian, Triassic, and Jurassic formations rising toward skyline. Layered sedimentary rocks such as these constitute the surface of most of Utah. Photo: Utah Tourist and Publicity Council.

Geology is the study of the Earth, and rocks are its basic documents. Few areas of equal size are more rocky than Utah; solid stone is underfoot or buried beneath only a shallow cover of soil or sand over at least two-thirds of the surface. The rock record is notable for its variety, comprehensiveness, and simplicity. The three great classes of rocks—sedimentary, metamorphic, and igneous—are represented by numerous varieties and associations. Unusually rich and diverse mineral deposits are scattered across the state.

Every fossil-bearing geologic period is preserved in the sedimentary sections. The diversity of colorful, non-marine rocks is notable. Geologic structures abound and are exposed with textbook clarity in imposing mountains and deep canyons.

It is for its surface expression that the geology of Utah is best known. Professional geologists dignify their studies as geomorphology or physiography. Hikers, tourists, river runners, and wilderness lovers enjoy the same scenery for other, no less important, reasons.

Generations of geologists have studied, trained, and worked in Utah. Their maps and reports number in the thousands. Although much remains to be done, the broad outlines of the geologic history of Utah can now be summarized.

GEOMORPHOLOGY

Large segments of four major physiographic provinces, the Colorado Plateau, Middle Rocky Mountains, Basin and Range, and Colorado Plateau/Basin-Range Transition make up the State of Utah. The Colorado Plateau is a sparsely vegetated landscape of plateaus, mesas, deep canyons, sloping pediments, imposing linear cliffs, and barren badlands that closely reflect the attitudes and differential erosion of a sedimentary section that is predominently continental sandstone and shale (fig. 1-1). A few intrusive mountains of Middle Tertiary age dot the rugged landscape. Choice sections of this colorful province have been set aside in 16 National Parks (fig. 1-2), National Monuments, Recreation Areas, and State Parks.

Figure 1-2. Air view of Zion National Park looking south. West Temple on right skyline. The massive light-colored Navajo Sandstone is well exposed. Photo: Allen Hagood, National Park Service.

The Middle Rocky Mountains Province is represented by the very dissimilar Uinta Mountains and Wasatch Range. The Uinta Mountains (fig. 1-3) trend east-west, reach a maximum elevation at Kings Peak (13,528 feet), are superficially anticlinal in structure, and are practically devoid of igneous rocks. The Wasatch Range (fig. 1-4) trends north-south, reaches a maximum elevation at Mt. Nebo (11,877 feet), is essentially a tilted fault block, and is an unusual assemblage of sedimentary, igneous, and metamorphic rocks. It has been uplifted along the Wasatch Fault so that cross sections of a number of west-trending structures, including the projection of the Uinta Mountains axis, are exposed. The two ranges intersect near Park City, Summit County, and the geology of this "crossroads" is extremely complex.

The Basin and Range Province consists of approximately 35 north-south-trending "ranges" and an equal number of alluvial valleys. The basic structure is that of alternating horsts and grabens. In the present state of geomorphic evolution, about equal areas of bedrock and alluvium make up the surface.

The Basin and Range/Colorado Plateau Transition Province is a broad belt in which geologic features gradational between typical plateau and basin and range features merge and overlap. Dominantly north-south structural alignments, parallel to those of the Great Basin, are evident in the High Plateaus and typical Colorado Plateau stratigraphic units extend well into the Basin and Range. The eight High Plateaus, ranging between 8,000 and 11,000 feet in elevation, are the most distinctive features of the Transition Province. Drainage is almost entirely into the Great Basin.

STRUCTURE AND TECTONICS

The Wasatch Line, named after the Wasatch Range, crosses Utah from southwest to northeast in a great curving arc. Contrasts across it are so marked that it is said to be one of the most profound geologic discontinuities of North America. It originated in late Precambrian time as a rift defining the western margin of North America. The rift widened to become the Paleozoic Cordilleran geosyncline and later, under compressive forces in the Mesozoic and early Cenozoic Eras, the eastern wall acted as a buttress against which eastward-moving slices of sedimentary rock were buckled and overthrust. Since the middle Cenozoic, the Wasatch Line has marked the eastern margin of the collapsed Basin and Range Province.

The smooth curve of the Wasatch Line is interrupted in north-central Utah by the east-trending Uinta axis. The Uinta Mountains, superficially a simple anticlinal structure, are composed of sediments that filled the Uinta trench or aulacogen 2 to 1 billion years ago. The 20,000-foot-thick sedimentary prism was undisturbed until it was extruded and underthrust by compressive forces associated with the Laramide Orogeny. Geologic effects as old as Ordovician, (see geologic time chart, back cover), along a westward projection of the Uinta axis, have not been satisfactorily explained.

Associated features are the so-called Hingeline south of the Wasatch Range, and the Thrust Belt north of Salt Lake City. Both are marked by great thrust sheets that have moved eastward from the Basin and Range onto the shelf areas of the Colorado Plateau and southwestern Wyoming. The source areas are now topographically lower than the thrust sheets, indicating great changes in relative elevation.

Several of the longest normal faults in North America have been mapped along the Wasatch Line. From north to south, they are the 225-mile-long Wasatch Fault; an offset continuation, the equally long Sevier Fault that begins near the center of the state and terminates near the southern border; and the Hurricane Fault, beginning near Richfield, Sevier County, and leaving the state southeast of St. George, Washington County. The surface expressions are

Figure 1-3. Glaciated crest of the western Uinta Range. The barren rounded remnants, mostly above timberline, are composed of Precambrian quartzite formations. Photo: U.S. Bureau of Reclamation.

Figure 1-4. Southern Wasatch Range looking east across Utah Lake. Snow capped Loafer Mountain, right, and Spanish Fork Peak, center, are composed of the thick Pennsylvanian-Permian Oquirrh Formation. Truncation of foothill spurs by the Wasatch Fault is a well-marked feature of this section. Photo: U.S. Bureau of Reclamation.

Figure 1-5. West face of Wellsville Mountain, northern Wasatch Range. Representatives of marine formations of late Precambrian, Cambrian, Ordovician, Silurian, Devonian, Mississippian, and Pennsylvanian are seen in this mountain. Photo: Hellmut H. Doelling.

impressive west-facing scarps such as the Wasatch Front and Hurricane Cliffs. Studies of stratigraphic facies, disrupted lava flows and geophysical reactions across the fault zones show complex histories including reversals of movement along the same planes.

Ordinary normal faults abound; one study charted more than 3,000 mappable faults in Utah's Great Basin. Most of the western ranges are bounded by normal faults with large displacements; numerous lesser faults cut the interiors of the mountain blocks. There are also many mappable lineaments. Because of clean exposures, those of the Colorado Plateau have received particular attention. One of the most important and least understood is the Colorado River Lineament (also called the Colorado Lineament). It extends into northern Arizona and has effects along the transcontinental arch as far as Lake Superior, Michigan. Evidences of recurrent movements beginning perhaps 200 to 150 billion years ago are apparent.

Every fossil-bearing period of the standard time scale is represented in Utah by significant thicknesses of sedimentary rock. Long intervals of Precambrian time are also represented by distinctive aggregations of sediments and metasediments. Maximum estimated thicknesses of the individual Phanerozoic (fossil-bearing) systems are: Cambrian, 10,000 feet; Ordovician, 4,700 feet; Silurian, 1,600 feet; Devonian, 5,500 feet; Mississippian, 5,500 feet; Pennsylvanian, 17,000 feet; Permian, 9,000 feet; Triassic, 4,500 feet; Jurassic, 10,000 feet; Cretaceous, 19,000 feet; Paleocene, 4,000 feet; Eocene, 8,000 feet; Oligocene and Miocene (chiefly igneous), 8,000 feet; Pliocene, 3,000 feet; and Pleistocene, 2,500 feet. The cumulative thickness of all sedimentary rocks, with no time intervals duplicated, approaches a minimum of 150,000 feet.

In more formalized terms the sedimentary section has been divided into about 578 named formations and members. Those in current good standing are distributed as follows: 29 Precambrian, 71 Cambrian, 16 Ordovician, seven Silurian, 23 Devonian, 32 Mississippian, 27 Pennsylvanian, 41 Permian, 44 Triassic, 44 Jurassic, 74 Cretaceous, 60 (approximately) Early Tertiary (Paleocene and Eocene), 72 (approximately) Middle Tertiary (Oligocene and Miocene), and 38 (approximately) Pliocene and Pleistocene units. Some of these are shown in the west face of Wellsville Mountain (fig. 1-5). Not all possible subdivisions have been named and many new formation and member descriptions remain to be added to the existing list.

Another indication of the unusually complete stratigraphic record is the fact that many conventional boundaries between the systems of the classical time scale lie in sections of continuous sedimentation; thus, in the most complete sections, there are no discernable lacunas between Cambrian/Ordovician, Devonian/Mississippian, Mississippian/-Pennsylvanian, Pennsylvanian/Permian, Triassic/Jurassic and Cretaceous/Tertiary rocks. Since Cambrian/Ordovician and Pennsylvanian/Permian boundaries lie in marine sections with abundant index fossils such as trilobites and fusulinids, they are candidates for stratatype designations. The Triassic/Jurassic boundary, in contrast, lies in continental beds virtually devoid of datable fossils. According to the criteria currently being used, the boundary has been placed at various levels in the interval from the top of the Chinle Shale to the top of the Navajo Sandstone. The discovery of Late Cretaceous dinosaurs and Paleocene mammals in what appears to be continuously deposited North Horn Formation has received worldwide attention. This was a key case in discrediting the validity of diastrophism as the basis for dividing the geologic column.

Known Precambrian igneous rocks include one probable batholith, the Vernal Mesa Quartz Monzonite, dated at 1.48 billion years, located on the northwestern flanks of the Uncompahgre Plateau, Grand County. Several intrusive bodies of adamellite in the Raft River Mountains are the oldest, well-dated rocks in the state (2.5 billion years). Basalt flows in the late Precambrian Browns Hole Formation furnish very important key dates. A half-dozen mafic dikes, dated as Cambrian/Ordovician, cut Precambrian strata in the Uinta Mountains. Mesozoic igneous rocks include one known Triassic basalt flow and a number of Late Jurassic granitic intrusions in western Utah. Volcanic derivatives, now chiefly bentonites, are prominent in Triassic (Chinle Shale), Jurassic (Morrison Formation), and Cretaceous (Mancos Shale) units. Tuff beds in the Eocene Green River Formation indicate active volcanism in nearby centers.

Most of the igneous rocks were produced during a brief period in the Oligocene/Miocene. Intrusive bodies are mostly small quartz monzonite stocks. Flows of andesite, rhyolite, latite, and dacite comprise a number of volcanic centers, the most important being in the Tushar (fig. 1-6), Tintic, and Thomas Mountains. Tuffs, breccias, and agglomerates accompany the flows. Great accumulations of welded tuff or ignimbrite formed by eruption of incandescent clouds of pulverized rock, constitute a special province.

Figure 1-6. Central Tushar Mountains; Mt. Baldy, left, elevation 12,082 feet and Mt. Belnap, elevation 12,134 feet. The range consists mainly of complex volcanic formations. Photo: Eugene E. Callaghan.

Mid-Tertiary igneous rocks, regardless of their modes of occurrence, are classified as calc-alkalic or intermediate implying a higher than average content of silica. Such rocks are associated with continental margins where crustal material is melted at intermediate depths.

The most recent volcanic phase, producing mostly basalt and rhyolite (a bimodal association), began about 6 million years ago and continued almost to the present. Shallower levels of the crust were tapped to produce these rocks. Surface expressions are mainly fresh-looking, dark-colored cones and flows in the southwestern quarter of the state.

PALEONTOLOGY

Utah has yielded fossils from every Phanerozoic period and a few from the Precambrian. Plants, invertebrates and vertebrates are well represented. A systematic survey gives the highlights: **Cambrian**: Trilobites, brachiopods and sponges common; worms, phyllocarids, carpoids, and medusoids important; early conodonts and chordates are very significant. The Middle Cambrian Wheeler Shale has yielded thousands of well preserved trilobites (fig. 1-7). **Ordovician**: Trilobites, graptolites, and brachiopods common; gastropods, cephalopods, pelecypods, bryozoans, and conodonts important as early representatives of their kind; bony fragments locally; the Lower and Middle Ordovician has been suggested as a world stratatype. **Silurian**: Important fossils mostly dolomitized brachiopods and corals. **Devonian**: Early, Middle, and Late epochs are represented: brachiopods common; corals, conodonts, and cephalopods important; significant fish faunas in the Water Canyon Formation. **Mississippian**: Brachiopods (spirifers and productids) and corals are abundant; bryozoans, trilobites, cephalopods, gastropods, pelecypods, echinoderms (crinoids), conodonts, and endothyroids locally abundant and easily correlated with worldwide zones. **Pennsylvanian**: Fusulinids dominate and give almost complete phylogenetic lines; brachiopods common; molluscs, bryozoans, and echinoderms locally abundant; a few trilobites; there is an important floral assemblage in the Manning Canyon Shale. **Permian**: Fusulinids continue in early deposits; molluscs, bryozoans, brachiopods, echinoderms, corals, and molluscs common; sponges locally very abundant; the phosphatic fauna is important and includes a variety of sharks; many vertebrate footprints and a few bones in the non-marine facies.

Triassic: Cephalopods of worldwide affinities abundant in early stages with associated brachiopods and molluscs; last known conodonts; later stages contain important gym-

Figure 1-7. Specimens of the so-called "blind trilobite," *Peronopsis interstrictus*, from the famous Middle Cambrian collecting grounds, House Range, Millard County. Length of individual specimens about 1/2 inch.

nosperm floras, fossil forests, and rare vertebrates, including fish and early dinosaurs. **Jurassic**: Extensive molluscan assemblage in the early stages followed by a unique desert biota and culminating in the Morrison Formation by one of the most complete known terrestrial assemblages. Dinosaurs are outstanding; Dinosaur National Monument and Cleveland-Lloyd Quarry are important public viewing sites (fig. 1-8). **Cretaceous**: In the Late Cretaceous marine facies, molluscs, especially cephalopods, are abundant; coal-forest floras are extensive, and the latest non-marine beds yield some of the last dinosaurs.

Early Cenozoic (Paleocene and Eocene): Lake and river-side animals abundant; mammalian faunas of Utah are the basis for defining the Dragonian, Uintian, and Duchesnian Provincial Ages; fossils of the Green River lake beds are unique and diversified. **Middle Cenozoic (Oligocene and Miocene)**: Sparse fossil record, volcanism and erosion prevail. **Late Cenozoic (Pliocene and Pleistocene)**: Climates were generally arid but the brief late Pleistocene humid phase (Bonneville) was accompanied by a characteristic fauna of large mammals.

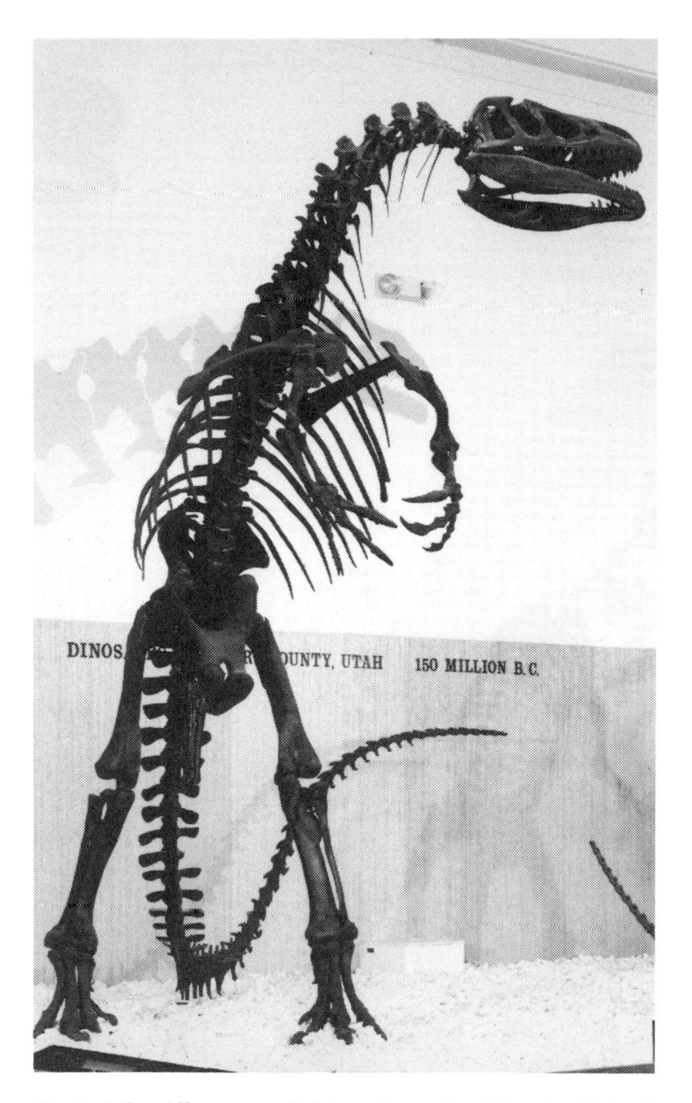

Figure 1-8. *Allosaurus* skeleton from the Cleveland-Lloyd quarry, Emery County, mounted in the Utah Museum of Natural History. Length of specimen, 33 feet. Photo: Glen Ungerman.

MINERALOGY

According to a recent compilation, 572 mineral species have been reported from Utah. This does not include a variety of hydrocarbons and non-combustible gases. The usual rock-forming minerals are abundant and the ore-forming ones are irregularly distributed to consitute the basis for 136 organized mining districts. Utah minerals have been collected and studied for many reasons. Those which contribute to valuable ore deposits are studied for purely economic reasons, both as individual species and as assemblages. Many minerals, perhaps the majority, are not commercially important and are chiefly significant as indicators of special chemical or physical environments of formation. Not everyone interested in minerals is motivated by purely scientific or economic reasons. Several rock and mineral societies, composed of serious amateurs, have been organized and rock collecting ranks (fig. 1-9) as one of the significant reasons tourists visit the state.

Utah minerals may be listed in various ways. According to chemical composition there are four antimonates-antimonites, 30 arsenates-arsenites, 47 carbonates, 26 halides, 319 hydroxyl-hydrous, one manganate, four molybdates, 11 native elements, one nitrate, one oxalate, 60 oxides, 49 phosphates, four selenates-selenites, 157 silicates, 81 sulfates, 45 sulfides, 20 sulfasalts, six tellurides, seven tungstates, 40 uraninates, and 27 vanadates.

About two dozen minerals were originally named from Utah localities and about 10 are found nowhere else. Rare, unusual, and unique minerals are associated with certain uncommon environments; thus, the uranium-vanadium ores of the Colorado Plateau were formed in a low-temperature sedimentary environment and contain a great

Figure 1-9. Colorful geodes from world famous collection grounds near the Dugway Mountains, west-central Utah. Sliced open geodes such as these reveal a variety of bands and crystals. Photo: Jim Howell.

number of unusual minerals including bequerelite, coffenite, uranite, bayleyite, rutherfordite, navajoite, and many others.

A second source of unusual minerals is the lacustrine sediments of the Eocene Green River Formation. Although they may not be minerals in the technical sense, the rare hydrocarbons, gilsonite, elaterite and wurtzulite, are noteworthy. For reasons that are not entirely clear, environments in the lake-bottom sediments gave rise to other unusual minerals such as abelsonite (nickel porphyrin), carbonate apatite, acmite (sodium iron silicate), neighborite (sodium magnesium floride), northrupite, reedmergnerite, garrelsite and shotlite. Much more famous and characteristic is a group of minerals characterized broadly as hydrous aluminum phosphates. Included are variscite and metavariscite, much prized as semiprecious gemstones. Incidently, the state gem of Utah is topaz (fig. 1-10); collecting grounds on Topaz Mountain are a veritable Mecca for collectors.

Figure 1-10. Crystals of topaz, the official Utah gemstone. This group is attached to the matrix of rhyolitic lava in which it was collected in the Thomas Range, Juab County. Length of largest crystal about 1 inch. Photo: Glen Ungerman.

ECONOMIC GEOLOGY AND ORE DEPOSITS

The earliest mining in Utah was by prehistoric native tribes seeking obsidian. The transient Spanish explorers found little of value and it was not until the coming of the Anglo-Saxons in 1848 that mining became important. The Mormons, under Brigham Young, were discouraged from searching for gold but they did exploit more utilitarian materials such as salt, coal, sulfur, iron, and lead. In 1863 gold was discovered in Bingham Canyon and a subsequent wave of prospecting uncovered most of the state's other metal-producing districts.

Three great districts, Bingham, Park City and Tintic, are especially notable. Bingham, centered at the great open-pit copper mine (fig. 1-11), is said to encompass the richest single ore deposit on Earth; Park City, and Tintic, once major producers, may have passed their prime. Other districts like Mercur and Gold Hill may see a resurgence through fine-gold technology but Ophir and San Francisco are definitely ghost towns.

As production of gold, silver, lead, and zinc declined there was increased interest in copper, coal, iron, uranium, and the hydrocarbons. Copper was a minor item until open-pit mining began early in the century; it has remained the state's most important mineral product until the early 1980s. Iron continued to be a major commodity until the 1970s. Industrial materials such as limestone, dolomite, clay, and gravel are abundant and rank in value with metals and hydrocarbons.

Uranium, a major product for many years, is mined mainly from fluvial Triassic and Jurassic sandstones in the Colorado Plateau. Ore deposition was governed by groundwater circulation through ancient buried stream channels and the presence of fossil organic material.

Bituminous coal is a major mineral resource. It is found almost exclusively in Late Cretaceous sediments deposited in marginal marine environments along the shoreline of the interior seaway that occupied eastern Utah. Cannel coal and anthracite are found locally. Oil and gas have been produced in Utah from all systems younger than the Silurian. In addition to the conventional marine source and reservoir rocks, oil has been obtained from salt, lacustrine shale, and fluvial and aeolian sandstones.

HYDROLOGY

Great Salt Lake is a well-known landmark, appearing on most maps and visible on photos taken hundreds of miles above the Earth (fig. 1-12). Located where it is, it can be neither avoided nor ignored; its sterile waters, muddy shores, and marginal salt-encrusted flats have been an obstacle to travel and a discouragement to human activities generally. Nevertheless, it is of great scientific interest, and technical studies have made it one of the best known bodies of water in the world. It is the shrunken remnant of a much larger body of fresh water, ancient Lake Bonneville. The present size, geochemistry, and sedimentology of Great Salt Lake are best regarded as a temporary stage in a history that began millions of years in the past and will continue through the foreseeable future. Locked in the lake sediments is a record of climatic change that may be one of the most complete on Earth.

So delicate is the balance between influx and evaporation that all statistical statements must be qualified to take note

Figure 1-11. The Bingham open-pit copper mine, Oquirrh Mountains, near Salt Lake City. Low-grade ore is associated with a middle Tertiary intrusion. Photo: U.S. Bureau of Reclamation.

of wide fluctuations. In historic time, the depth has varied through a range of 20 feet and the surface area has ranged between 1,750 and 2,125 square miles. Other statistics from historical observations are: Mean surface elevation, 4,200 feet; average depth, 13 feet; greatest depth 32 feet to 54 feet; drainage basin, 22,000 square miles and average salinity, 25.52 percent.

Important contributing streams flowing directly into Great Salt Lake are the Bear and Weber Rivers. They drain areas beyond the topographic boundaries of the Great Basin and without their contributions Great Salt Lake could not exist. Another source of fresh water is Utah Lake that receives the Provo and Spanish Fork Rivers and drains into Great Salt Lake by way of the 40-mile-long Jordan River. Utah Lake is the largest natural fresh-water lake west of the Mississippi River; it is artifically maintained at a fairly stable area of approximately 148 square miles, an average depth of 9.5 feet and an elevation of 4,489.3 feet above sea level.

The Colorado River crosses southeastern Utah. Its chief tributary, the Green River, drains most of the northeastern quarter of the state and joins the Colorado in the Inner Canyonlands. Other important tributaries of the Colorado are the Dolores, White, Duchesne, Price, San Rafael, Muddy, Escalante, Paria, Virgin, and San Juan Rivers. The Colorado system (including the Green) is one of the great river systems of North America and its geologic history one of the most puzzling. Flowing mostly through a desert, the Colorado supplies water to expanding populations in five southwestern states and Mexico. Flaming Gorge Reservoir, Lake Powell, and Lake Mead hold back the water and reduce the great river to little more than a trickle by the time it enters the Gulf of California. The accumulation of sediment behind the dams that form these three reservoirs is creating a difficult problem for engineers and environmentalists in the distant future.

Figure 1-12. The Great Salt Lake as of March 1966. At this date the lake level stood at 4,195 feet. Compiled by Intermountain Aerial Surveys from photos taken 12,000 feet above ground level. Length of causeway 20 miles. Reproduced with permission.

PLEISTOCENE GEOLOGY

The most significant deposits of Pleistocene age in Utah are the bottom sediments of Lake Bonneville and marginal equivalents in neighboring terraces, spits, bars, and deltas. Second in importance are glacial and periglacial deposits including moraines, ground till, and outwash at higher elevations. The correlation and age of lacustrine and glacial deposits and the sequence of events has engaged the attention of many investigators with significant, but not always consistant, results. Climatic factors governed the rise and fall of Lake Bonneville and the expansion and contraction of mountain glaciers.

So far, Pleistocene geologists have had to rely on natural outcrops, fortuitous commercial excavations, and a few experimental drill holes for relevant data. Until funds are available for investigating selected localities of greater information potential, many problems of Pleistocene stratigraphy and climatology will not be solved.

Non-glacial and non-lacustrine deposits of Pleistocene/Recent age are varied, widespread, and include pediment cover, alluvial fans, river terraces, loess, dune sand, soil, colluvium, and talus. All have implications for determining climatic change and exist today in various stages of developmental construction or destruction. With few exceptions these deposits are retained in their original depositional forms and may be related to processes that are still in operation.

Pediments are unusually prominent in Utah. Those skirting the Book Cliffs and Henry Mountains have been the subject of special study and have revealed much about the particularly difficult subject of pedimentation. Pediments are apparently not forming today; how existing remnants correlate with past lakes and glaciers is not well understood. Utah has a number of small active sand dune fields that are easily related to existing winds and sand sources. Stabilized dunes indicative of past climatic changes are also known.

Having been almost entirely swept clean of surficial deposits, the Colorado Plateau has no extensive record of Pleistocene time. Clearly much of the deep erosion, canyon cutting, and general denudation has been accomplished in the past few million years. To discover details of what has gone on, particularly in response to climatic change, is a challenge to geomorphologists.

Human inhabitants (prehistoric, pre-Columbian, and present day) exist at the mercy of climatic influences, chiefly precipitation. In spite of close adjustments to nature, the inhabitants of the Colorado Plateau were forced from their homelands by a severe drought about 800 years ago. Modern inhabitants, in spite of vast water conservation schemes, must also realize that they may be fighting an uncertain battle against creeping aridity. Studies of the geologically recent past, as revealed in a variety of surficial deposits, should be vital in predicting the future.

SCENERY

Scenery is usually mentioned only in an incidental way in geologic textbooks. With time this should change. Scenery has economic value and, in the end after mines and quarries are exhausted, tourism will remain a valuable resource because people will still come to Utah to view the scenery. Five great National Parks, two extensive National Recreation Areas, six of seven National Monuments, several Wilderness Areas, and 18 of 34 Utah State Parks have been established because of geologic scenery.

Tourists spend money, time, and energy to view something different. That they come to Utah to see rocks is an indication that there is something different about the ones

Figure 1-13. Looking upstream along Bridge Canyon through the arch of Rainbow Natural Bridge. Bridge is carved from Navajo Sandstone, abutments rest on Kayenta Formation. Human figures give scale, Navajo Mountain in the distance. Photo: Hal Rumel.

here compared to those of other areas. The officially designated scenic areas are there because of human reactions to massive sandstone formations cleanly exposed in an arid climate. Zion, Canyonlands, Arches, Capitol Reef, Natural Bridges, Rainbow Bridge, Snow Canyon, Deadhorse Point, Goblin Valley, Monument Valley, Kodachrome Basin and Paria Canyon exist because of the unusual erosion of sandstone (fig. 1-13). They are all part of a broad region called Canyonlands, Red Rock Country, or Slick Rock Country, in allusion to the colorful erosional forms that characterize them. Colored rocks are much less common than drab ones; white rocks are even more rare. Light color makes the Navajo Sandstone that forms the dazzling towers of Zion Park and rounded domes of Capitol Reef a major attraction for tourists. The Great White Throne is one of the two best known monoliths in North America (see chapter 13, fig. 13-17). Vertical cliffs and narrow, dimly lit canyons attract hikers and offer strong contrast to the open valleys of more humid regions. Canyons and cliffs in various combinations are evident on all sides in the Colorado Plateau. To persons accustomed to life on flat lands or in humid, heavily vegetated areas, it is the impassable cliffs that are most impressive. No place on Earth displays great linear escarpments such as those in southeastern and southern Utah. Many are prominant enough to deserve specific names. The Chocolate, Vermillion, White, Orange, Gray, Pink, Roan, Book, and Badland Cliffs extend for miles as barriers to travel and as bastions of scattered, sequestered settlements.

Two opposing cliffs make a canyon. Six of the great canyons of the Green/Colorado River system are in Utah: From north to south they are Split Mountain, Gray, Desolation, Labyrinth or Stillwater, Cataract, and Glen Canyons. Made famous by Major Powell's great expeditions, these canyons have become the river-runners domain which only a relatively few ordinary tourists can afford to share.

2 THE WASATCH LINE - BACKBONE OF UTAH

The most prominent geographic and geologic feature of Utah is the high curving belt of mountains and plateaus that divides the state into distinctly different western and eastern provinces. The name Wasatch Line, taken from the Wasatch Range, was applied to this geologic discontinuity by Marshall Kay, a Columbia University geologist (1951). The Line extends beyond Utah, north and south, into adjoining states and is, by any standard, one of the most important geologic features of North America. An abbreviated tabulation of geologic and geographic features east and west of the line is a good way to introduce a study of Utah geology and its prehistoric past. (Refer to the physiographic and geologic maps, envelope in back of book, and to the geologic time scale, front of book, for the chronological framework.)

Table 2-1. Comparison of the general features and basic geophysical properties east and west of the Wasatch Line, Utah.

Feature	West	East
Drainage	Internal drainage—runoff does not reach the ocean. The Great Salt Lake receives most of the drainage but other smaller closed basins may hold temporary water bodies (playas).	External drainage—runoff reaches the Pacific Ocean by way of the Colorado River and its tributaries. Some streams cross the Wasatch Line into the Great Basin.
Chief geologic activity	Deposition dominates. Material eroded from the mountains is deposited on their flanks or in nearby lakes. Much is carried away by wind.	Erosion dominates. The Colorado River and its tributaries are very powerful in tearing down and removing rock and soil.
Landscape	Sawtooth mountains (Sierras), sloping alluvial fans and wide flat-bottomed valleys.	Flat-topped mesas, buttes, stripped surfaces and hogbacks that follow hard flat-lying beds and deep canyons with steplike walls.
Structure (position and condition of the internal rock layers)	Complex structure with many large and small faults. Beds (strata) are mostly intensely folded, crumpled and tipped from a horizontal position.	Simple structure, many of the sedimentary rock layers are generally flat-lying as originally deposited.
Rock types	Exposed sedimentary rocks are mainly carbonates; limestone and dolomite of marine origin. Very little sandstone. Extensive exposures of igneous rocks. Valleys filled with alluvial material.	Most exposed formations are sandstone and shale, together called clastics. They are mostly of non-marine origin. Very little limestone in exposed sections.
Age of rocks (Refer to geologic time scale inside back cover)	Mostly Paleozoic and late Cenozoic. There are extensive thick formations of Cambrian, Ordovician, Silurian, Devonian, Mississippian, Pennsylvanian, and Permian ages making up the exposed ranges. Valley fill consists of less indurated Cenozoic sediments.	Mostly Mesozoic and early Cenozoic. Formations are chiefly of Triassic, Jurassic, Cretaceous, Paleocene, and Eocene ages. Only in the deeper canyons and major uplifts are formations older than Triassic exposed. Exposures in the Uinta Basin are chiefly Eocene.

Table 2-1. Comparison of the general features and basic geophysical properties east and west of the Wasatch Line, Utah (continued).

Feature	West	East
Geologic history.	Western Utah was a geosyncline during the Paleozoic, was uplifted in the Mesozoic, and collapsed to its present elevation in the mid-Cenozoic.	Eastern Utah was a shelf area under shallow water or exposed to erosion during much of the early Paleozoic. There were local uplifts in the Pennsylvanian Period, shallow seas in the early Mesozoic and deeper seas in the late Mesozoic. Lakes abounded in the early Cenozoic and erosion dominated in the late Cenozoic.
Igneous rocks and events	Many extrusive (surface deposited) and intrusive (subsurface) igneous rocks. Extrusive rocks are mainly Cenozoic. Basalt (dark lava rock) is the latest and most common type. Ash, dust, and cinders are common in the filling of the valleys. Granite intrusions are fairly abundant.	Few extrusive rocks except those spilling over the Wasatch Line to cover the High Plateaus. Four mountain groups have cores of intrusive material: Henry Mountains, LaSal Mountains, Abajo Mountains, and Navajo Mountain.
Mineral resources	Chiefly metallic mineral deposits of hydrothermal origin. Deposits of copper, gold, silver, lead, zinc, iron, molybdenum, tungsten, uranium, mercury, antimony, and less common metals are widely dispersed. Mostly they are associated with the igneous intrusions. Gravel and other rock products are also present.	Chiefly hydrocarbons such as oil, natural gas, coal, oil sands, oil shale, gilsonite, and less common solid organic materials. Most of the urnaium deposits present are in association with minor vanadium and copper. Gravel and other rock products are present.
Heat flow	Relatively high heat flow that amounts to 2 or more heat flow units (HFU).	Relatively low heat flow that amounts to about 1.3 HFU.
Underlying Crust	Crust is relatively thin, about 18.6 miles thick.	Crust is relatively thick, about 24.8 miles thick.
Earthquake waves	P waves have velocities of 4.6 to 4.7 mi/sec. (P waves are primary earthquake waves; they advance by push-pull or compression; also known as longitudinal waves).	P Waves have velocities of 4.8 to 4.9 mi/sec.
Magnetic variations	The Curie point is at relatively shallow depths. (The Curie point is the temperature at which a material loses ability to retain magnetism. For iron (Fe) it is 789°C.	The Curie point is at relatively greater depths.
Gravity variations	Anomalously high gravity field values; -150 to -175 milligals (g is the acceleration of a mass caused by the pull of gravity. A milligal is nearly equal to 1/1,000,000 of this value ($1 \times 10^{-3} cm/sec^2$).	Lower gravity field values than for the Basin and Range; -200 to -280 milligals.
Electrical variations	Relatively higher electrical conductivity of the mantle.	Relatively lower electrical conductivity of the upper mantle.

The most striking present-day indication of the Wasatch Line is its association with a chain of elevated mountains and plateaus (fig. 2-1). If portrayed as a single line and not as a zone, it follows the western base of the Wasatch Range from the northern state line to Salt Creek near Nephi, Juab County. South of Salt Creek the line continues but is identified with the western margin of a string of high flat-topped plateaus; the Gunnison, Sevier, and Markagunt Plateaus being nearest the actual transition from the Colorado Plateau to the Great Basin as it would be drawn purely on surface evidence.

In addition to the mountains and plateaus that accompany the Wasatch Line, a number of other geologic and geographic features such as hot springs and earthquake epicenters are concentrated along its course.

FAULTS

Thousands of faults have been mapped in the western United States and a number are long enough and cut through such great thicknesses of rock that they must be classed as of major importance. Several such faults follow the course of the Wasatch Line (fig. 2-2). The movement on most major faults is not usually concentrated on a single clean break but may be spread among a number of splinter-like breaks. As one branch dies out another usually begins on a nearby parallel course. Although the simple term "fault" is usually used, most major fractures are, in reality, zones or systems of displacement.

The greatest vertical displacement in Utah is concentrated on the Wasatch Fault system which extends from near

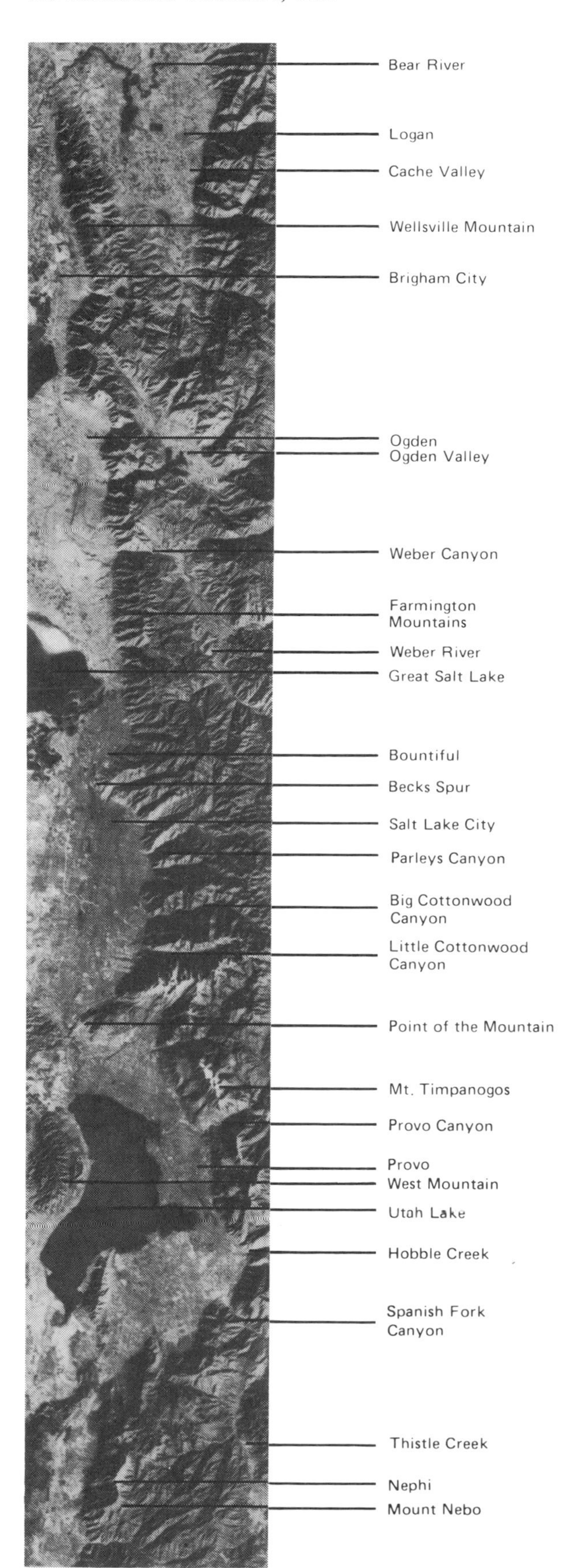

Figure 2-1. The Wasatch Front, present day expression of the Wasatch Line, as photographed from space. Major physical features and cities are indicated. Photo: U.S. Department of Agriculture.

Soda Springs, Idaho, to the vicinity of Nephi, Juab County, Utah, a distance of about 210 miles. It closely follows the front of the Wasatch Range with subsidiary branches in adjacent valleys and mountains. Vertical movement along this system exceeds 3 miles, without which there would be no Wasatch Mountains and no Wasatch Front. Near Nephi, beyond which the Wasatch Fault can no longer be traced, the Sevier Fault begins and continues southward another 240 miles. The Paunsaugunt Fault commences about 15 miles east of Monroe, Sevier County and continues to the Arizona line with a total length of about 175 miles. The Hurricane Fault, more closely related with the Wasatch Line, commences near Parowan, Iron County, and extends southward to the Grand Canyon, Arizona. There continue to be considerable differences of opinion about the names and configurations of the great faults of southwestern Utah.

HOT SPRINGS

When all the springs of Utah are charted, it is apparent that they show a heavy concentration along the Wasatch Line. This is to be expected as springs are mostly fed by surface water and much of Utah's precipitation falls on elevations associated with the line. If only the hot springs are considered, they too are concentrated along the Wasatch Line. Hot springs may yield water that has never before been at the surface or it may be water from the surface that has descended to areas of heated rock or steam and then returned to the surface. In either case, the concentration of thermal springs indicates a deep-seated heat source along the Wasatch Line. It is probably correct to associate the hot springs with the great faults and to assume that heated vapor or liquid water is rising along the fault planes. A map of hot springs (fig. 2-3) shows that in the Wasatch Range most springs rise at the projecting points or spurs such as Becks and Point-of-the-Mountain. An important study of selected hot springs has been reported by Parry and others (1976).

EARTHQUAKES

Of all the ways in which the Wasatch Line makes itself felt in a literal way, the greatest is by earthquakes (fig. 2-4). The effects extend beyond Utah into Wyoming and Idaho on the northeast and into Nevada and California on the west. The concentration of earthquakes along the line is so great that it has earned the name Intermountain Seismic Belt. In terms of destructive potential this belt is rated second only to the San Andreas Fault zone of California.

IGNEOUS ACTIVITY

Igneous activity has affected many parts of Utah but there are more intrusive and extrusive rocks in a broad band along the Wasatch Line than either east or west of it.

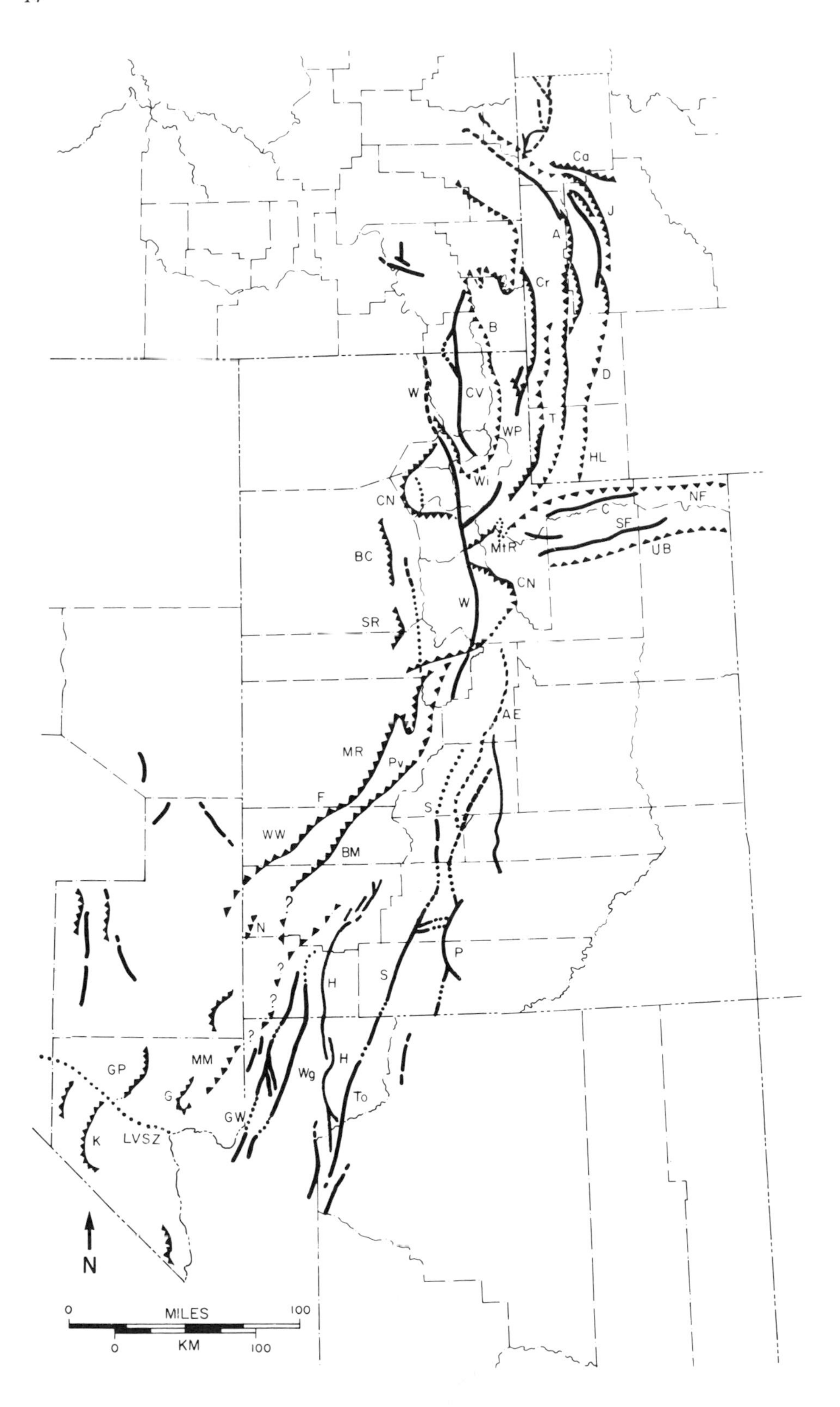

Key

Thrust faults barbed,
Normal faults plain.

A	Absaroka
AE	Ancient Ephraim
B	Bannock
BC	Broad Canyon
BM	Blue Mountain
C	Crest
Ca	Cache
CM	Cedar Mountain
CN	Charleston-Nebo
Cr	Crawford
CV	Cache Valley
D	Darby
F	Frisco
G	Glendale
DP	Gass Peak
GW	Grand Wash
H	Hurricane
HL	Hogsback Labarge
J	Jackson
K	Keystone
LVSZ	Las Vegas Sheer Zone
MR	Mineral Range
MM	Muddy Mountain
N	Needles
NF	North Flank
P	Paunsaugunt
PV	Pavant
S	Sevier
SF	South Flank
T	Teton
To	Toroweep
UB	Uintah Boundary
W	Wasatch
Wi	Willard
WP	Woodruff-Paris
WW	Wah Wah
Wg	Washington

Figure 2-2. Faults associated with the Wasatch Line. Normal faults are represented by the plain lines, thrust faults have barbs that point away from the direction of movement. The abbreviations are explained alphabetically in the adjacent list. (Reproduced from the Rocky Mountain Association of Geologists, Symposium on the geology of the Cordilleran Hingeline, 1976, p. 21.)

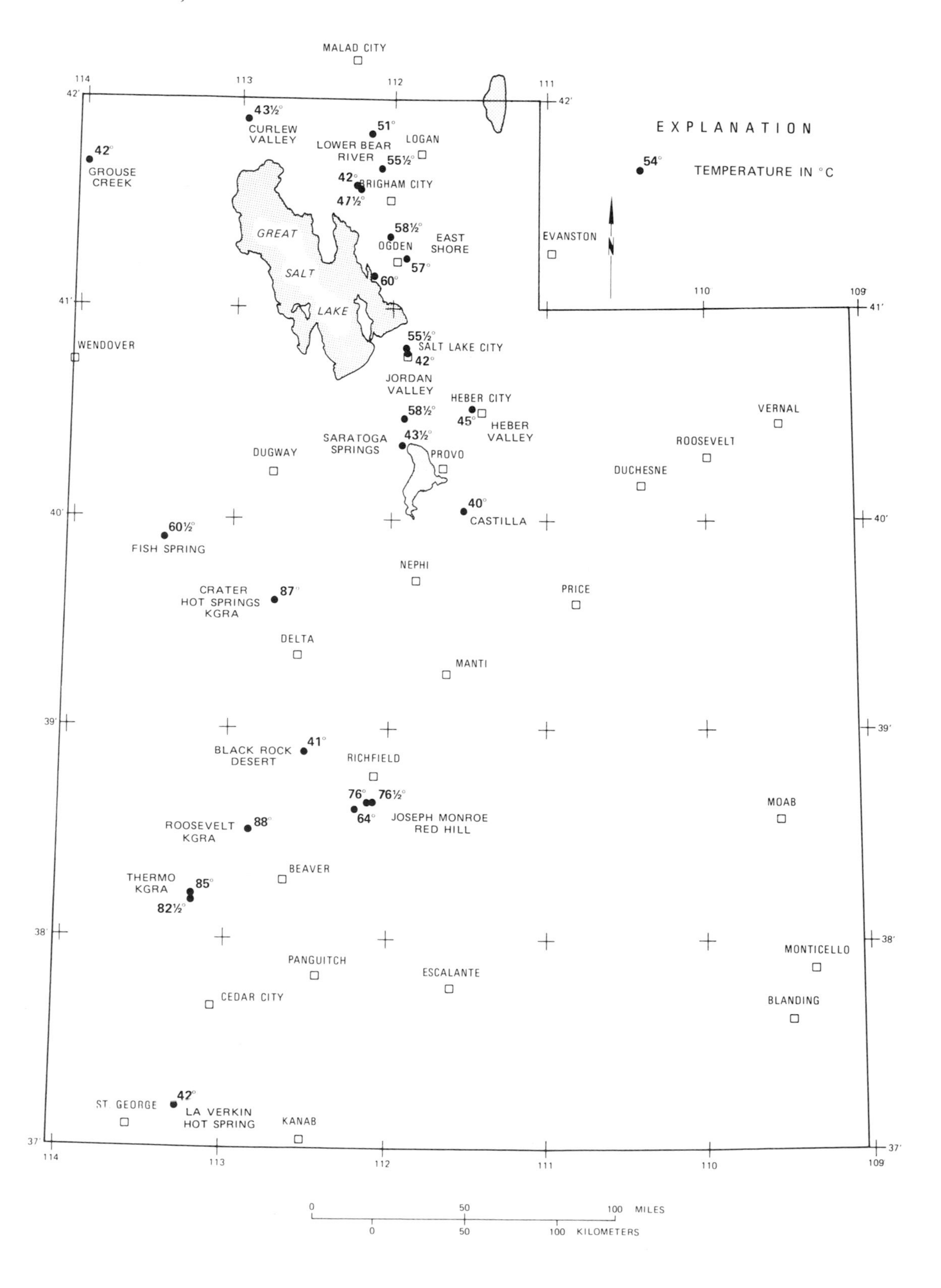

Figure 2-3. The hot springs of Utah. Localities are shown by dots, figures give temperatures in centigrade. Note concentration along the Wasatch line. (Reproduced from Rocky Mountain Association of Geologists and Utah Geological Association, 1979 Basin and Range Symposium, 1979, p. 372.)

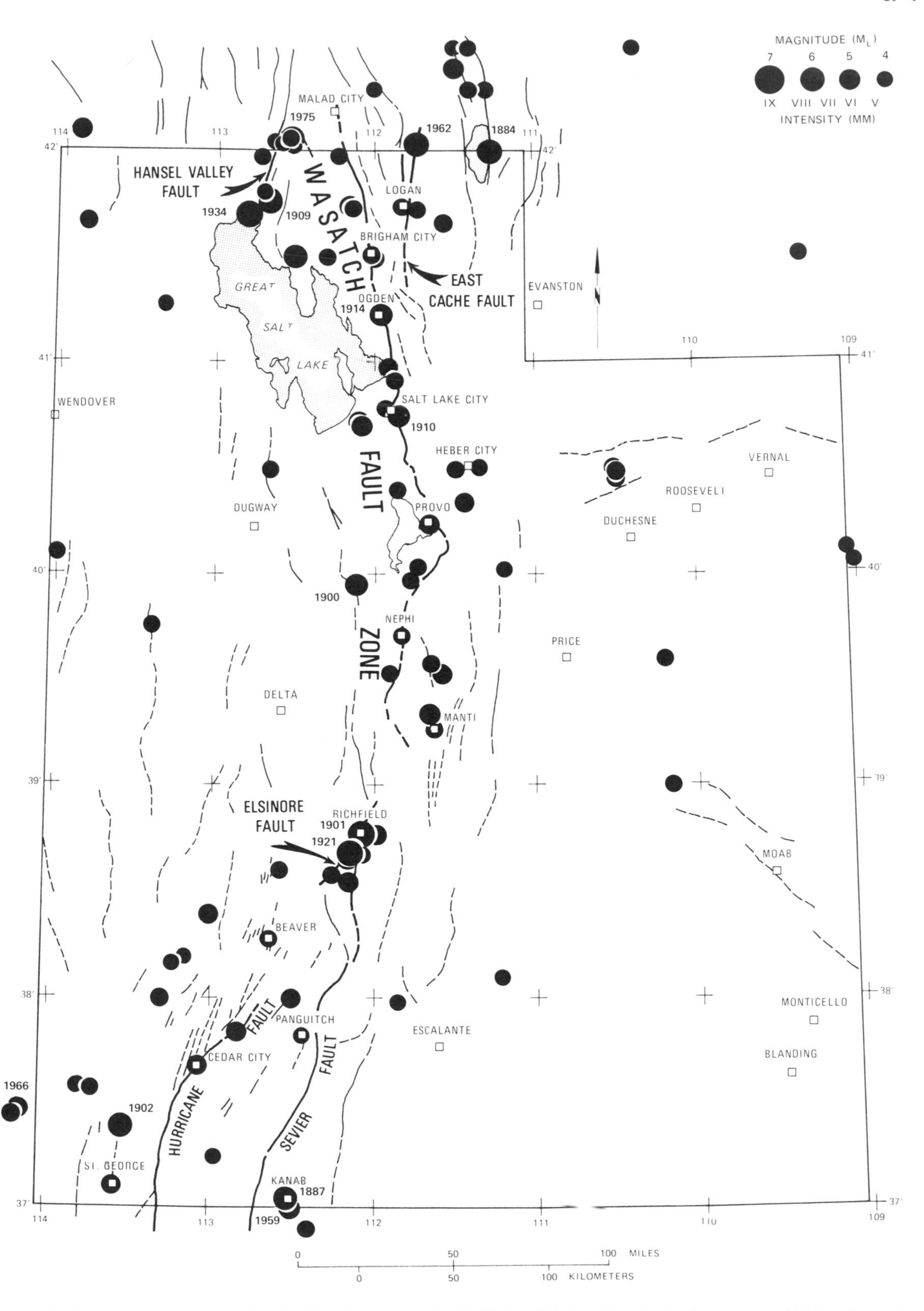

Figure 2-4. Distribution of epicenters of major historic earthquakes in Utah. Chief earthquake faults are named. Note that only quakes of 4 or greater on the Richter scale are charted. (Reproduced from Walter J. Arabasz, Robert B. Smith and William D. Richins, editors, 1979, Earthquake Studies in Utah, 1850 to 1978, University of Utah Seismograph Stations, Department of Geology and Geophysics.)

Both intrusive and extrusive effects are common in the area around Salt Lake City, Salt Lake County. Another center is near Nephi/Eureka, Juab County and still another makes up much of Piute County. The large and spectacular lava flows of the high plateaus that continue southwesterly into Nevada are the greatest in the state and they clearly follow the trends of the Wasatch and Las Vegas Lines. The flows have spread out many miles from their place of origin; if the actual vents were known they would probably show a close relationship to the Wasatch Line and the associated fault system.

WHAT IS THE WASATCH LINE?

The foregoing list of geologic features associated with the Wasatch Line still does not answer the question of what caused it to be where it is and why it acted as it did. It is clearly a zone of weakness in the crust but it is more than a great fault system and more than a simple earthquake zone. The fact that it has been in existence for at least 800 million years under one guise or another is, in itself, a major phenomenon. Part of the difficulty in describing it lies in the fact that it appears to be the only one of its type on Earth.

Although space does not permit lengthy speculation about the origin of the Wasatch Line, we cannot leave the topic without mention of some additional lines of evidence based on the nature of various disturbances of the line that break its continuity or cause it to split or deviate from a relatively smooth curve.

DISRUPTIONS OF THE WASATCH LINE

The Uinta Mountains

The course of the Wasatch Line is not strictly a simple unbroken curve. It is disrupted by several other major geologic features, one of which is clearly related to the Uinta Mountains (fig. 2-5). The Uinta Mountains are unusual in many ways. The east-west trend is nearly at right angles to other nearby ranges of the Rocky Mountain system and also to the Wasatch Line. They are also unusual geologically. Rocks that make up the high central core are mostly quartzite strata totaling more than 20,000 feet in thickness and clearly of shallow-water origin. In contrast, nearby Rocky Mountain ranges have cores of igneous or metamorphic rocks such as granite, gneiss, and schist. The known geologic history begins at least as long ago as that of the Wasatch Line, more than 800 million years in the past. As with most mountains, the beginning was not as an elevated highland but as a deep downfold or trough in which an unusually thick accumulation of shallow-water sediments was deposited. Features such as this are called aulacogens, hence the name, Uinta aulacogen, seems appropriate. The present unusual trend is clearly due to the east-west course of the ancestral sedimentary trough. When the trough was forming it must have had the appearance of a relatively narrow valley or an arm of the sea which opened westward into the Cordilleran geosyncline and extended more than 150 miles eastward into the continental interior. The trough seems to have deepened and possibly widened with the passage of time as westward-flowing streams eventually filled it with many cubic miles of sandy sediment.

After it was filled, the ancestral Uinta aulacogen remained relatively quiet; however, at times when the crust was under local tension there was slight additional subsidence and consequently a thickening of the sediments being deposited. When there was compression the result was slight bulging, causing thinning of contemporary deposits. The most severe compression came with the formation of the Rocky Mountains in the Paleocene Epoch (about 55 million years ago) when much of the contents of the trough was squeezed upward and outward to create the present range. A curious and unexplained fact is that at no time during this long history did igneous rocks of any consequence appear in the Uinta Mountains area. The scarcity of

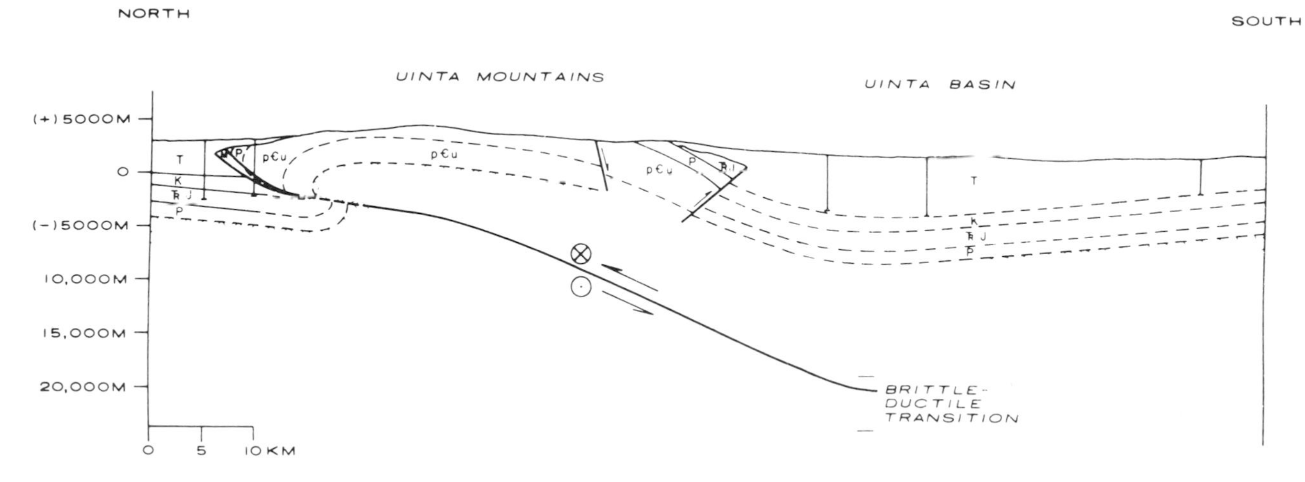

Figure 2-5. Generalized cross section inferred deep structure of the Uinta Mountains and Uinta Basin. Explanation: pЄu, upper Precambrian; P, Paleozoic; ₸J, Triassic and Jurassic; K, Cretaceous; T, Tertiary. Vertical lines, oil wells. (Ronald L. Bruhn, with permission.)

igneous activity is evidently the reason why no important ore deposits have been found. To the prospector and miner the Uinta Mountains have always been a great disappointment.

In some deep-seated and as yet not understood way, the same forces that gave rise to the Uinta Mountains produced effects extending westward into what is now the Basin and Range Province. For this projection, the term "Tooele Arch" was applied by Hintze. The name is taken from Tooele County where the effects are most noticeable. Marginal to the Tooele Arch, many formations thin and even completely disappear. Effects are most noticeable in Ordovician, Mississippian, and Pennsylvanian rocks. The arch separates two deeper basins: one to the north, called by some the North-central Utah Basin and another, the Ibex Basin, to the south.

The Great Thrust Faults and Hingeline Zone

The course of the Wasatch Line is marked at present by the Wasatch, Sevier, and Hurricane Faults. All are normal faults, meaning they are of the usual or common variety, one side down the other up. Less easily described and understood are the thrust (fig. 2-6) or reverse faults that are also related to the line.

In describing faults, reference is made to the block that lies above the plane of movement in relation to the block that lies below it. In a normal fault, the block above moves relatively downward and the block below relatively upward. In thrust or reverse faults, the block above moves relatively upward or forward and the block below relatively downward or remains static. Thrust faults may involve movement ranging from a few inches to scores of miles. Major thrust faults tend to follow relatively weak or incompetent beds for great distances. If they break upward to the surface and the upper block comes under attack by erosion, the lower block becomes essentially the existing land surface. The forward-moving slice may be tens, hundreds, or thousands of feet thick. It is common to find the slices created by thrust faults piled one upon another so that such faults usually occur in belts or groups. Additional complexity arises from the fact that the thrust slices may be carved into irregular discontinuous shapes by erosion. Erosion may also cut holes, or windows, through thrust sheets or it may leave remnants, called klippen, capping hills or mountains. Added complications arise when the traces of inactive thrust faults are covered by sediments, as many are.

Areas of intensive thrust faulting must be studied and mapped with great care. If ore deposits, coal beds, or oil pools have been affected, proper understanding of thrust faults is essential in finding them.

Thrust faults are clearly associated with the Wasatch Line in two areas, one southwest of the Uinta Mountains, the other northwest of them. In fact, the Uintas seem to have strongly affected the fault pattern. It is as if the mountains, like a pointed finger, remained stationary while the moving rock masses slid eastward on either side. The great plates of moving rock clearly started their journey west of the Wasatch Line, passed partly over it in places, and came to rest with the forward edge resting upon rocks that had not taken part in the movement. In other words, rocks out of the Cordilleran geosyncline moved eastward across the Wasatch Line onto the shelf area. Geologists refer to rocks that have moved as *allocthonous*, those that are in place as *autocthonous*.

Most of the movement southwest of the Uinta Mountains is in the form of one gigantic thrust plate, the Charleston-Nebo Thrust, called by some the Strawberry Thrust. The name is taken from the town of Charleston, Wasatch County, and Mt. Nebo, Juab County, near which two exposed segments of the fault trace can be seen. Between these exposures in the Wasatch Range the fault trace is mostly covered by deposits of early Cenozoic age. The Charleston-Nebo Thrust passes under Strawberry Reservoir hidden by a cover of thousands of feet of Tertiary and Quaternary sediments (see geologic map). It then turns westward, passing under Deer Creek Reservoir and across the Wasatch Range to the Traverse Mountains where it is cut off by the Wasatch Fault. The trace is thought to pass under Salt Lake Valley and westward between Antelope Island and the Oquirrh Mountains. There is good evidence that it swings northward around Antelope Island and then eastward south of Fremont Island. The northward continuation is uplifted to view again in the Wasatch Range where it is known as the Willard Thrust. There are spectacular exposures of fault planes in the mountains east of Ogden, Weber County. According to Crittenden (1972), the Charleston-

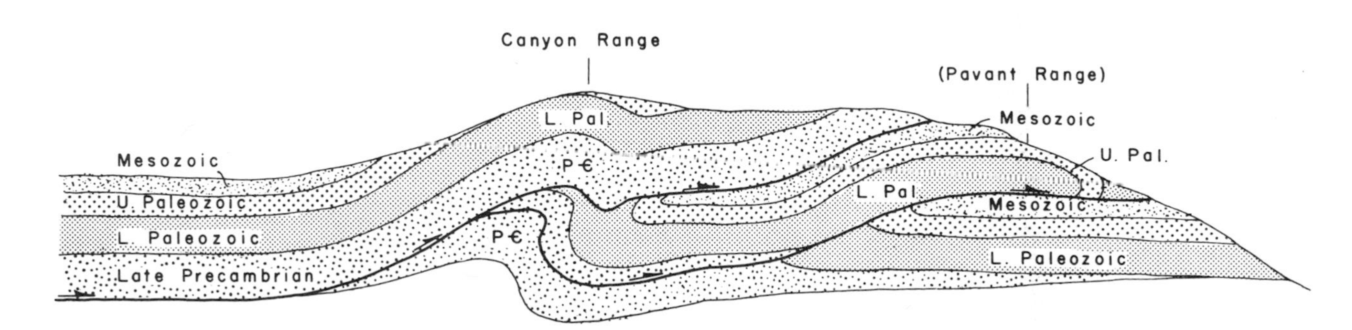

Figure 2-6. Diagrammatic cross-section of the Pavant thrust fault. See figure 2-2 for location. (Reproduced from Utah Geological Association Publication 2, Plateau-Basin and Range Transition Zone, Central Utah, 1972, p. 65.)

Nebo Thrust and the Willard Thrust are structurally continuous.

Several great thrust faults have been mapped northwest of the Uinta Mountains. Best exposures are along the Idaho-Wyoming border between Bear Lake, Idaho and Jackson Lake, Wyoming. The belt as a whole is crescent shaped, curving from a southerly course in Wyoming to a southwesterly course in Utah. The area is known geologically as the Wyoming-Idaho thrust belt or the Overthrust Belt. Traces of the larger thrusts that pass southward into Utah are mostly covered by deposits of Cenozoic conglomerate and sandstone. Two major thrusts entering Utah from Wyoming are the Woodruff Thrust, running from the west shores of Bear Lake to the vicinity of Willard Peak, and the Absaroka Thrust which enters Utah near the Wyoming corner. Some of the problems relating to this great zone of overthrusting will be mentioned later in this chapter.

The Marysvale Bifurcation

The Wasatch Line gives rise to a major branch in south-central Utah. This branch, called the Las Vegas Line, leaves the state slightly north of the southwest corner and continues into Nevada. The original Wasatch Line of Kay continues into Arizona. There are significant differences in the two branches. From Piute County southward the great faults do not curve westward with the Las Vegas Line, instead they continue in relatively straight courses into Arizona where they cross the Grand Canyon at approximately right angles. In contrast earthquake epicenters mainly follow the Las Vegas Line and are less common along the Arizona branch.

The actual area in which the branching of the fault system seems to take place is not clearly evident, but appears to be very near Marysvale, Piute County, on the east flank of the Tushar Mountains. I am suggesting the name *Marysvale Bifurcation* for this branching of structure and tectonic activity.

It is probably not entirely a coincidence that the area of branching between the ancient and modern courses of the Wasatch Line is marked by intense volcanic effects. The great lava flows of the High Plateaus seem to have originated in an area of the crust where southwest-trending faults and almost south-trending faults converge or terminate. It is not difficult to imagine that an area of numerous cross-cutting faults would be weaker and more easily penetrated by magmas from depth than areas with no faults or with all faults running in the same direction. This explanation for the concentration of volcanic action is certainly too simple but it does tie together several great geologic features related to the Wasatch Line.

THE WASATCH LINE THROUGH TIME

The Precambrian Beginnings

The earliest geologic features that coincide in location and trend with the Wasatch Line were apparent at least 800 million years ago, in the late Precambrian. This has been pointed out by Stewart (1972) who noted many features of Precambrian western North America that seem to set a pattern for later developments. Stewart believes there was a fragmentation of crustal material about 850 million years ago during which a large slice of western North America rifted away and disappeared (fig. 2-7). The relatively straight, slightly curving inner wall of the rift became the new continental margin and the space to the west vacated by the massive removal of the bordering land mass became the site of the Cordilleran geosyncline. The initial deposits of the geosyncline show a high degree of north-south continuity not apparent in older rocks.

The Paleozoic Cordilleran Geosyncline

The Cordilleran geosyncline that occupied much of what is now the Great Basin was one of the world's great repositories of late Precambrian and Paleozoic sediments. The Pacific Ocean lay to the west and lapped far beyond the present-day continental border into what is now the continental interior. A rather abrupt shoaling along the Wasatch Line from deeper water on the west to shallower water on the east is evident (fig. 2-8). West of the line, downsinking was slow but almost uninterrupted; east of the line there were frequent emergences with consequent unconformities and lapses in the record.

During middle and late Paleozoic time, drastic orogenic movements broke up the pattern of earlier periods. The Antler Orogeny (Devonian-Mississippian) crumpled the continental edge in Nevada and destroyed the western part of the geosyncline. Sand and conglomerate then prevailed in the central Great Basin where limestone had dominated before. The Wasatch Line would be evident on many maps that might be drawn of Middle Paleozoic rock units, but after that a new set of tectonic elements created by the Ancestral Rockies Revolution came into being and temporarily broke across and obliterated the line. The ancestral Rockies trend is definitely west-northwest from Oklahoma to western Utah. A significant point is that, although the Wasatch Line was temporarily obscured during the late Paleozoic, it reasserted itself for a short time in the Early Triassic.

Early Mesozoic—A Page Missing?

Between the Late Permian and Late Jurassic (see time chart, back of book) the record of happenings along the Wasatch Line leaves much to be desired. Late Permian formations are found fairly well represented on both sides of the line so the setting can be reconstructed in a satisfactory way. Not so with succeeding Triassic and Jurassic strata which are thick and varied east of the line but almost totally absent west of it. Many formations that thicken westward are abruptly cut off at the Wasatch Line. The Woodside, Thaynes, Ankareh, Gartra, Chinle Shale, Nugget Sandstone, Twin Creek Limestone, and Stump Formations, with an aggregate total thickness of more than 8,000 feet, reach the front of the Wasatch Range near Salt Lake City where they are cut off near the Wasatch Front. This is not, in itself, too remarkable but no trace of any of these units

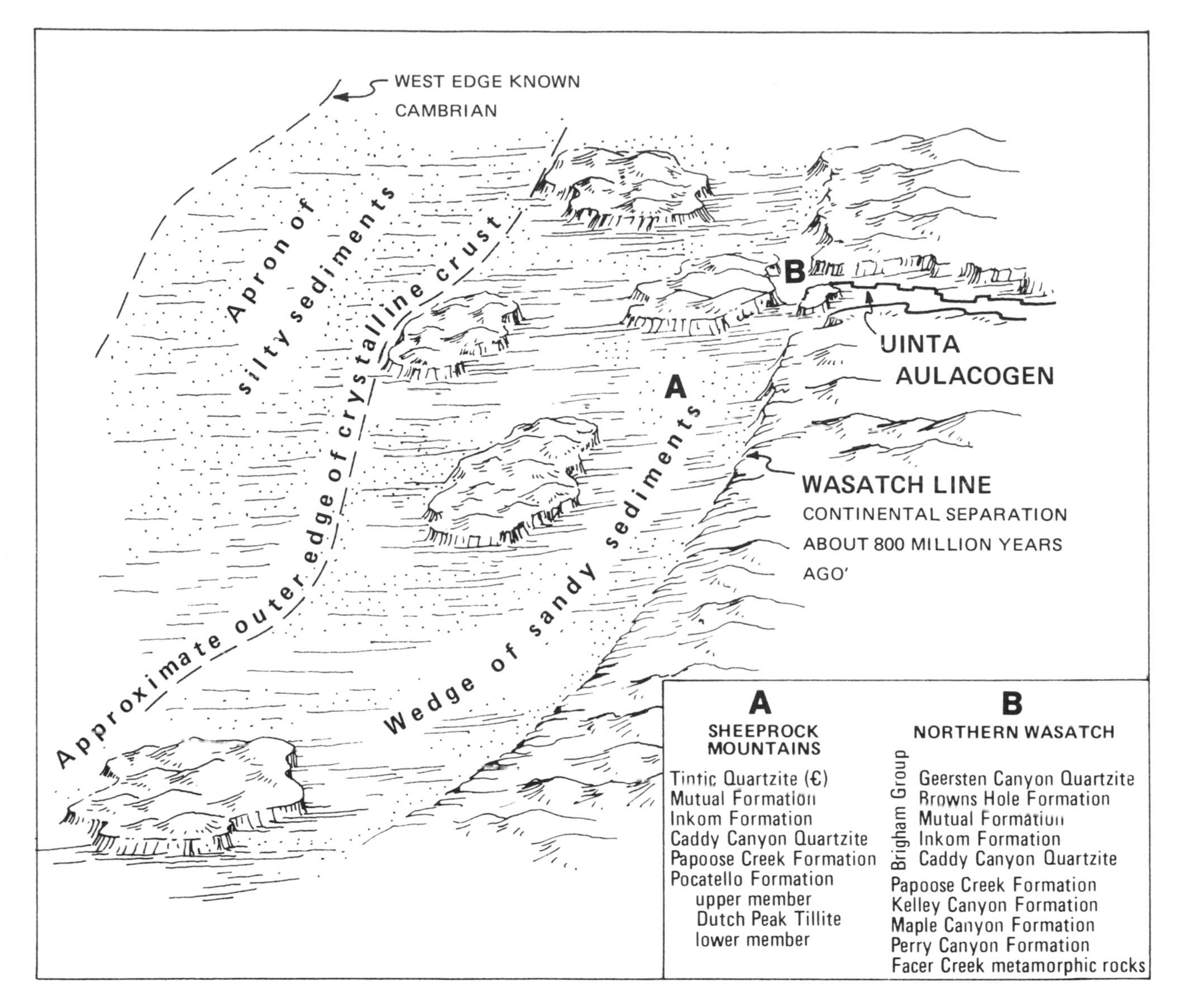

Figure 2-7. Reconstruction of a portion of western North America in late Precambrian time, over one-half billion years ago. This is based on the hypothesis that the Wasatch Line commenced as a rift from which pieces separated and drifted westward. Precambrian formations deposited after the rifting are shown at two localities. (Adapted from the Rocky Mountain Association of Geologists and Utah Geological Association, 1979 Basin and Range Symposium, 1979, p. 199.)

has been found to the west except for small remnants of Lower Triassic strata.

At first thought one might conclude that since the Wasatch Fault is a normal fault the early Mesozoic section dropped to the west and is still present in the trench under Salt Lake Valley. This may prove to be true but if so this section should also be, but is not, exposed somewhere in the succession of uplifted blocks to the west. How much, if any, of the missing Mesozoic section covered this region when normal faulting commenced remains to be determined. Most of the Mesozoic formations are soft sandstone, siltstone and shale, not durable rocks that would be expected to leave large identifiable pebbles or cobbles in contemporaneous deposits. How voluminous the early Mesozoic strata may have been immediately west of the Wasatch Line and what the behavior of the geosynclinal belt was during the corresponding time interval are among the items of information needed before the full history of the Wasatch Line can be reconstructed.

Mesozoic Disturbances and the Wasatch Line

In 1959 H. D. Harris presented evidence for a major geologic disturbance in south-central Utah during Late Cretaceous time. He called it the Sevier Orogeny. His observation assumed increasing importance with the discovery that other areas along the cordillera had been affected by disturbances at the same time. Many critical areas are still not adequately investigated but it seems likely that the Sevier Orogeny will be found to have had effects well into the northern Rocky Mountains.

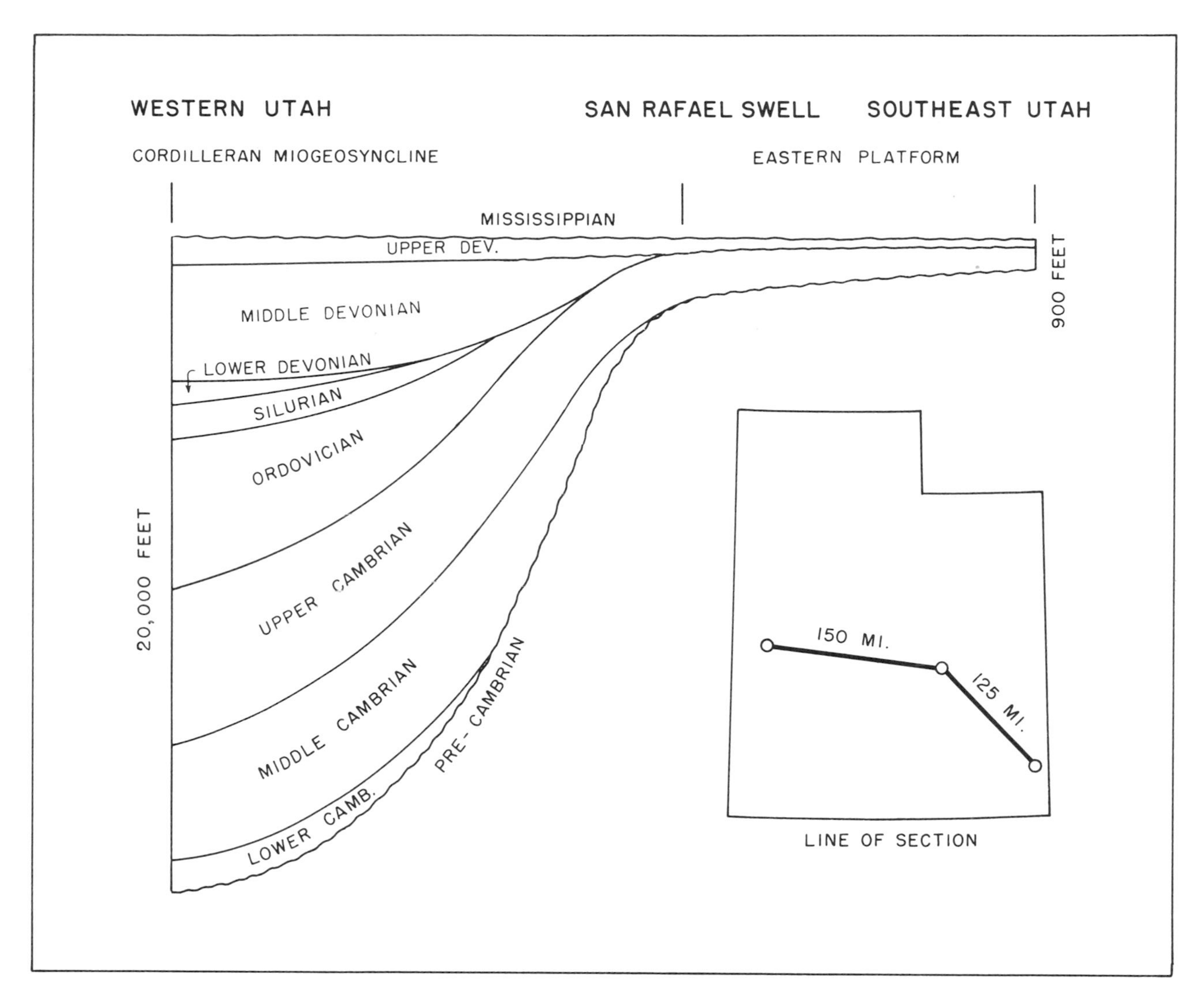

Figure 2-8. Simplified cross-section across central and southern Utah at the close of Mississippian time. A thickness of about 20,000 feet of sediment had accumulated in the Cordilleran Geosyncline to the west while only about 900 feet had been deposited on the shelf or platform to the east in what is now the Colorado Plateau. The transition from the thick to the thin section coincides with the Wasatch Line. The deep structure of the line might be drawn as a great buried fault, as a sharp bend in the crust, or as a high mountain-like front caused by rifting as hypothesized in figure 2-7.

The most notable effect of the orogeny was a great eastward movement of miogeosynclinal sediments to constitute the thrust faulting mentioned earlier. The evident facts are these: 1) There is a concentration of fault traces parallel to the Wasatch Line; 2) the movement of fault blocks was from west to east; and 3) movement was concentrated in the Late Cretaceous.

The problem of how Late Cretaceous and early Tertiary thrusting relates to the Wasatch Line has many aspects and only a few general statements are possible in this brief review. No matter what forces were acting to initiate the thrusting and keep the slices moving, there must have been something in the pre-existing arrangement of rock masses that caused the fault plane to cut upward in the vicinity of the Wasatch Line. Two possible controls come to mind. The initial dip of successive Paleozoic strata was to the west and had been accentuated over a lengthy period of relative subsidence. Fault planes following any particular favorable level of weakness tended to rise eastward and broke to the surface where such planes ended or became too thin to exercise significant effects. This same concept would apply to any movement along surfaces between the solid crystalline basement rocks and the weaker overlying sediments. That the surface of the older rocks rises eastward is a consequence of the subsidence incident to the formation of the Cordilleran geosyncline. Any visualization of conditions within the geosyncline, as shown by east-west cross sections, must invariably show an eastward rise at the top of the oldest sediments. This configuration alone would seem sufficient to guide subsequent thrust faults upward out of the thicker geosynclinal section.

Other constraints enter the picture. An extensive area west of the Wasatch Line is known to have been vertically elevated in the Mesozoic so as to have been much higher than the area to the east. This has a bearing on the thought that thrust faults generally slide under the pull of gravity from higher to lower positions. This must have been true of thrusts associated with the Wasatch Line but those faults, as they presently exist, cannot be directly related to higher areas on one hand and lower areas on the other. For example, the area of central Utah where the Charleston-Nebo Thrust plate clearly originated is now lower in elevation than the area where it finally came to rest. Likewise, east-central Idaho is now generally lower than the mountains of the Overthrust Belt to the east in Wyoming. This agrees with sedimentological evidence that a belt of territory including western Utah and central Idaho was supplying sediment eastward and must have been higher during the Late Cretaceous and early Tertiary time when the great thrust slices were in motion. Later the source areas sank leaving the displaced material at a relatively higher position.

Other interesting problems should be mentioned. How far have the displaced slices moved? Estimates for the thrusts along the Wasatch Line range from 10 to more than 100 miles. Consider Mount Timpanogos, carved from the over-riding slice of the Charleston-Nebo Thrust, and now resting on the Wasatch Line. The rocks of which it is composed were laid down to the west; in terms of today's geography the original site may have been as far west as Cedar Valley (20 miles) or Rush Valley (40 miles). An estimate has been made that Triassic rocks now exposed near Strawberry Reservoir were laid down in the position of Utah Lake. Rocks in the northern Wasatch Range, for example those making up Wellsville Mountain west of Logan, Cache County, have also been moved eastward for an unknown distance, possibly from the vicinity of the northwest arm of Great Salt Lake.

Great force is obviously needed to move the slices forward but rocks are too weak to be pushed very far without breaking or piling up. Comparison with a table cloth on a table is frequently made. Any part of the cloth can be pushed only a short distance before it folds or bunches. If the table as a whole is tipped, however, the whole cloth slides forward rather easily.

The Wasatch Line in the Early Tertiary

A great reversal of tectonic effects took place after the Sevier Orogeny. It might be called the second great reversal, the first having been accomplished in the Triassic when the geosynclinal belt began to rise. The second reversal has been referred to as the decline of the Great Basin or the Basin-and-Range Orogeny. Basically the Great Basin geosynclinal belt subsided with respect to the shelf area to the east. The subsidence involved scores of elongated blocks and produced the distinctive horst-and-graben structure (fig. 2-9) that is unusual, if not unique in global geology (see physiographic and geologic maps, inside front cover). The disturbance is usually referred to as having affected the area between the west-facing scarp of the Wasatch Range (generally called the Wasatch Front) and the east-facing scarp of the Sierra Nevada in western Nevada. The parallelism and nearly coincident trends of the easternmost great normal faults and the Wasatch Line must have deep seated significance. As a matter of fact, in the thinking of most geologists, the Wasatch Fault and the Wasatch Front are almost synonymous with the Wasatch Line.

Figure 2-9. Looking south along the Joes Valley graben in the Wasatch Plateau. The narrow block that has subsided to form the trench that extends to the skyline in the distance is over 60 miles long. Photo: U.S. Bureau of Reclamation.

It is obvious that stretching or extensional forces were operating to bring about the collapse of the Great Basin (fig. 2-10). Some workers have proposed that the collapse began along the central axis of the Great Basin and progressed outward toward the margins. Others see evidence of early faulting along the eastern margin near the Wasatch Mountains. The evidence from drilling in Great Salt Lake is that Great Salt Lake graben was deep enough to divert drainage from the Uinta Mountains westward across the Wasatch Line and into the Great Basin as early as early Miocene. Geophysical investigations along the Wasatch Front (fig. 2-11) have resulted in discoveries that have been described as follows: "The gravity data indicate that in the valley areas between this fault block (Oquirrh Mountains, Boulder Ridge, northern East Tintic Mountains), and the Wasatch fault block, an intermontane trough (designated by us as the Wasatch Structural Trough) more than 100 miles in length, comprises a great belt of grabens and smaller fault blocks whose dislocations are varied and more complex than previously realized. Several large block fragments lying just west of the Wasatch block have apparently dropped deeper than some other fragments, as if slipping into a great crevass. From north to south, the major grabens are the Farmington, Jordan Valley, Utah Valley, and Juab Valley Grabens" (Cook and Berg, 1961).

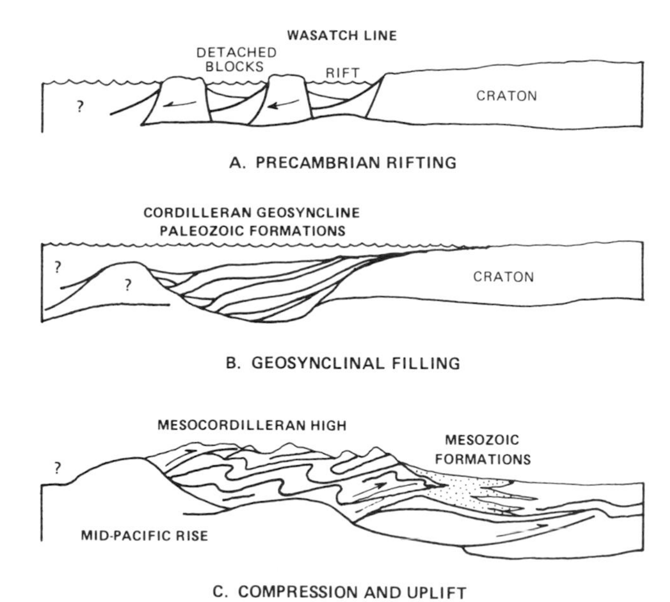

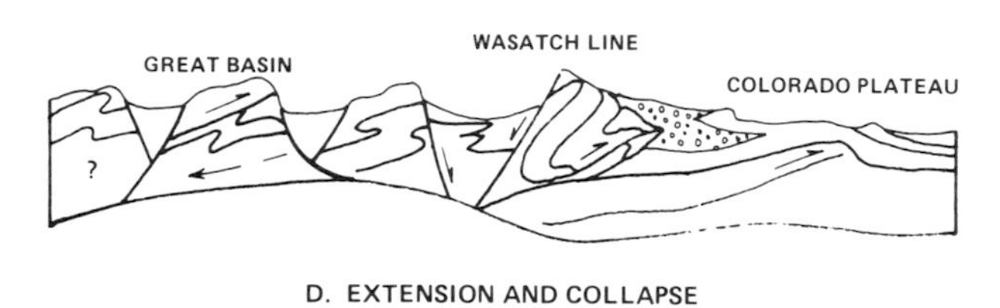

Figure 2-10. Generalized geologic cross-sections illustrating development of Great Basin and continental interior through geologic time. (A) Precambrian rifting, about 800 million years ago; (B) filling of Cordilleran geosyncline, 800 million to 220 million years ago; (C) westward drifting and compression, 200 million to 40 million years ago; (D) extension and collapse, 40 million years ago to present.

It is known from drilling that Tertiary and Quaternary sediments under Great Salt Lake reach a thickness of more than 12,000 feet. An exploratory well drilled near Spanish Fork, Utah Valley, penetrated more than 13,000 feet of Tertiary sediments. Further south near Cedar City, along the Hurricane Fault that has about the same relation to the Wasatch Line as the Wasatch Fault, workers have detected a similar system of grabens with unconsolidated fill nearly 4,000 feet thick.

Information is also available from shallow wells. A 1,000-foot core taken near Burmester, Tooele Valley (see chap. 20), is considered to have bottomed in sediments about 3.4 million years old. Extrapolating the rate of sedimentation downward to 10,000 feet would give a rough age of 34 million years for the sediments on the bedrock. This is almost at the Eocene/Oligocene boundary. Using a more conservative thickness of 5,000 feet of unconsolidated fill gives a date of 17 million years, sometime in the middle Miocene. These estimates seem to have been verified by drilling in Great Salt Lake.

Although the Wasatch Fault is active along this stretch and the maximum displacement of 15,000 feet could possibly have been reached in Quaternary time, the evidence is that the sinking of grabens not necessarily bounded by the Wasatch Fault, but closely related to it, began in middle Tertiary time. How this relates to the decline of the Great Basin in general and to the theory that failure of the rock units began in the center of the basin and spread outward will have to be decided on better evidence.

Is the Wasatch Line Migrating?

Shuey and others (1973) present evidence that the transition between the Colorado Plateau and the Basin and Range Provinces, as drawn on geophysical criteria, is considerably east of the boundary as drawn by physiographers. Their map illustrates this and emphasizes the fact that block faulting is found in the Colorado Plateau well eastward of the physiographic boundary. It might be added that the easternmost grabens and half-grabens are apparently very young; post-glacial movement can be proven in some faults of the Wasatch Plateau, for example.

An eastward migration of volcanic effects in the Grand Canyon area has also been well documented. A distinctive type of basalt called hawaiite appeared in the vicinity of the Grand Wash Fault 6.5 million years ago, in the central belt of the Shivwits Plateau 5 to 15 miles to the east about 3 million years ago, and along the Hurricane and Toroweap Faults 40 miles or so to the east 1 million or less years ago.

Seismic data may tell the same story. Many earthquakes occur east of the Wasatch Fault and Smith (1974) suggests that the zone of seismic activity may be migrating eastward. This possible shift may be the explanation of a puzzling, quiet condition that prevails along the Wasatch Fault in the central Wasatch Range.

The Wasatch Line in a World Setting

Many diverse facts have been explained by the theory of plate tectonics (fig. 2-12). In simplified terms, this is the concept that the Earth is encased in a shell of brittle rock, the lithosphere, which ranges from 50 to 200 miles thick which rests and moves upon a deeper, hot, plastic layer, the asthenosphere. The lithosphere is subdivided into a number of great curving plates, six large ones and about 12 small ones, the whole being roughly comparable to the cracked shell of a hard-boiled egg. The amazing thing is that individual lithospheric plates are in a state of relative motion and are colliding, pushing apart, and sliding past each other in a complicated but interrelated way. The major plates are separating along a great submarine mountain system that runs beneath the major oceans. At the time of separation, lava pushes up from depth so that new crust comes into being and no gaping cracks are created. Where plates move together the usual reaction is for one of them to be forced downward along an oceanic trench where it is remelted into the asthenosphere. Such trenches are called subduction zones. In some instances the underthrust plate is not destroyed but is added or welded to the overlying

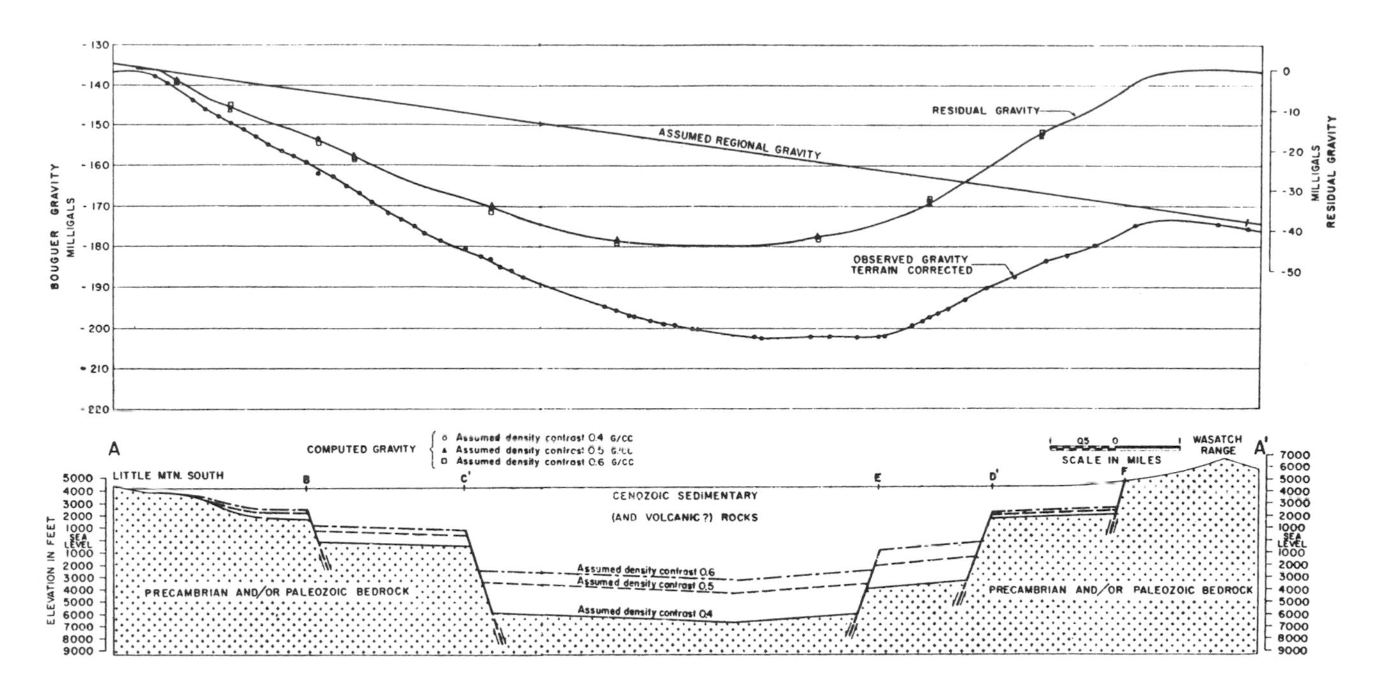

Figure 2-11. A geophysical cross-section of the Wasatch trench in the Ogden area. Depending on assumptions made as to the density of the valley fill, different depths to bedrock are obtained. The greatest thickness near the center of the profile with an assumed density contrast of 0.4 is 11,000 feet, making the bottom of the trench 6,000 feet below sea level. Note that the elevation of the crest of the Wasatch Range in this vicinity is 3,000 feet.

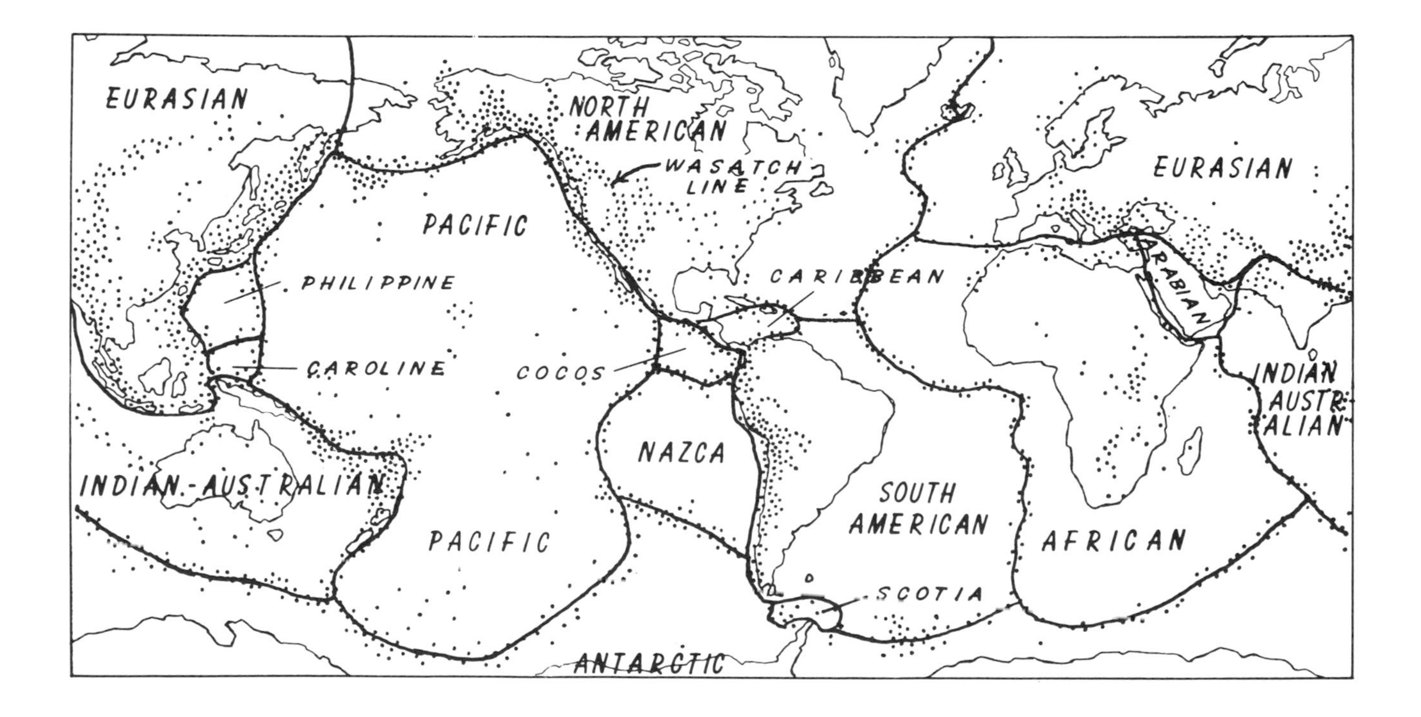

Figure 2-12. The great lithospheric plates of the earth in relation to continents and ocean basins. Dots show relative distribution of major earthquakes. Note the earthquake belt representing the Wasatch Line. Although the line is active geologically, it is not a plate boundary. (Adapted from various sources.)

plate so as to create a doubling-up of material. The Tibetan Plateau in Asia is held to be an example. Where two plates slide past each other a great transverse fault is created, the San Andreas Fault system in California is such a zone. Areas within plates are geologically less active with relatively simple folds, fewer earthquakes, and less igneous activity.

Much of the history of western North America can be explained in terms of plate tectonics, particularly activity during the past 200 million years. During this lengthy period the American continents have pushed westward to collide with the Pacific plate or plates. This coincided with the opening of the present Atlantic Ocean. As it became wider the Pacific became correspondingly narrower. For a very long time the American plate pushed over and obliterated the ocean floor to the west. There was much volcanic activity and material was literally scraped from the ocean floor and forceably added to the continent. In effect the continent grew at the expense of the ocean. In the Early Triassic, about 195 million years ago, the shores of the Pacific lay near the Wasatch Line; by the Middle Triassic, they traversed central Nevada; and by Late Cretaceous time, the shoreline ran through central California. By 25 million years ago, the two great plates ceased to collide; perhaps westward movement of the North American continent slowed, but at any rate the Pacific Plate began to move northwesterly. This created the strong oblique sliding action which is going on today along the San Andreas Fault zone.

The Wasatch Line should be explainable under the concept of plate tectonics but at present (1985) there is considerable disagreement as to how the line relates to the broader picture. It definitely does not seem to be a subduction zone where the Pacific plate has dipped down beneath North America. There are not enough signs of volcanic action, and the volcanic rocks that are present are not the right varieties. Also, the line bows inward and not outward as present-day subduction zones do. The line, as presently known, shows evidence of the crust being pulled apart. Valleys along the Wasatch Fault, for example, are deep narrow sediment-filled grabens where space has been created by extension and subsidence. The structure of the Wasatch structural trough has been compared with the so-called "rift valleys" of east Africa. In Africa large volcanoes are present in and along the zones of separation, but in Utah practically no volcanic activity is present where the splitting has been greatest. More and more it seems that the Wasatch Line is "one of a kind" that cannot be matched with any other great Earth fracture.

Many competent geologists have mapped and written about the Overthrust Belt, Hingeline, and other sections of the Wasatch Line. Most of the papers are in guidebooks that emphasize associated oil fields. Important future discoveries are to be expected.

For additional reading about the topics discussed in Chapter 2, see works by the following authors:

Arabez and others, 1979
Armstrong, 1968, 1972
Astin, 1977
Atwater, 1970
Baker, A. A. J., 1949, 1959
Best, 1969
Best and Brimhall, 1974
Bick, 1966
Bissell, H. J., 1952, 1957, 1964
Buss and Peterson, 1969
Callaghan, 1939
Cook, D.R., 1957
Cook, E.F., 1960a
Cook, K.L., 1966, 1969, 1970
Cook and Berg, 1961
Cook and Smith, 1967
Crittenden, 1964, 1972
Crittenden and others, 1970
Eardley, 1933, 1969
Erickson, A. J., 1968
Goode, 1965
Hamblin, 1970
Hansen, W. R., 1965, 1969b
Heisey and others, 1977
Hill, 1976
Hilpert, 1971
Hintze, L. F., 1959, 1963, 1971, 1973
Johnson, K. D., 1959
Lindsay, 1970
Marsell, 1964a, 1964b
Miller, G. M., 1966
Morisawa, 1971
Moulton, 1976
Mundorff, 1970, 1971
Proctor and Bullock, 1963
Ridd, 1960
Ritzma, 1974
Rowley and others, 1975
Smith, R. B., 1974, 1974b
Stokes, 1976, 1977
Swenson, 1975
Threet, 1959
Welsh, 1959
Woodward, 1976.

For complete bibliographic citations, please see List of References.

Figure 2-13. Waste dumps and surface installations of silver mines in the Alta district, late 19th century. Skiers take note of landmarks. Photo: Utah State Historical Society.

3 WHAT LIES BELOW

As of 1985, the deepest mine in Utah, slightly more than 3,000 feet deep, was the Chief Mine in the Tintic district near Eureka, Juab County. The deepest oil well was Texaco, Inc. No. 1 Thousand Peak Ranch in northern Summit County, an unsuccessful test that reached 21,847 feet. From these and other deep penetrations of the crust a great deal has been learned about what lies beneath the surface. There are many reasons for probing still deeper, but even the most optimistic geologists see little possibility of drilling more than a few miles beyond present records. Technical difficulties and cost increase dramatically with depth. Even so, the desire and need to know about conditions below the economic limits of drilling remain and lead to the development of indirect exploration methods, including many geophysical techniques that have been developed from surface studies and adapted to deeper and deeper situations.

LAYERS WITHIN THE EARTH

A basic generalization about the Earth is that it has a layered structure at almost every level. The characteristics of the layers reflect different geologic processes and histories. The outermost layers, laid down by wind and water, are the familiar beds or strata of geologists and engineers (fig. 3-1). Aggregations of sedimentary strata, lumped together for convenient reference and mapping, are called geologic formations and are, by their very nature, created at the Earth's surface. Extensive mapping has demonstrated that they seldom exceed a few thousand feet in thickness or cover more than a few thousand square miles. In comparison to igneous or metamorphic rocks, most sedimentary formations consist of minerals that are relatively light in both weight and color.

The minerals of which sediments are made have risen to the surface because of their low specific gravity. It is difficult to return this lightweight material into the deeper, denser environments from which it was segregated. When a pile of sediments becomes excessively thick, on the order of 60,000 to 80,000 feet, it approaches a position of equilibrium and will sink no farther unless forced by strong external pressure. At those depths the effects of heat begin to appear, expansion takes place, buoyancy increases, and subsidence ends. The principle that crustal rocks float, somewhat like icebergs on and in a heavier medium, is called isostasy. C. E. Dutton, a pioneer student of Utah geology, introduced this concept in 1889.

At depths of about 10 miles, heat and pressure obliterate practically all evidence of stratification and convert sediments into denser rocks like slate, schist, and gneiss that are in equilibrium with higher pressures and temperatures. Gneiss is indicative of temperatures high enough to destroy original features but not sufficient to bring about complete melting. The thin, twisted layers of light- and dark-colored

Figure 3-1. Cataract Canyon of the Colorado River, east-central Utah. Rocks of Pennsylvanian and Permian age are exposed in the walls. Undeformed strata such as these make up most of the Colorado Plateau. Photo: Parker Hamilton and Utah Travel Council.

minerals are clearly not the result of sedimentary processes (fig. 3-2). In slate and schist, the original material is compressed into platy layers. The terms "banded" or "foliated" are usually applied to gneiss, while the term "cleavage" is appropriate for slate and schist. Highly altered sediments cropping out at the surface are indicative of deep burial followed by uplift and erosion. Such rocks are seen on Antelope Island and along the central Wasatch Front east of Farmington, Box Elder County.

Figure 3-2. Boulder of banded and contorted gneiss from Farmington Canyon Complex. Photo: Arthur C. King.

With the application of geophysical techniques, chiefly seismology, another type of layering has been discovered. The layers are created by movement along great horizontal, or nearly horizontal, breaks called detachment faults. The Great Basin furnishes the best examples. Here as many as three superimposed plates or layers have been detected between 2 and 9 miles beneath the surface. The term "detachment fault" implies a separation of overlying and underlying material. Smith and Bruin (1984), in a study of deep-seated structures of the eastern Basin and Range, conclude that there has been large-scale movement on planes that seem to follow zones of weakness between brittle and plastic material. Faults seen at the surface mostly curve downward and disappear at the level of the detachments. Also, most shallow earthquakes are known to originate at these levels. Other differences between layers are not well understood.

According to long established usage, the outer, relatively thin, brittle shell of the Earth is called the crust. The continental crust consists of sedimentary strata at the surface and metamorphic rock below. The oceanic crust consists mainly of basalt, an igneous rock, covered by a thin veneer of sedimentary ooze. Below the crust, at depths ranging to as deep as 25 miles below the surface, is a very prominent plane known as the Mohorovicic Discontinuity, or Moho. This is 15 to 18 miles below the surface of the Great Basin and 24 miles beneath the Colorado Plateau. Still deeper and making up the great bulk of the globe is the more homogeneous mantle and below that, at the center of the Earth, is the partly molten core. The crust is about 20 miles thick, the mantle is 1,700 to 1,800 miles thick, and the core has a diameter of about 2,000 miles. With the understanding of continental drift and sea-floor spreading, a more meaningful division of the Earth's outer shells is coming into use. Two great divisions, called the lithosphere and asthenosphere, are recognized (fig. 3-3). The lithosphere consists of sedimentary and metamorphic rocks that are solid and relatively cool. It comprises the crust, the Moho, and the upper part of the mantle and ranges from 200 to 400 miles in thickness. The asthenosphere, ranging from 60 to 250 miles thick, lies entirely within the mantle and is relatively plastic, hot, and mobile. According to the concept of plate tectonics, movements of lithospheric plates upon the asthenosphere produce most of the deformation of the Earth's surface.

GEOPHYSICAL EVIDENCE

Each of Utah's four physiographic divisions presents contrasting manifestations of deep subsurface conditions that challenge study and explanation. The Great Basin is characterized by numerous alternating valleys and mountains bordered by steeply dipping faults. In strong contrast is the Colorado Plateau, an elevated block with stratified rocks virtually as level and undeformed as when they were deposited. The Wasatch Line between these provinces is a zone of transition marked by geologic activity so intense that geophysicists regard it as dividing the United States into two superprovinces, each involving both the crust and mantle.

Geophysics is the study of the reaction of earth material to vibrations, gravity, magnetism, electricity, and heat. Each of these five manifestations of energy can be measured by specific techniques and instruments. Geophysics, aided by conventional geologic techniques, is applied extensively to practical problems of locating economic, mineral, and energy resources and to the study of earthquakes, including their possible prediction and control. Application of geophysics has revealed most of what is known and inferred about conditions below depths reached by drilling and mining.

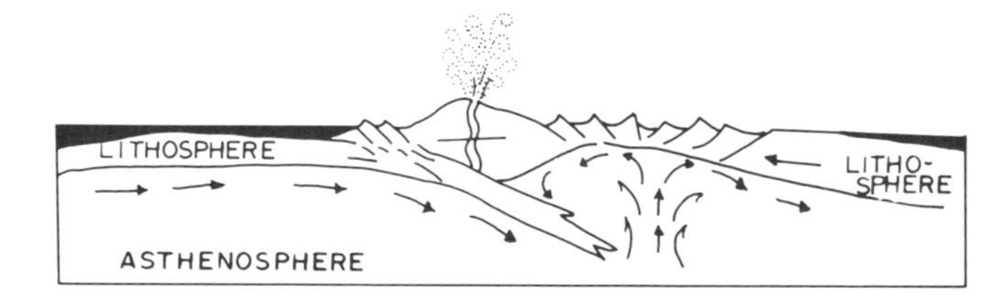

Figure 3-3. Diagrammatic cross-section of the western margin of North America showing continental lithosphere moving westward onto the Pacific plate which is plunging downward beneath it. The Basin and Range province is represented as undergoing extension as a convecting current of plastic material rises beneath it. Black represents water - Pacific Ocean on the left, shallow interior sea on the right.

Seismology

The study of mechanical vibrations in the Earth is called seismology and the seismograph is the basic instrument for procuring the data. This instrument records vibrations created by naturally occurring earthquakes and by man-made explosions or impacts (fig. 3-4). Hundreds of quakes of magnitude 2 or less on the Richter scale occur each year. They are not normally felt by humans. It is estimated that during the past 115 years Utah has been shaken each year by an average of about 11 quakes of magnitude 3 and three quakes of magnitude 4 on the Richter scale. In the same 115-year period there have been 10 damaging quakes of magnitudes between 4 and 5, five between magnitudes 5 and 6, and two between magnitudes 6 and 7. Some minor earthquakes are caused by rock bursts and collapse due to coal removal from underground mines. Adjustments of local strata can release enough energy to cause tremors in the range of 2 to 3 on the Richter scale; maps depicting earthquakes show many epicenters near the mines in Carbon County.

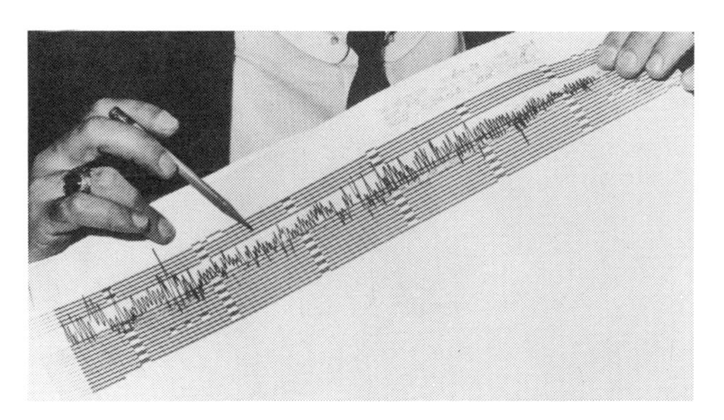

Figure 3-4. Seismogram of a moderate intensity earthquake as recorded on a University of Utah seismograph. (From Cook, 1972 with permission of Utah Geological Association).

Geophysicists have found uses for the earth-shaking energy of the powerful blasts that break up rock and ore at the Bingham Canyon open-pit copper mine. Explosions are set off on a regular schedule and can be identified exactly as to time and place of origin. By calculating the speed of seismic waves from Bingham Canyon, a number of profiles have been constructed across adjacent territory. The still more powerful explosions of underground nuclear tests in the nearby Nevada Proving Grounds are also recorded and studied.

Much of what is known about conditions at depth comes from studying the reflection and refraction of seismic waves and the speeds at which they travel. Velocity through different materials gives clues to the nature of these materials and the physical conditions under which they exist. Seismic reflection is widely employed in petroleum exploration; refraction studies are important in discovering the probable composition of deep-seated layers or masses of rock. In addition to almost universal use in petroleum exploration, seismology has been employed to map favorable locations for uranium ore bodies in the Colorado Plateau, to detect water-bearing gravels near Ogden, Weber County, and to map the thickness of valley fill along the Wasatch Front.

As described in chapter 2, a zone of intense earthquake activity crosses Utah, parallel with and including the Wasatch Line. The study of this earthquake belt is of much more than academic interest because of the high risks to human life and property that exist along the heavily populated Wasatch Front. The Intermountain Seismic Belt extends from the Mojave Desert area of California across southern Nevada, central Utah, western Wyoming, eastern Idaho and west-central Montana. In North America this zone ranks second only to the San Andreas Fault zone of California for earthquake risk and potential damage. The University of Utah operates a network of 30 to 40 stations equipped with fixed and portable seismographs that constantly monitor vibrations occurring along the Utah and Idaho segment of the Intermountain Seismic Belt. Data produced by the network are needed to develop earthquake-detection systems, to define the associated hazards in various parts of the state and to aid in understanding the causes of earthquakes.

Gravity

Gravity is defined as the force of attraction to the Earth felt by a body divided by the mass of the body; the unit of gravity measurement is the gal (after Galileo), but measurements are usually given in milligals (1×10^{-3} cm/sec^2). It is known that the acceleration of gravity is not uniform but varies slightly from place to place due to the nonspherical form of the Earth, topographic irregularities, and difference in density of buried rock masses. Other anomalies stem from deep-seated causes that are subject to various interpretations.

The gravimeter is the basic instrument for measuring gravity. Deviations from what would be expected of a mathematically ideal Earth are called gravity anomalies and it is these anomalies that geologists and geophysicists seek to interpret. Gravity studies have been successful in detecting buried faults and igneous rock bodies.

A number of gravity surveys have been made and compiled to produce a gravity map of Utah (fig. 3-5). This shows, by contours, the anomalies that exist after the effects of elevation above sea level and latitude are discounted. A value of 2.67 milligals divides positive and negative values. Dense masses of igneous or sedimentary rock give positive, or higher, values; the core of quartzite in the Uinta Range is an example. Low values indicate less dense rock such as the sedimentary contents of the nearby Uinta Basin. The thickening of the crust east of the Wasatch Line is indicated by an increase in values of -150 to -175 across the Basin and Range Province to a value of -200 across the Colorado Plateau. Geophysicists interpret this to mean that the boundary between the crust and mantle descends from about 15 to 18 miles in the Basin and Range to 25 to 28 miles under the Colorado Plateau and Middle Rocky Mountains.

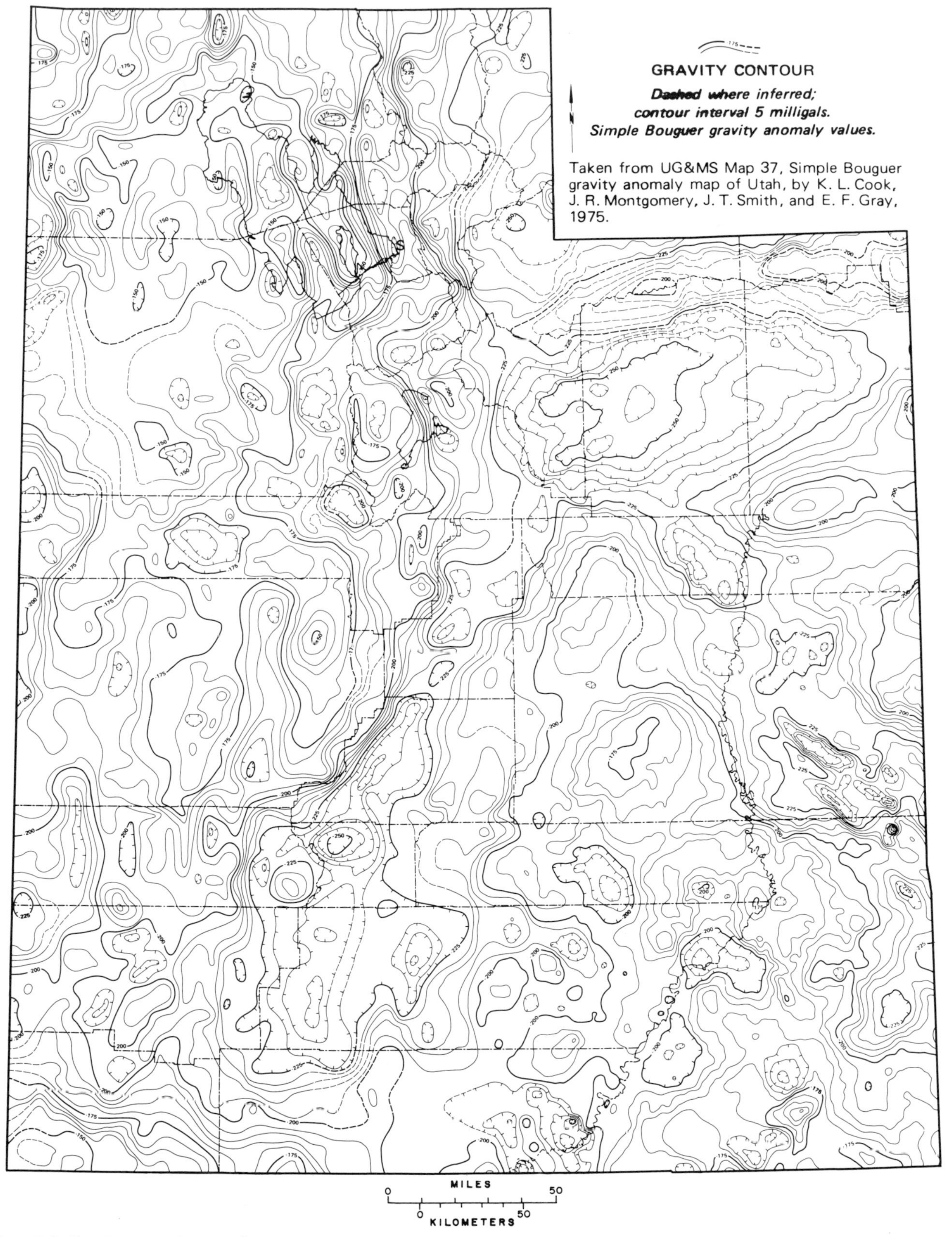

Figure 3-5. Gravity anomaly map of Utah. Contours connect lines of equal gravity anomaly values; figures are in milligals. A reading of -175 is approximately average. Note expression of Wasatch line, Uinta Basin and Uinta Mountains. Credits appear upper right corner.

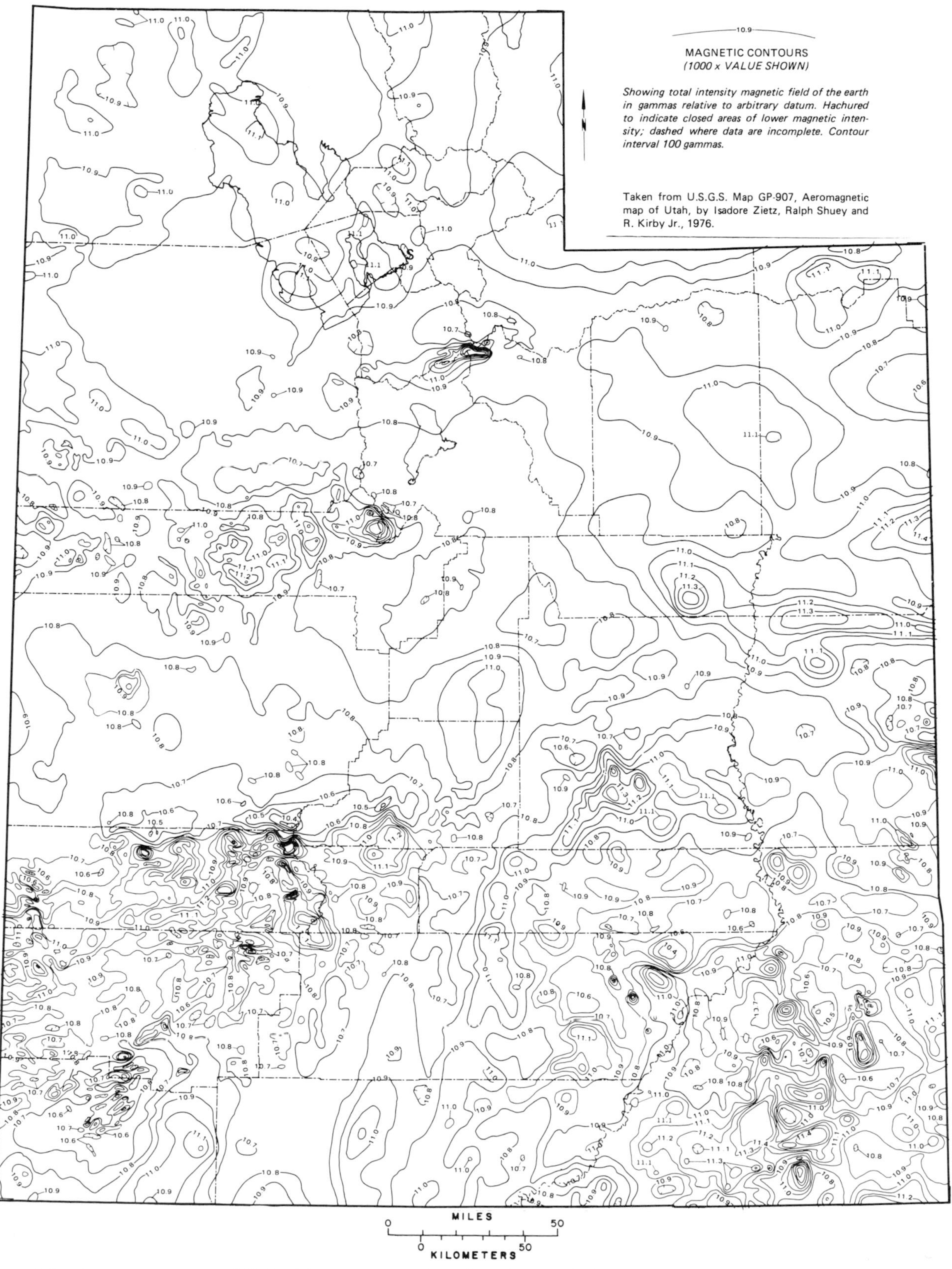

Figure 3-6. Aeromagnetic map of Utah. Lines connect points of equal magnetic intensity relative to an arbitrary datum. Figures are in gammas. In general, areas of higher iron content are accentuated and show higher readings. For eastern Utah the higher values reflect masses of iron-rich intrusions in the buried Precambrian. Credits upper right corner.

Geomagnetism

Many rock types are magnetic and the Earth possesses its own magnetic field. The units of electromagnetic measurement are the gauss (after Gauss), one gauss being the total magnetic field of the Earth, and the gamma, about 1/50,000 of a gauss. Magnetism is measured by a magnetometer which can be operated on the surface, carried by aircraft or towed through water. Compared to other geophysical procedures, magnetic surveys are relatively inexpensive.

Magnetic effects arise from: 1) Magnetism induced by the main magnetic field of the Earth; 2) magnetic fields generated by electrical currents, and 3) remnant magnetism of local rock masses. As with gravity, there are many anomalies, or departures from what would prevail in an ideal, theoretical magnetic field. Anomalies may arise from external as well as internal causes. Some are transitory while others are permanent; for example, the magnetic field associated with a body of iron ore is permanent, whereas the electromagnetic fields caused by sunspots are not. The Earth's magnetic fields gradually shift during periods of weeks or months and appear to be caused by movements within the core. The complexities of magnetic fields make the interpretation of anomalies difficult.

The pattern of magnetic anomalies shown on the aeromagnetic map of Utah (fig. 3-6) correlates well with surface observations and contributes to interpretations of subsurface geology. Complex and sharply defined anomalies indicate relatively near-surface igneous rocks such as the laccolithic intrusions of Tertiary rocks in the Henry, LaSal, and Abajo Mountains. Broader anomalies suggest deeper blocks of relatively high magnetic susceptibility. A distinct east-west belt of anomalies in southwestern Utah that seems to terminate at the Wasatch Line near Marysvale, Piute County, correlates with a belt of calc-alkalic volcanic rocks that dominates the surface outcrops. In contrast, the anomalies east of the Wasatch Line appear to indicate deep-seated metamorphic bodies. The anomalies of eastern Utah show no distinct pattern or common orientation except a vague tendency to follow the N. 70° E. trend of the transcontinental arch. Such patterns are used to interpret the broad structure of the United States.

The magnetic method has proven extremely successful in exploring for iron deposits in the Iron Springs district near Cedar City, Iron County (fig. 3-7). Since the ore is chiefly the magnetic mineral, magnetite, large deposits affect the local magnetic field even through hundreds of feet of non-magnetic overburden, displaying anomalies of more than 1,500 gammas.

Electrical Methods

The electrical properties of the Earth and its materials vary considerably from time to time and place to place. The unit for electrical measurements is the coulomb (after Coulomb). Electrical currents are introduced into earth and rock to reveal near-surface conditions; investigations of deeper zones utilize the naturally occurring currents of the Earth and atmosphere. Electrical disturbances in the ionosphere induce eddies in the crust and upper mantle. Measurements of these telluric currents allow inferences to be made about the distribution of deep-seated electrical conductivity and structure.

Electrical methods are well adapted to logging drill holes. Electrodes are lowered through successive stratigraphic units to produce "E-logs" that are routinely made and used in the petroleum industry. The instruments that measure electrical conductivity are similar to mine detectors and the more familiar devices used by treasure hunters to locate metallic objects. Mineral deposits of many types, especially where materials of contrasting resistivity occur in near proximity, can be probed by electrical means.

The presence or absence of underground solutions dramatically influences electrical conductivity. Resistivity decreases as the pore spaces of rocks are filled with water, salt solutions, or other fluids. Clay particles resulting from alteration of feldspars are often good conductors. Conductivity also increases with increases in temperature. These variations are important in determining the characteristics of underground fluids. Electrical methods have been successfully applied in exploring geothermal resources near Roosevelt Hot Springs where variables such as depth to water, porosity of fractured rocks, temperature, salinity of fluids, and presence of clay minerals and pyrite (FeS_2) provide evidence of hydrothermal action.

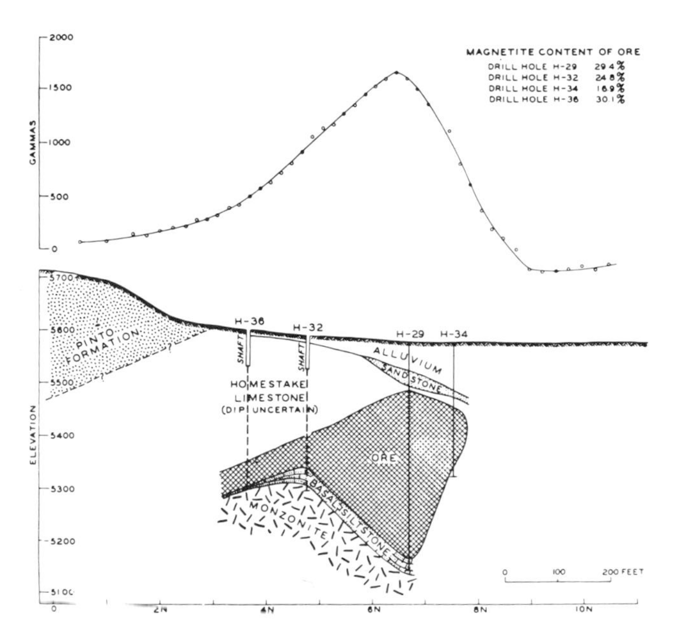

Figure 3-7. Diagrammatic cross-section illustrating use of magnetic surveys in locating a body of iron ore in the Iron Springs district, Iron County. Upper curve shows variations in vertical component of earth's magnetic field, in gammas, across the concealed ore body. (From Cook, 1950; reprinted from U.S. Bureau of Mines Report of Investigation 4586).

Heat Flow

The average outward flow of heat that reaches the Earth's surface is about 1.25 x 10^{-6} cal/sec/cm^2 (1 mcal/c-m^2/sec) or about 40 cal/yr. This quantity is so small that it could melt only a layer of ice no more than 0.2 inches thick each year. Direct sunlight on a clear day supplies 17,000 times as much energy as comes from below. Heat flow is measured in terms of Heat Flow Units (HFU).

Because temperatures deep in the Earth cannot be measured directly, thermometers placed at a known distance apart in drill holes measure changes in temperature in the accessible crust and, thus, establish thermal gradients (fig. 3-8). Most land-based measurements are taken in holes drilled for oil or mineral exploration at depths of from 98 to 328 feet; at these depths surface climatic effects are negligible.

Figure 3-8. Instruments for obtaining heat-flow data in operation in the Sevier Lake area. A thermistor probe is being lowered into a pipe leading into a deep drillhole at the upper left. A digital resistance meter, center, records temperature data. Photo: David S. Chapman.

As might be expected, the escape of heat from within the Earth's interior is not uniform but variations are difficult to measure. The actual temperature difference that determines a local gradient is influenced by the thermal conductivity of the subsurface rock masses and ground-water conditions. The thermal conductivity of specific rock types can be determined from laboratory experiments on suitable samples or from tests in drill holes.

Until 1976 very few heat flow measurements had been made in Utah. Recent studies give an average heat flow of 2 HFU for the Great Basin; corresponding values for the Colorado Plateau are about 1.3 HFU. The world average is about 1.5 HFU. Values characteristic of the Great Basin are found as far as 50 miles east of the Wasatch Line.

As molten magma rises from deeper levels of the Earth it may carry pieces of solid material torn from the walls of subterranean chambers and conduits. Such pieces are called xenoliths, or plutonic inclusions (fig. 3-9). Many types of xenoliths occur in igneous rocks in Utah. An intriguing

Figure 3-9. A xenolith (unmelted inclusion) of gneiss in quartz monzonite (so-called "Temple Granite") from Little Cottonwood Canyon.

example is described by Callaghan (1973) in his study of the mineral resources of Piute County: "Float blocks of a dark dike rock, evidently weathered out of volcanic breccia, were studied by S. O. Agrell some years ago at Cambridge University in England. The rock fragments contain an unusual group of minerals: Nepheline, corundum, spinel, hibonite, diaspore, forsterite, clinohumite, sillimanite, and orthoclase. Agrell found the rocks ranged as high as 70 percent alumina content. The blocks of rock containing the minerals, which are foreign to the natural sequence of igneous rocks in the Marysvale region, must have been broken loose by volcanic processes from a deep-seated source and incorporated in an eruptive outpouring of volcanic breccia."

No less intriguing are xenoliths found in the Henry and LaSal Mountains described by Hunt (1953 and 1958). These consist of amphibolite, a dark-colored rock composed chiefly of hornblende and characteristic of deep burial and metamorphism. They may represent the parent material of the magma that eventually pushed upward to form the cores of the mountains. If so, the increase of temperature and melting of the parent material probably took place at depths of 25 to 28 miles near the base of the crust.

The abundant basalt flows of southwestern Utah contain a variety of unmelted xenoliths derived from the mantle. They are chiefly dark, heavy basic rocks such as lherzolite, websterite, gabbro, and clinopyroxenite. In southeastern Utah a number of ancient vents or pipes called diatremes have also yielded rock and mineral specimens from great depths (fig. 3-10). Garnets from similar diatremes in nearby areas of Arizona have weathered free into the stream beds and have been collected for many years.

GEOTHERMAL ENERGY

The upward rise and escape of heat is the basis of geothermal energy. The term is commonly used in connection with

Figure 3-10. Oblique aerial view of the Mule Ear diatreme, south of the San Juan River, San Juan County.

the utilization of such energy by man. Heated steam or hot water may appear at the surface in natural hot springs (fig. 3-11) and fumaroles. Technically, a division between hot springs and warm springs is set at 90°C. Utah has about 50 warm or hot springs but no fumaroles. Geothermal energy is also present beneath the surface locked in bodies of hot, dry rock. The energy of such rocks may be captured by injecting water into the heated areas, then recovering it as it flows or is pumped to the surface.

In order to constitute a geothermal resource, an underground system must have: 1) A source of heat such as molten or recently molten rock; 2) a source of underground water; 3) a permeable or fractured body of rock in which steam or hot water may be stored; and 4) a cap rock to prevent the heat from leaking away. Utah has several locations designated as Known Geothermal Resource Areas (KGRAs): Monroe/Joseph near Monroe, Sevier County; Crater Springs north of Delta, Millard County, associated with the lava beds of Fumarole Butte; Cove Fort/Sulphurdale, Millard County; Thermo, north of Cedar City in Beaver County; Newcastle, west of Cedar City in Iron County; and Roosevelt Hot Springs northeast of Milford, Beaver County, where evidences of recently active springs include sulphur and siliceous material deposits (fig. 3-11), and where over a dozen wells have been drilled to depths of 1,000 to 7,000 feet. A typical well in the Roosevelt field is capable of producing 1 million pounds of steam (fig. 3-12) and water per hour at temperatures of 270°C (500°F), of which 25 percent will flash to steam capable of generating electrical power. The field is reported to have a proven capacity of 55 megawatts for 35 years from heat supplied by large bodies of igneous rocks that make up much of the nearby Mineral Mountains.

Full development of Utah's geothermal resources would be very expensive; millions of dollars are necessary to bring one field into production, as exemplified by the Roosevelt area. Optimistically, however, between 500 and 1,000 megawatts of power might be generated from geothermal energy by the year 2000 from a proven resource - the Geysers field in California is a good example. In comparison, the Huntington coal-fired power plant generates 446.4 megawatts per year. About 11,000 megawatts are consumed yearly in Utah. Hot water from small geothermal systems could possibly heat the nearby towns decreasing their use of otherwise imported, expensive power. Other geothermal waters that do not reach the temperature of steam production are usable for space heating, swimming, etc. (fig. 3-13). The hot water that rises and escapes in natural springs

Figure 3-11. Baker Hot Spring near Delta. Calcareous material (tufa) is being deposited due to loss of carbon dioxide. The subsurface rock from which the water is rising is estimated to have a temperature of at least 350° C. Photo: Jim Howell.

Figure 3-12. Steam escaping from a well in a Roosevelt geothermal area. Photo: James A. Whelan.

along the Wasatch Line could eventually heat homes and public buildings. The LDS Church office building utilizes thermal ground water and a heat pump for heating, supplemented by gas.

CONCLUSIONS

Geologists and geophysicists are cooperating to discover what lies below the highly diverse, near-surface rocks and structures and above the relatively uniform mantle. There is general agreement that the Mohorovicic Discontinuity separating crust and mantle lies from 15 to 18 miles below the surface in the Great Basin and from 22 to 26 miles under the Colorado Plateau. The deepening along the transition zone between the two great provinces is not a simple downward slope. A distinct bulge along the transition zone parallels the Wasatch Line and brings the mantle to within 16 miles of the surface; the east flank of this upwarp descends quite steeply under the Colorado Plateau and Rocky Mountains while the west slope declines gently to near horizontal west of the Utah-Nevada border (fig. 3-14).

The mantle upwarp has been identified by electrical and seismic data, and by thermal measurements. Electrical resistivity falls off gradually from eastern Nevada across western Utah, reaching a minimum in the transition belt. It increases rapidly east of a line about 31 miles east of the Wasatch Line. Evidence from heat-flow data substantiates these observations. In the Basin and Range the heat production measures from 1.8 to 2.4 HFU, whereas the Colorado Plateau has more normal heat production of 1.0 to 1.5 HFU. Although the transition zone shows many superficial geologic similarities with the Colorado Plateau, the heat-flow values are more like those of the Basin and Range to the west. The transition from high to low values seems to be abrupt along a narrow belt about 62 miles east of the Wasatch Line. This coincides with a zone of intensified earthquake activity.

Rocks immediately below the Moho appear to be highly heated but not molten. In mineralogical terms they are peridotites and eclogites, very heavy rocks composed of iron-magnesium-rich minerals. Fragments (xenoliths) of these rocks have been carried to the surface as inclusions in basaltic flows. Their place of origin has been calculated as between 40 and 50 miles where temperatures of 1,300 to 1,400°C prevail. These rocks are samples of the deeper lithosphere; the asthenosphere that begins some tens of miles below consists entirely of hot, plastic, well-mixed material. Geophysically the asthenosphere is known as the upper mantle low-velocity zone because seismic waves have lower velocities through it than they do through the cooler, more solid material above or the core below. How a hot, plastic shell can come into existence and continue to exist between two solid shells is not fully explained.

Perhaps the most important effect of the mantle upwarp has been the production of a second, higher layer of heated rock within the crust itself. Because this higher layer is characterized chiefly by a drop in the velocity of seismic waves it is called the upper crustal low-velocity layer (LVL). This

Figure 3-13. West-facing scarp of the Warm Springs fault exposed in gravel pits at the base of Becks Spur, north of Salt Lake City. Springs of warm water emerge along the fault zone and have provided water for public swimming. Photo: Henry Dequasie.

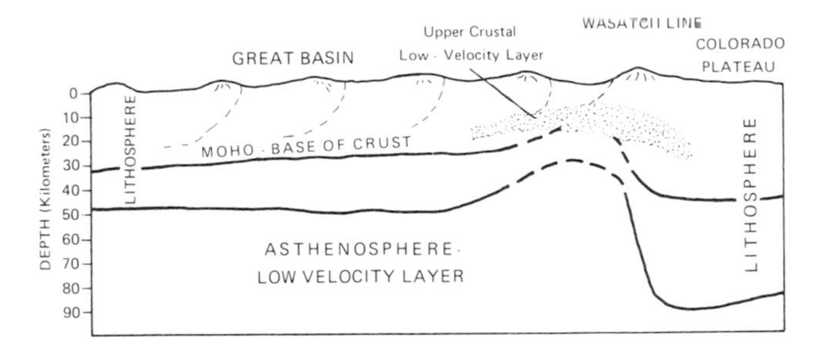

Figure 3-14. Diagrammatic cross-section from Great Basin to western Colorado Plateau. Subsurface conditions inferred from surface geology and geophysical evidence. Length of section about 125 miles.

layer extends westward to east-central Nevada and eastward to about 31 miles east of the Wasatch Line where it dies out abruptly. The top of this high-temperature zone ranges from 4 to 10 miles below the surface.

Although the deeper mantle upwarp may be the primary heat source, it is the crustal LVL that appears to be directly responsible for various surface phenomena along the Wasatch Line. The LVL coincides with the Intermountain Seismic Belt of shallow earthquakes and the belt of major Cenozoic faults and trenches. The earthquakes of the Intermountain Seismic Belt are relatively shallow, originating 0 to 6 miles below the surface, and appear to result from adjustments in brittle rocks above the less rigid LVL. Earthquakes cannot occur in plastic or liquid material where stresses are released by flowage instead of fracture.

Abundant normal faults of relatively recent origin cut the rocks above the LVL. Many of these, such as the great Wasatch Fault, are active and can cause damaging earthquakes. Movement may result from adjustments of the brittle upper crust to expansion of heated rock below. Seismic evidence indicates that most fault surfaces curve from a near-vertical attitude at the surface toward horizontal planes at relatively shallow depths.

Although the existence of a mantle upwarp beneath the Wasatch Line or transition zone is well substantiated, the cause of such a feature is not well understood. Many of the characteristics of this zone are present along mid-oceanic ridges and continental rifts such as in East Africa. The associated crustal tension and splitting may cause the upwarp or be caused by it. Perhaps a large segment of the North American continent west of the Wasatch Line is splitting away from the more solid continental interior just as has happened at other places in the great global interplay of lithospheric plates.

For additional reading of the topics discussed in Chapter 3, see the following list of authors:

Arabaz and others, 1975
Bodell, 1981
Chapman, 1980
Cook, K.L., 1961, 1964, 1967, 1970
Cook and Berg, 1961
Cook and Smith, 1967
Cook and others, 1975
Ellingson, 1973
Gilbert, 1928
Goode, 1971
Gregory, 1917
Hilpert, 1971
Mundorf, 1970
Nolan, 1943
Osmond, 1960
Parry and others, 1977
Petersen, C. A., 1973
Smith, R. B., 1974
Smith and Bruhn, 1984
Smith and Sbar, 1974
Smith and others, 1974
Stewart and Crosby, 1972
Stewart and others, 1977
Utah Geological and Mineral Survey, 1974
Williams, J. S., 1958
Wilson and others, 1977
Zeitz and others, 1976

For complete bibliographic citations, please see List of References.

4 THE PRECAMBRIAN

The interval designated as Precambrian begins with the origin of the Earth approximately 4.5 billion years ago and ends about 570 million years ago with the appearance of certain diagnostic fossils. It thus comprises more than 85 percent of geologic time. Textbooks often relegate the Precambrian to an inconspicuous narrow space at the bottom of the time chart and give much greater emphasis to the younger, better known, fossil-bearing divisions. If the space alloted to each geologic time division were proportional to its actual duration, the Precambrian would occupy most of the chart and recent geologic time would have only a narrow space at the top. As the great length and complexity of the Precambrian becomes better appreciated, increasing attention is being given to understanding the rocks and events that characterize it. Even so, it will be some time before a workable scheme of correlation comparable to that for younger rocks can be established.

Most Precambrian rocks are complexly deformed and highly metamorphosed. Fossils are present only in the very youngest portion and it is difficult to correlate surface exposures from one area to another on the basis of physical appearance. Fortunately, many Precambrian rocks contain minerals that can be dated by radiometric methods to provide a basis for correlation within and among continents. Worldwide, only a few small exposures are 4 billion years old or older and several sizeable areas are known to be composed of rocks between 3 and 4 billion years old. In contrast, great regions, thousands of square miles in extent, consist of rocks between 3 and 0.5 billion years old.

The Canadian Shield is typical of extensive regions consisting entirely of Precambrian rocks. The Precambrian units of the Shield disappear under cover of younger sediments in western Canada and the northern United States. In a few places in the Rocky Mountains, Colorado Plateau, and Great Basin Provinces, the Precambrian is so near the surface that limited exposures exist in eroded uplifts or in deep canyons.

Through the accidents of geologic history and arbitrary creation of state boundaries, Utah fails, by a few miles, to include some of the most important Precambrian exposures of the western United States. A very thick, representative section lies in the Albion Range which extends from the northwestern corner of Utah 25 miles into south-central Idaho. Another section, among the best of its age and type, is found in the Bannock Range near Pocatello, Idaho, 50 miles north of the Utah line. The great Wind River Range, with hundreds of square miles of complex Precambrian rocks, is not far away in Wyoming. Utah has only a small

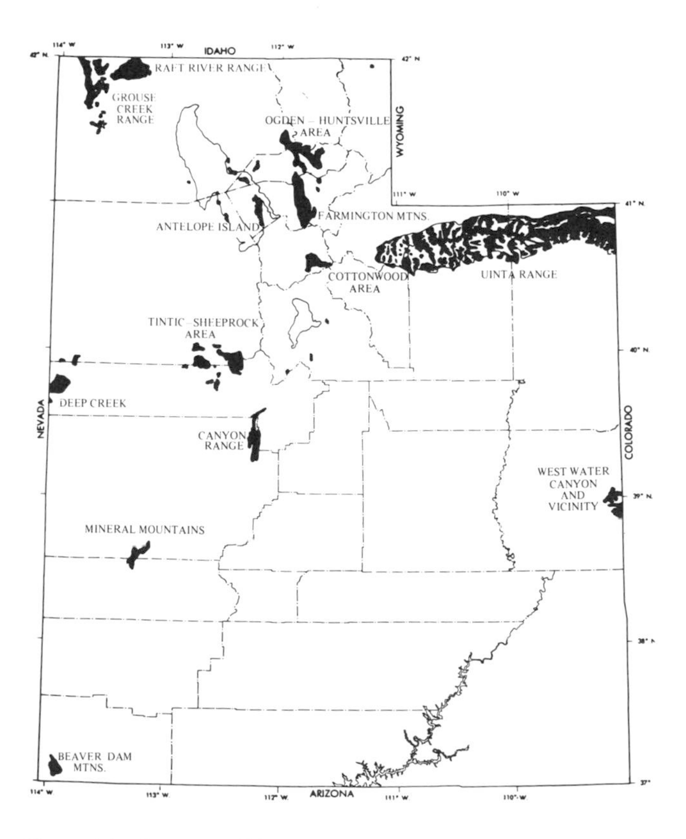

Figure 4-1. Outcrops of Precambrian rocks in Utah. Light areas in the Uinta Range are mostly thin glacial deposits; Precambrian sediments are essentially continuous throughout the core of the range.

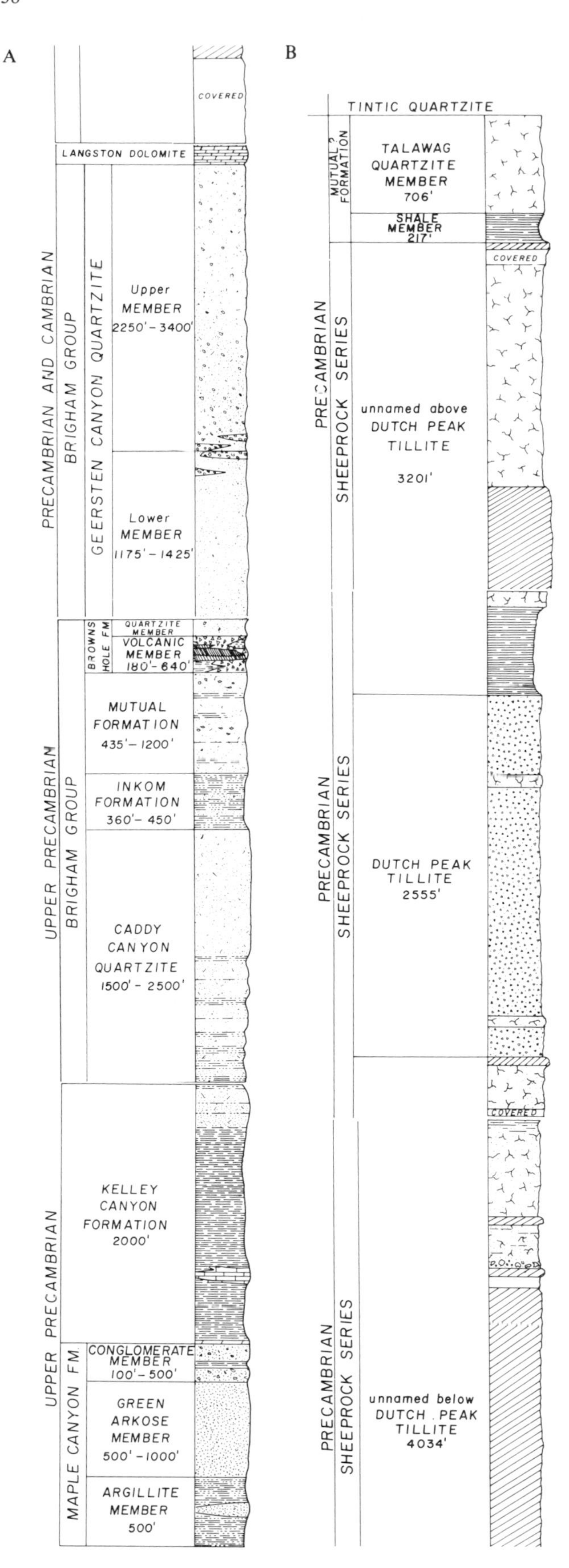

Figure 4-2. (A)Stratigraphic section of Precambrian sedimentary units exposed in the Ogden Valley region, northern Utah (from Crittenden, M.D., Jr.). (B)Stratigraphic section of Precambrian sedimentary units exposed in the Sheeprock Mountains, central Utah (from Cohenour, R.E., 1959, Sheeprock Mountains, Tooele and Juab Counties, Utah: Utah Geological and Mineral Survey Bulletin 63).

part of the Precambrian of the Uncompahgre Plateau which is mainly in Colorado, and the Precambrian outcrops of the San Juan Mountains are entirely in Colorado about 65 miles east of the Utah state line.

Utah misses by only 50 miles the world-famous Precambrian exposures of the Grand Canyon where 1,000 feet of complex Archean rocks are exposed below 8,200 feet of fairly uncomplicated, Phanerozoic, sedimentary formations. The very significant, fossil-bearing, Precambrian rocks of Death Valley and the Mojave Desert region lie 150 miles from the Utah border and one of the best and most complete sections of Precambrian rocks that are only slightly metamorphosed is in Nevada within sight of the Utah line west of Delta, Millard County.

Even so, Utah is not devoid of Precambrian outcrops although the distances between exposures are usually great and correlations among exposures are speculative (fig. 4-1). Two of the most complete Precambrian sections in Utah are depicted in figure 4-2. The following discussion treats the Precambrian from oldest to youngest units, relying upon exposures from nearby states as well as those in Utah.

THE CRYSTALLINE BASEMENT

Crystalline rocks are those igneous and metamorphic varieties which are made up chiefly of visible crystalline minerals. In contrast, the crystals of most sedimentary rocks are not visible as such. The term basement refers to the lowest (generally oldest and deepest) rocks of any region. Most basement rocks in the United States range in age from 3.9 to 1.5 billion years old. Unlike younger rocks, they have passed through several cycles of heat and pressure that have hardened and metamorphosed them. Thus, the top of the basement generally lies below well-stratified, sedimentary rocks but its base cannot be defined except by geophysical techniques.

Utah possesses a distinct and unmistakable crystalline basement which appears to underlie at least the eastern half of the state and is exposed in widely scattered outcrops in the Basin and Range (fig. 4-1). It may lie at depths as great as 40,000 feet in downwarped areas such as the Uinta Basin. The most extensive outcrops of Precambrian basement make up the Harrison Series in the Raft River Mountains of northwestern Utah; the Farmington Canyon Complex in the west-central Wasatch Range; the Little Willow Formation near the mouth of Little Cottonwood Canyon; and the the core of the Beaver Dam Mountains in Washington County. Less extensive outcrops can be seen on Antelope and Carrington Islands in Great Salt Lake; along the western base of the Mineral Mountains near Milford, Millard County; in Westwater Canyon of the Colorado River in Grand County; and at several slightly disconnected but related localities on the northern flanks of the Uinta Mountains, Duchesne and Uintah Counties, in the extreme northeastern corner of the state.

Radiometric dates, chiefly those based on K/Ar (potassium/argon) ratios, indicate that the crystalline basement of the western United States consists of rocks formed and consolidated during two distinct times of igneous action (both intrusive and extrusive), strong metamorphism and mountain building. Intensive geologic events are termed orogenies or diastrophies. During such events minerals are commonly formed which can later be dated by radiometric means. Great caution must be exercised in selecting specimens for radiometric age dating because later orogenies can reheat rocks and "overprint" or "reset" their atomic clocks.

Precambrian rocks within certain broad regions or provinces share approximately the same chemical characteristics and geologic ages. According to radiometric dating, the oldest rocks of Utah are found in the Raft River Mountains (figs. 4-3a and 4-3b) in the northwestern corner of the state and in the Red Creek Quartzite of the Uinta Mountains in the northeastern corner. Based on these age assignments, the northern portion of the state is included in the Wyoming Province, a semi-isolated area chiefly in Wyoming, with basement rocks 2.0 to 2.5 billion years old.

The 2.43 billion year date from the Raft River Mountains is from a granite which intrudes (and hence is younger than) the Harrison Series that continues into Idaho's Albion Range. The Harrison Series consists of an unknown thickness of mica schist, quartzite, and dolomite. The intrusive rock is medium-grained to porphyritic granite which has been altered in part to metamorphic granite. The unmetamorphosed rock gives the most reliable age dates. More sophisticated age-dating techniques are showing that similar crystalline basement rocks thought to be younger are actually this old or older. If these dates are proven, the Wyoming Province may be enlarged to include much of Utah.

Figure 4-3a. The Raft River Range, looking northward. All rocks in this view are Precambrian in age. Photo: Hellmut H. Doelling.

Figure 4-3b. Close view of the Precambrian Elba Quartzite, Raft River Range. The prominent surfaces along which the rock splits are not bedding planes, they are cleavage planes formed during intense deformation and metamorphism that has affected the area. This is an important Utah decorative stone. Photo: Hellmut H. Doelling.

The Red Creek Quartzite, named from Red Creek between Clay Basin and Browns Park in northeastern Utah, is a very significant formation. It records not only the conditions of its own formation but also a number of important subsequent happenings. Several age dates by various methods have been obtained from it; the best authenticated appears to be 2.32 billion years for a muscovite schist dated by the strontium-rubidium method. Most of the Red Creek Quartzite is metaquartzite, amphibolite, and mica schist. The term metaquartzite refers metamorphosed quartzite. Thin sections show the Red Creek Quartzite to be highly crystalline, very compact, crushed in places, and solidly recemented. Colors include white, gray, tan, and green. The formation is at least 20,000 feet thick.

Crystalline rocks thought to be younger than 2.3 billion years old are exposed in a number of localities south of the Wyoming Province.. They were formed either during an important period of disturbance, regional metamorphism, uplift and granitic intrusion called the Hudsonian, approximately 1.6 to 1.8 billion years ago, or they were already in existence and received a new radioactive date during that diastrophy. Exposures occur in the mountains east of Farmington, Davis County (fig. 4-4); at Little Mountain west of Ogden, Weber County; on Antelope and Carrington Islands in Great Salt Lake; at the mouth of Little Cottonwood Canyon; near Santaquin, Utah County; along the west flank of the Mineral Mountains, Beaver County; in the Beaver Dam Mountains, Washington County; and in Westwater Canyon, Grand County. These rocks are composed chiefly of granitic gneiss, schist, and migmatite with minor amphibolite and pegmatite. Extensive metamorphism and deformation have been so intense and most expo-

Figure 4-4. Crest of Farmington Mountain, Davis County, with Francis Peak on the left. The range is almost entirely composed of Precambrian rocks, chiefly gneiss and schist. Photo: Ward Roylance.

Figure 4-5. Wasatch Front near Willard, Box Elder County. Light-colored Cambrian-Precambrian quartzite resting on dark gneiss and schist of the Farmington Canyon Complex. A great unconformity, representing an estimated half-billion years separates the two. Photo: Robert Q. Oaks, Jr.

sures are so limited that measurement of orginal or present thickness is highly speculative. Before metamorphism these rocks appear to have been impure shale and sandstone. To achieve the degree of metamorphism they now exhibit they must have been buried to depths of at least 20,000 feet. The great spread of age dates obtained is the result of a long series of disturbances that carried them from the surface to great depths and back to the surface where they are now exposed more than a mile above sea level. Based on this complex history there appears to be reason to doubt that the crystalline basement of most of Utah is really younger than that of the Raft River and Red Creek areas.

THE GREAT UNCONFORMITY

At no place is it possible to prove continuous deposition from the crystalline series to the next younger rocks. The top of the crystalline basement is consistently an eroded surface, or unconformity. The overlying rocks are totally different and much younger (fig. 4-5). This great break in the rock record extends far beyond Utah and represents 0.5 to 1 billion years of time when much of the continent was being eroded. The material removed includes entire mountain ranges and their surroundings.

The long-continued erosion of the basement rocks produced the raw material for many succeeding formations. Gneiss, schist, and granitic rocks provide the constituents of sandstone and finer grades of siliceous sedimentary rocks. These less soluble components are carried away as sedimentary particles while more soluble minerals such as calcite enter the ocean and may be precipitated almost anywhere much later. That the less soluble materials are available for immediate deposition while the more soluble may be retained in the ocean for a longer time may explain why the dominant rock type of the younger Precambrian in Utah and elsewhere in the United States is quartzite and why there is little limestone or dolomite of this age.

ROCKS OF TRANSITIONAL CHARACTER

Although most of the material eroded from the crystalline basement was transported out of the region to unknown sites of deposition, a small amount was deposited within what is now Utah. From these deposits a great deal may be learned about what occurred between the time of basement rock formation, 2.5 to 2.0 billion years ago, and the deposition of extensive younger sedimentary rocks less than 1.7 billion years ago. The record is far from complete; only one formation in the northern Wasatch Range and five formations in the Raft River Mountains appear to have been deposited during the transitional interval.

The Facer Formation, exposed in the Northern Wasatch Range, consists chiefly of quartzite colored green by the chromium mica, fuchsite; quartz-hematite schist, amphibolite, and igneous rock intruded into the sediments shortly after their deposition. Intensely deformed outcrops of the Facer Formation are found as slices between thrust faults. No one slice contains the entire thickness of the formation but it appears to be at least 3,500 feet thick and was deformed by metamorphism both before and after the deposition of the overlying late Precambrian and Cambrian rocks. The degree of metamorphism is less severe than that of the underlying basement rocks.

Six formations similar in composition to the Facer Formation have been mapped in the Raft River Mountains. They are, from oldest to youngest: Elba Quartzite (fig. 4-3b), Upper Narrows Schist, Yost Quartzite, Stevens Spring Schist, Clarks Basin Quartzite, and Mahogany Peaks Schist. The two upper units may be Cambrian in age. The Raft River section, like that in the Wasatch Range, rests unconformably upon much older crystalline rocks and contains green quartzite (Elba and Yost Formations), hematitic schist, and amphibolite. The Wasatch and Raft River outcrops are now about 90 miles apart but they were probably nearer, if not in actual contact, before thrust faulting moved the Wasatch section eastward.

LATER PRECAMBRIAN ROCKS

A very great quantity of sediment was produced between the deposition of the Facer Formation 1.5 billion years ago and the beginning of Cambrian deposition about 0.57 billion years ago. These later Precambrian rocks have not been greatly metamorphosed or deformed and resemble what might be called ordinary sediments of later age.

Later Precambrian rocks, mostly unmetamorphosed, are exposed in a number of places in Utah (see fig. 4-1). The most extensive exposure, consisting of the Uinta Mountain Group, makes up the core of the Uinta Mountains (fig. 4-6). Other large exposures are in the Brigham City-Huntsville area, Box Elder and Weber Counties; Big and Little Cottonwood Canyons, Salt Lake County; the Sheeprock Mountains, Juab and Tooele Counties; Dry Mountain east of Santaquin, Utah County; the Dugway Range, Juab

Figure 4-6. The High Uintas, near the crest and above timberline. The height of the eroded wall marks the depth of glacial erosion which produced the extensive, wide valleys. Sediments are part of the Precambrian Uinta Mountain Group. Photo: U.S. Forest Service.

County; the Deep Creek Range, Juab and Tooele Counties; the Canyon Mountains, Millard and Juab Counties; the Beaver Mountains (southern Cricket Mountains), Beaver and Millard Counties; and Antelope Island-Fremont Island-Promontory Point in Great Salt Lake. The best known and most fully described section is that in Ogden Valley area, Box Elder and Weber Counties (fig. 4-2a).

It is difficult to describe the younger Precambrian deposits using common terms for later rocks. Quartzite must be referred to either as orthoquartzite (cemented by ordinary sedimentary processes) or as metaquartzite (cemented by excessive heat and pressures). Siltite is a term used as a companion to quartzite to describe rock of firmly cemented or silicified silt-sized particles. Argillite refers to clay- or silt-rich rock that has been slightly metamorphosed but is not yet in the state of being slate. Phyllite refers to a silty rock in which small micaceous flakes have formed by mild metamorphism. Many geologists use the term graywacke for a type of sandstone, common in the Precambrian, that is dirty in appearance due to a high content of dark-colored rock and mineral fragments in addition to light-colored quartz. Graywacke is interpreted to have been accumulated and buried without much washing or reworking by water.

THE TILLITE PROBLEM

One rock type of particular importance and interest in the late Precambrian, not only of Utah but of essentially the entire world, is so unusual that geologists have had trouble agreeing on its origin and name. Earlier workers in Utah applied the name Mineral Fork Tillite under the firm conviction that they were dealing with a Precambrian glacial deposit. Tillite is the solidified equivalent of till, the crude, unsorted mixture of large and small rock fragments deposited by glaciers. Later workers were not entirely convinced that the Mineral Fork is a product of glacial action. Some added a question mark to the rock type or used the word, tilloid, meaning till-like. Still others who wished to be conservative and noncommital about any specific mode of origin employed the term diamictite a name for an unsorted sedimentary material consisting of sand and/or larger particles in a muddy matrix. Such a mixture might be produced by landslides or flows of muddy material from high to low ground, possibly in a submarine environment, and might or might not be associated with tillite. The characteristics that convince most students that the Mineral Fork is a true tillite are: 1) The presence of angular fragments as much as several feet across embedded without any particular orientation in a matrix of unsorted finer material (fig. 4-7a and 4-7b); 2) erosional contacts above and below the unit; 3) poorly defined bedding; 4) lack of vertical size gradation; 5) poor sorting; and 6) a great variety of foreign or exotic materials that appear to have been transported from a considerable distance. Almost positive evidences of glacial action such as striated, grooved, and polished surfaces or floors ground down by ice, and of faceted pebbles or cobbles shaped by grinding on the bedrock have also been reported.

Figure 4-7a. Outcrop of Mineral Fork Tillite in Mineral Fork of Big Cottonwood Canyon, Salt Lake County; shows rock fragments of various size in finer, dark-colored matrix. Photo: Peter Varney.

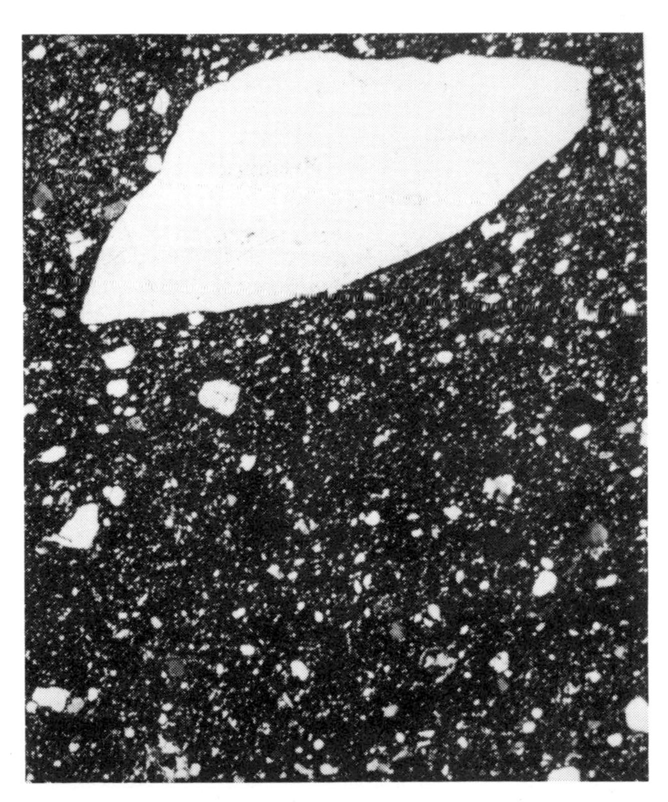

Figure 4-7b. Enlarged thin section of the Mineral Fork Tillite showing angular fragments in dark, fine-grained matrix. Photo: Peter Varney.

The Mineral Fork and equivalent formations have been identified in the Huntsville area, Weber County; Sheeprock Mountains; Northern Deep Creek Range; Antelope Island; and Little and Big Cottonwood Canyons. The maximum reported thickness is 4,044 feet, measured in the Sheeprock Mountains. By contrast only 50 feet are reported from Antelope Island.

Figure 4-8a. Kings Peak, highest point in Utah - elevation 13,528 feet. Carved from quartzite of the Uinta Mountain Group and named for Clarence King, pioneer geologist of the Uinta Mountains. Photo: U.S. Forest Service.

Figure 4-8b. Falls of the Provo River, southwestern Uinta Range. Rocks are quartzite of the Precambrian Uinta Mountain Group. Photo: U.S. Forest Service.

PRE-GLACIAL ROCKS

Regardless of the origin of the tillite or diamictite, it has become an important key for correlating formations on a worldwide scale. It has been suggested that the younger Precambrian rocks of North America could well be separated into two sequences, one younger than the tillite, the other older. This works well for those areas where the tillite is exposed; however, there are many areas where the unit definitely is not present. How do the rocks of the Uinta Mountains with no tillite correlate with rocks of the central Wasatch Range where tillite is well exposed? Three correlations are possible: 1) The Wasatch section is entirely older than the Uinta; 2) the Wasatch section is entirely younger than the Uinta; and 3) they are the same age. A 952-million-year age date for a rock sample from the upper part of the Uinta Mountain Group would seem to place deposition of the entire Uinta Mountain Group before the tillite. Since tillite overlies beds of this age elsewhere, it would, if present, overlie the Uinta Mountain Group. Possibly the environment that produced these rocks did not extend into the Uinta Mountains. Stratigraphic position would confirm this hypothesis and is an example of the great value of the tillite section in correlating Precambrian rocks in Utah. The unit is a component of the lowermost formation (Perry Canyon) of the Huntsville sequence and this provides evidence that the Uinta Mountain Group and the Big Cottonwood Formation are both older than the Huntsville sequence.

The Uinta Mountain Group (figs. 4-8a and 4-8b) provides an unusually thick and complete rock section because what is now an uplift was once an elongated subsiding valley or aulacogen where sediments could accumulate to unusual thickness. Although the Uinta Mountain Group is highly siliceous it does exhibit significant variations. The 15,000 feet exposed in the High Uintas Primitive Area have been informally subdivided into six units which are, from oldest to youngest: 1) Pebbly arkose; 2) quartzite and arkose; 3) micaceous shale, siltite, and quartzite; 4) fine- to medium-grained, moderately grayish-red dense quartzite; 5) dark-brick-red to dusty-red, medium- to coarse-grained quartzite; and 6) the Red Pine Shale consisting mainly of brownish-gray or olive-drab shale. The Red Pine Shale has yielded a curious fossil, *Chuaria*, that has value in correlating it with other Precambrian formations. The maximum thickness of the Uinta Mountain Group as exposed along the Green River east of the Utah border is 26,000 feet.

The Big Cottonwood Formation (fig. 4-9), although 16,000 feet thick, has much less volume than the Uinta Mountain Group. It consists of quartzite and shale in approximately equal amounts. The lower quartzite beds are pinkish to white, the higher ones are greenish or gray, all of them tend to weather rusty brown. The shaly intervals are bluish-gray, bluish-purple, greenish, or reddish-purple. Evidence of shallow-water origin such as ripple marks, cross-bedding, and mud cracks are seen in the upper units but the lower part displays few such features and appears to have been laid down in moderately deep water. The Big Cottonwood Formation has yielded neither fossils nor minerals by

Figure 4-9. Steeply dipping strata of the Big Cottonwood Formation in Big Cottonwood Canyon, near Storm Mountain, Salt Lake County. The formation is at least 18,000 feet thick in this vicinity. Photo: Hal Rumel.

which it can be dated. About all that can be safely said is that it is younger than the Little Willow Formation on which it rests and older than the Mineral Fork Tillite which overlies it. Little Willow rocks give unreliable radiometric dates because they have been severely heated by the nearby Cottonwood Stock of Tertiary age.

Although the Mineral Fork Tillite has not been dated precisely, an almost positively equivalent formation in Washington has been dated at 900 to 825 million years old. If this indirect dating is correct, the underlying Big Cottonwood Formation was probably deposited between 1,400 and 800 million years ago. This correlates well with the rubidium/-strontium date of 952 million years obtained for the younger part of the Uinta Mountain Group and is additional evidence that the Uinta Mountain Group and the Big Cottonwood Formation are time equivalents.

A third pre-glacial formation, the Facer Formation, has already been described as several thousand feet of metaquartzite and schist for which ages of 1.75, 1.7, and 1.4 billion years have been obtained. Also contained in this sequence are beds of apple-green (chromium-bearing) quartzite. Green is a rare color for rocks and when it occurs in hard durable material the result is an attractive building stone. Green quartzite, similar to that found in the Facer Formation, occurs in large quantities in the Raft River Mountains where it is quarried extensively as a decorative building stone.

POST-GLACIAL ROCKS

The thickness of Precambrian sediments above the tillite reaches 30,000 feet. In contrast to the pre-glacial sequence, post-glacial units appear to be relatively continuous; some identifiable litholgic units can be correlated from southeastern Idaho to central Utah, areas separated by more than 300 miles. In the well exposed, 12,000-foot section in the Huntsville, Box Elder County area the following formations have been described: Maple Canyon Formation (1,000 to 1,500 feet thick), Kelley Canyon Formation (2,000 feet thick), and the Brigham Group, consisting of five formations totaling about 8,500 feet in thickness. One unit of the Brigham Group, the Mutual Formation, is second only to the tillite as a marker formation. The Mutual Formation had been known informally for years as the "purple quartzite" until it received its official name in 1952. The type section is at the Mutual Mine in Big Cottonwood Canyon near Salt Lake City. Colors range from grayish red to purplish or pale pink and there is abundant cross bedding. The purple quartzite was the only Precambrian unit suitable for correlation before radiometric dates were available or the tillite had been recognized and traced. The Mutual Formation is recognized in both the Uinta and Sheeprock Mountains and appears to have been deposited on both sides of the Wasatch Line. Another significant unit of the Brigham Group is the Browns Hole Formation that contains a volcanic member 180 to 460 feet thick. The dominant rock is basalt which occurs as distinct flows and also as rounded cobbles and boulders. An age date of 570 million years has been obtained for this unit.

END OF THE PRECAMBRIAN

The Cambrian Period is the geologic period in which abundant fossils first appear. Many elementary textbooks describe an abrupt appearance of diverse kinds of advanced organisms imply that the base of the Cambrian can be drawn at the stratigraphic level where this influx occurs. This simple assumption encounters many practical problems; locating the Precambrian-Cambrian boundary has no simple solution. Some of the reasons for this difficulty are worldwide, others are local.

Although specific fossils have great value in establishing time planes in sedimentary rocks, index species do not appear or disappear everywhere in the rock sequences as needed. Also, paleontologists have not yet agreed on exactly which fossil species are to be used as guides. It is the spotty distribution of fossils that prevents an easy placement of the base of the Cambrian. No rocks with trilobites have yet been included in the Precambrian, but rocks with many other types of fossils have been. Should the line be drawn to include all many-celled animals in the Cambrian? This would require passing judgement on numerous vague "worm" trails and other questionable traces that are subject to different interpretations. In 1985 there was fair agreement that the base of the Cambrian should be placed at the plane where primitive brachiopods, *Obolella* for example, first appear and are followed, without a break, by the first trilobites of the Lower Olenellus Zone.

Even though specific fossils have been selected to mark the beginning of the Cambrian in the western United States, they have not yet been found in Utah. Here the oldest known Cambrian fossils occur in the Pioche Formation of the House Range in Millard County and are of late Early Cambrian age, at least several million years younger than the beginning of the Cambrian.

This late appearance of suitable index fossils does not mean that earlier Cambrian time is not represented by sediments. All evidence indicates continuous sedimentation from the Late Precambrian into the Cambrian. However, the environments during this interval appear to have been unfavorable for the existence of animal life and certainly unfavorable for its preservation as fossils. Quartzite or sandstone usually indicates a marginal marine or tidal-flat environment where life is generally precarious. Farther from shore, in deeper-water areas of Nevada and Southern California, conditions were more favorable and many Precambrian and Early Cambrian fossils were preserved.

Another way of establishing the Precambrian-Cambrian boundary is by mineral dating. Here again, there are worldwide difficulties. Fossils tend to occur in sedimentary rocks that are generally unfavorable for radiometric dating. Worse still, no agreement has been reached on an absolute date for the beginning of the Cambrian. Current estimates range from 644 to 516 million years ago; a date of 570 million years has recently been published by the Geological Society of America. As mentioned previously, a sample from the Browns Hole Formation of the Brigham Group has been dated as 570 million years old, placing at least part of it in the Cambrian. The Browns Hole Formation is overlain by the Geertsen Canyon Quartzite, approximately 4,200 feet thick, which is sparsely fossiliferous and considered probably Cambrian in age. Above the Geertsen Canyon is the Langston Dolomite which is well dated by fossils as early Middle Cambrian. Thus, the beginning of the Cambrian seems to have occurred during the deposition of the Browns Hole Formation. Conditions were unfavorable for preservation of fossils during the relatively long, perhaps 25-million-year, interval when the Geertsen Canyon Quartzite was deposited. Only with the arrival of deeper, lime-bearing seas in the early Middle Cambrian did datable fossils appear in northern Utah.

For additional reading on the topics discussed in Chapter 4, please see the following list of authors:

Armstrong, 1968
Barker, 1969
Bayley, 1963)
Bick, 1966
Blackwelder, 1932
Bowers, D., 1978
Breed and Road, 1976
Christiansen, 1952
Cohenour, 1959
Cohenour and Thomson, 1966
Compton, 1972, 1975, 1977
Compton and others, 1977
Condie, 1960, 1967, 1969
Crittenden, 1971, 1972, 1980
Crittenden and Wallace, 1973
Crittenden and Peterman, 1975
Crittenden and others, 1952, 1967, 1971, 1972
Dane, 1935
Demars, 1956
Eardley, 1944
Eardley and Hatch, 1940
Hansen, W. R., 1965, 1969

Hintze, F. F., 1913
Hodge and others, 1968
Hoffman, 1977
King, 1977
Larsen, 1957
Larson, 1954
Ludlum, 1943
Marsell, 1964
Misch and Hazzard, 1962
Neff, T. R., 1963
Ojakangas and Matsch, 1980
Olson, 1960
Powell, 1876
Reber, 1952
Robison and Hintze, 1972
Seeland, 1968
Staatz and Carr, 1965
Trimble and Schaeffer, 1965
Varney, 1972
Wallace, 1972
Williams, 1953
Williams and Maxey, 1941
Woodward, 1965, 1968, 1972

For complete bibliographic citations, please see List of References.

Figure 4-10. Bald Mountain, western Uinta Range, Summit County. Part of the Uinta Mountain Group is well exposed; the surrounding lower ground has been deeply eroded by glaciers. Photo: Utah Tourist and Publicity Council.

5 THE CAMBRIAN PERIOD

The Cambrian Period began approximately 570 million years ago and lasted 65 to 75 million years until the beginning of the Ordovician Period approximately 500 million years ago. The Cambrian system is the oldest and longest of the Paleozoic periods. Cambrian rocks were first intensively studied in North Wales by eighteenth century geologists who named the system from the Latin term for Wales, Cambria. Cambrian rocks are found on all continents and are especially thick, varied, and fossiliferous in western North America. Utah has one of the most complete records of the period with abundant and unusual fossil assemblages. Approximately 80 formations have been recognized, the most important are listed at the close of the book.

PALEOGEOGRAPHY

The forerunner of the Wasatch Line and the contrast between the geologic provinces to the east and west of it were evident when the Cambrian Period began. The Cordilleran geosyncline to the west gradually subsided and was occupied by deep, almost permanent, seas. To the east, the Utah-Wyoming shelf, an integral part of the North American craton, was generally covered by shallow oscillating seas. The Cambrian was dominated by a slow flooding, or transgression, of the western ocean onto the shelf area and across the continent. This eastward transgression of the ocean began long before Cambrian time so that when the period commenced the shoreline had already reached the approximate position of the Wasatch Line (fig. 5-1). During the Early Cambrian, sluggish river systems flowing westward across wide sandy flats characterized eastern Utah while western Utah received shallow-water deposits of silt and fine sand. As the continent continued to subside, the shoreline shifted gradually eastward and the western ocean became progressively deeper. As a result Cambrian sediments thicken westward (fig. 5-2). By the close of Middle Cambrian time, about 525 million years ago, the shoreline had almost reached the Utah-Colorado border. By then the only areas above water were small scattered islands and perhaps the northwest corner of the state (fig. 5-3). The seas continued to flood inward so that by the close of the period the shoreline was in Minnesota, Wisconsin, and southern Manitoba. In the Black Hills and Ozark Mountains, only Late Cambrian sediments were deposited.

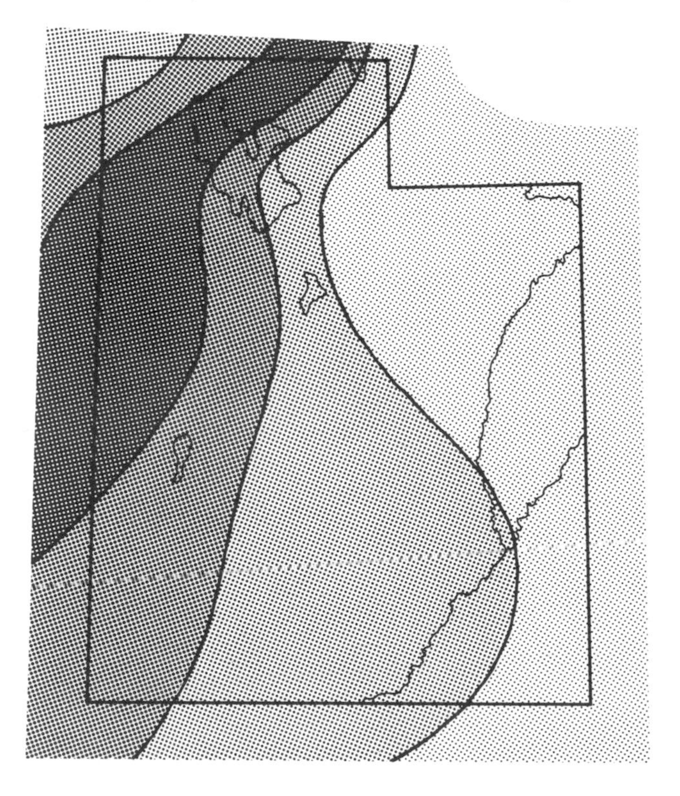

Figure 5-1. Generalized paleogeographic map of the Cambrian System. Relative darkness of patterns indicates the length of time represented and thickness of sediments preserved. Thus the darkest belt contains an almost complete record of Cambrian time. Compare with figure 5-2.

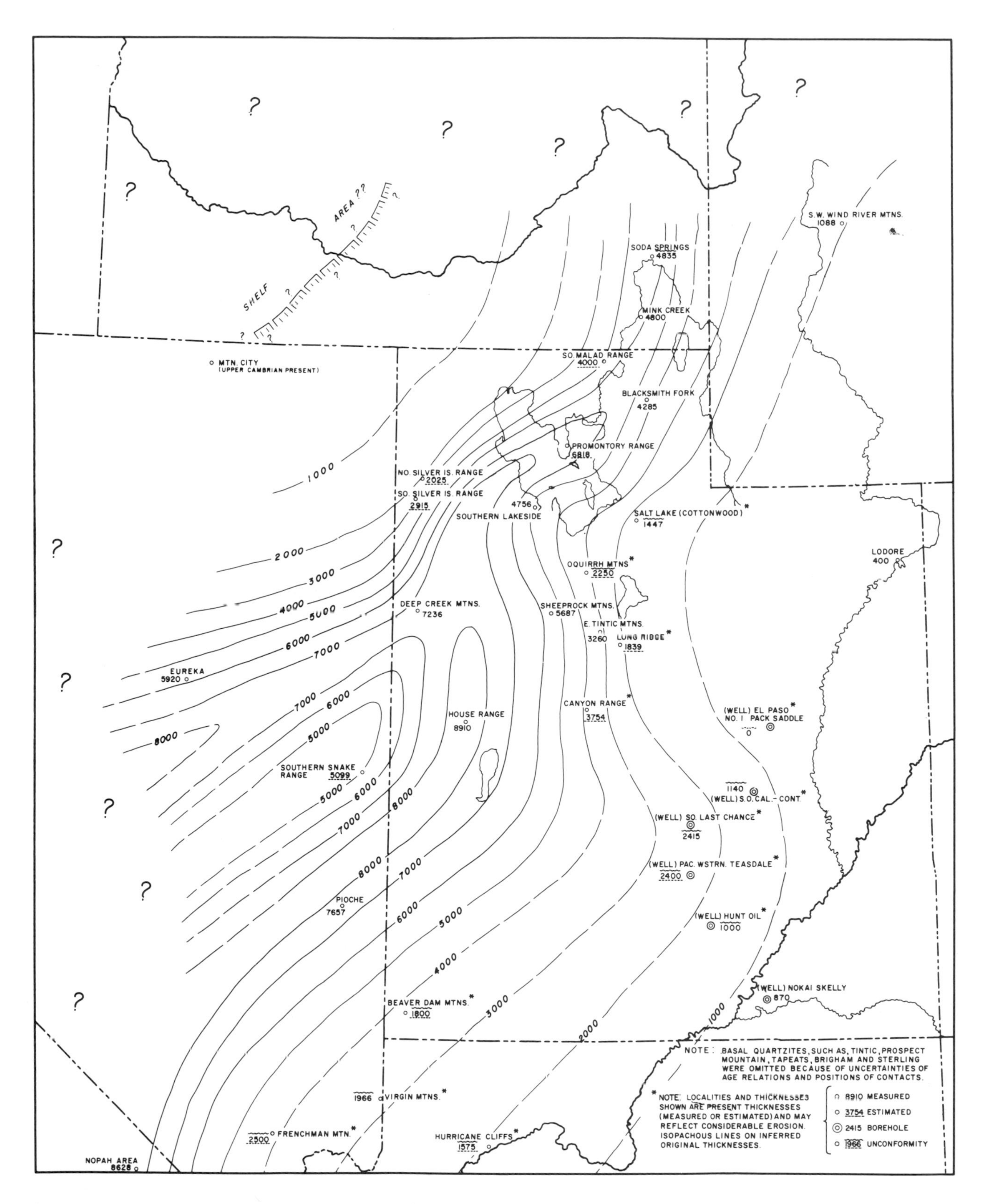

Figure 5-2. Isopach map of the Cambrian System exclusive of basal quartzites. In addition to the contours showing thickness, various important sections with thicknesses are also shown. From R.E. Cohenour, 1959.

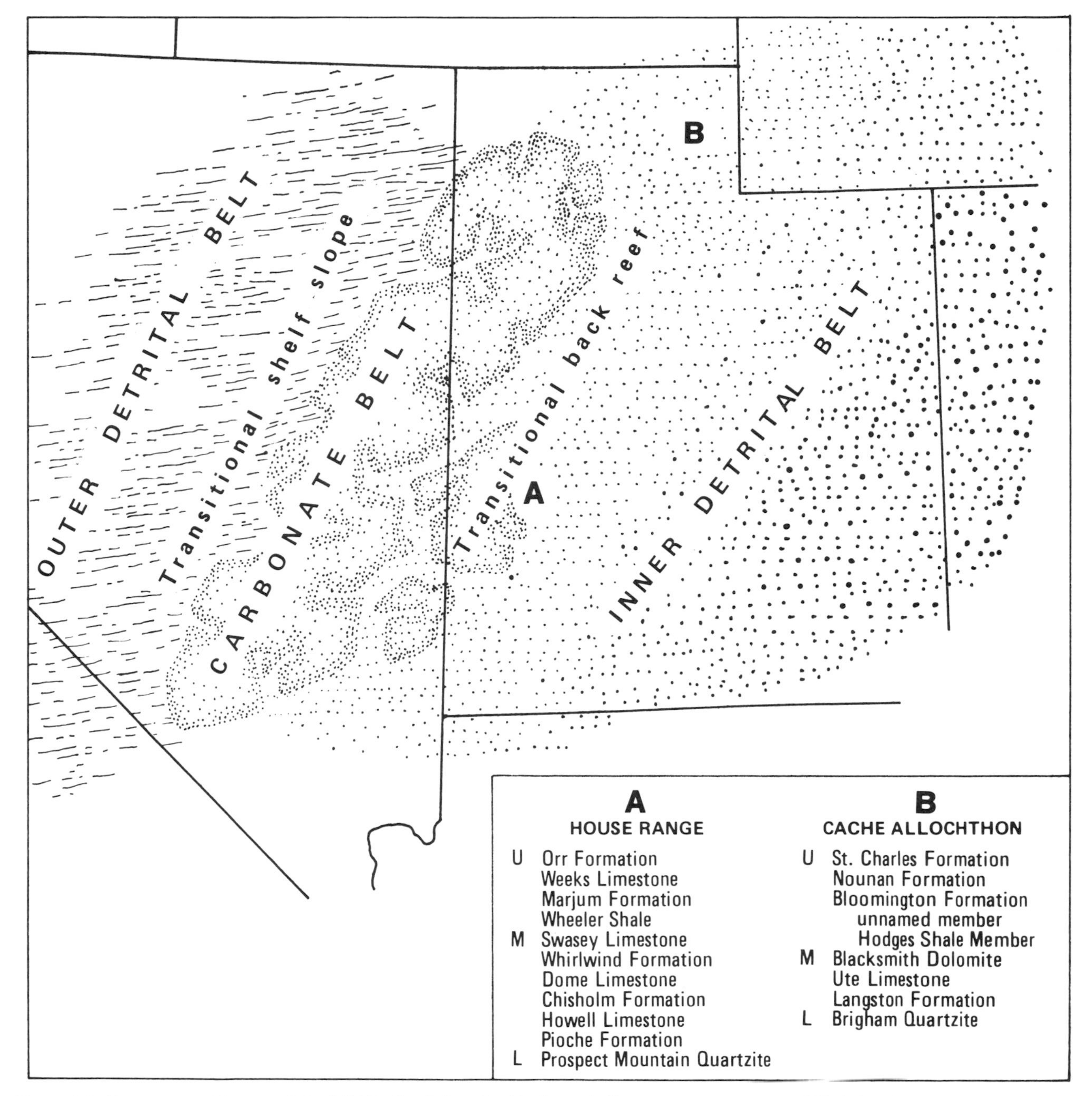

Figure 5-3. Paleogeographic map of the Middle Cambrian. At this time, shallow seas covered most of Utah but deposits to the east were relatively more sandy than those to the west. Formations of two important sites are appended. From Stokes, 1979.

ORIGIN AND NATURE OF CAMBRIAN ROCKS

Rock types of the Cambrian, in approximate order of abundance are: Limestone, sandstone, quartzite, dolomite, shale, and conglomerate. Sandstone and its metamorphic equivalent, quartzite, are the normal products of nearshore, floodplain, delta, and shallow marine environments. In marine situations it usually indicates proximity to a shoreline. As the Cambrian shoreline shifted eastward, so did the belt of sandy deposits. Such deposits are younger as they rise or transgress time planes. Transgressive sandstone marks the base of the Cambrian regardless of what the age may be. The zone of shallow water lying seaward of and parallel to the sandy beach also moved steadily eastward leaving behind a sequence of fine-grained deposits that are also older to the west and younger to the east. The Ophir Shale is the most extensive expression of this offshore environment. With time the deposits of fine-grained, silty clay and mud became shale, mudstone, and siltstone, common rock types in the late Early and Middle Cambrian of Utah.

In deeper water not dominated by sand or silt from adjacent land areas, deposits of limestone (chiefly $CaCO_3$) and dolomite (chiefly $MgCO_3$) precipitated directly from ocean water by chemical reactions and biologic activity. Mixtures and varieties of limestone (figs. 5-4a and 5-4b) and dolomite are differentiated chiefly on the basis of color, texture, and structure and not on the basis of exact chemical composition. For example, *Girvanella* limestone consists of rounded pea-sized bodies of supposedly algal origin whereas oolitic limestone consists of smaller bodies resembling fish eggs, called oolites. When pieces of partly consolidated sea-bottom are torn up, broken, and redeposited, the resulting rock is called intraformational breccia or conglomerate, or flat-pebble conglomerate. Many carbonate strata of the Cambrian show this feature. Other terms frequently used to describe Cambrian limestone and dolomite are banded, striped, ribboned, mottled, laminated and blotched. For certain features that may be organic, terms such as twiggy or wormy are applied.

Chert (SiO_2) is a relatively rare, but widely distributed, rock type in many calcareous sediments. Although uncommon in the Cambrian it appears in thin beds and nodules in the Ajax Formation, Notch Peak Limestone and a few other formations. Its relative scarcity in early Paleozoic rocks may be due to the small number of sponges which are known to have supplied much of the silica for chert in later periods.

Only one occurrence of Cambrian igneous rock is known. A diabase flow at the base of the Tintic Quartzite can be seen in a few scattered outcrops near Provo, Utah County, and in the East Tintic Mountains.

Figure 5-4a. Outcrop of Marjum Limestone, Middle Cambrian, Sheeprock Range, Tooele County. Photo: R.E. Cohenour.

Figure 5-4b. Specimen of Upper Cambrian dolomite. The rounded bodies, known as *Girvanella*, are attributed to lime-secreting algae. Photo: Jim Howell.

OUTCROPS AND SUBSURFACE FORMATIONS

Cambrian sediments were deposited across the entire state and were subject to erosion during all subsequent periods, especially following mountain building. At least one-half of the original volume of Cambrian rock has been removed by erosion.

The most complete exposures, or outcrops, of Cambrian rock that remain today are found in areas where the original deposits were thickest and most complete (fig. 5-5). The Confusion Basin of Millard County, and the Bear River Range in Cache County are world famous. Sections from the House Range in the Confusion Basin and from Blacksmith Fork Canyon in the Bear River Range are given in figures 5-6a and 5-6b. Most of Utah's Cambrian formational names are taken from these two sections.

Less complete Cambrian sections are found in the Promontory Mountains, central Wasatch Range, southern Wasatch Range, Newfoundland Mountains, Silver Island Mountains, Lakeside Mountains, Stansbury Mountains, Onaqui-Sheeprock Mountains, West Tintic Mountains, Dugway-Thomas Ranges, Fish Springs Range, Deep Creek Range, Needle Range, Wah Wah Mountains, Cricket Mountains, Pavant Range, Canyon Mountains, Long Ridge, Beaver Mountains (southern Cricket Mountains), and Beaver Dam Mountains. The thin Lodore Sandstone (fig. 5-7) of Late Cambrian age encircles the eastern Uinta Mountains but most outcrops are obscured by debris from overlying formations.

Cambrian rocks are not exposed in the deep canyons of eastern Utah; however, a number of wells provide evidence that they thin eastward. Cambrian strata are 1,130 feet

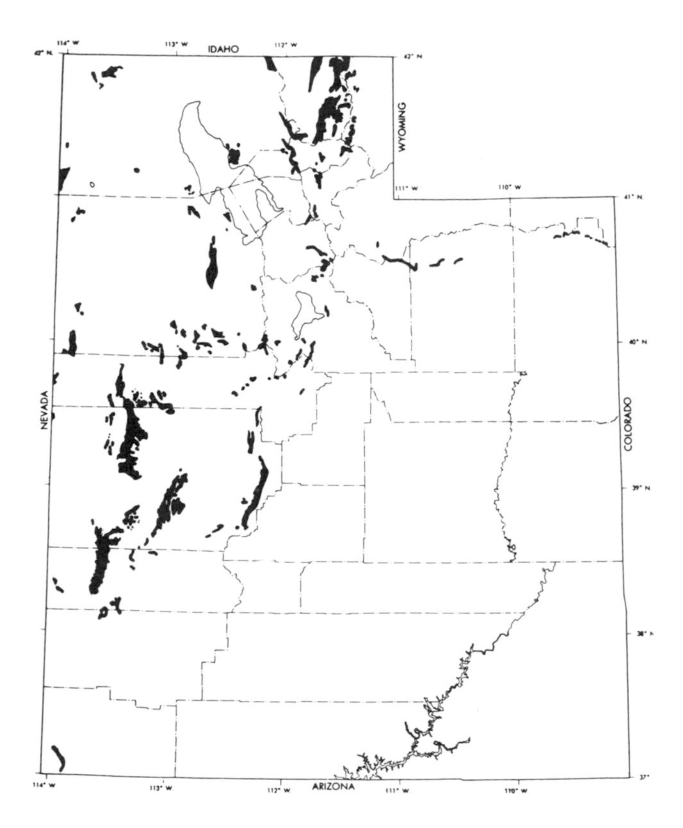

Figure 5-5. Outcrops of Cambrian rocks in Utah. Note concentration of closely spaced exposures in the Confusion Basin and Cache Valley areas.

thick in the San Rafael Swell, 780 feet thick on Cedar Mesa, 1,150 feet thick in the Inter-river area, and 850 feet thick in the Lisbon Anticline. In Westwater Canyon of the Colorado River, eastern Grand County, crystalline Precambrian rocks are directly overlain by Triassic and Jurassic formations. The Cambrian was probably eroded from this area following the Ancestral Rockies Revolution of Pennsylvanian time.

FOSSILS

Most Cambrian formations contain fossils indicative of the primitive beginnings of many evolutionary lines (fig. 5-8a). The best specimens are found in impure, platy limestone or siltstone. Few fossils are preserved in the sandy deposits of the earlier parts of the period and remains are rare in dolomite and shallow-water limestone formations.

The animal fossils of the Cambrian are, in approximate order of abundance: Trilobites, brachiopods, echinoderms, sponges, arthropods (fig. 5-8b) other than trilobites, gastropods, ostracodes, conodonts, pelecypods, and cephalopods. Dozens of species of trilobites belonging to many families have been discovered and have been of great value in correlating and dating rock outcrops, especially in the Basin and Range Province. The oldest known animal fossils of Utah are olenellid trilobites from the Early Cambrian Pioche Formation in the House Range, Millard County. Figure 5-9 illustrates the temporal ranges of some of the more common and stratigraphically useful Cambrian trilobites. Cores taken from deep wells in the Colorado Plateau Province have also yielded trilobite fragments of great value in understanding the subsurface stratigraphy.

Brachiopods are numerous and varied but paleontologists find them much less interesting and more difficult to study than the trilobites with which they are associated. Most Cambrian specimens belong to the class called inarticulates, are typically about 0.3 inch long, smooth shelled, oval or tongue-shaped, and are of phosphatic composition. From an obscure beginning early in the period, another class, the articulate brachiopods, increased and largely replaced the inarticulates in number and varieties. They are about 0.5 inch wide, having straight hinge lines, ribbed surfaces, and calcareous composition. A variety of other Cambrian groups including echinoderms, sponges, annelids, trace fossils, and conodonts are known from Utah formations.

ECONOMIC

The Cambrian was not suited to the production of fossil fuels; there was no significant land vegetation and marine life was somehow not favorable for the generation of oil and gas. Also, the period was relatively quiet tectonically with little ore-producing igneous activity. The only signifi-

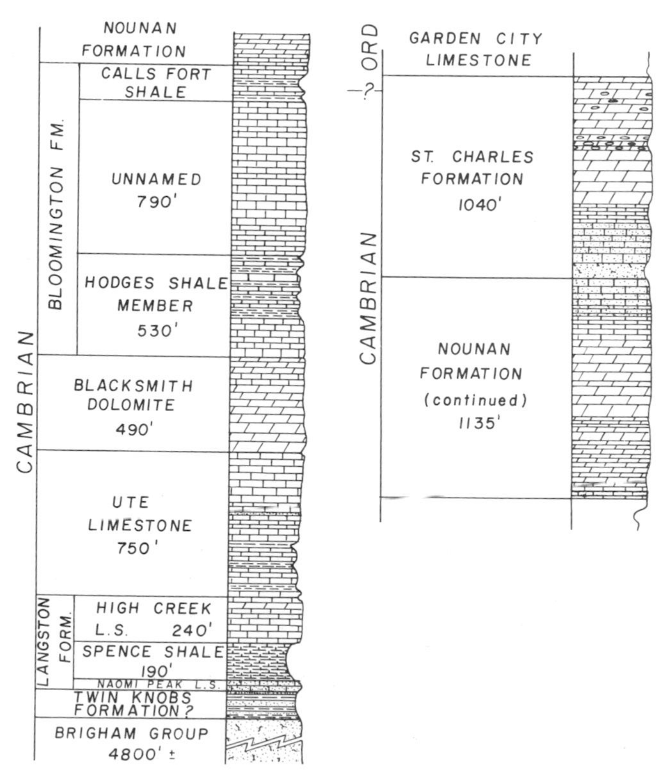

Figure 5-6a. Graphic stratigraphic column showing formations of the Cache Valley area, northern Utah. Section begins at the base of left hand column and continues to top of right hand column.

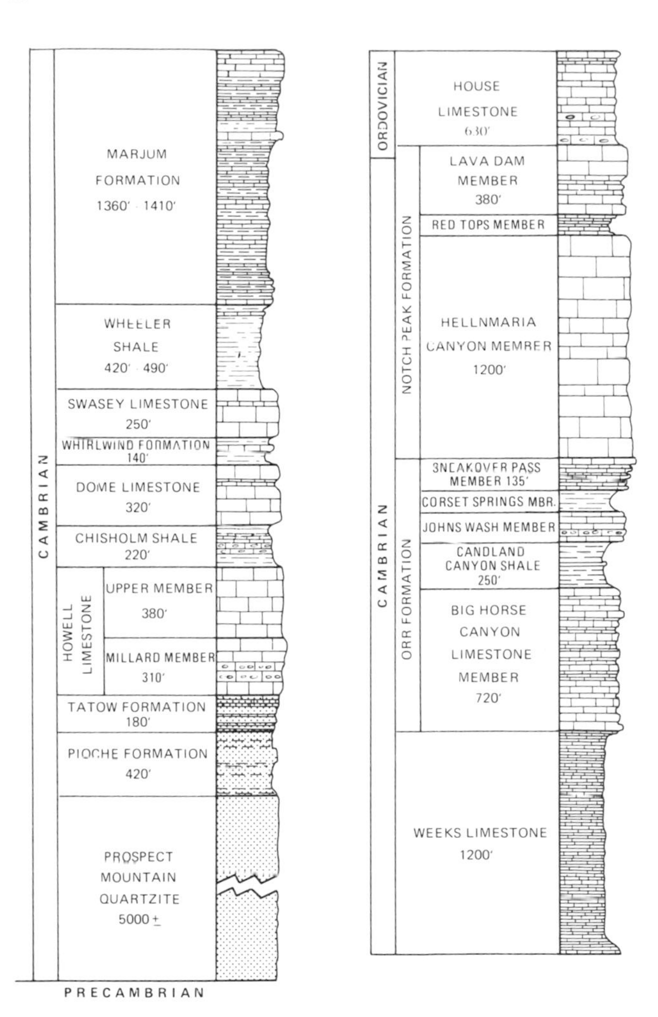

Figure 5-6b. Graphic stratigraphic column showing formations in the central Confusion Basin, western Utah.

Figure 5-7. Section of the Lodore Formation, eastern Uinta Mountains.

Figure 5-8a. Specimen of the Brigham Quartzite, Lower Cambrian, showing vertical tubes attributed to worm-like organisms. The name *Scolithus* has been applied to this fossil. Photo: Jim Howell.

Figure 5-8b. A phyllocarid, an arthropod very distantly related to the modern King Crab. From the Wheeler Shale of the House Range. Specimen about 3 inches across. Photo: Lloyd Gunther.

cant indigenous economic materials are stone products from the limestone and dolomite formations. Limestone is quarried from the Teutonic, Dagmar, and Herkimer Formations, and dolomite from the Bluebird and Cole Canyon Formations at the Keigley Quarries of northern Long Ridge and southern West Mountain, Utah County. Most of the output has been sold as fluxing stone for use in U.S. Steel's Geneva Mill, but a large amount has been used for road ballast, rock dust, and for manufacturing chemicals. An $85 million cement plant utilizing Cambrian limestone has recently (1980) been put into operation by Martin Marietta near Lemington, Juab County (fig. 5-10). In the Cricket Mountains, Millard County, the Continental Lime Company operates a quarry in carbonate rocks of Late Cambrian age.

Cambrian formations have served as host rocks for important metallic ores deposited during the Tertiary Period. Lying near the base of the sedimentary section, Cambrian carbonates afforded the first suitable environments in

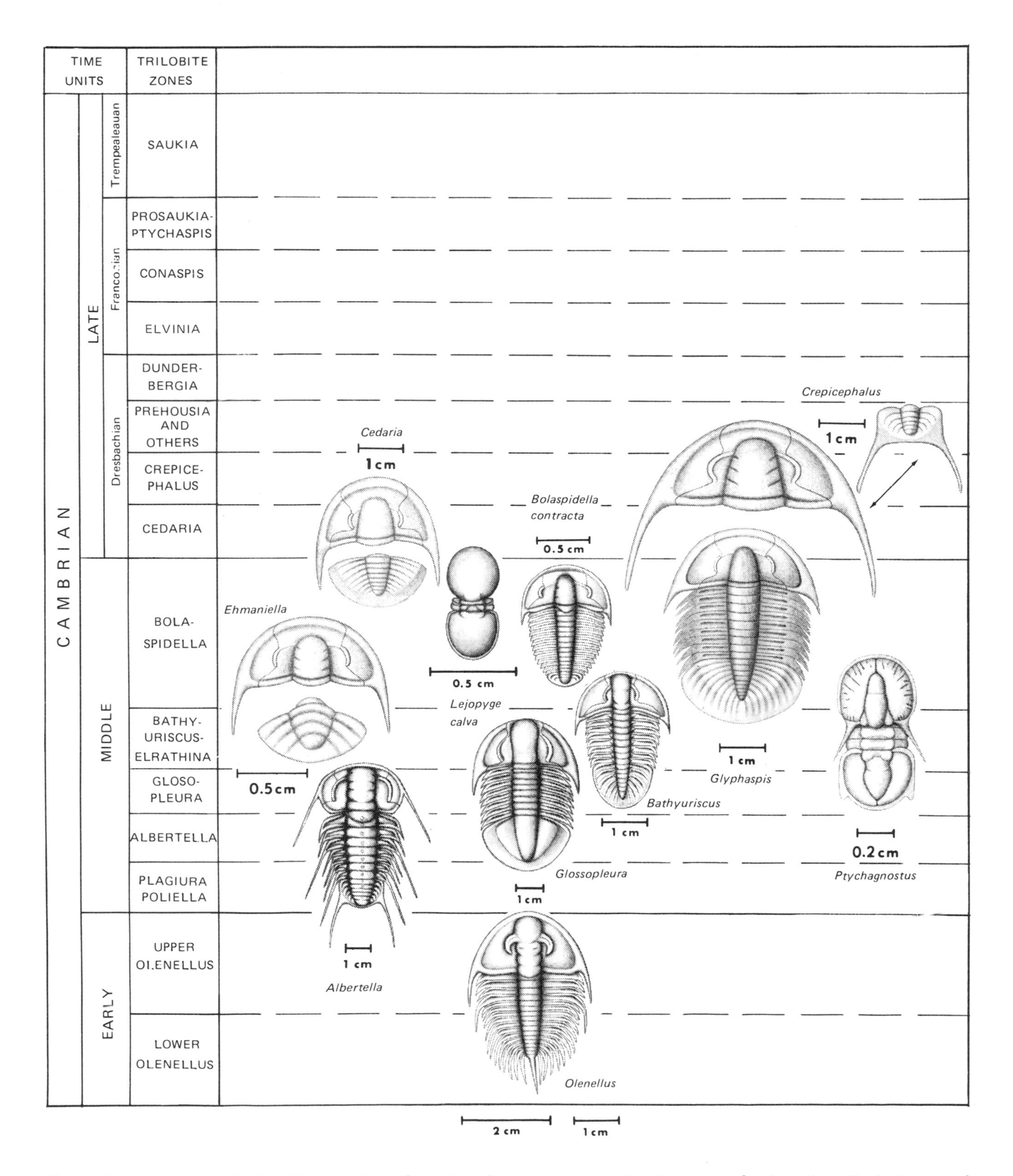

Figure 5-9. Selected index fossils of Utah Cambrian formations. Sketches are arranged so that center of each specimen lies in the zone of which it is characteristic. Currently used zones are listed on the left. Sketches: John K. Balsley.

Figure 5-10. The Chaffin quarry in Cambrian limestone formations, six miles east of Leamington, Juab County. At the time this photograph was taken the site was fully developed but no limestone had been removed.

which upward-moving, ore-bearing solutions could react. Ore bodies in Cambrian rocks are particularly important in the Tintic district.

SCENERY

Limestone and dolomite, typical products of marine deposition, are mostly drab shades of gray. Cambrian rocks illustrate this very well and any claims they may have of scenic attractiveness rest on characteristics other than color. Even so, a few scenic localities are worth mentioning: Highway 89 passes through many Cambrian outcrops as it crosses the Bear River Range between Logan, Cache County, and Bear Lake, Rich County. The same formations make up the walls of scenic Blacksmith Fork Canyon above the junction of Left Fork. This locality is world-famous for the study of Cambrian rocks and fossils.

Notch Peak (fig. 5-11), a spectacular cliff on the west side of the House Range, is in banded Cambrian rocks. This sheer exposure rises vertically almost 4,450 feet and is one of the highest cliffs in North America. The term House Range is said to have originated from the presence of several chimney-shaped buttes that give a house-like profile.

Although scarcely a scenic attraction, notorious Neff's Cave near Salt Lake City should be mentioned in connection with Cambrian rocks. This cave in the Ophir Formation extends from only one known entrance at the mouth of Neff's Canyon downward along a limestone bed to a total depth of at least 1,170 feet. A stream of water at the lower end prevents deeper exploration. Because of its steep incline, overhanging walls, and flowing water, this cave has proven to be so hazardous that the entrance has been sealed. The famous Lehman Caves, designated as a National Monument, located only 12 miles from the Utah line in White Pine County, Nevada, are in Cambrian limestone and dolomite formations.

Figure 5-11. Notch Peak, west side of House Range, Millard County. Except for light-colored outcrops of Notch Peak intrusion (granite) in the foothills, the entire face of the mountain is Cambrian strata. Photo: Peter Varney.

For additional reading about the topics discussed in Chapter 5, please see the following list of authors:

Abbott, 1951
Bick, 1966
Christensen, 1952
Cohenour, 1959
Cook, D.R., 1975
Crittenden, 1964
Dane, 1935
Deiss, 1938
Doelling, 1964
Elison, 1970
Green and Halliday, 1958
Hanks, 1962
Hintze and Robison, 1975
Kepper, 1972
Lochman-Balk, 1972
Lockman-Balk and Wilson, 1958
Maxey, 1946, 1958
Morris, 1961, 1964
Morris and Lovering, 1962
Muessig, 1951
Nolan, 1935
Oliveire, 1975
Olson, 1956
Paddock, 1956
Palmer, A. R., 1971
Podrebarac, 1976
Reiber, 1971
Rigby, 1958
Robison, 1960, 1964
Robison and Rowell, 1972, 1976
Schaeffer and Anderson, 1960

Staatz and Carr, 1964
Walcott, 1908
Wheeler and Steele, 1951
Williams, J. S., 1948, 1958
Woodward, 1965, 1968

For complete bibliographic citations, please see List of References.

Figure 5-12. Ladore Formation as identified by Forest Service sign in Sheep Creek, Daggett County. Photo: U.S. Forest Service.

Figure 5-13. Pillar-like algal heads or stromatolites, Ute Formation, Antimony Canyon, Wellsville Mountain, Box Elder County. Photo: Stanley S. Beus.

6 THE ORDOVICIAN PERIOD

The Ordovician Period began about 500 million years ago and lasted about 70 million years. The name, Ordovician, comes from the Ordovices, a tribe which inhabited Wales when the Romans arrived. The system is well represented by formations in many regions of North America, including exceptionally complete and highly fossiliferous sections in western Utah. About 28 formations of Ordovician age have been recognized in the state. The distribution of Ordovician outcrops is shown in figure 6-1. The formations are listed at the end of the book.

PALEOGEOGRAPHY

Ordovician deposits were laid down under essentially the same conditions as those of the preceding Cambrian Period. The Cordilleran geosyncline dominated the west and continued to subside while the shelf area to the east remained relatively stable and only slightly above sea level (fig. 6-1). Although the edges of most Ordovician formations, as now preserved, follow the Wasatch Line rather closely, it is probable that the original shorelines were somewhat farther east. The problem of drawing accurate shorelines is a common one in geology. The preserved edge of any formation, as shown by its wedgelike termination between overlying and underlying formations, marks either the original depositional edge or the point to which it was removed by erosion before the next formation was laid down. In the first case an ancient shoreline can be drawn quite accurately; in the second it cannot. If a marine formation can be studied over a considerable distance, evidence usually will be found indicating where the original shoreline or depositional edge had been. Among the clues indicating a nearby shoreline are a relative abundance of sand or pebbles such as would be deposited on a beach, the presence of abundant ripple marks or other indications of energetic wave or current action, a relatively greater proporation of shore-living organisms, and relatively more broken or water-worn fossils or no fossils at all.

It is certain that during Ordovician time, deeper water prevailed in the Confusion Basin of central southwestern Utah with gradual shallowing eastward to a shoreline not far from the present Wasatch Line. The western, deeper-water formations contain abundant fossils whereas the easternmost edges of the Ordivician formations are almost barren of identifiable remains. In the Tintic mining district, an area of shallow water during Ordovician time, two formations, the Opohonga Limestone (400 to 1,000 feet thick) and the Fish Haven Dolomite (275 to 350 feet thick), are much thinner than the equivalent 4,700 feet of

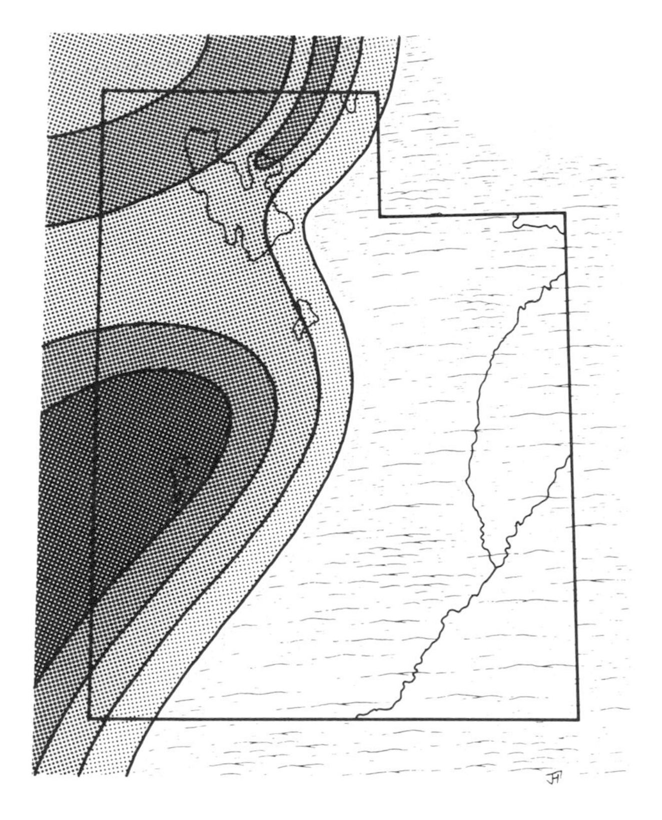

Figure 6-1. Generalized paleogeography of Utah during the Ordovician Period. Darker pattern indicates area covered by seas and receiving sediment during almost the entire period. Lighter zones show progressively thinner and less complete sedimentary record. Dry-land topography is shown diagrammatically.

deeper-water formations in the Confusion Basin. Only a few species of Ordovician marine fossils have been found in the Tintic area whereas scores of species are present in the Confusion Basin.

A study of Ordovician paleogeography shows that the shorelines and depositional areas shifted considerably, although not drastically, during the Early, Middle, and Late Epochs of the period. During the Early Ordovician, the western ocean reached the Wasatch Line and was populated by abundant and varied life, including many trilobites. Limestone was the dominant sediment. The sea gradually became more shallow and finally disappeared in early Middle Ordovician time. A radical change in sedimentation occurred later in the Middle Ordovician and sandy formations accumulated, not only in western Utah but also across wide regions in the central and northern United States. The sand was probably derived from land areas exposed in the interior of the continent and was carried westward by running water and/or wind before coming to rest in the shallow marginal seas. Individual sand grains are well rounded and entire units appear to have been thoroughly winnowed and washed as would be expected from lengthy transport.

Although fossil evidence and other means of dating the quartzite formations are lacking, it is believed that the earlier sand sheets were laid down by an advancing sea and the later ones by a retreating sea. If this is so, there should be, and probably is, an unconformity that may represent a rather long time above the upper quartzite.

In Late Ordovician time a warm ocean spread eastward across the sandy landscape. The shoreline of that part of the Late Ordovician sea which crossed western Utah seems to have corresponded rather closely to that of earlier time. Elsewhere, as in Wyoming, the seaway was much more extensive and the present Colorado Plateau was a large island surrounded by shallow seas.

For some poorly understood reason, the Late Ordovician dolomite formations have an entirely different fossil assemblage than those of the Early Ordovician. Trilobites are rare and corals, poorly represented before the Middle Ordovician, are correspondingly more abundant.

ORIGIN AND NATURE OF ORDOVICIAN ROCKS

Ordovician rock types, in order of decreasing abundance, are limestone, dolomite, sandstone-quartzite, shale-siltstone, and chert. Limestone dominates in the early part of the period, quartzite in the middle part, and dolomite in the late part. Outcrops of Ordovician rocks in Utah are shown in figure 6-2. Representative stratigraphic columns of Ordovician formations are shown in figures 6-3a and 6-3b.

The Early Ordovician limestone formations are fossiliferous and characterized by abundant patches and lenses of intraformational conglomerate which consists of flakes and flat pebbles enclosed in a matrix having the same composition as the pieces (fig. 6-4). Such rocks evidently originated in very shallow water through the stirring and tearing up of newly deposited and only partly consolidated sea bottom.

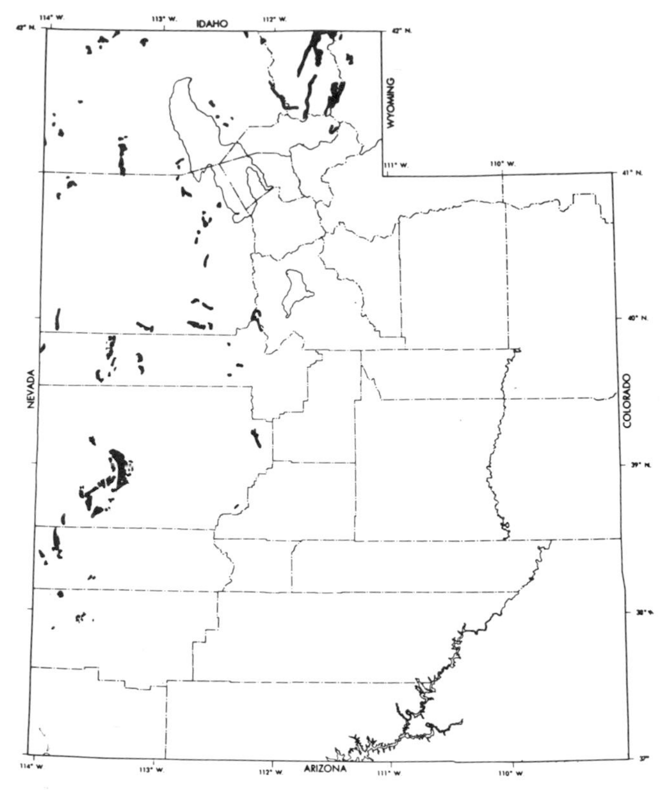

Figure 6-2. Outcrops of Ordovician rocks in Utah. There are no exposures east of the Wasatch line.

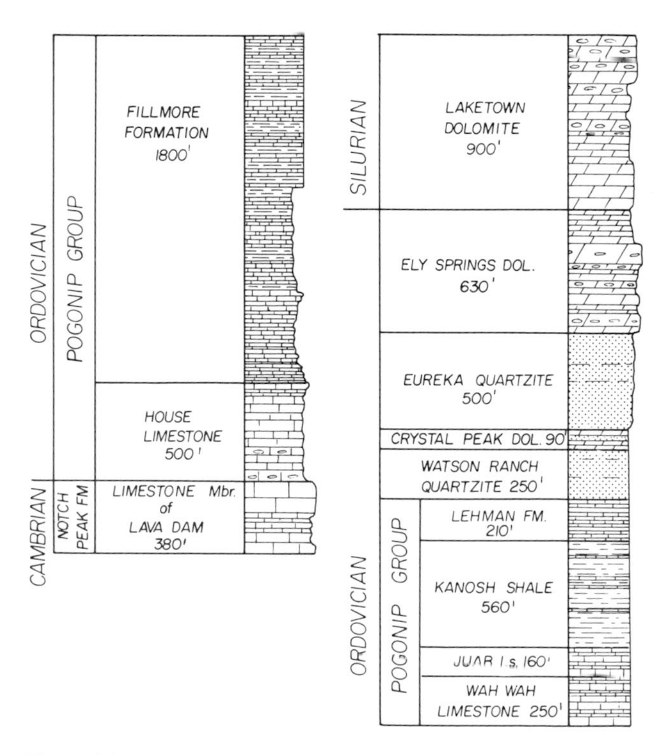

Figure 6-3a. Columnar section showing sedimentary formations of Ordovician age in the Confusion Basin, southwestern Utah.

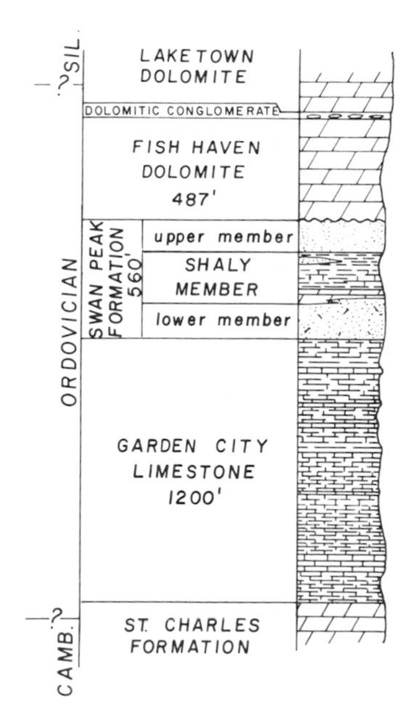

Figure 6-3b. Columnar section showing sedimentary formations of Ordovician age in the Cache Valley area, northern Utah.

Figure 6-4. Intraformational conglomerate from the Garden City Formation, Lakeside Mountains. The specimen has been cut and polished to show details. Photo: Jim Howell.

Figure 6-5. Fish Haven Dolomite exposed on the west face of Wellsville Mountain, Box Elder County. Swan Peak Quartzite below, Laketown Dolomite above. Photo: Stanley S. Beus.

Broken pieces of fossil organisms such as trilobites and brachiopods are frequently found in intraformational conglomerate.

Many beds of Ordovician limestone contain a high proportion of fine, silty particles distributed in thin, discontinuous, chiplike lenses. They take on red, yellowish, or brownish tints when weathered so that many outcrops have a characteristic crudely banded appearance. The silt may have been transported into the shallow seas by wind and the silty laminations could have resulted from the sorting action of gentle waves. Chert makes up as much as 50 percent of the middle part of the Lower Ordovician Garden City Formation and a lesser percentage of the younger Fish Haven Dolomite (fig. 6-5).

FOSSILS

Fossil content of Ordovician sediments ranges from abundant to rare (fig. 6-6). Animal fossils of Ordovician rocks in rough order of decreasing abundance are: Trilobites, brachiopods, graptolites, bryozoans, corals, ostracodes, various echinoderms, gastropods, cephalopods, and pelecypods. Conodonts probably should be included on the list, but they are rarely visible without magnification and special preparation techniques.

Many Ordovician fossils have been more or less obliterated by conversion of limestone to dolomite. This is particularly true of the Fish Haven Dolomite which contains only vague outlines or "ghosts" of several types of organisms, particularly brachiopods. Many specimens in both limestone and dolomite strata are silicified and can be released from the rock by dissolving the matrix with hydrochloric or acetic acid. The trilobites of the Garden City Formation and Pogonip Group are outstanding in this respect. Corals and brachiopods of the Fish Haven Dolomite also occur as silicified specimens. Graptolites, as is usual, are almost entirely restricted to fine-grained shale or mudstone (fig. 6-7). In contrast to most graptolite-bearing strata that are dark in color, many units in the Confusion Basin are light yellow or cream colored.

The deposition of sediment and the evolution of marine organism in the Confusion Basin evidently went on without interruption across the Cambrian-Ordovician boundary. Trilobites of the Early Ordovician are clearly descended from those of the Late Cambrian. Many species have been established by study of Utah specimens. Although it is difficult to make general statements about the evolution of Ordovician trilobites, a few trends are worth mentioning. Many species have broad, smooth tails and unornamented

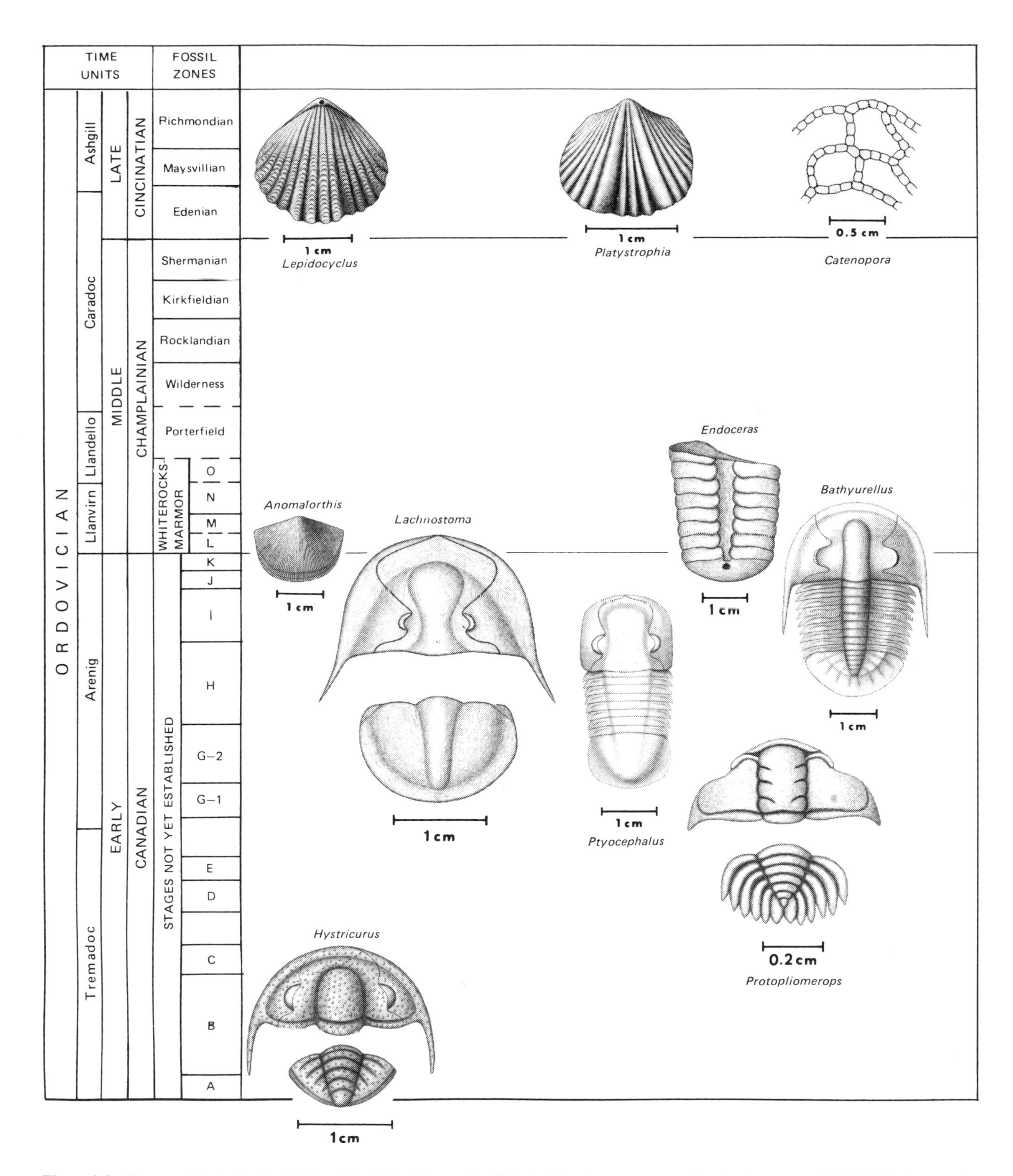

Figure 6-6. Characteristic index fossils found in Ordovician rocks of Utah. Sketches are centered in the time zone of which it is characteristic. Sketches: John K. Balsley.

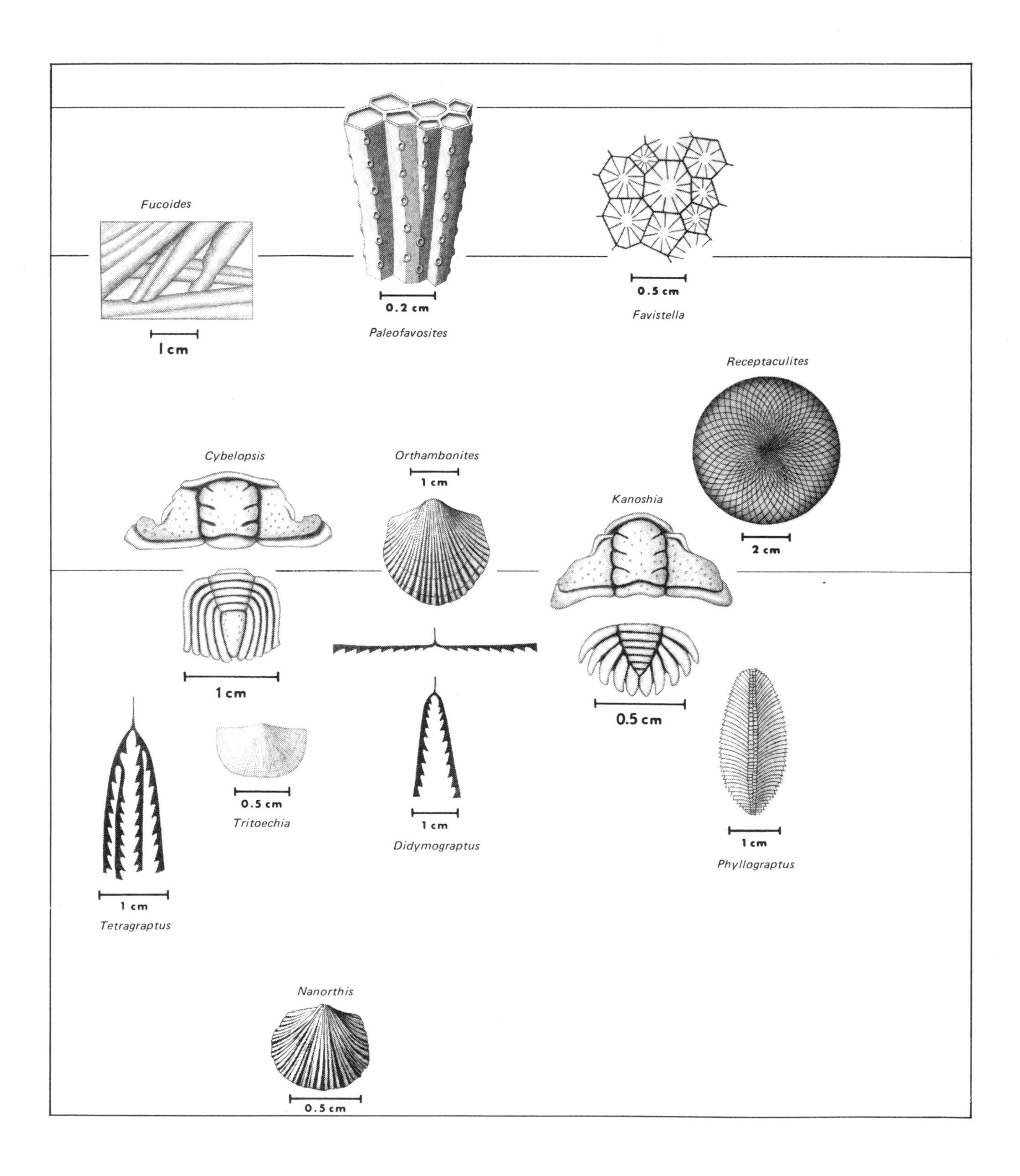

Figure 6-6. Continued.

Figure 6-7. Fossils of the graptolite, *Didymograptus bifidus* from the Middle Ordovician Swan Peak Formation, Mantua Valley. Photo: Jim Howell.

heads, another group has rough granulated surfaces, and still another is marked by spine-bearing tails.

Ordovician brachiopods are numerous but not particularly varied in appearance. The most common types are classified as orthids. They are mostly betwen 0.5 and 1.0 inch in diameter, with simple radiating ribs and a distinct, straight hinge line.

Graptolites are generally found in shaly formations of continental margins. They are present in Utah as far east as Cache Valley and increase in abundance westward across the Great Basin into Nevada. In the Confusion Basin, Early Ordovician graptolite-bearing shale interfingers with trilobite-bearing limestone. This provides an opportunity to compare the evolutionary advances and correlation of these two important animal groups.

Corals occupy a prominent place in Late Ordovician rocks but are rare in older ones. Other Ordovician fossils are of interest because many of them represent early or ancestral species. Unique and important echinoderms as well as early representatives of gastropods, pelecypods, sponges, bryozoans and ostracodes are found in Early Ordovician strata of the Confusion Basin.

A particularly notable locality for Ordovician fossils is Fossil Mountain in the northern end of Wah Wah Valley. At this site 700 feet of the Pogonip Group and 200 feet of Eureka Quartzite are well exposed and contain a number of highly fossiliferous units.

Perhaps the most puzzling of Ordovician fossils is found decorating the surfaces of many sandstone and quartzite beds of the Swan Peak and Eureka Quartzites (fig. 6-8). It is clearly something made by an organism rather than the organism itself. The appearance is that of a tangled, intertwining mass of large, spaghetti-like bodies that are elongate, tapering, and grooved rather than round and smooth. They are made of sand and stand out in relief from the surrounding matrix. They seem to be fillings of cavities made by living organisms or spaces left after something died and disintegrated. They have been interpreted as masses of seaweed, as probings made by the tentacles of cephalopods searching in the mud for food, and as burrows of some kind of worm or arthropod. Currently they are called *Phycoides* but there may be other interpretations and names for them in the future.

Figure 6-8. Slab of Swan Peak Quartzite showing masses of *Phycoides*, a fossil of unknown relationships. This specimen is seen on the roadside in Logan Canyon. Photo: U.S. Forest Service.

SCENERY

Although there are numerous conspicuous outcrops of Ordovician rocks, not many exposures of the dominantly gray strata can be said to constitute truly eye-catching, scenic attractions. The most striking and accessible outcrops are conspicuous cliffs of the Garden City Limestone seen at the mouth of Logan Canyon behind the hydroelectric plant (fig. 6-9). Logan Cave, one of the best known caves in Utah, located farther up the canyon, is a well known roadside landmark (fig. 6-10a and 6-10b). It is the subsurface conduit of Logan Cave Spring that yields a large flow of pure water. The accessible cave is about 2,000 feet long, 10 to 60 feet wide, and 50 to 70 feet high in places. Its course is determined by two sets of fractures in the Garden City Formation.

A striking cliff of Fish Haven Dolomite towers above the Forks in Logan Canyon (fig. 6-11). The Swan Peak Quartzite and the Fish Haven Dolomite crop out as rugged cliffs at Tony Grove and High Lakes (fig. 6-12). The U.S. Forest Service has set up a large slab of *Phycoides*-bearing quartzite about 10 miles up Logan Canyon. This is one of the best known and most photographed fossil specimens in Utah.

Figure 6-9. Outcrops of Ordovician Garden City Limestone near mouth of Logan Canyon. Photo: Clyde T. Hardy.

Figure 6-10b. Aragonite crystals in Logan Cave, Logan Canyon, Cache County. Photo: E.J. Williams.

Figure 6-10a. Rick Springs fault, Logan Canyon, Cache County. Spring emerges along fault in the Ordovician Garden City Limestone. Photo: E.J. Williams.

Figure 6-11. Ledge of Ordovician Fish Haven Dolomite along Logan River near the junction with Right Fork. Photo: U.S. Forest Service.

Figure 6-12. Tony Grove Lake, Bear River Range, Cache County. Mt. Magog on right skyline; light colored cliffs of Swan Peak Quartzite rise above lake level and are overlain by darker outcrops of the Fish Haven Dolomite, both Ordovician. Photo: E.J. Williams.

ECONOMIC

The only indigenous mineral products of value so far discovered in Ordovician rocks are building and industrial stone. Many buildings in Cache Valley, including Logan's Mormon temple, are constructed of stone from the Garden City and Swan Peak Formations quarried from nearby canyons. Farther south, in the Stansbury and Lakeside Mountains, important quarries in the Fish Haven Dolomite, have yielded exceptionally pure material for U.S. Steel's Geneva plant and for export out of state.

Ordovician carbonate rocks furnish host rocks for important ore bodies in the Tintic mining district. Ore taken from the Opohonga and Fish Haven Formations in the Main and East Tintic mining districts is estimated to exceed $20 million in value.

For additional reading of the topics discussed in Chapter 6, see the following list of authors:

Berden, 1976
Braithwaite, 1976
Budge, 1972
Church, 1942
Cook, D. R., 1957
Ethington and Clark, 1971
Flower, 1976
Hinds, R. W., 1970
Hintze, L. F., 1952, 1963, 1969
Hintze and others, 1961
Jensen, R. G., 1967
Ketner, 1968
Lane, N. G., 1970
Morris, 1961, 1964
Morris and Lovering, 1962
Pojeta, 1971
Rigby, 1958
Rigby and Hintze, 1977
Ross, 1951, 1953, 1974, 1976
Von Dorston, 1970
Webb, 1956, 1958
Williams, 1958
Yochelson and Jones, 1968
Young, G. E., 1973

For complete bibliographic citations, please see List of References.

7 THE SILURIAN PERIOD

The Silurian Period began about 440 million years ago and ended about 30 million years later. The time limits are somewhat uncertain because reliable radiometric dates for the upper and lower boundaries have not been obtained. The name was first applied in 1835 and derived from the Silures, an ancient tribe inhabiting the borderland of Wales and England. The most complete representations of Silurian rocks known in North America are in Nevada and New York State. The Silurian system in Utah has generally been mapped as one formation, the Laketown Dolomite. Locally it has been subdivided and approximately 14 additional stratigraphic units are now recognized. The most important are listed at the end of the book.

PALEOGEOGRAPHY

The seaway that covered most of western Utah during Silurian time was unusually narrow and shallow (fig. 7-1). At times, wide, flat, featureless tracts of limy sediment were exposed and any precipitation which fell merely accumulated in temporary shallow pools and could accomplish no significant erosion.

The eastern edge of Silurian rocks, as preserved today, may be near the original shoreline of the Silurian seaway or considerably west of it. Evidence favors the first hypothesis and would locate the shoreline not far from the Wasatch Line. Silurian rocks are unrecognized in northwestern Utah—either they were not deposited or have been obliterated by more recent disturbances. Some geologists would have the area under water, others consider it to have been a low-lying land, similar to an offshore island. Eastern Utah was out of water with a surface of previously deposited limy material.

ORIGIN AND NATURE OF SILURIAN ROCKS

Silurian strata are entirely of marine origin. They have smaller total volume, fewer outcrops, and are of more uniform composition than strata of any other system (fig. 7-2). The relatively simple, restricted rock record is due partly to the shortness of the Silurian Period which lasted only about one-half as long as either the Cambrian or Ordovician Periods and partly to the shallow water environment of deposition which did not favor thick accumulations of sediment. There was apparently little subsidence of the Cordilleran geosyncline so that very little space was available below sea level and no significant uplifts affected the adjacent shelf to provide coarse material for contemporary formations.

A surprising discovery came with the dating of a basic igneous dike in the Uinta Mountains as 412 ± 17 million years. This places its origin as very late Silurian. The dike cuts, and is surrounded by, Precambrian sediments and records at least one event in an otherwise great gap in the geologic history of the region.

OUTCROPS AND FORMATIONS

Until recently all of Utah's Silurian rocks were assigned to one formation, the Laketown Dolomite. The formation averages about 1,200 feet thick and is exposed in a number of mountains in the Basin and Range Province of northern and western Utah. The type section is in Laketown Canyon, near the southeastern shore of Bear Lake. Complete sections of the formation are found in the following areas: Bear River Range, Wellsville Mountains , Samaria Mountains, Promontory Mountains, Newfoundland Mountains, Silver Island Mountains, Lakeside Mountains, Sheeprock Mountains , Dugway Range, Deep Creek Range, Fish Springs Range, Confusion Range, Conger Range, Needle Range, and the Wah Wah Mountains.

Thinner sections are found on Stansbury Island, the East Tintic Mountains, West Tintic Mountains, Pavant Range, Beaver Lake Mountains, and Long Ridge. In the well-studied East Tintic Mountains, the Silurian strata are combined with Ordovician and Devonian strata to compose the Bluebell Formation.

No Silurian rocks have been positively identified in the transition belt represented by the Beaver Dam, Mineral, and Oquirrh Mountains. If it is present in these localities, it is thin and not readily distinguished from adjacent formations.

In areas where particular attention has been paid to Silurian strata, investigators have been able to subdivide the

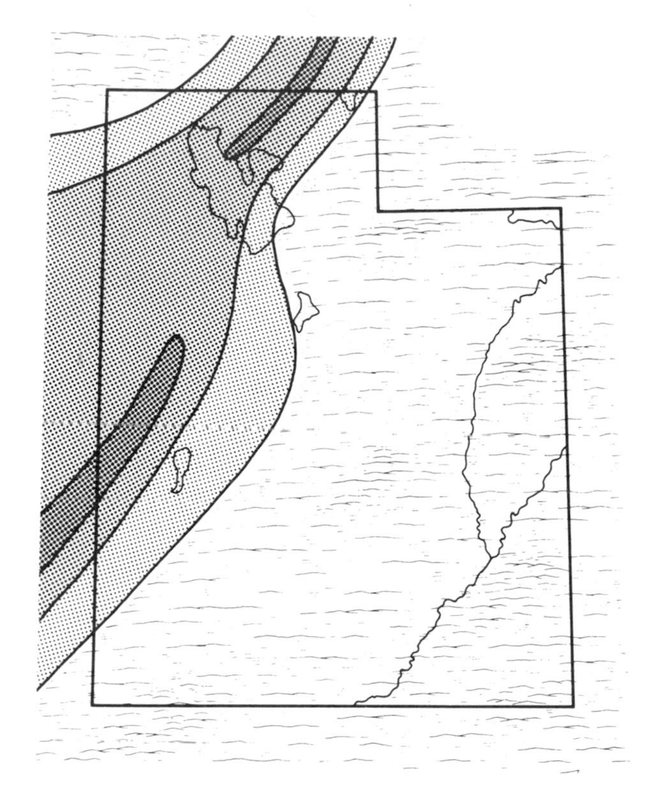

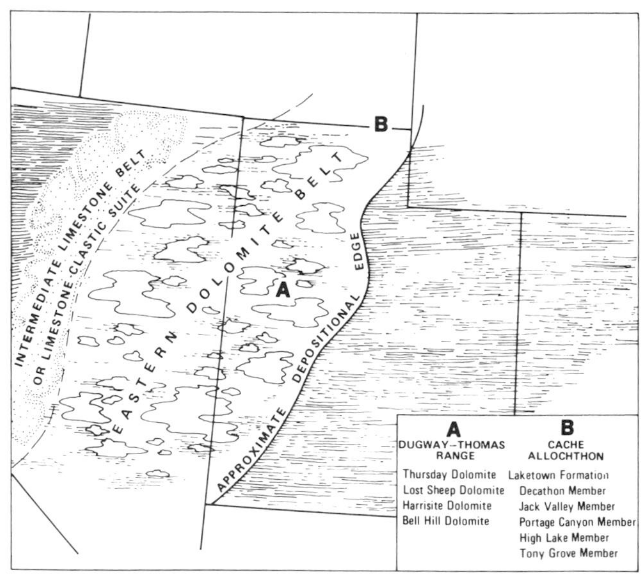

Figure 7-1. Two representations of the paleogeography of the Silurian Period. Upper illustration shows by shaded patterns the distribution of thicker (darkest) to thinner (lightest) deposits. In general more time is represented by sediments in the thicker sections. Lower illustration shows the reconstructed environments of the Cordilleran geosyncline at the time of maximum marine flooding. Typical formations and members are named in both illustrations. The topography of dry land areas is shown diagrammatically. (Lower illustration from Stokes, 1979.)

Laketown Dolomite into a number of members. Formal names have been given to some, while others have received only letter or number designations. In the Cache Valley area and the Bear River Range the approximately 1,200-foot section of Laketown Dolomite has been subdivided into five members which are, from oldest to youngest: Tony Grove Lake Member (625 feet), High Lake Member (354 feet), Portage Canyon Member (200 feet), Jacks Valley Member (10 feet), and Decathon Member (16 feet). The two youngest members were first identified in the Confusion Basin, the others have type sections in the Bear Lake area. These units may or may not become established by future useage. In the Thomas Range the 1,200-foot section of Laketown equivalent has been divided into the following formations, from oldest to youngest: Bell Hill Dolomite (430 feet), Harrisite Dolomite (175 feet), Lost Sheep Dolomite (270 feet), and Thursday Dolomite (330 feet). Figure 7-3 shows graphic columnar sections of these representative areas.

FOSSILS

The Silurian has yielded fewer fossils than any other system in Utah (fig. 7-4). Not only is the volume of sediment small but the common rock type, originally shallow-water limestone, is not well suited for the burial and preservation of fossils. Silurian seas seem to have been shallow

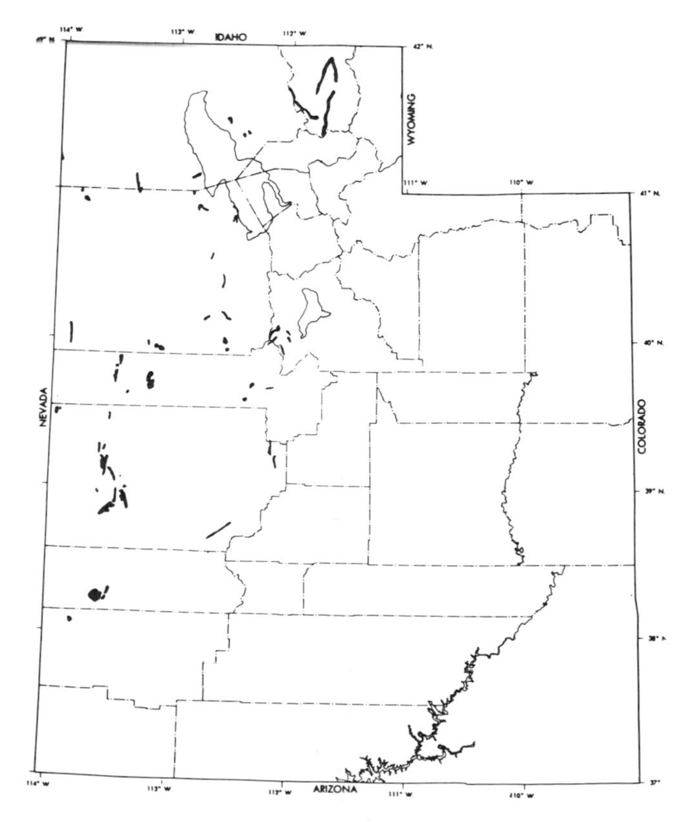

Figure 7-2. Exposures of Silurian rocks in Utah. Note relatively larger areas in the Cache Valley area and Confusion Basin.

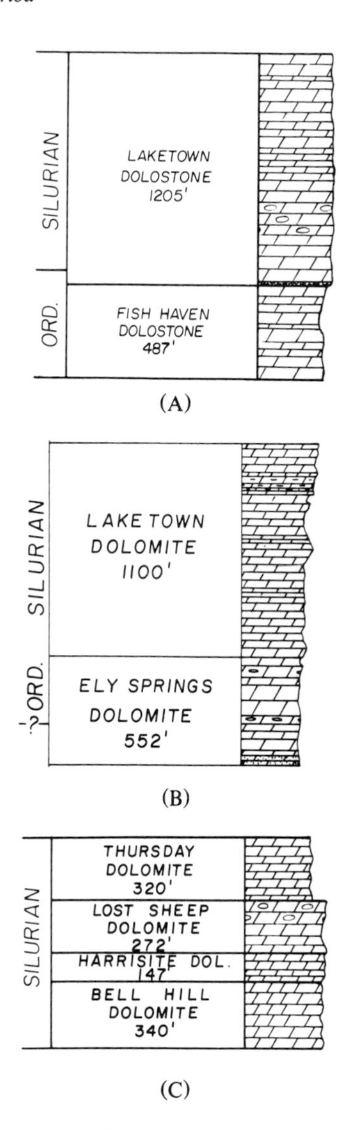

Figure 7-3. Graphic stratigraphic sections of Silurian sedimentary formations: (A) Cache Valley area, northern Utah; (B) Thomas Range, west-central Utah, and (C) Confusion Basin, southwest-central Utah.

and subject to constant stirring by waves and currents. Few marine animals can live permanently under such conditions. Those that do exist are subject to the danger of being left exposed to the air or of being dislodged from their living spaces by wave action. Illustrative of this is the fact that few of the brachiopods are preserved in growth positions and most coral specimens have flattened, platelike forms.

In addition, many fossils which were originally present have been destroyed by a process called dolomitization that alters the orginal calcareous ($CaCO_3$) shells and matrix to dolomite ($MgCO_3$) by reactions with sea water. The substitution of calcium ions by magnesium ions results in recrystallization which more or less obliterates any fossils that may be present. In small areas, and even in parts of a single fossil, the effects of yet another process, silicification, may precede or interfere with dolomitization. As the name suggests, calcareous shell material is replaced by silica (SiO_2). This process results in the preservation of fossils that range in quality from very good to very poor. If only enough silica enters the fossil to replace the exact original material, the fine details that are needed for identification are preserved; if additional silica enters, details are obliterated and a coarse, granular, texture results. Collections suitable for study may be obtained by selecting the best silicified specimens and removing the matrix by acid treatments.

In rough order of decreasing abundance, the fossils of the Silurian are: corals, brachipods, stromatoporoids, crinoids, cephalopods, gastropods and sponges (fig. 7-4). The corals are predominantly colonial, having lived in compact groups of many individuals. There are a few solitary types as well. The chain coral, *Halysites*, is very common in Silurian rocks, not only in Utah but worldwide. It has a chainlike configuration of individual elements strung end to end in curving patterns, each link of which is the work of a separate animal. Different species may be identified by the shape, size, and arrangement of the "links." Two other characteristic Silurian fossils are *Favosites*, the "honeycomb" coral, and *Syringopora*, the "pipe organ" coral (fig, 7-5). Even partly silicified or dolomitized specimens are adequate to identify most Silurian marine formations. Less common Silurian corals are *Bighornia, Agetolites, Axofistulophyllum,* and *Palaeophyllum.*

Many Silurian brachiopods are rather large, smooth, and distinctly five-sided (pentameral); some can be identified even by their shadowy outlines. Common specimens are *Virginia* and *Pentamerus.* The great group of brachiopods known as spirifers originated in the Silurian, but few are known from Utah. An excellent collection of silicified brachiopods from the Desert Range, Tooele County, has been described by Sheehan (1976).

Stromatoporoids are fossils that seem to be related to certain reef-dwelling sponges and commonly associate with corals to build reefs of various sizes. They are preserved as crust-like or mound-like masses with a distinctive inner structure consisting essentially of thin layers separated by pillar-like structures.

SCENERY

The Laketown Dolomite (fig. 7-6) usually forms very steep and rugged cliffs that are not easily distinguished from cliffs of the underlying Ordovician and overlying Devonian dolomite formations. In Cache County, the Laketown cliffs are particularly impressive and two stretches are notable: between the hydroelectric plant near the mouth of Logan Canyon and the American Legion Home and near the junction of Card Canyon and Logan Canyon. Clay Valley, east of Mantua, appears to be a solution valley in the Laketown Dolomite.

ECONOMIC

No significant quarries for building or industrial stone have been opened in Silurian rocks, but there is no reason

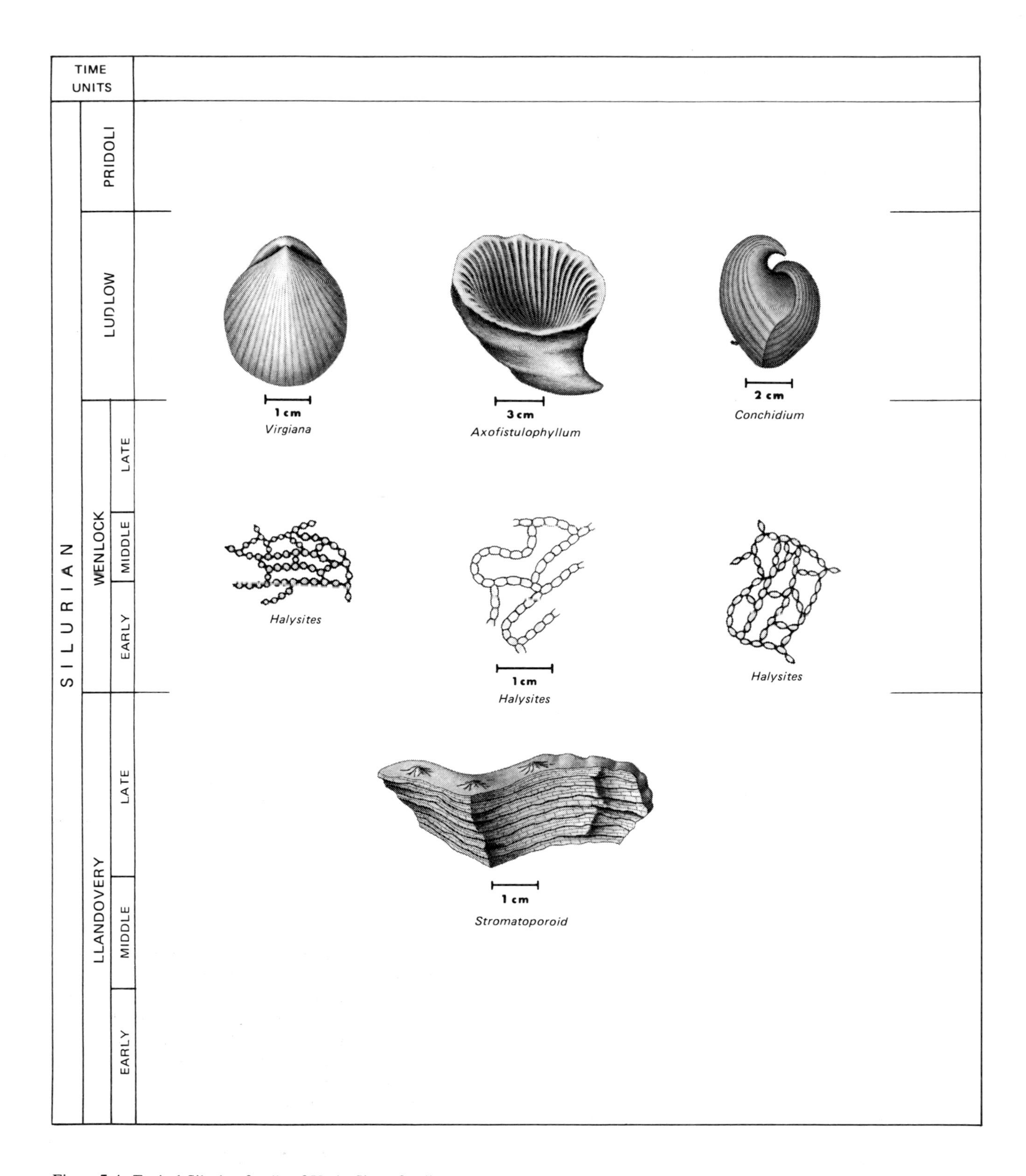

Figure 7-4. Typical Silurian fossils of Utah. Since fossil zones have not been established in Utah formations the species illustrated here have no value in identifying particular parts of the system.

A

B

C

Figure 7-5. Characteristic Silurian fossils of Utah: (A) *Halysites*, the "chain" coral; (B) *Favosites*, the "honeycomb" coral; and (C) *Syringopora*, the "pipe organ" coral. All of these specimens are silicified in a matrix of carbonate rock. *Halysites* specimen about 5 inches across. Photo: Jim Howell.

Figure 7-6. Banded dolomite of lower part of Silurian Laketown Dolomite, Wellsville Mountain, Box Elder County. Photo: Stanley S. Beus.

why they might not be exploited in the future. Important ore bodies occur in the Bluebell Dolomite of the Tintic mining district and much of the fluorspar ore of the Spor Mountain district is in pipes and veins that cut Ordovician and Silurian dolomite formations. Since no ore is known below the top 10 feet of the Swan Peak Quartzite (Ordovician) or above the lower 100 feet of the Sevy Dolomite (Lower Devonian), the host rocks must be largely Late Ordovician and Silurian.

For additional reading of the topics discussed in Chapter 7, see the following list of authors:

Barosh, 1960
Beus and Rush, 1968
Beus and Gelnott, 1958
Bick, 1966
Budge, 1972
Chapusa, 1969
Christiansen, 1977
Cohenour, 1959
Doelling, 1964
Duncan, 1956
Groff, 1959
Kepper, 1960
Lautenschlager, 1954
Maxey, 1946
Miller, G.M., 1966
Morris and Lovering, 1961
Muessig, 1951
Olson, 1956
Paddock, 1956

Richardson, 1913, 1941
Rigby, 1967
Ritzma, 1974
Rush, 1956, 1963
Schaeffer and Anderson, 1960
Seeland, 1976
Staatz, 1963
Staatz and Carr, 1964
Williams, J. S., 1948, 1958
Wilson, J. R., 1976

For complete bibliographic citations, please see List of References.

8 THE DEVONIAN PERIOD

The Devonian Period began about 410 million years ago and lasted an estimated 50 million years. It was first studied intensively in Devonshire, England, and named in 1840. Many important Devonian formations have been mapped in North America. Representative deposits of all major subdivisions of the period are found in Utah and about 30 named Devonian formations have been recognized. Important Devonian stratigraphic units are listed at the end of the book.

PALEOGEOGRAPHY

Devonian seas followed the pattern of previous periods, shallow and temporary to the east, deeper and longer lasting to the west. A gradual eastward migration of the shoreline is documented by a Lower Devonian rock sequence of small volume and limited extent, Middle Devonian units of wider extent and intermediate volume, and Late Devonian formations of greatest extent and volume (fig. 8-1). Only in Late Devonian time did the sea extend eastward beyond the Wasatch Line.

It is uncertain how much of northeastern Utah, including the Uinta Mountains area, was covered by seas during the Devonian. Although thin remnants of Late Devonian marine rocks have been found below Mississippian formations in the western Uinta Mountains, it is probable that the original deposits did not extend much farther east. Deep drill holes in southeastern Utah outline the approximate eastern edge of Devonian rocks as they now exist. It is generally agreed that the deep erosion of mountains uplifted during the Pennsylvanian Period removed all earlier sediments, including Devonian strata, from east-central Utah. Figure 8-1 shows northeastern Utah as a lowland being eroded and east-central Utah as under shallow seas in Late Devonian time.

Local uplift during the Late Devonian interrupted the steady accumulation of marine sediments that had been going on for a very long time in west-central Utah. Evidence for such an uplift can be recognized in the Stansbury Mountains south of Great Salt Lake. A Late Devonian event, called the Stansbury Disturbance, elevated a long narrow section of the crust into a prominent ridge above sea level. A geologic disturbance is a relatively minor event when compared to the more extensive mountain building and radical alterations of land and sea known as revolutions—for example, the Rocky Mountain Revolution. Although the ancient Stansbury Mountains were topographically important for only a short time, they are shown on the paleogeographic map as significant features of the Devonian.

ORIGIN AND NATURE OF DEVONIAN ROCKS

A listing of Devonian rock types, in order of decreasing abundance is: limestone, dolomite, shale, sandstone-quartzite, and conglomerate. The basal or Lower Devonian formations (Sevy Dolomite and Water Canyon Formation) are almost pure dolomite, Middle Devonian formations (the Simonson Dolomite and Jefferson Limestone) are mixed limestone and dolomite, and Upper Devonian rocks (Guilmette and Stansbury Formations and the Pinyon Peak Limestone) are limestone, shale, sandstone, and conglomerate (figs. 8-1a and 8-1b). The Devonian sequence clearly shows a trend, away from the production of dolomite that had prevailed during the Late Ordovician and Silurian Periods, toward the production of limestone that was to dominate Mississippian seas. Clastic sediments, for example sand and shale, also increased during and after the Late Devonian.

Extensive dolomite formations in the Great Basin constitute an important natural laboratory for the study of the origin and varieties of dolomite. Understanding the formation of this rock type is a major problem for sedimentologists because very little dolomite is forming today, whereas limestone deposition is taking place over great areas of shallow ocean bottom. Conditions that favor the deposition of dolomite rather than limestone appear to include shallow, warm, marine water where sunlight evaporates and heats the brine.

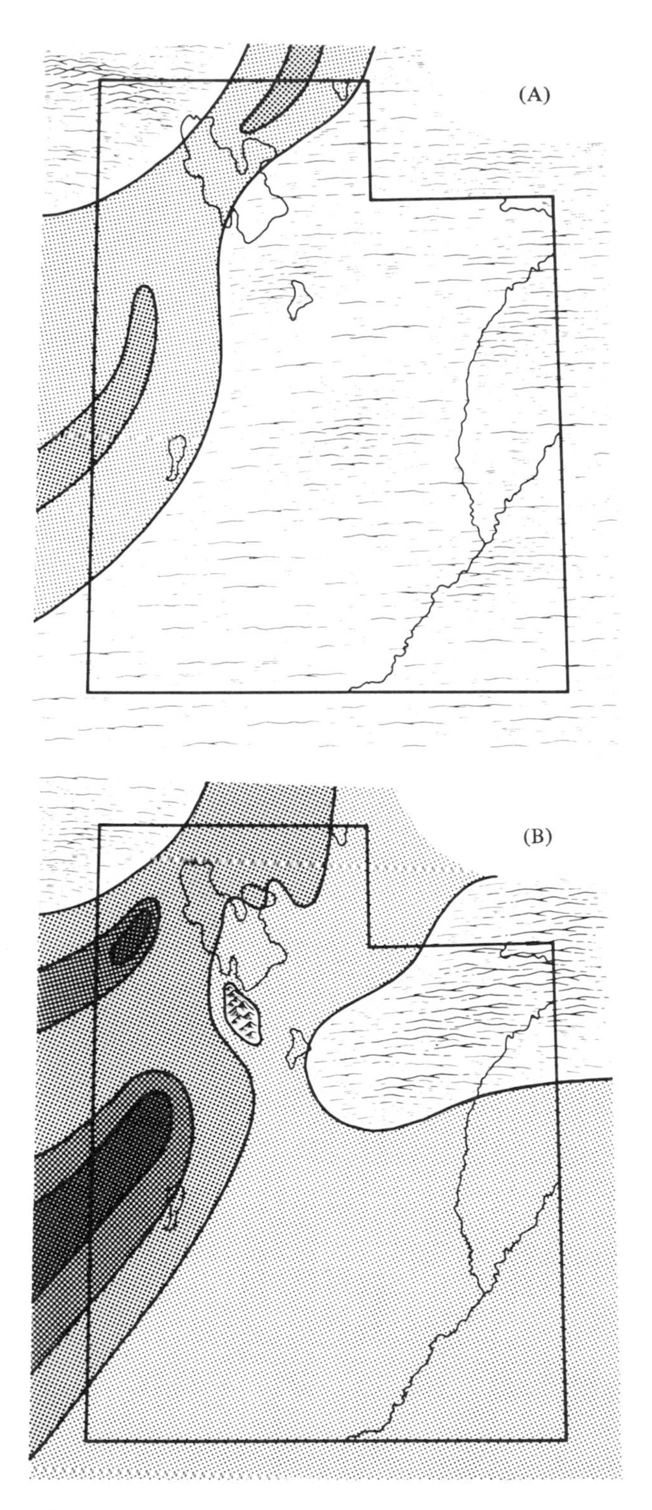

Figure 8-1. Generalized paleogeography of (A) Early Devonian time and (B) Late Devonian time. Relative darkness of patterns indicates length of time represented by preserved deposits. Darkest areas have the most complete record and greatest thickness of sediments. Topography of exposed land is shown diagrammatically. Note small uplift caused by the Stansbury disturbance near the southern end of Great Salt Lake.

OUTCROPS AND FORMATIONS

Devonian rocks form significant parts of many mountain ranges in western Utah (fig. 8-2). Complete stratigraphic sections (figs. 8-3, 8-4, and 8-5) that include Lower, Middle, and Upper Devonian sequences are found in a number of uplifts: Bear River Range, Wellsville Mountains, Samaria Mountains, Lakeside Mountains, Newfoundland Mountains, Silver Island Mountains, Stansbury Mountains, Onaqui and Sheeprock Mountains, Deep Creek Range, Confusion Range, Thomas Range, Fish Springs Range, Conger Range, Wah Wah Mountains, and the Needle Range. Less complete, but still significant, sections are found in the central Wasatch Range, Long Ridge, Oquirrh Mountains, East and West Tintic Mountains, Stansbury Island, Canyon Mountains, Pavant Range, Mineral Mountains, San Francisco Mountains, and Beaver Dam Mountains. At present only a thin remnant of Late Devonian age strata has been identified on the northwestern flank of the Uinta Mountains; however, further study will undoubtedly identify additional Devonian strata there.

Devonian formations have been named at a number of Utah localities, including Cache Valley (the Water Canyon Dolomite and two members of the Jefferson Limestone, the Hyrum Dolomite Member, and the Beirdneau Sandstone Member), Gold Hill (Sevy Dolomite, Simonson Dolomite, and Guilmette Formation) and in the subsurface of southeastern Utah (McCracken). The Ouray Limestone and Elbert Formation were originally named from surface outcrops in Colorado, but the McCracken Formation, discovered by drilling to 8,049 feet in the Four Corners area, was named for McCracken Mesa, a surface feature at the drill-site.

FOSSILS

Marine animals left numerous remains in the Devonian formations of Utah but critical studies of these fossils have been conducted mostly in states adjoining Utah. Important Devonian fossil groups include brachiopods, corals, crinoids, conodonts, echinoderms, bryozoans, trilobites, stromatoporoids, gastropods, pelecypods, and cephalopods (fig. 8-6). Conodonts are of most value in correlation but because of their small size they cannot be used directly in the field.

By Devonian time, the brachiopods had reached a high in numbers and varieties. Of the 12 Devonian fossil zones recognized in the western United States, 11 are named for brachiopods and one is named for a coral. A most common Devonian brachiopod is *Atrypa*, of which many species are found. The wide, pointed, wing-shaped brachiopods known as spirifers are also abundant and several species with closely spaced radiating ribs are characteristic of the Late Devonian. One of the largest brachiopods of all time is *Stringocephalis*, with shells as large as 6 inches across. Specimens are found in Middle Devonian strata around the world, including western Utah.

Both solitary and colonial species of corals abound and in places (not including Utah) the Devonian was a period of

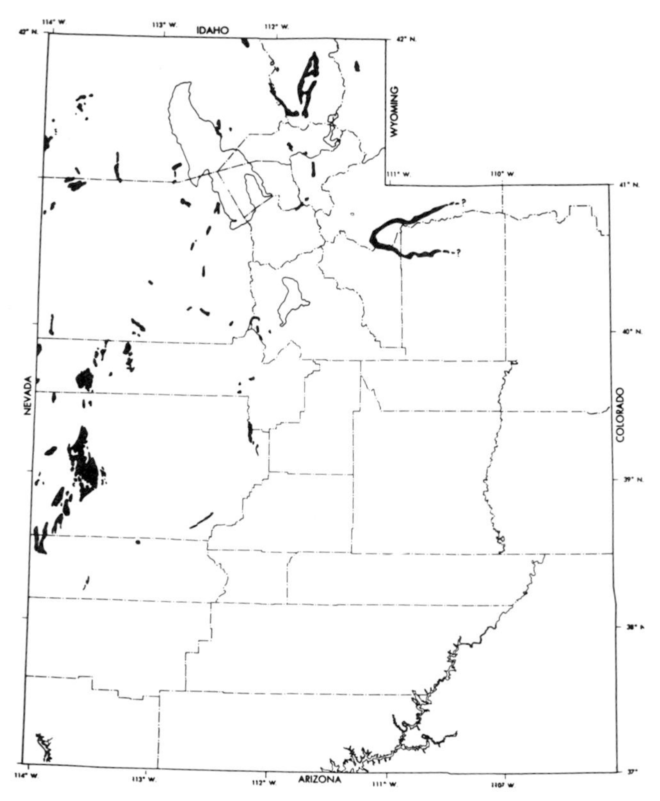

Figure 8-5. Graphic columnar section of Devonian formations exposed in the Thomas-Dugway Ranges, west-central Utah.

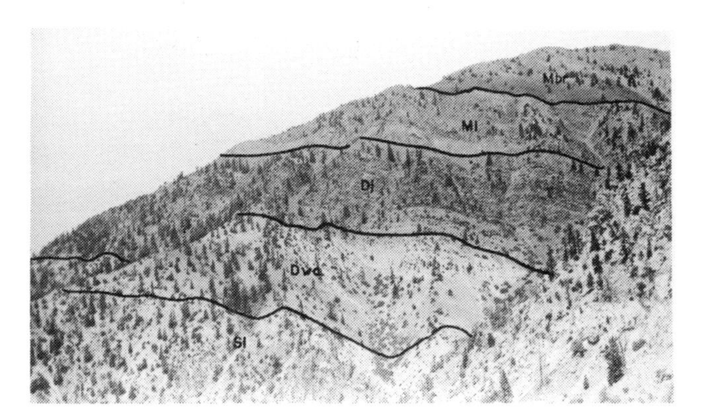

Figure 8-3. Paleozoic formations exposed on west face of Wellsville Mountain, Box Elder County. Sl, Silurian Laketown Dolomite; Dwc, Devonian Water Canyon Dolomite; Dj, Devonian Jefferson Formation; Ml, Mississippian Lodgepole Limestone; Mbr, Mississippian Brazer Limestone. Photo: Stanley S. Beus.

extensive reef building. Colonial corals are those with many individuals uniting to build solid compartmentalized structures; solitary corals are those in which a single animal lives in each structure. Common colonial genera are *Hexagonaria*, *Phillipsastraea*, *Amphipora*, and *Cladopora*. Small corals such as *Amphipora* and *Cladopora* occur in large masses making what field geologists call "spaghetti rock"

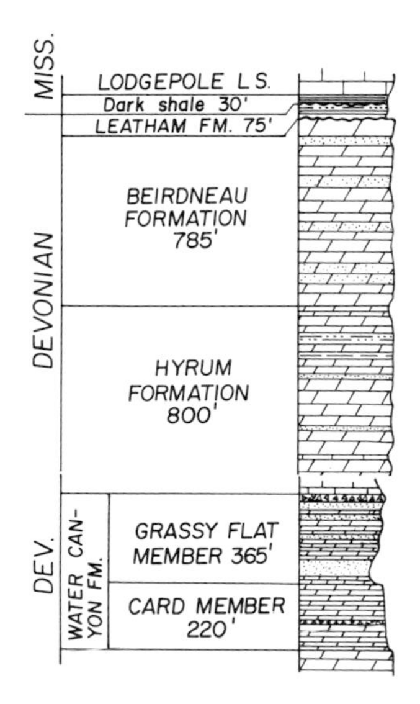

Figure 8-4. Graphic columnar section of Devonian formations in the Cache Valley area, northern Utah.

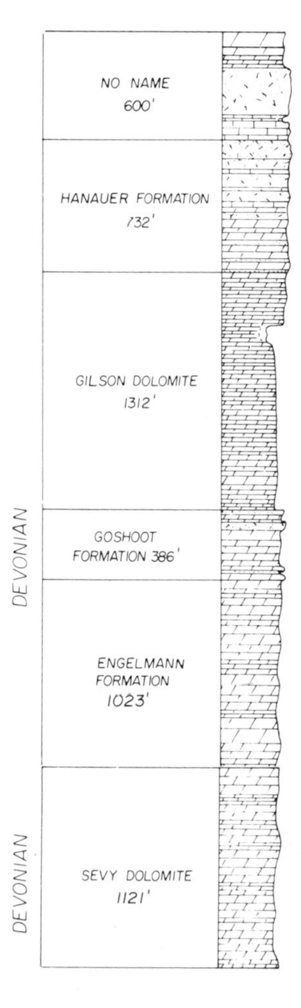

Figure 8-5. Graphic columnar section of Devonian Formations exposed in the Thomas-Dugway ranges, west-central Utah.

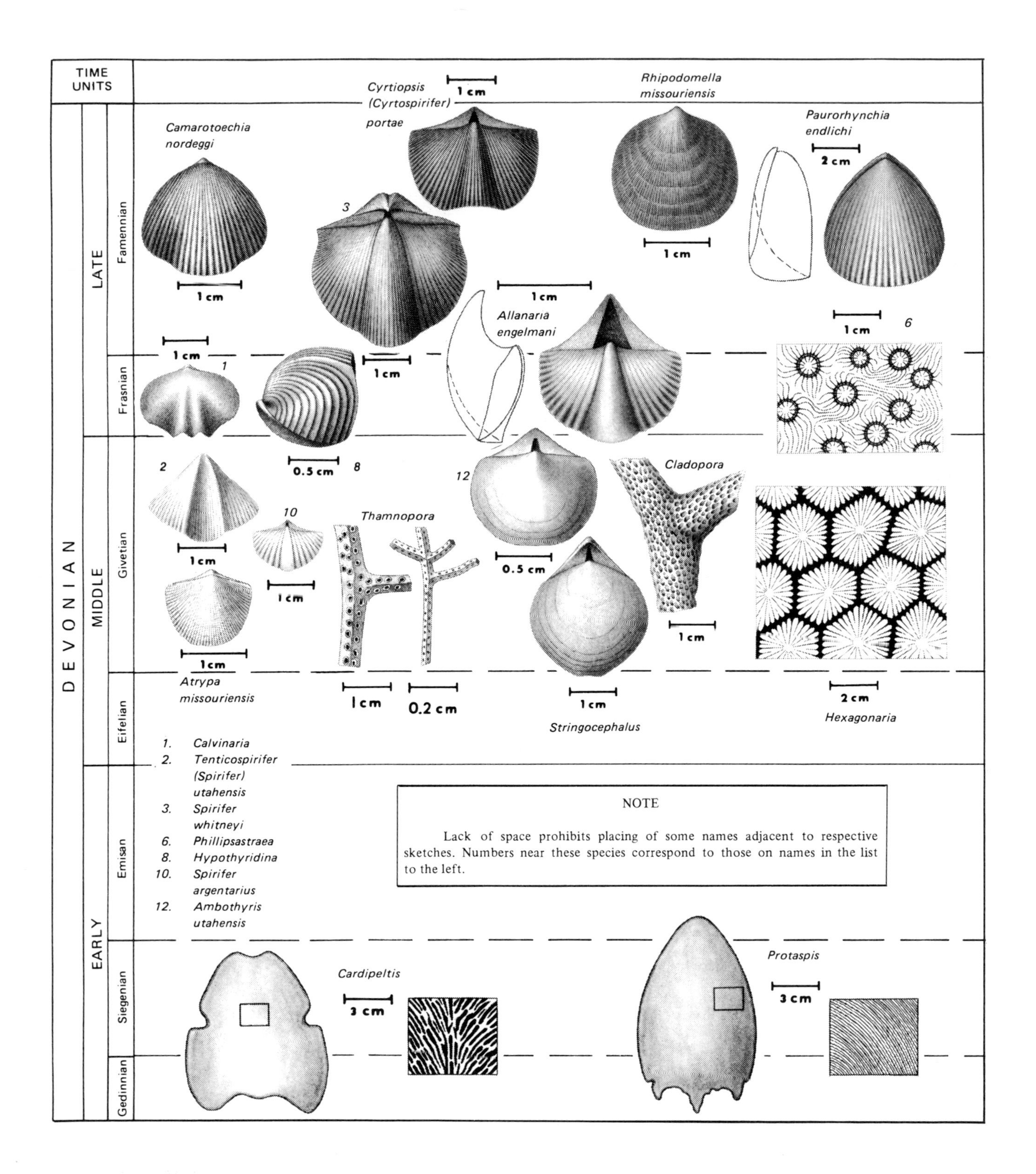

Figure 8-6. Typical index fossils for Devonian rocks of Utah. Sketches are arranged so that center of each specimen lies in the zone of which it is characteristic. Sketches: John K. Balsley.

(fig. 8-7). The Devonian was also a high point in the history of stromatoporoids, colonial animals probably related to sponges, that build extensive reefs in association with corals and other organisms.

Figure 8-7. So-called "spaghetti-rock," Middle Devonian. The twig-like bodies are broken and recrystallized sections of small coral colonies. Ten-cent piece gives scale.

All other invertebrate fossils are relatively rare. Cephalopods, used extensively in correlating formations worldwide, are represented by only scattered specimens of a few species, each of which is of unusual value as a guide fossil.

The Devonian is best known as the Age of Fishes. In many ways the most important fossils of the period are those of primitive, bone-bearing fish called ostracoderms (bone-skins). Ostracoderms are greatly unlike modern fish; they had neither teeth nor jaws and the fore-parts of their bodies were encased in bony shields. Their fossils are found in the Lower Devonian Water Canyon Dolomite and in the Beirdneau Sandstone Member of the Jefferson Limestone of Middle Devonian age. Most of the fossils are fragmentary, but remains of a dozen or so different types have been identified as in figure 8-8. At the present time ostracoderms are the oldest bone-bearing animals known; their fossils are basic to an understanding of what the primitive beginnings of the vertebrates were like.

ECONOMIC

Although great volumes of potentially valuable limestone and dolomite are contained in Utah's Devonian formations, they are not currently being utilized. Small quarries have been opened in the quartzite beds of the Stansbury Formation to obtain silica as a raw material for refractory bricks.

The oldest Utah formations known to contain oil and gas reserves are the Elbert Formation, the Ouray Limestone, and the McCracken Formation. Production of oil and gas has been obtained from these formations at depths of from 8,300 to 9,200 feet in the Lisbon Valley Field, San Juan County.

Figure 8-8. Almost complete head shield of *Cardipeltis*, Early Devonian fish, from the Water Canyon Formation, Lakeside Mountains.

SCENERY

Devonian strata have produced little noteworthy scenery. Where limestone and dolomite beds crop out they generally form ragged step-like cliffs such as those in Logan Canyon and on Wellsville Mountain (fig. 8-3). The town of Wendover, in Tooele County on the Utah-Nevada state line west of the salt flats, is surrounded by barren hills and cliffs of Devonian strata and a famous nearby archaeological site, Danger Cave (fig. 8-9), is in the Guilmette Formation. Colorful strata of the Hyrum Dolomite and Beirdneau Sandstone Members of the Jefferson Limestone are seen along the shores of Causey Creek Reservoir in Weber County.

Figure 8-9. Entrance to Danger Cave, near Wendover, Tooele County. The cave is in the Guilmette Formation, Middle Devonian. Evidence of human occupancy dating from 11,000 years ago was discovered here. Photo: Archaeology Center, Department of Anthropology, University of Utah.

For additional reading of the topics discussed in Chapter 8, see the following list of authors:

Baetcke, 1969
Beus, 1958
Beus and Rush, 1968
Bick, 1966
Chapusa, 1969
Christiansen, 1962, 1977
Clark, D. L., 1960, 1967
Clark and Ethington, 1966, 1967
Cohenour, 1959
Doelling, 1964
Edvalson, 1947
Elison, 1952
Gould, 1959
Hooper, 1951
Hose, 1966
Kepper, 1960
Ketner, 1969
Knight and Cooper, 1955
Kunkel and Schick, 1963
Lautenschlager, 1954
Maxey, 1946
Miller, G. H., 1966
Morris and Lovering, 1961
Osmond, 1954
Paddock, 1956
Parker, J. M., 1961
Petersen, C. A., 1974
Preston, 1961
Reber, 1952
Rigby, 1958, 1963
Rigby and Bissell, 1958
Schaeffer and Anderson, 1960
Staatz and Carr, 1964
Williams, J. S., 1948

For complete bibliographic citations, please see List of References.

Figure 8-10. Outcrop of the Stansbury Formation at the southern end of Stansbury Island; Stansbury Mountains in the distance. The outcrop is quartzite. Photo: Jim Howell.

9 THE MISSISSIPPIAN PERIOD

The Mississippian Period began about 360 million years ago and lasted about 40 million years. This subdivision of geologic time was suggested in 1869 by the American geologist, Alexander Winchel. Geologists outside of North America prefer to use the term Early Carboniferous for approximately the same period of time American geologists call the Mississippian. Mississippian strata are widely distributed across North America. The type area for the system is in the Mississippi River Valley near the junctions of the Mississippi, Missouri, and Ohio Rivers. The period is usually formally divided into Early and Late portions. In Utah the system is well represented in spite of the fact that as much as half of the original strata has been removed by erosion. About 55 Mississippian stratigraphic units have been recognized in Utah. The more important are listed and briefly characterized at the end of the book.

PALEOGEOGRAPHY

At maximum extent the Mississippian seas covered almost the entire state except perhaps the northwest corner (fig. 9-1). Significant quantities of Mississippian rocks were removed by erosion during the next period (Pennsylvanian) and there has been a steady destruction of Mississippian rocks ever since.

During the Early Mississippian much of the western United States, including Utah, was under water. This sea was evidently shallow, warm and well mixed by currents so that limestone with a relatively uniform assemblage of fossils was deposited over an unusually wide area. Contributions of sandy sediments were insignificant during this interval.

Following the Early Mississippian, eastern Utah emerged from the sea and was subject to a lengthy period of erosion, including widespread solution of previously deposited limestone. A layer of insoluble residue and deeply weathered limestone, known as the Molas Formation, was created over much of eastern Utah and western Colorado. While eastern Utah was being eroded western Utah continued to subside and additional sediments accumulated throughout the remainder of the period (figs. 9-2 and 9-3). In north-

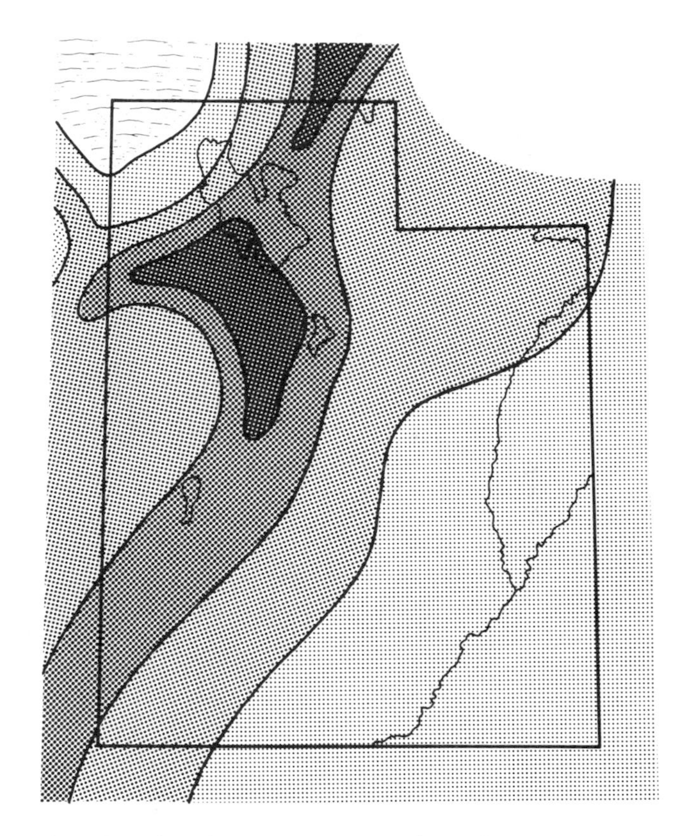

Figure 9-1. Simplified paleogeography of Utah for the Mississippian Period. Darkest shaded areas have thickest and most complete sedimentary sections. Lighter zones contain correspondingly less complete sections. Land area shown diagrammatically in the northwest corner is somewhat hypothetical.

central Utah and extending into Idaho, Late Mississippian deposits are limy and record rather warm, shallow-water environments (figs. 9-4a and 9-4b). In the Confusion Basin of southwestern Utah the Late Mississippian strata contain less limestone and more shale, sandstone, and even some conglomerate. The non-limy constituents were derived from sources in west-central Nevada where Antler Orogeny

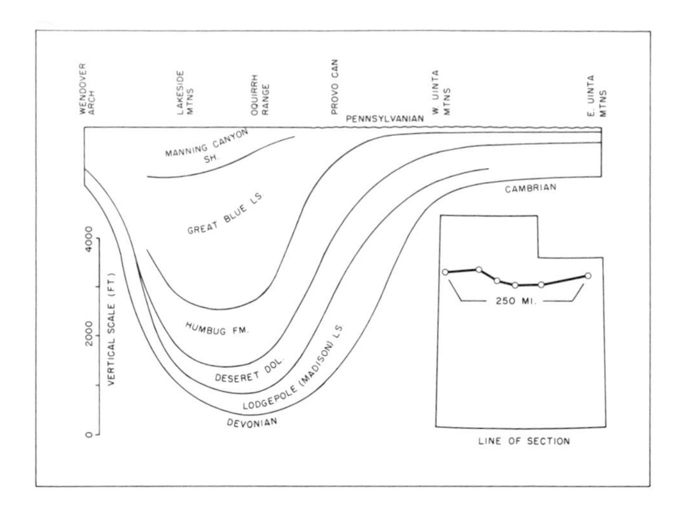

Figure 9-2. Cross-section from western to eastern Utah showing Mississippian formations (from Stokes and Heylmun, 1957).

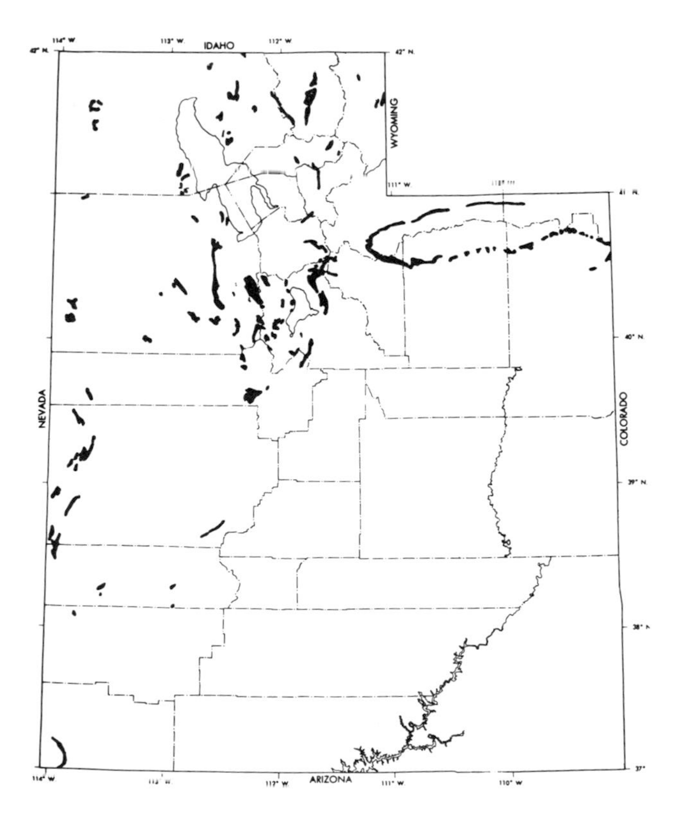

Figure 9-3. Outcrops of Mississippian rocks in Utah. Although Mississippian rocks underlie most of eastern Utah they have not yet been exposed by erosion.

mountain-building was actively in progress. It has been estimated that conglomerate rock fragments now found in Utah were derived from highlands as far as 70 miles away.

ORIGIN AND NATURE OF MISSISSIPPIAN ROCKS

Mississippian deposits almost everywhere contain much limestone. The period, considering its short duration, may be the greatest limestone-producing interval of geologic time. Limestone was also a common rock type of the Cambrian, a period of similar paleogeography with shallow widespread seas well mixed by warm currents.

The study and classification of limestone is a specialized field that is somewhat more complicated than the classification of sandstone and siltstone because calcium carbonate can originate in a variety of ways and can be dissolved and redeposited much more easily than can silica, the common constituent of sand and silt. One classification scheme recognizes that most carbonate rocks are made of three components: 1) allochems, which are discrete aggregates or particles such as pellets, oolites, or pieces of limy shells; 2) micrite, which is extremely fine-grained mud or calcite ooze; and 3) sparry calcite, which is chemically precipitated, crystalline, pore-space-filling cement. Another classification scheme is based on the type and arrangement of the original components: types with and without mud; types in which the grains are abundant enough to support themselves; and those in which the grains are supported by the muddy matrix.

All common types of limestone are present in the Mississippian of Utah. One particular type, called encrinite, is particularly abundant. It is composed chiefly of disarticulated and broken pieces of crinoids, marine stemmed animals having plant-like form and consisting of skeletons of numerous calcareous plates. Each plate is a single crystal of calcite which can readily be incorporated in sediments, either as part of the complete animal skeleton or as a single cleavage fragment.

Dolomite (magnesium carbonate, $MgCO^3$) is much less common than limestone in the Mississippian. It comprises individual beds within a few Mississippian formations and, in the vicinity of strong igneous activity, large volumes of rock originally deposited as limestone became dolomitized through the action of hot solutions. Such rock is called secondary, or hydrothermal, dolomite.

Because of its very close association with limestone and dolomite, another rock type, chert, should be mentioned. Chert consists almost entirely of silicon dioxide (SiO_2) and occurs as rounded or irregular masses within or between beds of carbonate rocks. Minor impurities impart various colors and textures; most Mississippian varieties range from light gray to black. Chert of the Deseret Limestone is commonly banded in shades of brown and gray (fig. 9-5). Fossils are frequently found embedded in chert that seems to have precipitated as a gel and hardened around them rather quickly. Chert is undesirable in rock that is intended for use as cement or as flux.

Sandstone is a prominent consitutent of only one Mississippian formation, the Humbug Formation. This formation consists of about equal parts of limestone and sandstone. The sandy sediment appears to have been swept into

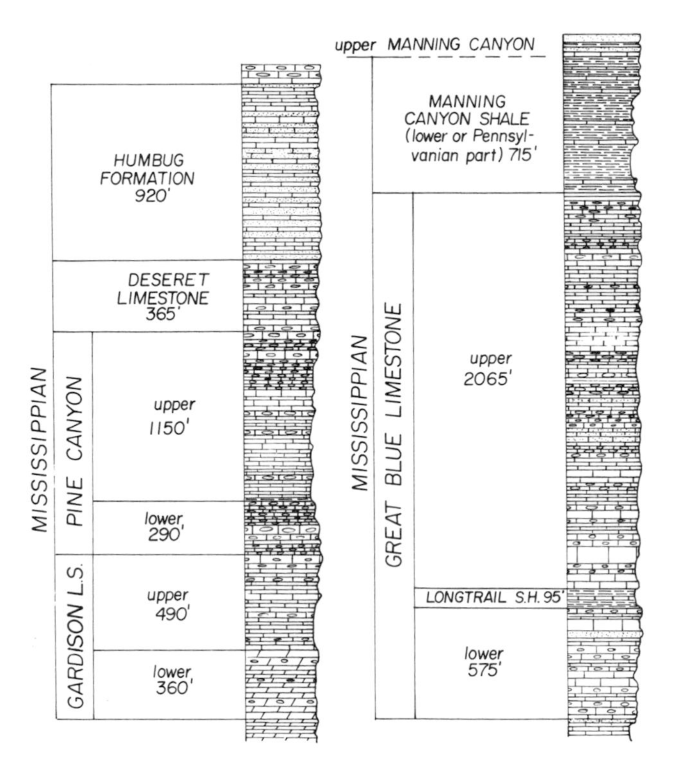

Figure 9-4a. Graphic columnar section of Mississippian formations of north-central Utah.

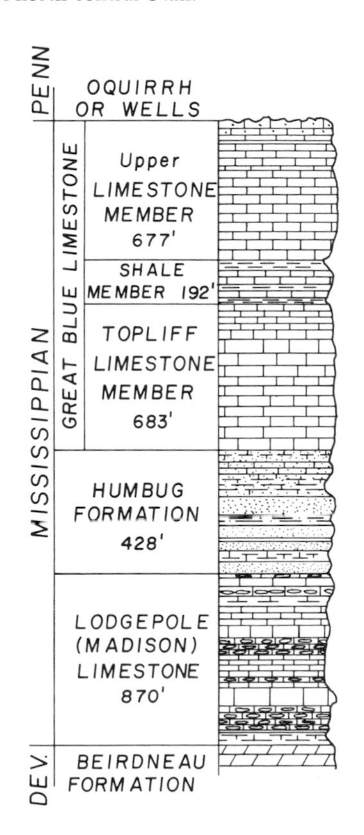

Figure 9-4b. Graphic columnar section of Mississippian formations of the Cache Valley area.

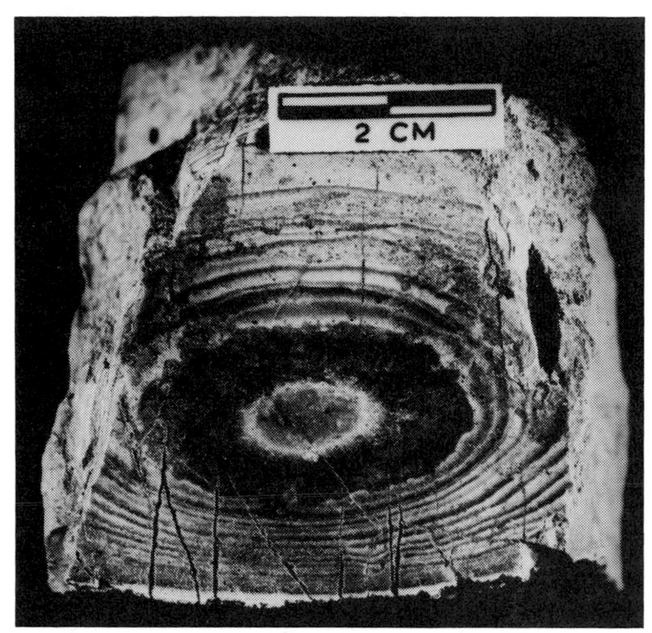

Figure 9-5. Banded chert nodule, Deseret Limestone, western Uinta Mountains. Photo: Jim Howell.

the shallow seas from source areas in south-central Idaho. Siltstone and mudstone make up a large part of several units that are entirely or partly of Mississippian age. Several mappable shale units have received separate names as formations or members of formations. Two such units have been mapped in the Great Blue Limestone, the Long Trail Shale Member and the Chiulos Shale Member.

Another dominantly shale unit is the Manning Canyon Shale that includes both Mississippian and Pennsylvanian strata (fig. 9-6). It is recognized in northern and central Utah. The Doughnut Formation in northeastern Utah is an approximate correlative. Because of their softness, these formations are seldom well exposed. The Manning Canyon Shale is unusual in that it contains considerable organic matter, including scattered plant remains and one coal bed in the Pennsylvanian portion.

The Chainman Formation, deposited in the Confusion Basin and much of adjacent eastern Nevada, also contains an unusually complete representation of Late Mississippian rocks. It has been divided into six members, from oldest to youngest: the Needle Siltstone Member (500 feet), the Skunk Springs Member (5 feet), the Camp Canyon Member (515 feet), the Willow Gap Limestone Member (290 feet), the Donner Member (300 feet), and the Jensen Member (450 feet). The formation is rich in fossils including cephalopods, otherwise rare in western rocks of this age. Part of this formation, the Donner Member, contains considerable conglomerate with siliceous pebbles from identifiable sources in central Nevada.

FOSSILS

As might be expected from the relatively stable, quiet, shallow, warm marine conditions that favored a diverse

Figure 9-6. Outcrop of Manning Canyon Shale, western Summer Ranch Mountains, Box Elder County. Photo: O.C. Adams.

fauna and its eventual preservation, Mississippian rocks are rich in fossils (fig. 9-7). Fossils in shaly formations are excellently preserved. Many in limestone are well silicified and may be freed in good condition by acid treatment or by weathering. Fossils that have weathered free can be picked off the surface of many outcrops. Many good specimens which appear to be firmly embedded can be carefully chipped out with a chisel or hammer.

In rough order of decreasing abundance, Mississippian fossils include: brachiopods, bryozoans, crinoids, corals, gastropods, pelecypods, echinoderms other than crinoids, protozoans, cephalopods, trilobites, and sponges. The first four of the above list may be said to be common, the others are rare, except locally.

Two types of brachiopods are notable, the spirifers and the productids. The Mississippian is a high point in the evolution of spirifers. During this period they reached their greatest size, as large as 8 inches across. Productids, so named because they produced shells with large numbers of slender, sharp, hollow spines, also flourished and they too had gigantic members, as large as 13 inches across. Many other brachiopods of various shapes and sizes are to be expected in any good Mississippian collection.

During the Mississippian, bryozoans became common and abundant for the first time. These are exclusively colonial animals and many individuals combine to make each fossil. The most striking forms in Mississippian rocks are the fenestellids, commonly called "lace fossils", of which many species have been named. Specimens have the appearance of pieces of coarse lacy fabric and are the remains of many small individual animals (fig. 9-8a). Associated with the fenestellids is the curious screw-shaped fossil *Archimedes*, which some regard as also a bryozoan. Other bryozoans have twig-like or mound-like forms and some form thin crusts or overgrowths on other objects.

Crinoids may actually be the most abundant fossils of Mississippian rocks although they are difficult to recognize as such. Large volumes of limestone, perhaps even cubic miles, are composed chiefly of crinoid plates. In spite of the obvious abundance of these animals preserved calyxes, or heads, are extremely rare, perhaps because they were easily broken up by currents or destroyed by predators. One exception is the small, marble-shaped, stemless crinoid, *Agassizocrinus*, which has left thousands of fossils in the Chainman Shale.

Fossil corals of many types are abundant in Mississippian strata. The simple, solitary cup coral, *Ekvasophyllum*, is probably the most striking and easily collected. Many varieties of the branching, colonial, pipe-organ coral, *Syringopora*, are also found. Solid colonies of such species as *Lithostrotion* locally built reef-like masses (fig. 9-8b).

Rarer fossils such as trilobites and cephalopods have attracted much attention. Certain types of trilobites seem to have had a resurgence in the Mississippian, and in local areas may have been the dominant species. All had large tails and relatively few body segments. Most cephalopod fossils are less than an inch across and many tend to be globular in shape. Certain environments were especially favorable for cephalopods and specimens are consequently abundant in certain limited areas; fossils are often found closely packed in concretionary masses.

Pelecypod and gastropod fossils are rare but may be found in almost all collections. Their relatively simple forms and generally poor preservation have not made them popular items of study in comparison to their more showy contemporaries. The Mississippian contains abundant small fossils (mainly endothyroids) that must be studied in thin section. The thin sections are relatively easy to prepare if the matrix is limestone. Small tooth-like conodonts are locally abundant but they must be studied as microfossils.

SCENERY

Many eye-catching scenic spots and tourist attractions are seen in Mississippian rocks. A Lower Mississippian limestone, known variously as the Leadville, Redwall,

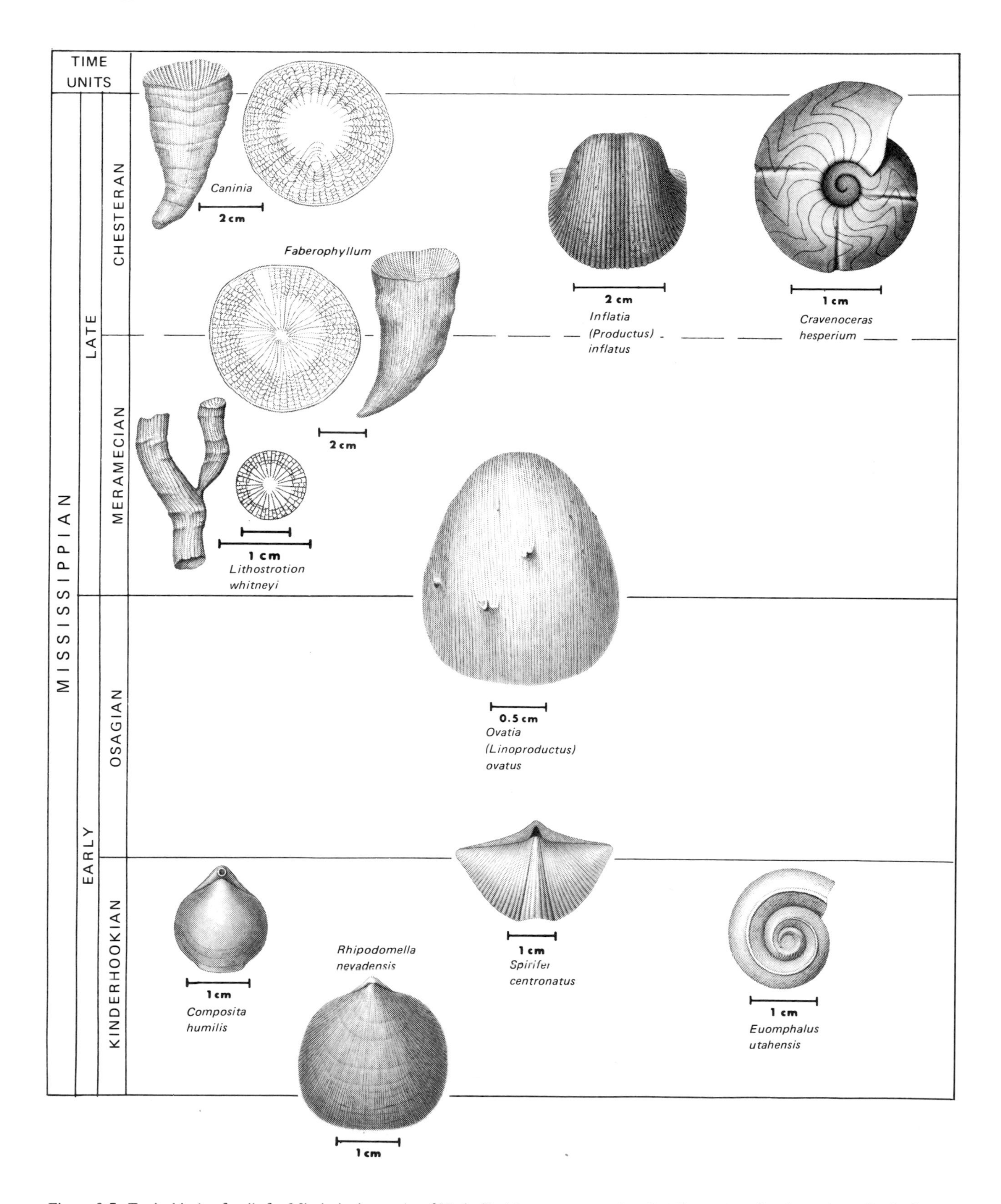

Figure 9-7. Typical index fossils for Mississippian rocks of Utah. Sketches are arranged so that the center of each specimen lies in the zone of which it is characteristic. Sketches: John K. Balsley.

Figure 9-8a. Fossil bryozoans (*Fenestella* and related genera), Manning Canyon Shale (Mississippian-Pennsylvanian), Oquirrh Mountains, Tooele County.

Figure 9-8b. Fossil colonial coral weathered in relief from the Great Blue Limestone, southern Lakeside Mountains. Photo: Wm. Lee Stokes.

Lodgepole, Madison, and Joanna, tends to form a massive, solid cliff at many localities. One of the most famous exposures, though not in Utah, is the almost impassable Redwall Cliff in the Grand Canyon. In the Bear River Range, especially in Logan Canyon, the Lodgepole Limestone forms a double cliff, locally referred to as the Chinese Wall (fig. 9-9).

Figure 9-9. The "Chinese Wall" in Logan Canyon. This prominent cliff is formed by the Lodgepole (Madison) Limestone. Photo: Sue Ann Bilby Bowman.

Mississippian limestone formations are very susceptible to solution and contain many caverns. Mammoth Cave, Kentucky, is the best known example in North America. Timpanogos Cave, formed in the Early Mississippian Deseret Limestone, is a well-known example in Utah. It has been designated as a National Monument and is located 2 miles above the mouth of American Fork Canyon on the northern flank of Mt. Timpanogos.

Timpanogos actually consists of three caves, Hansen , Middle, and Timpanogos Cave proper, joined by artificial tunnels to give a total length from entrance to exit of about 1,500 feet. The caves were formed by the same general sequence of events which operates to create limestone caves anywhere: 1) the original unaltered strata were uplifted from the place of origin near or below sea level; 2) at some later time underground water percolated through fractures and along bedding planes, removing the limestone and creating spacious openings; 3) still later, water percolating into and through the caverns deposited travertine, or dripstone, making the caves scenically interesting and scientifically important (fig. 9-10).

Sixteen types of depositional features have been cataloged in the Timpanogos Cave system: Long, thin, tubular stalactites; massive stalactites; joint-plane stalactites; bacon-like sheets; helictites; club-like, wart-like and nodular forms; small, uniform stalagmites; broad-based, flat-topped stalagmites; disc or stepped stalagmites; massive stalagmites; columns; ledge deposits; fluted columns and wall deposits; lake terraces (rims); cappings (fake floors), and aragonite crystals. Perhaps the most interesting are the helictites, or branching stalactites. Traces of iron compounds in many of the deposits give colors not commonly seen in dripstone.

Many other caves are found in the Mississippian formations of Utah. One is Brush Creek Cave (fig. 9-11) into which Brush Creek, a sizeable stream draining from the Uinta Mountains near Vernal, Uintah County, disappears. This is a dangerous cave to enter but it has been explored for a length of several thousand feet. Details of what has been discovered have not been published.

Figure 9-10. Stalactitic dripstone formations in Timpanogos Cave. Photo: Ward Roylance.

ECONOMIC

Missippian limestone formations are quarried extensively for rock products of various kinds. The largest quarries are in the Great Blue Limestone at Flux, Tooele County (fig 9-12). Other quarries include those of the Amalgamated Sugar Company in Providence Canyon, Cache County, and the Lakeside Lime and Stone Company near Pelican Point, Utah County. Lime products are used in cement, calcium carbide, chemicals, aggregate, fill material, whiting, flux (used in smelting), rock dust for coal mines, filter material, roofing granules, railroad ballast, rip-rap, and poultry grit. Reserves of limestone are, for all practical purposes, unlimited.

Figure 9-11. Entrance to Brush Creek Cave about 18 miles north of Vernal. The entire flow of Big Brush Creek disappears into the cave. The entrance is approximately 130 feet wide by 40 feet high. The cave is in Mississippian limestone and is of unknown length. Photo: Sue Ann Bilby Bowman.

Clay is mined extensively from the Manning Canyon Shale, the lower part of which is Mississippian age. The chief mines are in Utah County, west of Utah Lake, on the east flanks of Lake Mountain and in Five-Mile Pass. The clay is used for brick and tile.

Subsurface Mississippian formations are also of great economic importance as reservoirs for oil and gas. The Leadville Formation (Madison equivalent) is the chief target and producer in the Lisbon and Big Indian oil fields, San Juan County, Utah. Other oil and gas fields exploiting Mississippian reservoirs are Big Flat and Salt Wash in Grand County. Total production from these four fields was 46.5 million barrels of oil and 456.3 million cubic feet of gas as of September, 1984.

Mississippian formations furnish host rocks for deposits of metallic minerals that entered and replaced the limestone long after its deposition and lithification. Such replacement ore bodies have been mined at two great districts in Utah,

Figure 9-12. Stone quarries in Great Blue Limestone, Mississippian, northeast flanks of Stansbury Mountains, Flux, Tooele County. Beds here are nearly vertical, older Mississippian and Devonian formations make up hill above quarry. Photo: John A. Burger.

Park City and Tintic. Chief production has come from the thick limestone formations but at Park City many of the better ore bodies are in the Humbug Formation in which beds of sandstone and limestone alternate.

For additional reading of the topics discussed in Chapter 9, see the following list of authors:

Arnold, 1956
Bissell, H. J., 1959
Breed and Roat, 1976
Burckle, 1960
Chamberlain, 1969
Cook, D.R., 1957
Cramer, 1954
Crittenden, 1959
Davis, 1956
Erickson, A.J., and others, 1968
Foutz, 1966
Gordon, 1975
Holland, 1951, 1952
Kunkle and Schick, 1964
Livingston, 1955
Miller and others, 1952
Morris, 1964
Moyle, 1958
Parker, 1960
Parks, 1951
Patterson, 1969
Preston, 1961
Rigby and Clark, 1962
Rose, 1976
Sadlick, 1965
Stowe, 1970
Tidwell, 1962, 1967
Tooker and Roberts, 1970
Van Sant, 1964
Welsh, 1972
Williams, J. S., 1958, 1963
Wood, 1976
Zeller, 1957

For complete bibliographic citations, please see List of References.

10 THE PENNSYLVANIAN PERIOD

Like the Mississippian Period which preceded it, the Pennsylvanian Period was proposed as a major geologic division by an American geologist. The name was first used in 1891 by H.S. Williams and is taken from the state of Pennsylvania where the system is well exposed and contains abundant coal. European geologists prefer the term Late Carboniferous for an approximately equivalent span of time.

The Pennsylvanian Period began an estimated 320 million years ago and lasted for about 35 million years. Pennsylvanian strata are widely distributed across North America and are extremely varied and economically important. About 80 formations of this age have been mapped in the state, the more important of which are listed at the end of the book.

PALEOGEOGRAPHY

One of the most important events in the geologic history of the western United States took place in the Pennsylvanian Period. This was a strong, mountain building, orogenic event called the Ancestral Rockies Revolution. The name is derived from the fact that it created zones of weakness that were followed by many uplifts of the modern ranges of New Mexico, Colorado, and Wyoming. The Ancestral Rockies consisted of several ranges running northward through New Mexico with one branch continuing almost due north through Colorado into Wyoming and another branch curving westward into Utah. The westward component has been named the Uncompahgre Uplift. It enters Utah in eastern Grand County and can be traced as a buried ridge as far west as Range Creek in Carbon County (fig. 10-1). The appearance of the Uncompahgre Uplift was geologically abrupt. In just a few million years the range appeared and grew to an estimated elevation of 12,000 to 15,000 feet. As soon as the range was topographically in evidence, it was attacked by erosion. The Utah section of the range was finally worn down and buried in Late Triassic time. The Colorado portion of the range was not buried until Jurassic time. Only a few square miles of Precambrian rocks are exposed in eastern Grand County, but the depth and configuration of the westward subsurface projection of the uplift has been determined from drill hole information.

The Uncompahgre Uplift is representative of a type that is accompanied by a depression of corresponding magnitude (fig. 10-2a). In Utah the Paradox Basin appeared immediately south of the Uncompahgre Highland. This was the deepest basin formed during the Ancestral Rockies Revolu-

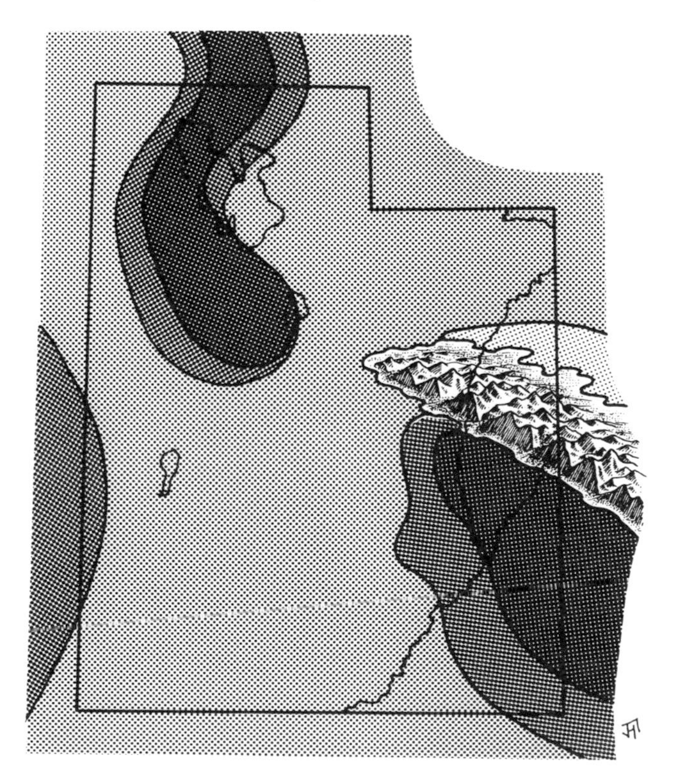

Figure 10-1. Generalized paleogeography of the Pennsylvanian Period. This view emphasizes the newly formed Uncompahgre Uplift in eastern Utah, the adjacent Paradox Basin and the Oquirrh Basin to the northwest. The darker the pattern the thicker and more complete the rock record of the period. Dry land topography is shown diagrammatically.

tion. As the range rose, the adjacent basin sank to receive great quantities of sediments transported from the nearby uplift. Other areas of Utah were uplifted during the Ancestral Rockies Revolution but not so much as those in the east-central portion. The Emery High (or Piute Platform as it is now called) and the Kaibab Uplift (a poorly defined band of uplifts) have been identified by the thinning or absence of Pennsylvanian rocks. The Grand Canyon crosses one of these areas of thin Pennsylvanian formations.

The Oquirrh Basin, a depression of major proportions and even deeper than the Paradox Basin, appeared in north-central Utah as a westward expression of the Ancestral Rockies deformation (fig. 10-2b). It is named from the Oquirrh Mountains which eventually appeared near the approximate center of the ancestral basin. Subsidence began in Late Mississippian time, reached its most rapid rate in the Pennsylvanian and continued into the Permian, resulting in a total accumulation of 25,000 to 30,000 feet of marine sediments.

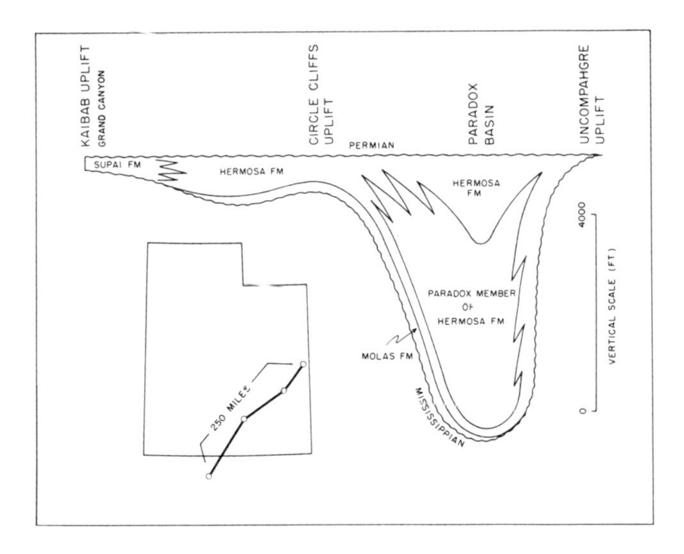

Figure 10-2a. Simplified cross-section of the Paradox Basin and adjacent areas (from Stokes and Heylmun, 1957).

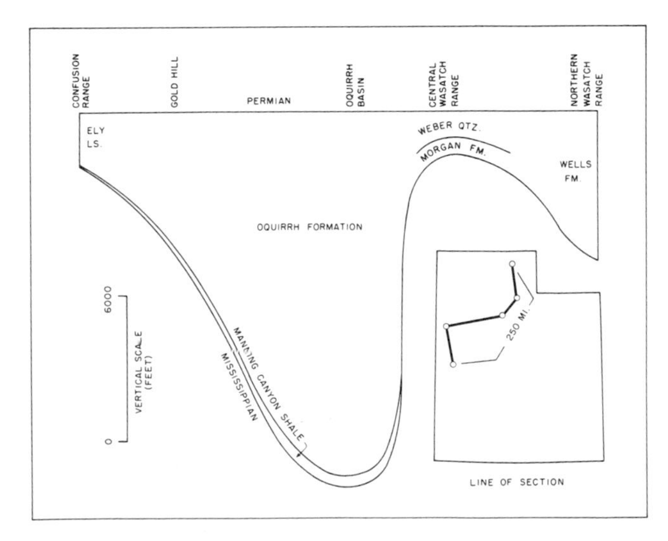

Figure 10-2b. Simplified cross-section of the Oquirrh Basin and adjacent areas (from Stokes and Heylmun, 1957).

The effects of the Ancestral Rockies Revolution seem to have extended across the Wasatch Line from one great geologic province into another. Although much of the state was either uplifted or depressed during this time, some areas appear to have remained relatively stable including much of south-central Utah, the site of the present Uinta Mountains and Uinta Basin, and the extreme northwestern corner of the state.

ORIGIN AND NATURE OF PENNSYLVANIAN ROCKS

A greater variety of sedimentary rock types (figs. 10-3, 10-4a, and 10-4b) was produced during Pennsylvanian time than in any other comparable period. This is partly because continental (dry land) environments are represented extensively in Utah for the first time and partly because marine environments were unusually varied. Eastern Utah changed from a stable shelf area to one of pronounced diversity, thus creating unique new environments. Pennsylvanian seas seem to have covered most of Utah before the Ancestral Rockies Revolution. Afterward the only area not receiving continental or marine deposits of one type or another was the Uncompahgre Uplift. The volume of accumulated deposits is probably greater than that of any other Paleozoic period. Much of this material is still preserved in both eastern and western Utah where it is deeply buried in the Paradox, Uinta, and Oquirrh Basins.

Pennsylvanian rock types, in rough order of decreasing abundance are: limestone, sandstone, shale, dolomite, conglomerate, halite, sylvite, and other minor salts. Nonmarine conglomerate and sandstone are confined to a narrow fringe along the base of the Uncompahgre Uplift in east-central Utah. Much of the material in this belt is a distinctive kind of sandstone called arkose. In technical terms, arkose is defined as sandstone with 25 percent or more feldspar in the non-clay detrital fraction. It consists of fragments derived directly from granite with little or no weathering of the mineral grains.

Repetitive sequences of strata are characteristic of the Pennsylvanian system in many parts of the world, including Utah. The sequence of limestone-sandstone-shale is repeated to make up large volumes of the Oquirrh, Wells, and Ely Formations. Any one cycle is from 10 to 150 feet thick and sometimes includes other rock types. This regular arrangement is repeated many times in single exposures.

The salt deposits of the Paradox Basin also display repetitive cycles. They are unusual as sediments and constitute a vast reserve of valuable saline minerals. The Paradox Basin is chiefly in Utah and Colorado with edges in New Mexico and Arizona. It has an irregular oval shape about 190 miles long in a southeast-northwest direction and 95 miles across, in a northeast-southwest direction. The salt deposits thicken toward the Uncompahgre Uplift and were originally at least 5,000 feet thick in the deepest part of the basin. Much salt

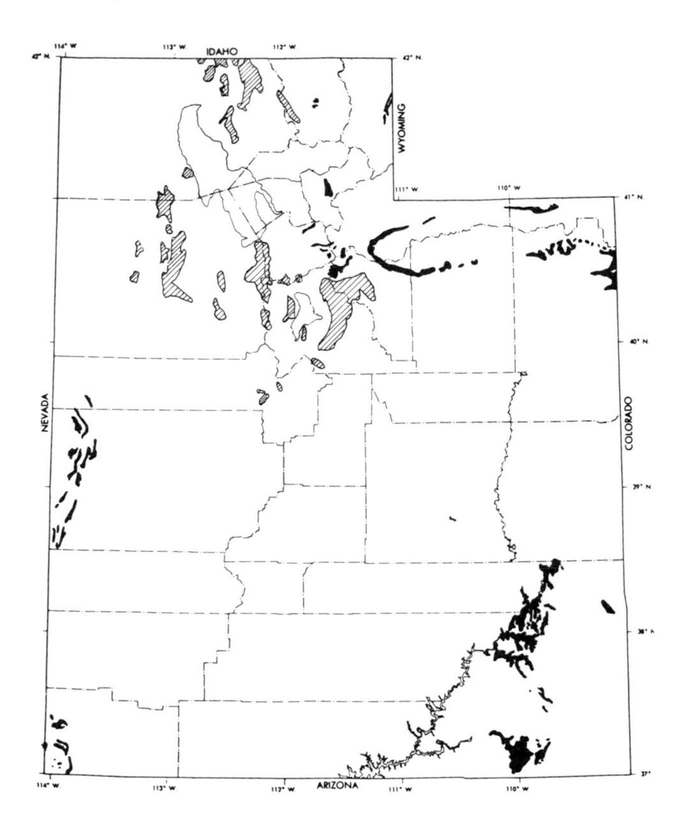

Figure 10-3. Outcrops of Pennsylvanian rocks in Utah. Exposures in which Pennsylvanian and Permian rocks cannot be shown separately have cross-lined pattern. These are chiefly outcrops of the Oquirrh Formation.

has been removed by solution in the past few million years and none is seen on the surface in natural outcrop.

The Paradox Basin was nearly hemmed in by highlands to the north, northeast, and east and by shallow barriers or sills along the other sides. It is the nature and location of the connections between the open sea and the nearly isolated basin that resulted in the deposition of salt and important source rocks for oil and gas. The rim of the southwestern margin of the basin, which is now known as the Four Corners area, was almost at sea level so any slight rise of the ocean allowed seawater to spill into the basin and any lowering cut off the supply of water. The spillway was a favorable place for the growth of marine organisms which tended to build up large banks or shoals of limy material. The large amount of organic material also restricted circulation of water in and out of the basin and later, when buried, became a favorable reservoir for oil and gas.

The details are not easy to decipher, but there appear to be 27 complete cycles of deposition in the Paradox Salt Member of the Hermosa Formation. Each cycle consists, in ascending order, of black shale, carbonate rocks (chiefly dolomite), anhydrite, halite, potash, and magnesium salts. The irregular top of each cycle is interpreted as an erosional surface created by the solution of the most recently deposited salts by fresher seawater that spilled periodically into the basin to initiate the next cycle. Not all cycles are complete.

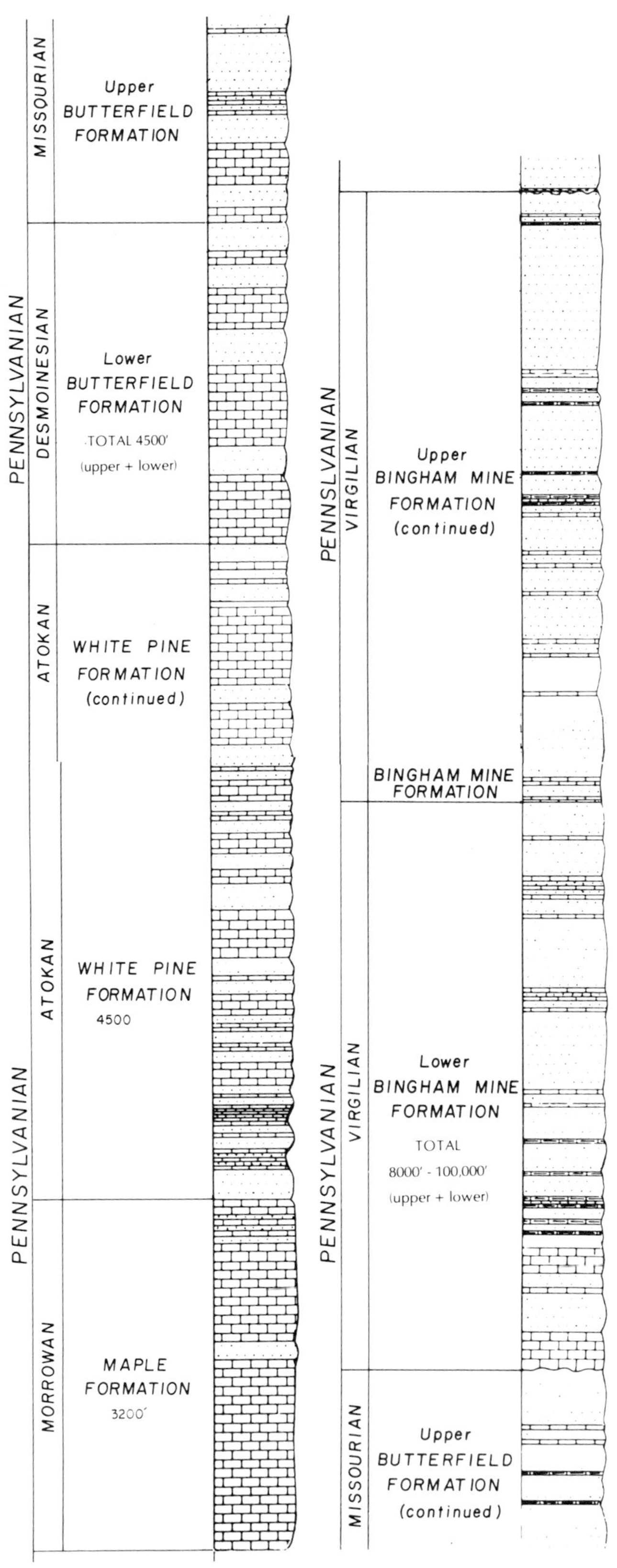

Figure 10-4a. Graphic columnar section of Pennsylvanian formations of the northern Oquirrh Range. Other alternative interpretations of this section have been published. Continued on next page.

The thickness of a single cycle ranges from 100 to 200 feet (fig. 10-4c).

The cyclic deposits of salt in the Paradox Basin must be related in some fundamental way to the cyclic deposits in the Oquirrh Basin. Other expressions of contemporaneous cyclic deposition related to rise and fall of sea level include the famous coal-bearing cyclothems of the east-central United States.

The cause of cyclic deposition in the Pennsylvanian Period is not yet fully understood. It is interesting that the salt beds record not only cycles that lasted thousands of years but also lesser cycles. Certain sections show well defined layers averaging 1 inch thick that are considered to be of yearly origin. Any layer of rock recording a year's depositions is called a varve. Thousands of superimposed varves present in cores taken from the Paradox salt represent, literally, cycles within cycles.

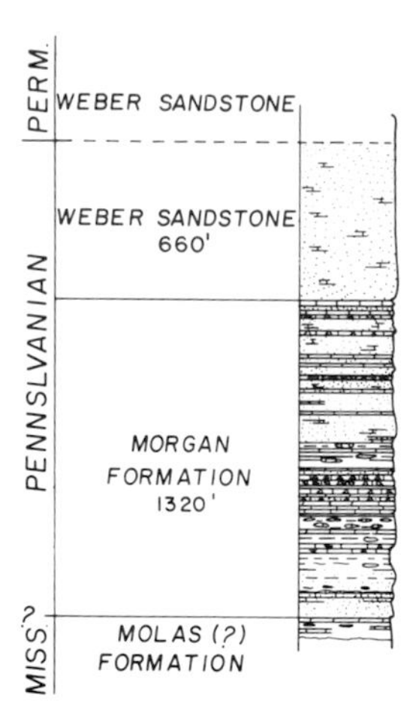

Figure 10-4b. Graphic columnar section of Pennsylvanian formations in the Wasatch Range near Salt Lake City.

FOSSILS

The Pennsylvanian Period was a time of varied and abundant land and sea life. Great numbers of plant fossils are found in association with coal-bearing strata in the eastern United States. In Utah, Pennsylvanian rocks and fossils are mostly of marine origin. However, one notable assemblage of Late Pennsylvanian plants is preserved in the upper part of the Manning Canyon Shale in central Utah and a small quantity of coal has been mined from the Manning Canyon Shale in Sols Canyon, Daggett County.

Pennsylvanian rocks locally contain abundant fossils (fig. 10-5). In rough order of decreasing abundance they are: fusulinids, brachiopods, bryozoans, corals, pelecypods, crinoids, and gastropods. Fusulinids are extinct shell-bearing protozoans which resemble seeds of wheat, oats, rice, and other grains (fig. 10-6a); they reached their greatest importance during the Pennsylvanian. Hundreds of species have been described and their remains are numerous enough locally to make up entire beds of rock.

The fusulinids are more than merely rock-making organisms. They are one of the most valuable guide fossils available to geologists. Rock containing fusulinids must be cut into thin slices so the specimens can be identified and studied under magnification. Fusulinids seem to have been a detrimental influence on most other forms of marine life. Perhaps they were such efficient food gatherers that they left little for anything else. Before they became common and after they declined, other shallow-water organisms seem to have existed in greater numbers.

The Pennsylvanian was a high in the evolution of brachiopods, many of which were large and highly ornamented. Productids and spirifers were common but the simple form, *Composita*, is probably the most widely represented genus of the period. Most collections of Pennsylvanian fossils include bryozoans of many types, of which the peculiar, screw-shaped *Archimedes* is probably the most distinctive. The so-called "lace fossil," *Fenestella*, and related types are also present in many Pennsylvanian limestones (fig. 10-6b). Not to be overlooked is the so-called "hair coral," *Chaetetes*, which left many compact colonies as large as 1 foot in diameter (fig. 10-6c). Pelecypod and gastropod fossils are less common. The almost total lack of cephalopods, important inter-regional guide fossils, is difficult to explain.

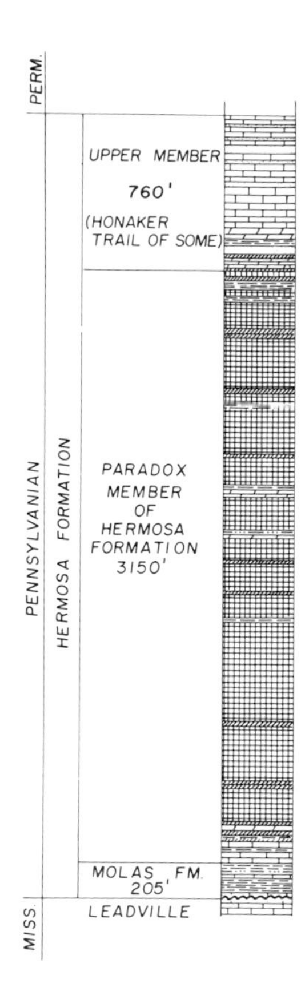

Figure 10-4c. Graphic columnar section of Pennsylvanian rocks in the south central Paradox Basin.

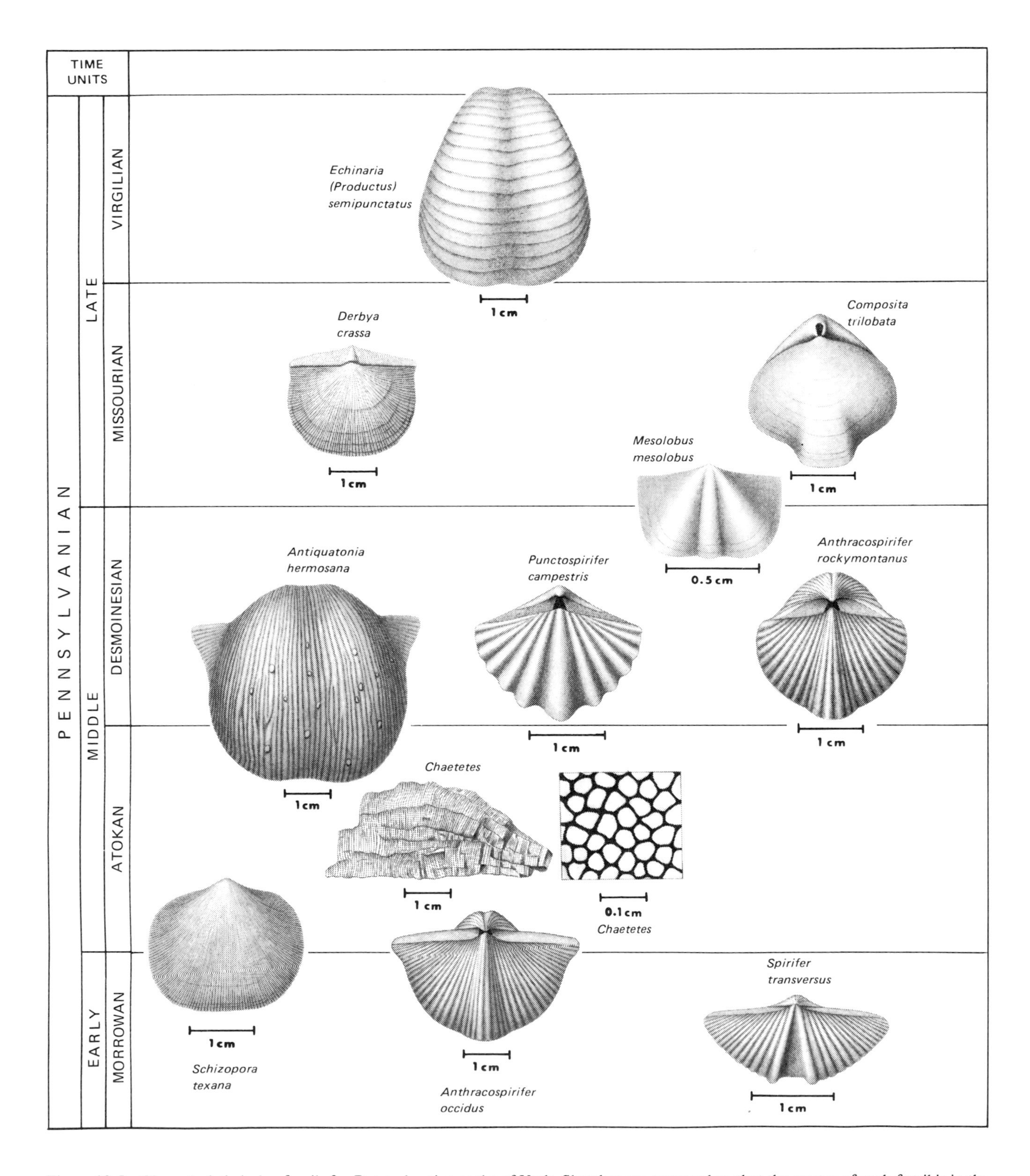

Figure 10-5. Characteristic index fossils for Pennsylvanian rocks of Utah. Sketches are arranged so that the center of each fossil is in the zone of which it is characteristic. Sketches: John K. Balsley.

Figure 10-6a. Pennsylvanian rocks containing many specimens of fossil fusulinids (wheat-like objects). Coin gives scale. Photo: Jim Howell.

Figure 10-6c. Water-worn siliceous cobbles of the "hair" coral *Chaetetes* derived from the Morgan Formation, Pennsylvanian, Uinta Mountains. Often mistaken for petrified wood. Twenty-five cent piece gives scale. Photo: Jim Howell.

Figure 10-6b. Fossil bryozoans (fenestellids) from the Hermosa Formation, Spanish Bottom, Grand County. Photo: Jim Howell.

SCENERY

Pennsylvanian rocks form numerous striking scenic features in both the eastern and western provinces of Utah. Many Wasatch Front communities are within sight of the two highest peaks of the Wasatch Range, Mt. Nebo, elevation 11,877 feet (fig. 10-7a) and Mt. Timpanogos, elevation 11,750 feet (fig. 10-7b). The summits of both mountains are carved from the Oquirrh Formation. As a matter of fact, the entire crest of the range between the two peaks is carved in this formation, including Provo Peak, Spanish Fork Peak, and Boulder Mountain. Most of the steep-sided,

Figure 10-7a. Mt. Nebo from the west. Long Ridge in middle distance. The three cirques of Mt. Nebo are well shown. Photo: Ward Roylance.

Figure 10-7b. Mt. Timpanogos (highest point 11,750 feet) looking west. Exposed rocks are almost entirely Pennsylvanian Oquirrh Formation. Photo: A.J. Eardley.

deeper stretches of Provo Canyon, Hobble Creek Canyon, and Spanish Fork Canyon are also in Pennsylvanian strata. Well known Bridal Veil Falls in Provo Canyon descends over step-like beds in the lower part of the Oquirrh Formation (fig. 10-8).

The Oquirrh Mountains, which bound populous Salt Lake Valley on the west, consist almost entirely of the Oquirrh Formation. The name is said to have come from an Indian word meaning "shining mountains", an apt description of the rounded peaks when covered with snow. The higher summits of Wellsville Mountain and the Bear River Range are carved from the Wells Formation, an Oquirrh equivalent.

Pennsylvanian strata crop out at intermediate elevations around the Uinta Mountains. Spectacular cliffs of the Weber Sandstone are seen at the exit of the Green River from Split Mountain (fig. 10-9) and in the canyons of Brush Creek in Dinosaur National Monument.

In southeastern Utah, exposures of the Pennsylvanian formations are chiefly in the deeper canyons of the Colorado and San Juan Rivers. The Colorado River in Cataract Canyon has cut extremely rugged cliffs of alternating beds of Pennsylvanian-age limestone and hard sandstone almost to the level of the Paradox salt. Perhaps the best known tourist attraction displaying Pennsylvanian strata in southeastern Utah is the Goosenecks of the San Juan River (fig. 10-10). The boundary between the Pennsylvanian and Permian, as determined by fossil evidence, is about 150 feet below the rim of the canyon.

ECONOMIC

Pennsylvanian rocks yield a great variety of valuable products, some of which are indigenous materials (salts), some of which have migrated from their place of origin (oil), and some of which were introduced at a later date (metallic ores). Taking all these resources into account, the

Figure 10-8. Bridal Veil Falls, Provo Canyon, Utah County. Water descends in two stages over ledges of the lower Oquirrh Formation. Photo: Utah State Historical Society.

Pennsylvanian probably has yielded greater mineral wealth than any other system in Utah.

Potassium, in the form of KCl (sylvite), is mined on a large scale from the Paradox Formation at the Cane Creek Mine of Texasgulf, Inc. (fig. 10-11). The product is commonly referred to simply as potash. The mine was orginally planned and developed as an ordinary underground operation and a 2,700-foot shaft was put down. In 1970 operations were converted to solution mining. Water, at the rate of 2,000 to 3,000 gal/min, is introduced into the salt beds for about 30 days until it is fully saturated with salts, then it is pumped to the surface and the concentrated brine is spread in large solar evaporation ponds. The final product, containing about 60 percent K_2O, is obtained by gravity separation. Potash is being produced (1985) at a rate of 15,000 to 20,000 t/year. The supply of potash in the Paradox Basin is, for all practical purposes, inexhaustible.

Potassium, nitrogen, and phosphorus are primary mineral fertilizers. Potassium is also used in the manufacture of matches, dyes, pharmaceuticals, synthetic rubber, detergents, films, insecticides, ceramics, and solid fuels. Sodium chloride (NaCl; table salt) is a by-product of most potash

Figure 10-9. Aerial view of the rugged outcrops of the light-colored Weber Sandstone, Split Mountain, near Jensen, Utah. The Green River flows out of the view to the right. The Split Mountain view area at the edge of the picture and the river's edge is visited by thousands of tourists annually. Photo: Hal Rumel.

operations and the reserves are essentially beyond calculation.

A large number of oil and gas fields are located in Pennsylvanian rocks of the Four Corners region in adjacent parts of Utah, Colorado, New Mexico, and Arizona. In Utah, the most productive pools are in the Hermosa Group, which includes the Paradox and Honaker Trail Formations. About 25 separate fields have produced oil and gas in the Utah section of the Four Corners. The most productive field is Greater Aneth, which has an estimated ultimate recovery of 350 million barrels of oil. Production is from algal and oolitic carbonate rocks in the Desert Creek substage of the Paradox Formation. Wells average about 6,000 feet in depth.

The Weber Sandstone is the chief producer in the Rangely oil field in Rio Blanco County, Colorado, a few miles east of the Utah line. Oil from this field is piped to refineries in Salt Lake City and contributes greatly to the economy of Utah. The Weber Sandstone also produces oil at the Ashley Valley field in Uintah County. This is recognized as the first commercial oil field in Utah; total production as of September, 1984, was 19.6 million barrels of oil and 221 million cubic feet of gas.

Much of the ore of the Bingham mining district (fig. 10-12) is taken from Pennsylvanian rocks associated with a Teriary intrusion. Ore minerals are disseminated in quartzite and limestone beds in the Bingham Mine Formation of the Oquirrh Group, as well as in the igneous intrusion through a vertical interval of several thousand feet. This unit is about 5,400 feet thick and contains two very important host beds, the Jordan and Commercial limes.

Figure 10-10. Canyon of the San Juan River near The Goosenecks, San Juan County. The step-like walls of the canyon are cut in the Hermosa Formation. The Pennsylvanian-Permian contact is several hundred feet below the rim of the canyon. Photo: Utah Tourist and Publicity Council.

Figure 10-11. Surface installation of the Texasgulf Cane Creek Mine. The salt beds lie about 2,700 feet below the surface. Photo: Utah State Historical Society.

Figure 10-12. The great open-pit mine of Utah Copper Division of Kennecott Minerals Company in the Oquirrh Mountains near Salt Lake City. This is the center of what is said to be the most valuable mineral deposit on earth. Low-grade copper ore, contained partly in an igneous intrusion of middle Tertiary age and partly in surrounding sediments of Pennsylvanian and Permian age, is being mined. Photo: Kennecott Minerals Company.

Pennsylvanian rocks also contain ore in the Milford, Millard County, area (San Francisco, Preuss, North Star, and adjacent districts), and the Gold Hill district in western Tooele County. Minor vein deposits are also mined in the Weber and Round Valley Formations in the Park City district

For additional reading of the topics discussed in Chapter 10, see the following list of authors:

Baars, 1966, 1973a, 1973b
Baars and Molenar, 1971
Bissell, H. J., 1947, 1959, 1962a, 1962b, 1963, 1967
Bray and Wilson, 1975
Butler, 1913
Campbell and Bacon, 1976
Chamberlain, 1969
Condra and Elias, 1944
Curfman, 1975
Dane, 1935
Doelling, 1975
El-Shatoury and Whelan, 1970
Fetzner, 1960
Getzer, 1960, 1963
Gordon, 1975
Groenwald, 1961
Herman and Barkell, 1957
Herman and Sharps, 1956
Heylmun, 1959
Hintze, 1973
Hintze and Whelan, 1973
Hite, 1960, 1961, 1968
Hite and others, 1972
Holmes, 1956
Lane, B. O., 1962
Mallory, 1972a, 1972b
Nolan, 1935
Peterson, J.A., 1963, 1966;
Peterson, J.A. and Hite, 1969
Peterson, V.E., 1957
Picard and others, 1960
Preston, 1961
Rigby and others, 1971
Ritzma, 1959
Roberts and others, 1965
Sando, 1965, 1969
Stokes, 1948
Tidwell, 1962, 1967
Tooker and Roberts, 1970
Untermann, 1950
Untermann and Untermann, 1954, 1955, 1968
Wengerd, 1956
Wengerd and Matheny, 1958, 1966
Wengerd and Strickland, 1954

For complete bibliographic citations, please see List of References.

Figure 10-13. Spanish bottom, on the Colorado River, looking west. Masses of gypsum upthrust from the Paradox Formation (Pennsylvanian) appear in foreground. The Hermosa, Elephant Canyon and Cutler Formations make up the opposite wall. Photo: U.S. Bureau of Reclamation.

11 THE PERMIAN PERIOD

The Permian Period began about 285 million years ago and lasted an estimated 40 to 45 million years. Roderick I. Murchison first applied the name in 1841, referring to the Perm plains on the western flanks of the Ural Mountains in U.S.S.R. Most of the Permian outcrops in North America are in the southwestern United States. The period is well represented in Utah by approximately 47 formations which are listed at the end of the book.

PALEOGEOGRAPHY

Permian geography follows closely that of the preceding Pennsylvanian Period (figs. 11-1 and 11-2). No radically new features were added to the landscape; the same basins and uplifts continued to control erosion and deposition. The Uncompaghre Uplift still dominated the topography of eastern Utah and furnished a variety of sediments which spread out on all sides. Evidence is that a warm, dry climate prevailed over the region so that streams from the highlands were either too small or too ephemeral to move sediment far from the base of the range. A landscape of alluvial fans, shallow seasonal lakes, and shifting dune fields is easily reconstructed for eastern Utah during most of Permian time. The Paradox Basin, lying southwest and south of the Uncompahgre Uplift, continued to be the dumping ground for much of the detritus from the uplift. It is not certain, however, whether the highland actually became higher and the basin deeper during the Permian. It is certain that the highland was steadily eroded to lower and lower levels and was mostly buried during the succeeding Triassic Period.

The stratigraphy of the Permian system is complex, due chiefly to several shallow marine incursions. Except for a rather broad belt including the Uncompahgre Uplift, most of Utah was periodically submerged during much of Permian time. Early in the period, an arm of the ocean penetrated eastward into what is now the Canyonlands area, almost to the Colorado border. Although the eastern portion of this embayment silted up and disappeared, marine deposition continued almost uninterrupted in the geosynclinal belt to the west. During the later stages of the Permian Period marine waters from the Gulf of Mexico flooded across northern Arizona into Utah to the latitude of Salt Lake City, Salt Lake County. This is named the Kaibab Sea after its chief deposit, the Kaibab Limestone. Slightly later another marine incursion, this one from the north bringing organisms with Siberian affinities, spread into Utah to leave deposits as far south as the Confusion Basin and as far east as Dinosaur National Monument. This

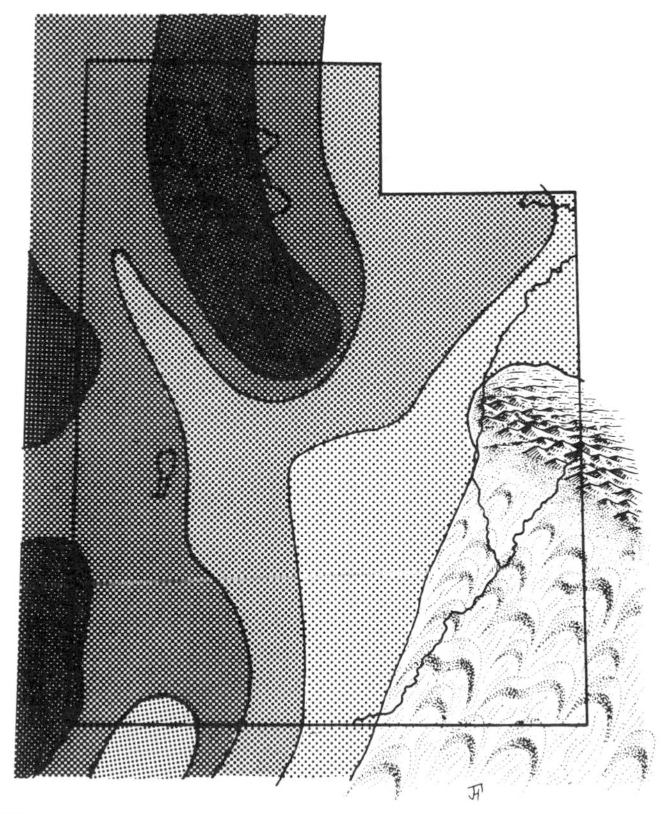

Figure 11-1. Generalized paleogeography of Utah for the Permian Period. Darkest patterns represent areas of thicker marine deposits; lighter patterns show relatively thinner, less complete sections. The Uncompahgre Uplift and dune-fields are shown diagrammatically in the southeastern part of the state.

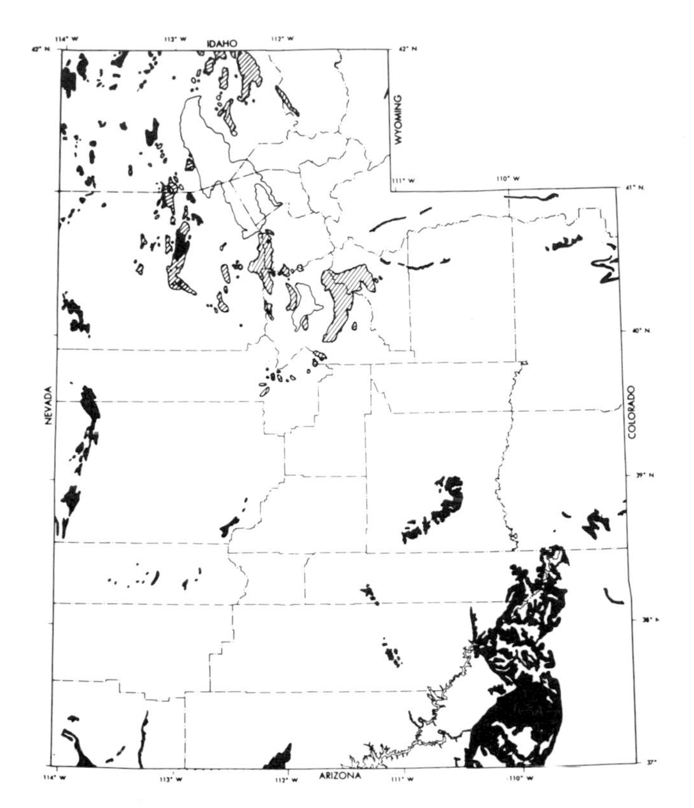

Figure 11-2. Outcrops of Permian strata in Utah. Solid black indicates exclusively Permian rocks, cross-lined pattern designates areas where Pennsylvanian and Permian have not been mapped separately. These areas are chiefly the thick and complex Oquirrh Formation.

is called the Phosphoria-Park City Sea. Through this combination and overlap of successive marine invasions western Utah received what is probably the most complete record of Permian time to be found in the United States.

The actively subsiding Oquirrh Basin that had already received at least 15,000 feet of Pennsylvanian strata continued to be a depositional center during the Permian. It sagged in an uneven way as it filled, and active deposition shifted from place to place within it. Near the close of the period, when the Phosphoria-Park City Sea withdrew, the basin seems to have stabilized.

The Confusion Basin in southwestern Utah also has a relatively thick Permian section in comparison with the underlying, thin, and incomplete Pennsylvanian section.

ORIGIN AND NATURE OF PERMIAN ROCKS

With the possible exception of the Pennsylvanian, the Permian displays the greatest variety of sedimentary rock types of any geologic system (figs. 11-3a, 11-3b, and 11-3c). Non-marine conditions governed the deposition of many cubic miles of material in the Colorado Plateau and, for the first time, wind action became a major agent of erosion and deposition.

This was also the great period of red-bed production, or more accurately, the production of potential red beds. The present-day red color of Permian units results from an "aging" process of iron-bearing minerals in what may originally have been drab-looking sediments. Through a long sequence of geologic events, Permian red beds are now widely exposed throughout the Colorado Plateau. In popular vernacular, this is the "Red Rock Country." It is not entirely coincidental that sediments, orginally produced in an arid climate, should now be exposed in a similar climate. The absence of soil and vegetation coupled with vigorous erosive action have combined to create what is possibly the most scenically attractive series of formations to be viewed anywhere.

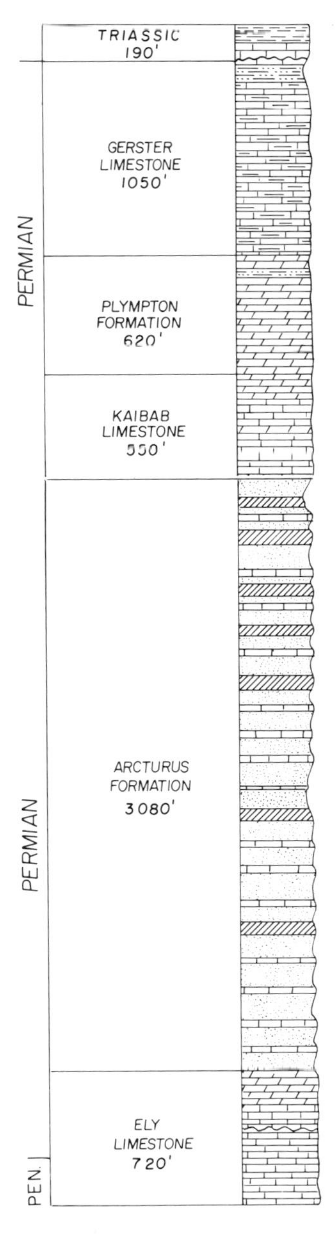

Figure 11-3a. Graphic columnar section of Permian formations in the Confusion Basin, southwestern Utah.

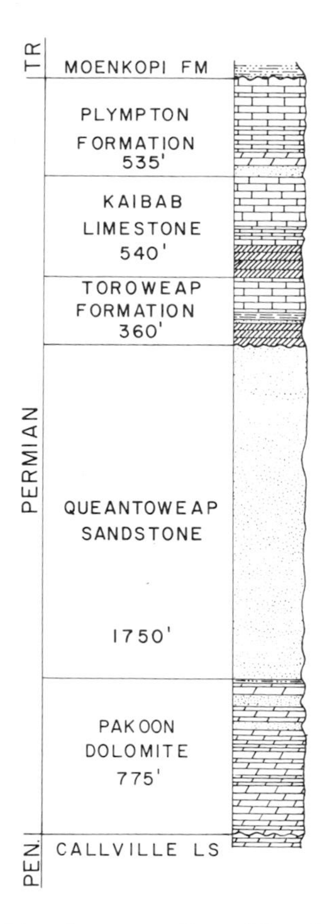

Figure 11-3b. Graphic columnar section of Permian formations in the St. George area, southwestern Utah. Information from an exploratory oil well. From John Welsh.

In addition to continental sediments, almost every type of ocean-deposited material, except perhaps the more soluble salts (halite and sylvite), are represented in the Permian. Compared with other systems, the Permian is also noted for a high chert content. Another type of sediment is not only relatively abundant and highly unusual, but also economically important. This is phosphorite, a general term for phosphate-bearing material.

In rough order of decreasing abundance, the chief Permian rock types of Utah are sandstone, siltstone, mudstone, limestone, dolomite, chert, gypsum and phosphorite. It is difficult to find common environmental origins for such diverse rock types. Perhaps a uniform climatic influence dominated sedimentary conditions in the latter part of the period. At that time the equator crossed the southern Colorado Plateau along a northeasterly trend putting the entire area under an almost vertical sun. This orientation, coupled with shallow shelving seas, favored the production of sediments characteristic of warm, shallow water and high evaporation rates. This theory is supported by the fact that gypsum and dolomite are common units in Utah's Permian rocks.

Permian sandstones also make it possible, for the earliest time in geologic history, to learn something quite definite about paleo-wind directions in the western United States.

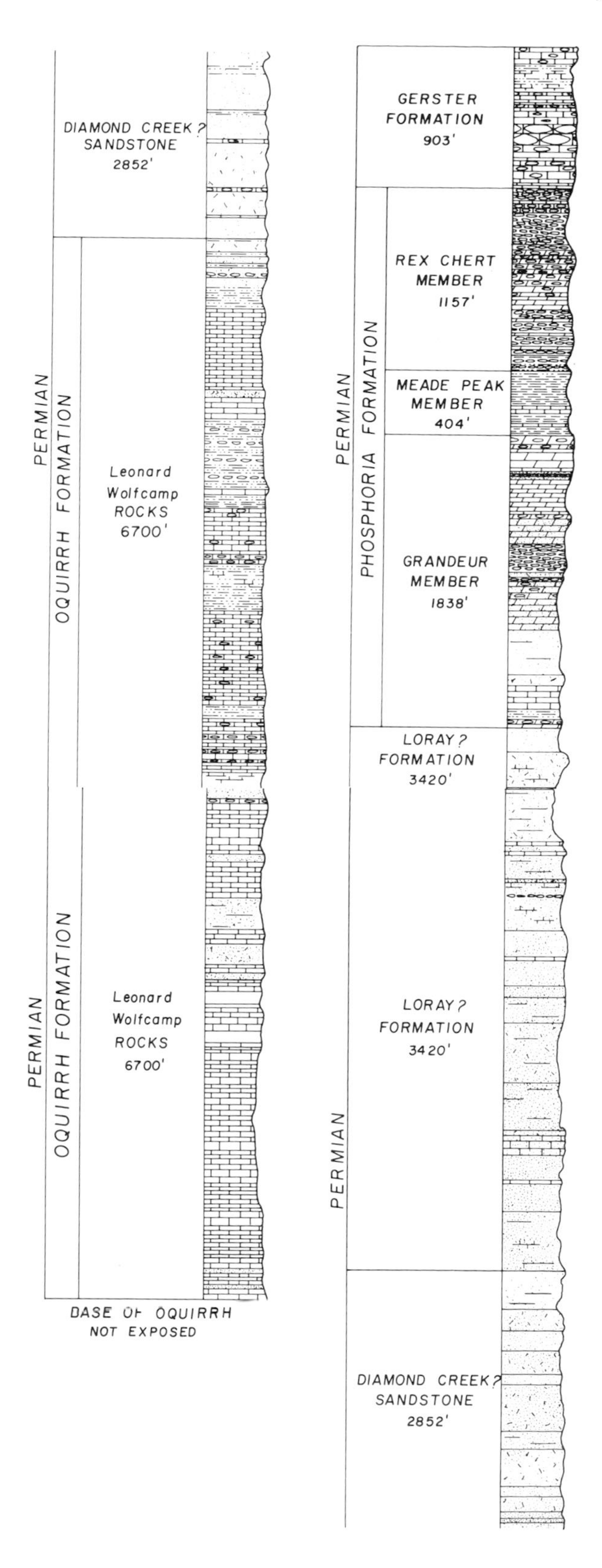

Figure 11-3c. Graphic columnar section of Permian formations exposed in the Terrace-Hogup Mountains, Box Elder County. From Stifel, 1964.

By studying the cross bedding of many thick sandstone deposits that stretch from Wyoming through Utah into Arizona, it has been deduced that the prevailing winds were from the north and northeast, directions analogous to the northeast trade winds of present-day atmospheric circulation (fig. 11-4).

Warm water, provided it is circulating and not too saline, is more favorable to life than cold water under the same conditions. Permian seas of the southwestern United States were warm and supported exceptionally abundant plant and animal life. The Kaibab (fig. 11-5), Park City, and Gerster Formations, for example, are richly fossiliferous almost everywhere. The significance of chert is not well understood, but much of it accumulated through the activity of warm-water organisms, particularly sponges.

The Permian of Utah and nearby territory is characterized by a combination of structural and sedimentary features called platforms. A platform is a relatively wide, block-like, elevated area between basins. Its surface is relatively flat and the descent along its sides is abrupt enough to constitute a mappable boundary. A platform may commence as an anticline of relatively rounded form, but a more angular cross section is produced as the upper surface is planed away by erosion, deposition accelerates on the flanks, and the growth of marine organisms creates fringing reefs and banks.

Figure 11-5. Exposures of marine Permian formations in the Hurricane Cliffs about 15 miles north of St. George. The Harrisburg Member of the Kaibab Formation appears on the skyline and the Fossil Mountain Member in the bare, much-jointed cliff. The Toroweap makes up all the lower cliffs except the light-colored outcrops below the triangular dark patches. Below these is the Coconino Sandstone. Photo: LaRell Nielson.

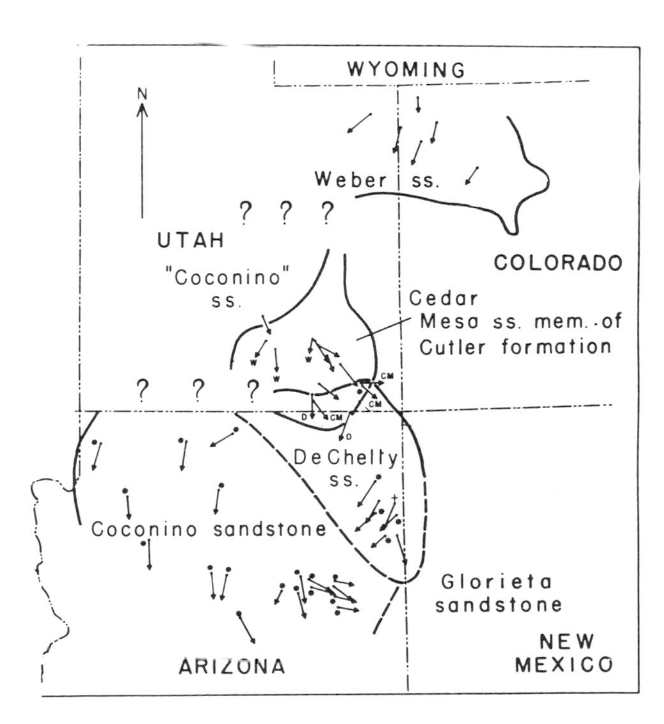

Figure 11-4. Wind directions of Lake Permian time as inferred from cross-bedding in sandstone formations in and adjacent to Utah. Arrows fly with the wind. W designates White Rim Member of the Cutler Formation, CM, the Cedar Mesa Sandstone Member and D, the DeChelly Sandstone. From Stewart, Poole and Wilson, 1957.

Geologists have named several such uplifted platforms in Utah that originated in the Ancestral Rockies Revolution. The Emery High, including most of Emery County and extending westward into Juab County, and the Kaibab Uplift, extending into the High Plateaus area from the Grand Canyon in Arizona, are combined under the name Piute Platform. Permian rocks rest directly on Mississippian rocks across this platform. The Callville-Pakoon-Queantoweap Platform, has been defined as running from the southwestern corner of Utah into Sevier County and most of northeastern Utah has been designated the Morgan-Weber Platform.

All of northeastern Utah, including the Uinta Basin, northern Wasatch Range, and Uinta Mountains, constituted the southern part of the extensive Utah-Wyoming shelf area during Permian time. There are no unusual thicknesses of Permian sediments here in strong contrast to central and southeastern Utah. The rich phosphate deposits of the Phosphoria-Park City Group are located along the western edge of the Utah-Wyoming shelf where currents from the ocean to the west were apparently forced upward and onto the shelf area, a process known as upwelling. A prolific growth of marine life extracted phosphate and other elements from the upwelling currents to eventually build up important ore deposits.

FOSSILS

A great variety of fossils, including invertebrates, vertebrates and plants, is found in Permian formations (fig.

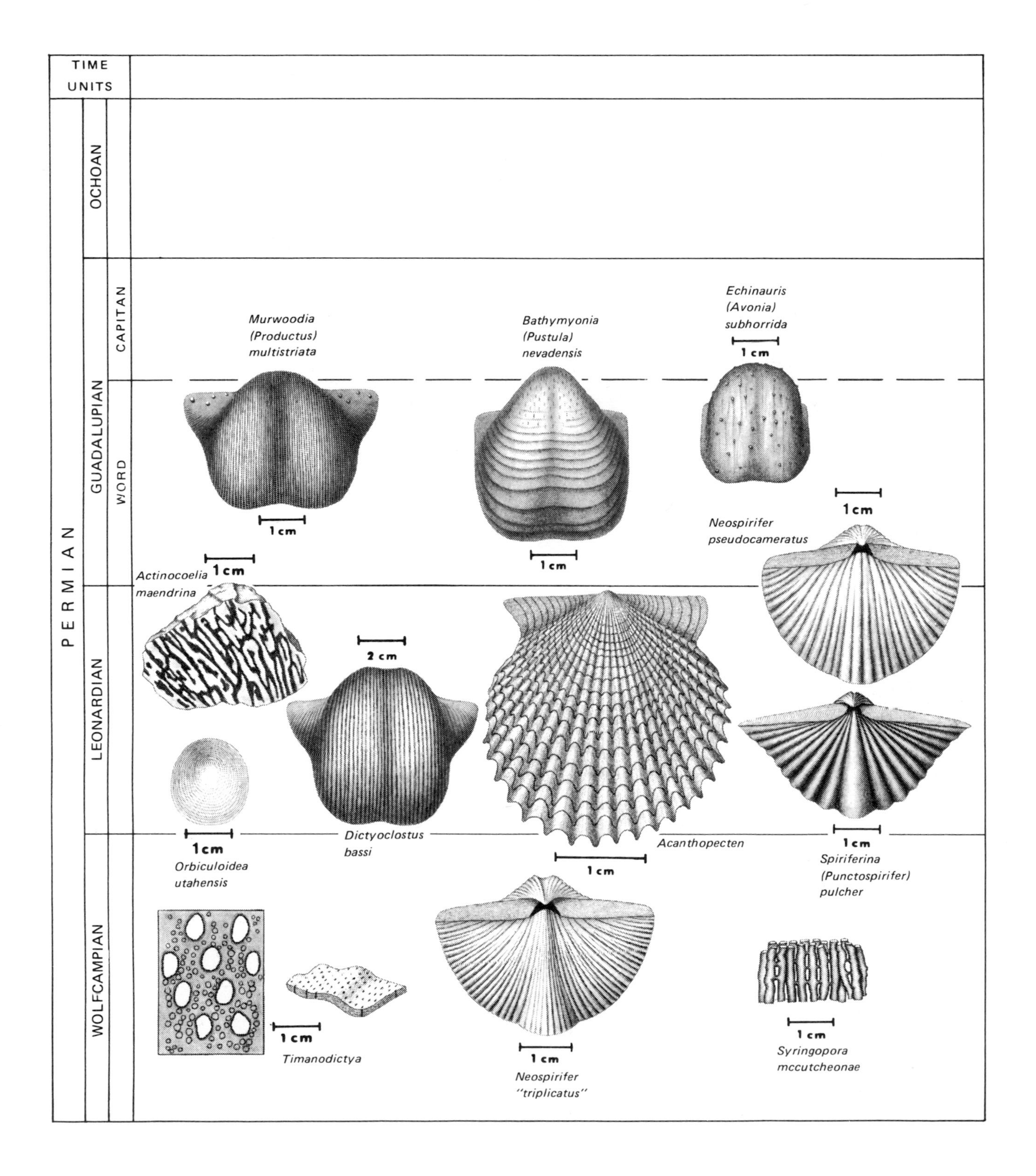

Figure 11-6. Characteristic marine fossils from the Permian of Utah. Sketches are arranged so that the centers of each specimen is in the zone of which it is characteristic. Sketches: John K. Balsley.

11-6). In rough order of decreasing abundance there are fusulinids, brachiopods, pelecypods, gastropods, bryozoans, echinoderms (crinoids mainly), cephalopods, corals, scaphopods, plants, and vertebrates. The groups might be listed in somewhat different order if importance to paleontologists were taken as the guide. For example, although vertebrate fossils of the red beds are extremely rare, they are important in understanding not only the evolutionary status of land life in Permian time, but also the environments of dry-land deposition. Many amphibians and possibly a few reptiles are represented by their tracks only (fig. 11-7). Bones are rare and complete skeletons exceptional. Although plants are included in the above list, they have been reported from only a few localities. Important plant collections have been taken from the Hermit Shale of the Grand Canyon; however, none have been described in Utah.

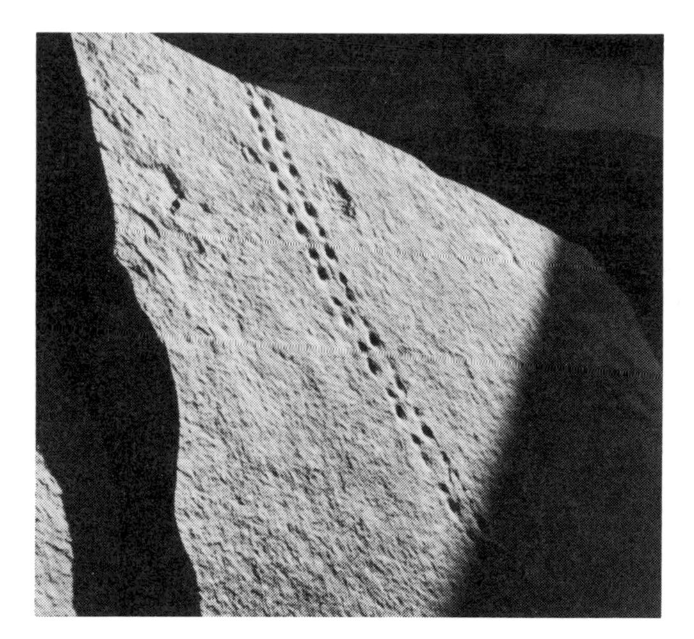

Figure 11-7. Footprints of an unidentified animal, probably an amphibian, Cutler Formation, lower Labyrinth Canyon of the Green River.

Permian marine invertebrates tend to occur in well-defined assemblages or faunas. Thus, for the earlier part of the period the dominant animals were fusulinids. They seem to have been well adapted to the limy-sandy cyclic deposits characteristic of the Oquirrh Formation and its equivalents. Other locally abundant fossils are brachiopods, bryozoans, and crinoids.

Fusulinids decline and essentially disappear from Utah rocks near the middle of the Permian when the cyclic type of deposition characteristic of the Oquirrh ceased. After this, new and different environments appeared to harbor new groups of organisms. The incursion of the so-called Kaibab Sea from the Texas-New Mexico region brought many brachiopods of which the large productid, *Dictyoclostus*, is a key member. Molluscs dominated certain localities and were at least equal in importance to the declining brachiopods. Noteworthy in the Kaibab Sea was a proliferation of sponges, such as *Actinocoelia meandrina*, and an abundance of silica which was deposited as large quantities of light-colored chert.

Shortly after Kaibab time, the Park City-Phosphoria Sea encroached from the north with mostly different brachiopods and molluscs. An excellent guide fossil, both common and distinctive, is *Punctospirifer pulcher* (fig. 11-8). An unusual fauna of small molluscs accompanies and contributes to the phosphate-bearing beds. It is called a depauperate or dwarfed assemblage and may reflect adverse living conditions. Chert is even more common in the Park City-Phosphoria units than in the Kaibab. The only formation of Utah which is entitled to include chert as part of the formal name is the Permian Rex Chert Member of the Phosphoria Formation. It is composed largely of sponge spicules. Not to be overlooked in any review of Permian fossils are the conodonts. Although these minute fossils are practically invisible without magnification, they are of great use in age correlations.

As the Permian drew to a close, many fossil groups declined or disappeared in what is generally known as the Time of the Great Dying. Only a few cup corals and trilobites are found in the Kaibab Formation, the last remnants of formerly thriving groups. Crinoids and bryozoans declined dramatically but brachiopods appear to be thriving until the end of the period. In the Terrace Mountains (on the northwestern margin of Great Salt Lake), distinctive Permian and Triassic conodonts have been collected within a few inches of each other, an interval which includes the youngest Permian rocks in North America and the Permian-Triassic boundary.

Figure 11-8. Silicified specimens of the common brachiopod, *Spiriferina Pulcher*, from the Park City Formation. Coin gives scale. Photo: Jim Howell.

Figure 11-9. Monument Valley, Utah-Arizona looking south. All but a few of the mesas, buttes and spires of this famous landscape are in Arizona. The state line runs across the foreground flats and between the large mesa on the right and the small spire beyond it.

SCENERY

A number of especially scenic areas in Permian rocks have been officially set aside as parks and monuments. Best known is Monument Valley, shared by Utah and Arizona and administered in part as a Navajo Tribal Park (fig. ll-9). Here an assemblage of promontories, mesas, buttes, and spires rises starkly above an extensive, nearly level plain. The angular monoliths are formed of the DeChelly Sandstone; they rest on flaring bases of the softer Organ Rock Formation which also floors the intervening plain. Where the DeChelly has fallen away, the underlying Organ Rock erodes into lower monuments of a distinctly different type. Train Rock and Organ Rock (from which the formation gets its name) are examples. Shifting sand dunes embellish the landscape and only a few shallow water-courses impede those who travel across it.

A second area of special scenic interest is Natural Bridges National Monument in west-central San Juan County. Here within near proximity of each other are three great stone bridges: Kachina (108 feet from the stream bed to the base of the bridge and a span of 203 feet), Sipapu (167 feet from stream bed to the base of the bridge and a span of 268 feet), and Owachomo (100 feet from stream bed to the base of the bridge and a span of 180 feet (fig. 11-10). These are all correctly identified as bridges, for they span stream beds that occasionally carry water. All are in the Cedar Mesa Sandstone, usually regarded as a member of the Cutler Formation and older and lower in stratigraphic position than the DeChelly Sandstone.

The greatest display of scenic Permian rocks is in Canyonlands National Park, mostly in northeastern San Juan County (fig. 11-11a). At least half of the surface outcrops of the Park are Permian rocks, including those areas traversed by virtually all the access roads and the upper walls of all the deeper gorges, including Cataract Canyon, the Canyon of the Colorado River above its confluence with the Green River almost to Moab, Grand County; and Stillwater Canyon of the Green River to a point opposite Steer Mesa, Emery and Grand County.

Unique scenic features are seen in The Needles section of Canyonlands National Park where the Cedar Mesa Sandstone is sliced into countless narrow blocks by faults and joints (fig. 11-11b). Some slices have dropped several hundred feet, pulled by gravity into space left vacant by the sliding of near-surface rocks toward the nearby Colorado river. Probably the most striking single formation of the central section of Canyonlands National Park is the White Rim Sandstone, well named from its habit of appearing as a band of light-colored bare rock curving around the headwaters of many miles of side canyons (fig. 11-11c).

Permian rocks also appear in the central area of three of Utah's great anticlinal uplifts: the San Rafael Swell, Circle Cliffs, and Monument Upwarps. In the San Rafael Swell is

Figure 11-10. Owachomo Natural Bridge in the Cedar Mesa Sandstone (Permian). Natural Bridges National Monument, 180 foot span, 100 foot from stream bed to arch, San Juan County. Photo: Utah Travel Council.

Figure 11-11a. Angel Arch, Canyonlands National Park, San Juan County. Formed by breaking and weathering of a narrow wall of Cedar Mesa Sandstone Member of the Cutler Formation. Photo: U.S. Bureau of Reclamation.

Figure 11-11c. The White Rim and Standing Rock Basin, Canyonlands, San Juan County, looking southeast to Abajo Mountains. The curving light-colored outcrop is the White Rim Sandstone of Permian age. Below it in the Standing Rocks is the Cutler Formation. Photo: Utah Tourist and Publicity Council (Parker Hamilton).

Figure 11-11b. Needles area, Canyonlands National Park, San Juan County. Intricate jointing and erosion of the Permian Cutler Formation has produced the distinctive scenery. Isolated area called Chesler Park is in center of view. Photo: U.S. National Park Service.

the remote and little visited Black Box of the San Rafael River, a vertical narrow gorge in the White Rim and Cedar Mesa Sandstones. Other striking exposures of Permian rocks are seen in rugged Grand Wash which traverses Cedar Mesa, Grand County. The upper few hundred feet of the walls of the Goosenecks of the San Juan River is also of Permian rocks indistinguishable, except to the eyes of the trained geologist, from the Pennsylvanian rocks that extend to river level far below.

Farther north, in Dinosaur National Monument, Permian formations reappear in spectacular scenic outcrops. For many miles, the walls of the Yampa River above its junction with the Green River are in the Weber Sandstone. Steamboat Rock is the best known landmark of this stretch. The great sandstone wall where the Green River emerges from Split Mountain is also in Weber Sandstone (fig. 11-12). This outcrop continues eastward where it dips steeply southward and has been eroded into a vast jumble of irregular knobs, pinnacles, and deep canyons visible from many miles away. The Weber is older than either the Cedar Mesa Formation or the DeChelly Sandstone. In fact, the lower part of it is Pennsylvanian.

The Permian is probably represented in more geographic sections of Utah than any other Paleozoic or Mesozoic system. There are extensive exposures in both the eastern and western halves of the state, along the entire length of

Figure 11-12. Mouth of Split Mountain Gorge where Green River passes between cliffs of Weber Sandstone. The Weber is considered part Pennsylvanian and part Permian. Photo: U.S. Park Service.

the Wasatch Range and practically encircling the Uinta Mountains. Probably two-thirds of the Permian sediments originally deposited remain intact, mostly under younger, sedimentary cover in eastern Utah.

ECONOMIC

Permian formations are important economically for a wide variety of resources. The Phosphoria-Park City unit contains large reserves of phosphate rock, of which only the richest and most accessible have so far been mined (fig. 11-13). Currently, a grade of about 24 percent P_2O_5 is required to be economic. The middle part of the formation, the Meade Peak Member, is the principal source of phosphate ore. This member is 180 to 300 feet thick in the central and southern Wasatch Mountains, 10 to 90 feet thick in the western Uinta Mountains, and thins to a feather edge at the Colorado state line. The richer beds must be selectively mined to obtain maximum value from the ore.

Phosphate has also been mined from the Crawford Mountains in Rich County where the richest and thickest deposits of the state are found. The only other operating mines are on the south flank of the Uinta Range near Vernal, Uintah County. Here the best ore is found from Rock Creek eastward to the vicinity of Little Brush Creek.

Permian rocks contain oil and gas in only a few Utah formations. The Kaibab Limestone is productive in the Upper Valley field, Garfield County, and in the Virgin field, Washington County. The Ashley Valley field, Uintah County, draws oil from the Pennsylvanian/Permian Weber Sandstone. The Coconino Sandstone is known to contain gas at several localities, including carbon dioxide in the Gordon Creek field, Carbon County. This non-flammable gas may be of great importance in the future but is not produced at present.

Much more important are the oil-impregnated sandstones, or tar sands. The most extensive deposit is in the

Figure 11-13. Phosphate-bearing beds of the Park City Formation as exposed in workings of the San Francisco Chemical Company. Photo: L.T. Grose.

White Rim Sandstone of Wayne (fig. 11-14) and Garfield Counties. The deposit occurs in the triangular area defined by the Colorado, Green and Dirty Devil Rivers. The thickness of oil saturation ranges from 5 to more than 300 feet and the deposit has been estimated to contain about 6.5 billion barrels of oil. Another large deposit, estimated to contain 12 to 15 million barrels of oil, is in the Hoskinnini Member of the Cutler Formation in White Canyon, San Juan County. Minor deposits are known in the Kaibab Limestone of the San Rafael Swell and the Park City Formation at Split Mountain, Uintah County.

Permian formations contain many of the important bodies of lead-zinc-silver ore in the Park City Mining District. The ore solutions rising from depth have replaced favorable limestone beds in the Park City Formation. Triassic and Mississippian limestones also contain ore in this important district but the major part of the production is from Permian strata. Ores of copper, lead, zinc, and silver are widely distributed in the Kaibab, Toroweap, and Plympton Formations of the Milford area, Beaver County. These

Figure 11-14. Flowing oil seep in Permian White Rim Sandstone, Elaterite Basin, Wayne County. Large masses of rock in this vicinity are classified as rich tar sands. Photo: Howard R. Ritzma.

same formations contain the ore bodies of the Deer Trail Mine in the Tushar Mountains.

Large reserves of gypsum are known in the Kaibab and Toroweap Formations but no production is recorded.

For additional reading about the topics discussed in Chapter 11, see the following list of authors:

Baars, 1962, 1971, 1972, 1973, 1975
Baars and Molenar, 1971
Behnken, 1975
Bissell, 1959, 1962a, 1962b, 1964
Bissell and Childs, 1958
Byrd, 1967
Callaghan, 1973
Cheney, 1953, 1957a, 1957b
Clark and Behnken, 1971
Clark and others, 1977
Cook, E.F., 1963
Crittenden, 1976
Cummings, 1910
Erickson, A.J., 1968
Gere, 1964, 1967
Girty, 1910
Gregory and others, 1938
Hallgarth, 1962
Hintze, 1973
Hintze and Whelan, 1973
Hose, 1959
James, H.L., 1973
Lohman, 1974, 1975
McGill and Stromquist, 1975
McKee, 1938
McKelvey and others, 1956, 1959
McKnight, 1940
Mallory, 1972a
Marcantel, 1975
Peterson, V.E., 1961
Poole, 1962
Preston, 1960
Rascoe and Baars, 1972
Ritzma, 1969
Roberts and others, 1965
Sharp, 1976
Stokes, 1961
Stowe, 1972
Untermann, 1949, 1950
Untermann and Untermann, 1954, 1964
Vaughn, 1973
Wardlaw, 1975
Wardlaw and Collinson, 1977, 1978
Warner, M. A., 1956
Welsh, 1972
White, D., 1929
Williams, J. S., 1943, 1949
Williams, J. G., 1949
Wilson and Pierson, 1958
Withington, 1964
Yochelseon, 1963, 1968

For complete bibliographic citations, please see List of References.

12

THE TRIASSIC PERIOD

The Triassic Period began about 245 million years ago and lasted for approximately 37 million years. It received its name as a formal geologic period in 1834 from a three-fold stratigraphic division in Germany. Triassic rocks have since been recognized on all the great land masses and are especially varied and well exposed in the western United States. The Triassic of Utah is characterized by a variety of marine and non-marine deposits and about 67 formations are found partly or entirely within the state. The most important are listed at the end of the book.

PALEOGEOGRAPHY

During the Triassic Period great geologic changes occurred in the western United States that permanently influenced the future development of the continent. A reconstructed view of the earlier part of the period differs entirely from that of the later part (figs. 12-1a and 12-1b). The pattern of Early Triassic lands and seas was much like that of the Paleozoic periods with the shore of the Pacific Ocean curving into central Utah along a shelving lowland that rose

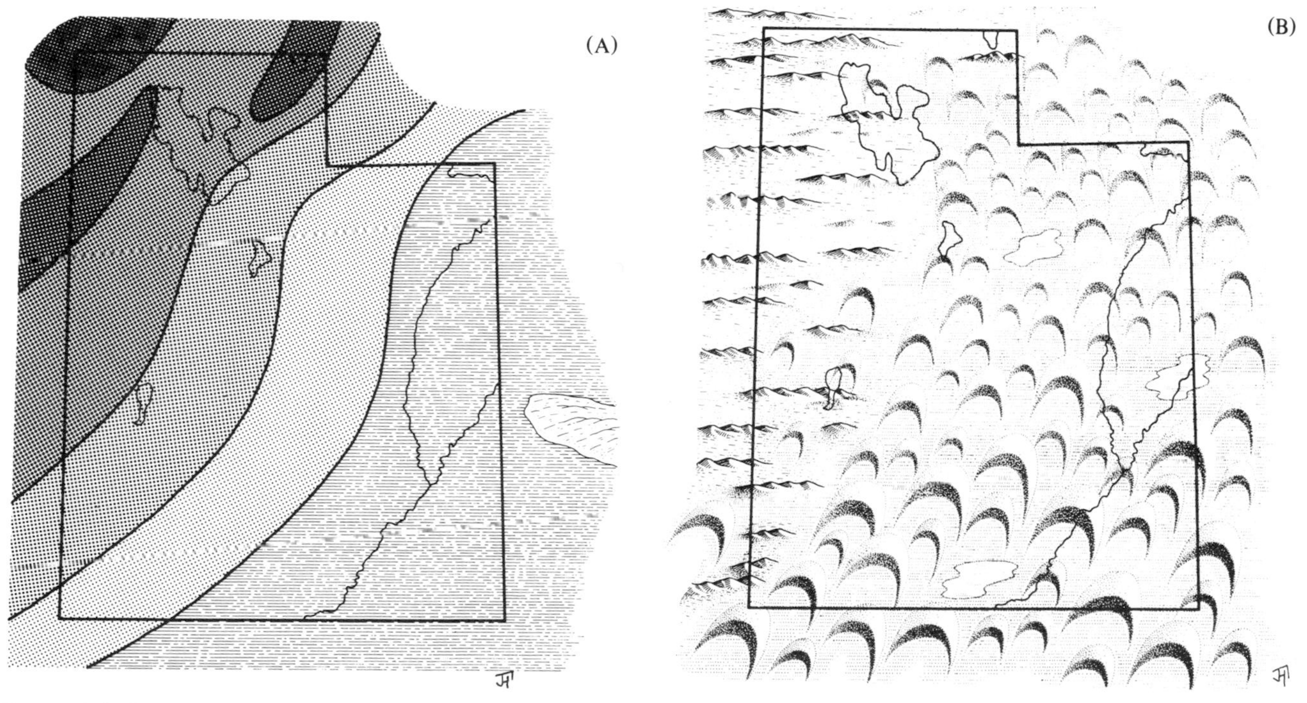

Figure 12-1. Generalized paleogeography of (A) Early Triassic time, and (B) Late Triassic-Early Jurassic. For the Early Triassic, the darkest pattern indicates areas of thicker, more complete formations; lighter patterns indicate correspondingly thinner, less complete sections. Areas of horizontal dashed pattern are mainly marginal marine mud flats. Note remnants of the Uncompahgre Uplift in west-central Colorado. In (B), representing Late Triassic-Early Jurassic time, deposition was exclusively wind-deposited sand. A succession of barchan dunes crossing the region from north to southwest is diagrammatically represented. Sketches: Jeffery B. Hulen.

gently toward the eroded remnants of the Ancestral Rockies to the east. It is from these mountains that much of the Triassic sediment of the Colorado Plateau was derived. So great was the volume of eroded material that it not only filled and smoothed over the ancient Paradox Basin, but also began to bury the mountains themselves. By the close of the Triassic no surface remnants of the Uncompahgre Uplift remained in Utah.

During Early Triassic time, shallow seas occasionally spread inward across wide, marginal mud flats and at their greatest extent reached eastward to a line running roughly north-northeast from Zion National Park across the Circle Cliffs, Green River Desert, and Uinta Basin to the central Uinta Mountains. When the seas withdrew, either from being crowded out by abundant silty deposits or from relative lowering of sea level, the land-derived sediments extended far into western Utah.

No sediments of Middle Triassic age have been positively identified; the nearest known deposits of this age are in west-central Nevada and it is assumed that much of the interior region of the continent, including Utah, must have undergone erosion for at least 10 million years.

During Middle Triassic time a barrier of some sort seems to have come into existence in what is now eastern Nevada. The name, Mesocordilleran High, intentionally gives no clue as to whether it was a high mountain range, low hills, or only a gentle arching. In any case it was sufficient to prevent inward flooding of the ocean. The creation of this barrier was, in itself, a significant event but it was only the first step in a 220-million-year-long gradual westward shift of the Pacific coastline to its present position. Jurassic seas from the west reached only into western Nevada, while the shoreline of Cretaceous time seems to have been even farther west along the western margin of the Sierra Nevada. In effect, about 800 miles of solid continental territory was added between Utah and the Pacific Ocean during the interval from mid-Triassic to mid-Tertiary time. Once the barrier developed, this strip was never again flooded by the sea.

The westward expansion of North America is very satisfactorily explained by plate tectonics and continental accretion. It began during the initial splitting of the Americas from Europe-Africa and the creation of the modern Atlantic Ocean. The Atlantic widened by a corresponding westward displacement of North America. Not only did the continent push westward across the margin of the Pacific Ocean, it also gathered up whatever islands and marginal sediments were in its path. Some of the sea bottom was forced downward and returned to the hot athenosphere and some buckled up to become the new coastal ranges of North America. The particular oceanic segment overridden and destroyed is called the Farallon lithospheric plate. The splitting of the Atlantic is near enough in time to the rise of the Mesocordilleran High that a cause and effect relationship is reasonable. During the time of maximum disturbance, the Middle Triassic, no sediments seem to have been deposited in Utah.

The rock record resumes in Late Triassic time but the paleogeography was significantly different. A semi-enclosed basin between the remnants of the Ancestral Rockies to the east and the Mesocordilleran High to the west was now in evidence. In this interior depression a great variety of land-laid sediments were deposited. The climate seems to have ranged from humid to semi-arid and resulted in a very complex intermingling of rock types deposited in rivers, floodplains, swamps, and lakes that are difficult to map and classify. The Chinle Shale designates the overall assemblage but a dozen or more subdivisions have been named within it. Not all of the subdivisions, however, are found in Utah.

The final scene of Triassic time is again very different. The broad lowland basin remained, but wind-blown sand dominated the previously diversified landscape for many millions of years. Three great sandstone formations centered in the Colorado Plateau were created during the latest part of the Triassic and Early Jurassic. At the base is the cliff-forming Wingate Sandstone known to be of Late Triassic age. Above it is the bench-forming Kayenta Formation which most geologists consider to be Triassic as well. It too is dominantly sandstone but shows evidence of deposition by running water as well as wind much more clearly than the formations above or below it. The uppermost formation of the sandstone section is the Navajo Sandstone, mostly—if not entirely, of Jurassic age.

A major problem with any reconstruction of Middle and Late Triassic rocks is how far west to extend the environments that are easily recognized in the Colorado Plateau (fig. 12-2). At present the Wasatch Fault and its counter-

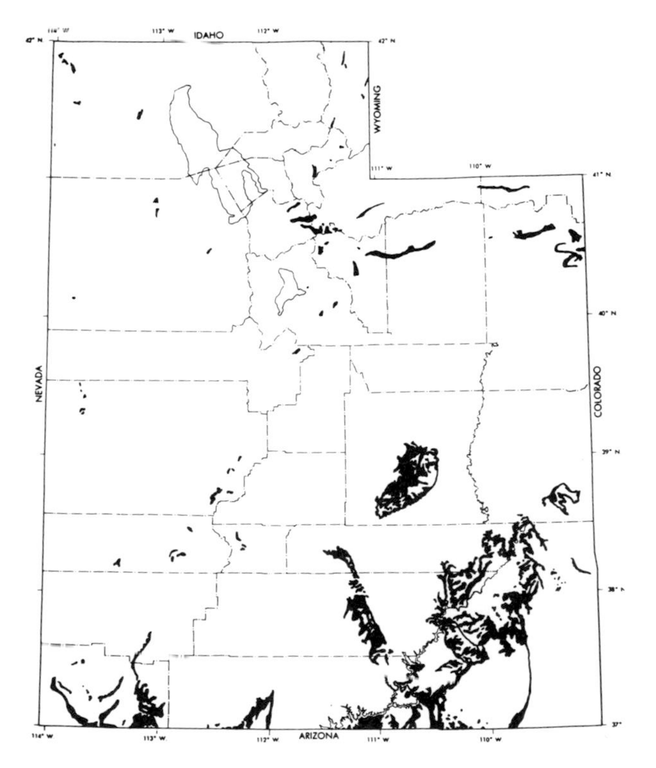

Figure 12-2 Outcrops of Triassic rocks of Utah. Most of the eastern part of the state between the outcrops is underlain by Triassic formations.

parts in central Utah abruptly terminate the Chinle Shale and the great sandstone formations along a western edge. How much farther did they extend? Not all the evidence can be discussed here; however, it seems possible that the western edge of wind-blown deposition was not far from the Utah-Nevada border.

ORIGIN AND NATURE OF TRIASSIC ROCKS

Lower Triassic rocks are similar in origin and composition to their Upper Permian predecessors. During this time interval, deeper and more permanent seas lay to the west. Occasionally, shallow embayments flooded eastward across extensive mud flats to create tapering, eastward-pointing tongues of marine rocks. As the seas retreated, the marine tongues of limestone were overlain by westward-tapering tongues of non-marine red beds (figs. 12-3a, 12-3b, and 12-3c). Earlier explorers could find no easy way of dividing these rock units and the symbol Permo-Triassic Red Beds appears on many older maps. Even today the boundary between the periods has not been fixed exactly in most areas.

During the Triassic, the production of red silty sediments reached a maximum. The Triassic was, in fact, a great Red Bed Age for the entire Earth. A climatic explanation seems the most logical for the prevalence of this phenomenon. Locally in the western United States the factors favoring red bed formation seem to have been a source of iron-bearing sediment and an arid or semi-arid climate under which oxygen or oxygenated waters could penetrate deeply and remain in contact with the previously deposited sediments while they lithified. According to a widely accepted theory, small amounts of the iron necessary for the production of red in red beds is contained in such minerals as hornblende, biotite, chlorite, and pyroxene. A small proportion of these minerals released from the older metamorphic rocks of the Ancestral Rockies were mixed with the quartz and other components of Permian and Triassic sediments. Over a long period of time the scattered grains were gradually oxidized to the color-bearing minerals hematite and limonite that spread through the matrix and coated the chemically inert, mostly colorless, quartz grains (fig. 12-4).

West of the Wasatch Line, Triassic rocks are known from only a few small scattered outcrops. They are remnants preserved in deep folds, fault blocks, or under fault plates. The best known exposures are in the Conger Range, Terrace Mountains, Gold Hill, Goose Creek Mountains, and the Grayback Hills. They are of great importance in understanding the structural deformation of western Utah, not only during the earlier part of the Triassic but in subsequent time as well.

In contrast to western Utah, Triassic rocks are widespread in the southern, central, and southeastern parts of the state. Nearly continuous exposures are found around the San Rafael Swell, Circle Cliffs, and Monument Upwarp. The spectacular Vermillion Cliffs extend for many miles near the southern border of the state. Triassic formations are also well exposed along the southern flank of the Uinta Mountains but less so along the northern flank. Notable outcrops are found on the eastern slope of Mt. Nebo in the southern Wasatch Range near Provo, Utah County; in Parleys Syncline near Salt Lake City, Salt Lake County; near Park City, Summit County, where type sections of several important formations are described; and near the east shore of Bear Lake, Rich County.

Any estimate of how much Triassic rock may have been removed from western Utah is a very risky guess. However, since all evidence indicates a steady westward thickening of the Moenkopi (fig. 12-5) and/or Thaynes Formations, at least to their truncation by the Wasatch Line, it seems reasonable to assume that the formations were once extensive and relatively thick over much of western Utah. It is probable that not quite half of the Triassic sediment once present in Utah is now preserved.

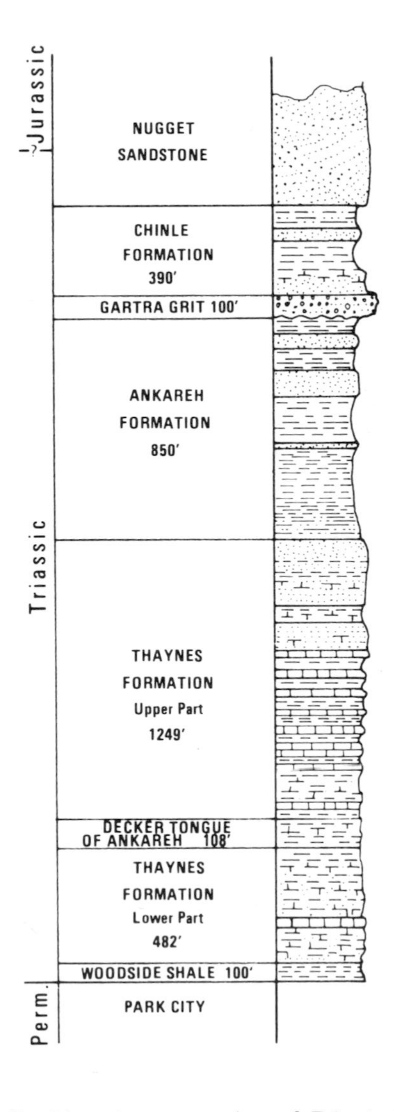

Figure 12-3a. Graphic columnar section of Triassic formations near Salt Lake City.

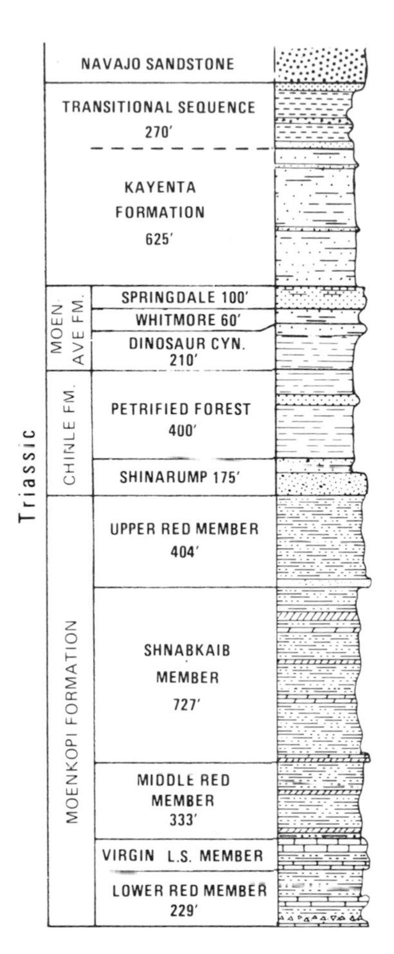

Figure 12-3b. Graphic columnar section of Triassic formations of St. George area, southwestern Utah.

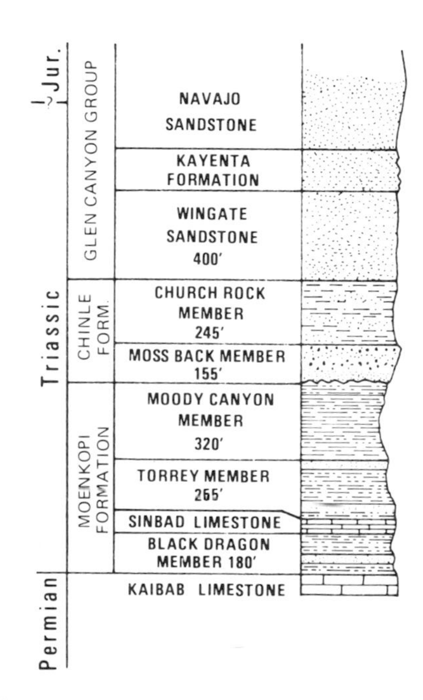

Figure 12-3c. Graphic columnar section of Triassic formations in the northern San Rafael Swell.

Figure 12-4. Specimen of a common Late Triassic rock type termed lime-pellet conglomerate. The color is dominantly red; the fragments were apparently torn up and redeposited in shallow water shortly after deposition. Specimen 3 1/2 inches across. Photo: Jim Howell.

FOSSILS

The Triassic is the first period of the Mesozoic Era. By this time all of the phyla of invertebrate and vertebrate animals and the divisions of the plant kingdom had appeared. However, a great extermination of practically all forms of life had occurred during the Late Permian and its effects were very much in evidence in the Triassic.

Triassic formations of Utah have yielded fossils of a great many significant groups of both plants and animals (fig. 12-6). The limestone tongues of the Lower Triassic are particularly fossiliferous. A rich assemblage of fossil cephalopods, collectively known as the *Meekoceras* fauna (fig. 12-7), is found near the base of the Thaynes Formation in the Wasatch Range and the Great Basin. Specimens ranging from less than an inch to a foot in diameter have been collected in great numbers, particularly in Cephalopod Gulch near Salt Lake City, Salt Lake County. The Thaynes Formation also contains pelecypods, gastropods, crinoids, starfish, and sponges. Conodonts furnish the best information for correlating Triassic marine rocks and important collections have been made in Utah.

Contributions from the non-marine red beds are not plentiful, but tracks of reptiles and amphibians are found locally. Footprints are known from the Moenkopi, Chinle Shale, Wingate, and Kayenta Formations. Tracks in the

Figure 12-5. Remnants of Wingate Sandstone resting on Chinle and Moenkopi red beds, Castle Valley, Grand County. This grouping has been called the Priest and Nuns. Photo: Utah Tourist and Publicity Council.

Moenkopi Formation are chiefly those of amphibians and small lizard-like reptiles. The mudflat environment favored trace fossils but few can be related to species known from actual bones. In younger formations, particularly the Chinle Shale and Kayenta Formation, the tracks of dinosaurs become increasingly common (fig. 12-8). The size of the dinosaur tracks increases with time. It is suspected that tracks found in the Chinle Shale belong to the dinosaur *Coelophysis*, which is known from many skeletons discovered in the same formation in New Mexico.

Excellent fossil fish have been found in Zion National Park and in Lisbon Valley, San Juan County. Fish discovered in the Chinle Shale include *Cionichthys*, *Lasalichthys*, *Seminotus*, *Hemicalypterus*, *Chinlea*, and *Ceratodus*. All are of fresh-water origin appropriate to Late Triassic environments. Bones of other vertebrates are rare.

Plant fossils are more common in Triassic formations than are animal fossils, especially if the "petrified forests" are taken into account (fig. 12-9). Petrified trees are so common in almost all outcrops of the Chinle Shale that the name, Petrified Forest Member, has been given to one of the subdivisions. Although Utah cannot match the great accumulations of the Petrified Forest National Park in Arizona, significant numbers of fossil logs, belonging chiefly to the coniferous genus *Araucarioxylon*, are found in the Circle Cliffs, San Rafael Swell, and other areas. Many other plants are represented by fossil leaves. They have been catalogued by Sidney R. Ash, Weber State College, who reports the following species from the Monitor Butte Member of the Chinle Shale: *Equisetites*, *Cladophlebis*, *Podozamites*, *Zamites*, and *Dinophyton*. The Shinarump Conglomerate Member of the Chinle has yielded *Equisetites*, *Phlebopteris*, *Cynepteris*, *Cladophlebis*, *Podozamites*, *Brachyphyllum*, *Pogiophyllum*, *Zamites*, *Eoginkgoites*, and *Nilssoniopteris*. Some of these genera are also reported from the Temple Mountain Member.

Fresh-water invertebrates of the Triassic include gastropods, pelecypods and arthropods. It is hoped that fossil evidence for or against the presence of Middle Triassic sediments in Utah may yet be discovered.

SCENERY

According to the Utah Historical Society, the term "Vermillion Cliffs" was applied by J. W. Powell (1875) to a long line of colorful slopes in southwestern Utah. Powell also selected the name Flaming Gorge for a stretch of the canyon of the Green River near Manila, Daggett County (fig. 12-10). These expressive names apply to especially striking outcrops of red Triassic strata at opposite corners of Utah. Between these classical scenic spots, many other out-

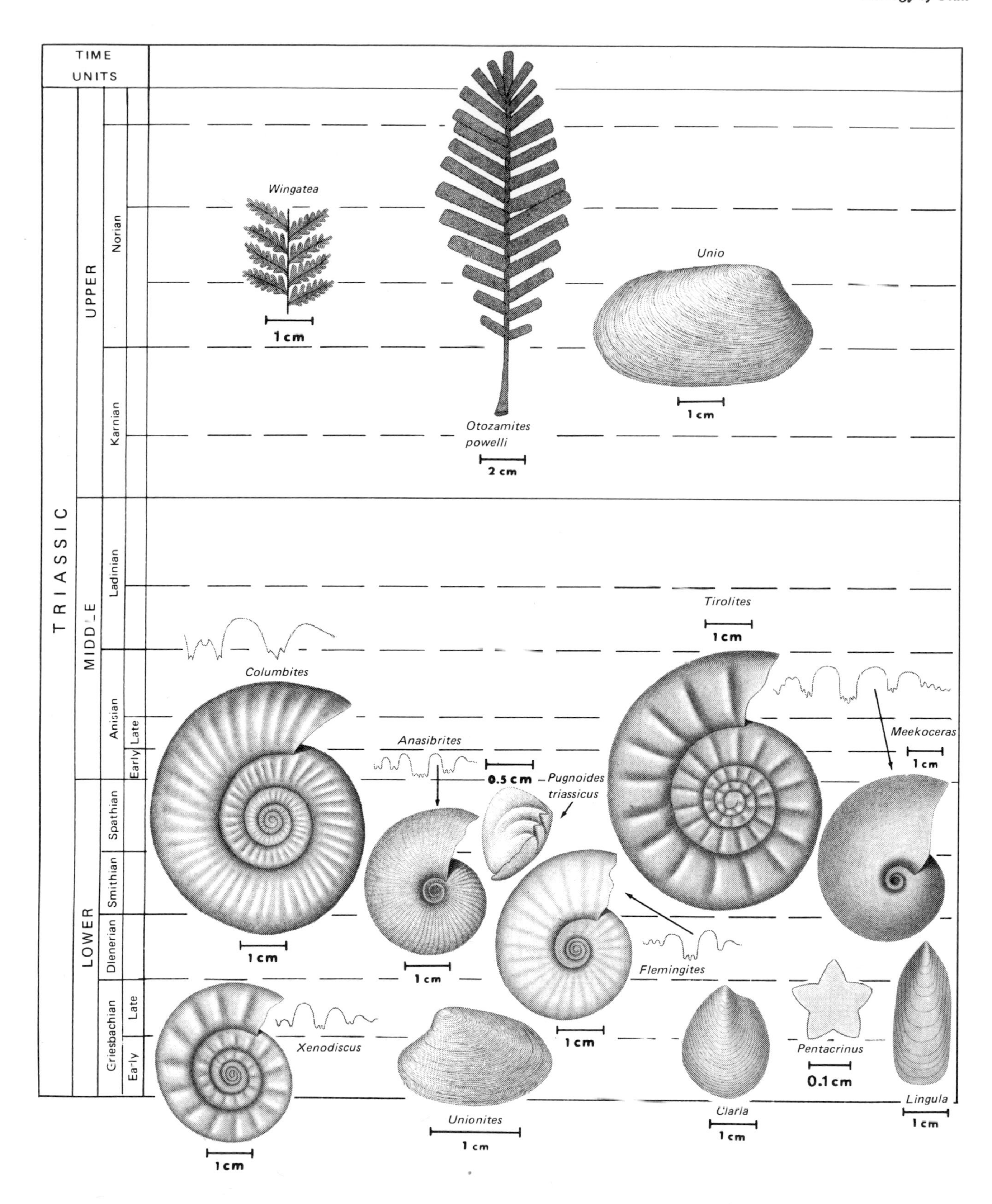

Figure 12-6. Characteristic Triassic fossils of Utah arranged according to world-wide zones. Sketches of individual specimens are centered in the zones of which they are characteristic. Sketches: John K. Balsley.

Figure 12-7. Typical fossil cephalopods from the Early Triassic *Meekoceras* zone. From largest to smallest these are *Wasatchites*, *Meekoceras*, and *Anasibirites*. Photo: Jim Howell.

Figure 12-9. Fossil logs weathering out of the Late Triassic Chinle Formation, Circle Cliffs, Garfield County. Photo: Utah Tourist and Publicity Council.

Figure 12-8. Dinosaur track from Triassic red beds near Kanab, Utah. Length about 5 inches. Photo: Jim Howell.

Figure 12-10. Flaming Gorge of the Green River, Daggett County, before deep inundation by water of Flaming Gorge Reservoir. Red strata which give the locality its name are Moenkopi, Gartra Grit, and Chinle Formations in the lower slopes and Nugget Sandstone in cliff. Photo: U.S. Bureau of Reclamation.

crops of the same colorful formations appear and have received appropriate names.

Triassic formations are of two contrasting types, hard and soft. Soft formations produce slopes while hard ones appear as cliffs. The most prominent hard formation, the Wingate Sandstone, is probably responsible for more miles of vertical cliffs than any other formation in the west (fig. 12-11). It appears as a highly indented wall surrounding the interior of Canyonlands National Park and forms the Orange Cliffs that parallel the Colorado River for scores of miles. It also appears in the highest ridge of such great hogbacks as the San Rafael Reef, Waterpocket Fold, Comb Ridge, and Capitol Reef. The Wingate Formation succeeds as a cliff maker chiefly because it is almost always capped and protected by the more resistant Kayenta Formation (fig. 12-12). When the Kayenta breaks down, the unprotected Wingate below soon disappears.

Underlying the Wingate Formation is the softer varicolored Chinle Shale (fig. 12-13). The most famous locality for this unit is the Painted Desert and Petrified Forest National Park in Arizona; however, many small localities in

Figure 12-11. Cliff face of Wingate Sandstone, Chimney Rock Canyon, Capitol Reef, Garfield County. Photo: K.L. Nichols.

Figure 12-12. Looking north along the San Rafael Reef. Rounded hillside on left is the Sinbad Limestone Member of the Moenkopi Formation, the valley is in upper Moenkopi and Chinle Formation, high hogback point is Wingate Sandstone, Kayenta and Navajo are in lower hogbacks to the right. Photo: A.J. Eardley.

Figure 12-13. Upper Triassic Chinle Formation exposed in varicolored barren slopes near the Paria. Photo: Herbert E. Gregory.

Utah duplicate scenic features of the famous park, including petrified logs and colorful pastel-tinted slopes and badlands. Someone has applied the term calico skirts to the spreading slopes of Chinle Shale that flare out below cliffs and monuments of the Wingate/Kayenta.

A typical profile of Triassic formations includes steep cliffs above and a slope below. A jog in the slope is created by a low cliff below the Chinle Shale and above the underlying Moenkopi Formation (fig. 12-14). This low cliff may be the Shinarump Conglomerate, Moss Back, or Gartra Member of the Chinle, depending on where the outcrop is located. These three units are mostly conglomerate and of such relative hardness that they form wide benches or protruding hogbacks. In places, the Moenkopi is so well protected by the Shinarump/Moss Back Member that the two join to form one vertical cliff such as the famous Mummy Cliffs near Torrey, Wayne County, or the younger, Early Triassic, red-bed exposures of Hurricane Mesa (fig. 12-15).

Figure 12-14. Massive sandstone lens making up most of the Gartra Grit Formation, Big Brush Creek, Uintah County. Note unconformable contact with underlying Moenkopi Formation. Photo: M. Dane Picard.

Figure 12-15. Hurricane Mesa, near Zion National Park and Rockville, Kane County. Practically the entire Moenkopi Formation is exposed in the slopes, the caprock is Shinarump Conglomerate. Photo: U.S. National Park Service.

Figure 12-16. A slab of "ripple rock" from the Moenkopi Formation. This type of red sandstone is much used as a decorative stone by builders and landscapers.

ECONOMIC

Triassic formations yield a variety of mineral products, some of which are indigenous to the rocks in which they occur and others that have been added at various times after the sediments were in place. Mineral deposits of actual or potential importance range from building stone to gold and include such unusual resources as native silver, red-bed copper, "ripple rocks" (building stone; fig. 12-16), petrified wood, and oil-impregnated sandstone. To an unusual extent, Triassic products have either been worked out entirely or have been exploited scarcely at all.

The Thaynes Formation of Early Triassic age contains important deposits of lead-zinc ores in the Park City district, Summit County. They are described as bedded replacement deposits because the ore minerals have replaced, and therefore follow, the original limestone beds.

A major metal-producing area is the Silver Reef (Harrisburg) district in eastern Washington County. In this area, ore bodies are restricted to the Silver Reef Sandstone Member of the Chinle Formation. This is the only known occurrence in the United States of commercial bodies of silver ore in sandstone. Minor amounts of copper and uranium also occur. The district has declined to almost total inactivity, but the estimated past production of about $7.5 million makes it one of Utah's great historic mining districts.

Triassic uranium deposits were mined for radium during World War I when mines were opened at Temple Mountain, Emery County (fig. 12-17). The metal was extracted in small amounts at tremendous cost from its parent uranium. The same deposits saw a second period of activity beginning about 1948 when uranium had great value. The most famous mine in Triassic rocks is probably the MiVida Mine in the Big Indian district, 35 miles southeast of Moab, Grand County. This deposit was discovered in 1952 and is said to have produced $40 million worth of uranium ore. In the interval from 1948 to 1974 about 54 other important properties in the near vicinity produced some 8.5 million tons averaging 0.35 percent U_3O_8.

Figure 12-17. Old mine workings for radium and uranium in the Moss Back Sandstone near Temple Mountain, Emery County. Photo: Ward Roylance.

The White Canyon mining district includes mines in White Canyon, Red Canyon, Deer Flat, Elk Ridge, Upper Cottonwood Canyon, and Upper Indian Creek. Most of the ore deposits are in the Shinarump Conglomerate Member of the Chinle Shale, in sandstone bodies that are clearly the filled channels of ancient rivers. A number of deposits have also been mined from the Shinarump Conglomerate in the Circle Cliffs.

The hydrocarbon reserves of Triassic rocks include gas, oil, and asphalt or tar. Since 1907 small amounts of oil have been produced at the Virgin field near Hurricane, Washington County, from the Timpoweap Member of the Moenkopi Formation; the field is the oldest in Utah. Gas is known to occur in the Last Chance Anticline of southwestern Emery County, but is currently not being produced. Of potential importance are the oil-impregnated sandstone lenses of the Moenkopi Formation in the Circle Cliffs and San Rafel Swell (fig. 12-18). Reserves in the Circle Cliffs are calculated at 1.7 billion barrels of oil in place.

Figure 12-18. Oil seep at the base of the Shinarump Conglomerate, White Canyon Flat, Circle Cliffs. Photo: Hellmut H. Doelling.

For additional reading on the topics discussed in Chapter 12, see the following list of authors:

Ash, 1975
Bahr, 1963
Baker, 1947
Baker and others, 1936
Blakey, 1973, 1974, 1977
Boutwell, 1912, 1933
Breed and others, 1972
Butler and others, 1920
Campbell, J. A., 1975
Campbell and Lewis, 1961
Clark, D. L., 1957, 1959
Clark and Stokes, 1956
Clark and others, 1977
Coffin, 1954
Collinson and Hasenmueller, 1978
Coney, 1978
Davidson, 1959, 1967
Davies, 1980
Dix, 1953
Eardley, 1933
Finnell and others, 1963
Garmoe and Erickson, 1968
Granger, 1953
Gross, 1955
Hansen, W.R., 1969
Hose, 1959
Irwin, 1971
Isachsen, 1954
Kummel, 1954
Lawson, 1913
Lohman, 1974
MacLachlan, 1972
Malan, 1968
Mathews, 1919, 1929, 1931
McKee, 1954
McKee and others, 1960
Miller, L. J., 1955
Nolan, 1935
Peabody, 1948, 1956
Phillips and Forsyth, 1972
Pitman and Talwani, 1972
Poole and Stewart, 1964
Powell, 1876
Preston, 1960
Proctor, 1953
Ritzma, 1969
Robeck, 1954
Schaeffer, 1950
Smith, H.P., 1968
Smith, J.P., 1932
Stewart, 1956, 1972
Stewart and others, 1972
Stifel, 1964
Stokes, 1958, 1958b, 1960, 1967, 1980
Stugard, 1951
Walker, 1967
Young, R.G., 1964

For complete bibliographic citations, please see List of References.

13

THE JURASSIC PERIOD

The Jurassic Period began about 208 million years ago and had an estimated duration of 64 million years. In 1879 Alexander Von Humboldt named it after the Jura Mountains on the border of France and Switzerland. In the United States Jurassic rocks crop out almost exclusively west of the Mississippi River. They have been studied intensively, chiefly because of the dinosaur fossils and the deposits of uranium they contain. About 58 formations of Jurassic age are known in Utah; both marine and nonmarine deposits are well represented and widely distributed (fig 13-1). Major stratigraphic units of Jurassic age recognized in Utah are listed at the end of the book.

ORIGIN AND ENVIRONMENT OF DEPOSITION OF JURASSIC ROCKS

The Mesocordilleran High (fig. 13-2) dominated Utah throughout the Jurassic Period. Recall that the Mesocordilleran High was the barrier lying between what is now California and central Utah. Although this feature is difficult to reconstruct or locate exactly, its existence is substantiated by much direct and indirect evidence. Because of it, the seas that invaded the interior of the continent in later Jurassic time did so by a route through Canada north of the obstacle. The barrier also seems to have had a blocking effect on moisture-bearing winds not greatly different from that of the Sierra Nevada today. This tended to create or intensify desert conditions in the interior, particularly in what is now the Colorado Plateau. Lastly, the Mesocordilleran High became a source of rivers carrying sediment that was redeposited eastward to form widespread formations of conglomerate, sand and mud.

The Mesocordilleran High influenced the three distinctly different environments that succeeded each other in the western interior during the Jurassic Period (figs. 13-3a, 13-3b, and 13-3c). The first of these paleoenvironments was a sandy desert, the second was a succession of shallow marine invasions and, finally, one of extensive river systems and shifting fresh-water lakes as the period ended. Each environment left distinctive deposits and fossils of more than usual interest to geologists.

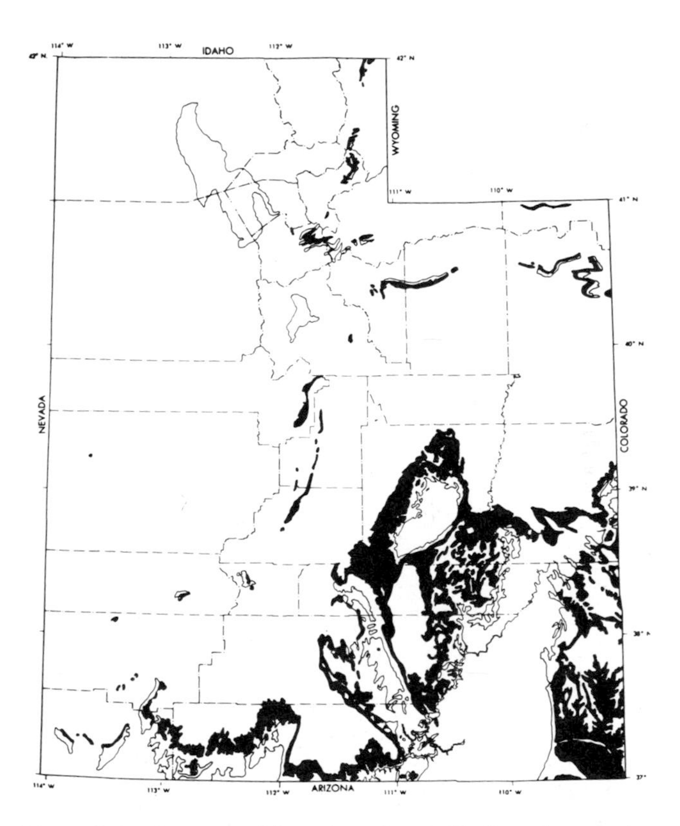

Figure 13-1. Outcrops of Jurassic and probable Jurassic rocks in Utah. Dark pattern includes all proven Jurassic sediments. Areas between these outcrops and the nearby uniform black line are occupied by the Navajo (or Nugget) Sandstone which is thought to be partly Jurassic and partly Triassic.

The Navajo-Nugget Sandstone was deposited during the earliest, sand-dominated, desert environment. It is not clear how far west this great sand sheet originally extended, but it may have covered most of Utah. Many significant remnants are found in southern Nevada, Arizona, and southern California. Hundreds of observations by many

MESOCORDILLERAN HIGHLAND

REMNANTS OF ANCESTRAL ROCKIES

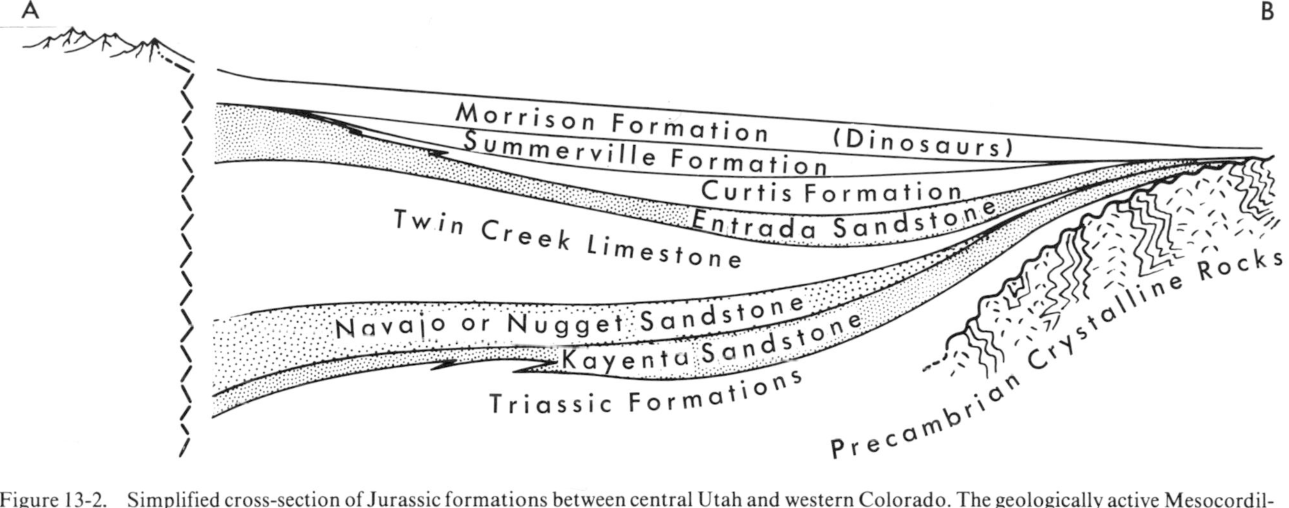

Figure 13-2. Simplified cross-section of Jurassic formations between central Utah and western Colorado. The geologically active Mesocordilleran Highland to the west and the eroded remnants of the Ancestral Rockies to the east created a basin-like depression in which Jurassic sediments accumulated.

geologists have established that the currents which deposited the sand were moving from the north or northwest relative to the present geography (fig. 13-4). Whether the transporting currents were wind or water has been hotly debated ever since the formation was first described more than 100 years ago. Furthermore, the ultimate origin of the sand itself has not been established.

Much of the Navajo-Nugget Sandstone is overlain by marine deposits (figs. 13-5a, 13-5b, and 13-5c). The lithologic change is abrupt (fig. 13-6) and may record a rapid advance of the sea over former dune fields. However, the transition may not have been as rapid as some suppose. For example, in southwestern and south-central Utah marine limestone tongues extend eastward into the upper part of the Navajo while sandstone tongues penetrate westward into the marine sections indicating shifting marine and nonmarine environments. Units known to have marine equivalents have been given a separate name, the Page Sandstone.

Although wind action was significant during the Permian and Triassic, the deposition of non-marine sandstone in Utah reaches an all-time maximum during the Early Jurassic. The succession of Permian, Triassic, Jurassic, and Early Cretaceous sandy formations forms a wide belt running from south-central Utah to east-central New Mexico to constitute what geologists call, half-jokingly, the Great Sand Pile. One thing is certain about the Great Sand Pile, it occupied an interior position where marine influences were at a minimum. This alone speaks strongly for a non-marine origin of many formations, including the Navajo. When the structure and composition of the formations are taken into consideration, the evidence to most geologists is overwhelming; the dominant agent of transportation and deposition in the Great Sand Pile was the wind. This is not to discount arguments of those who think otherwise; they point to the presence of glauconite (a mineral characteristic of marine environments) and to extensive slumping and contorted bedding that they suggest could not have been formed in dry sand. They also maintain that the minute markings on the sand grains are not characteristic of dunes, but rather of beaches.

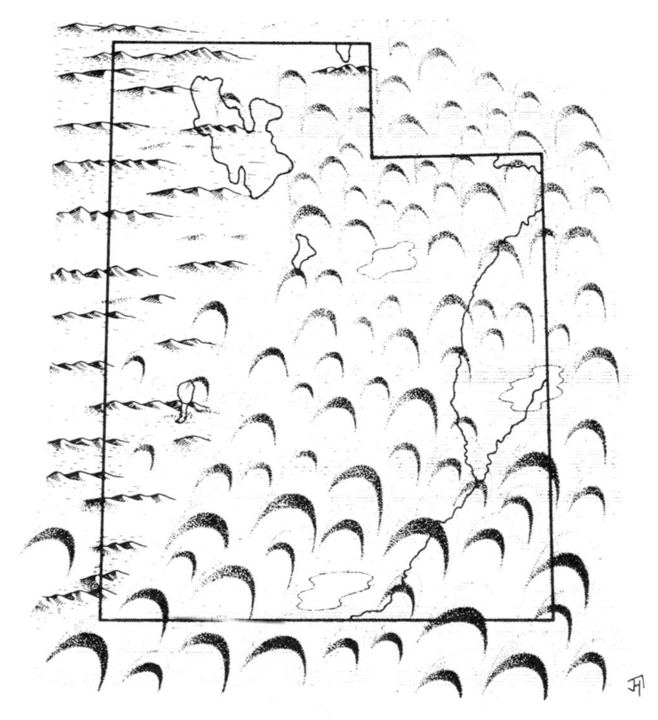

Figure 13-3a. Late Triassic-Early Jurassic, deposition was exclusively wind-deposited sand. A succession of barchan dunes crossing the region from north to southwest is diagrammatically represented.

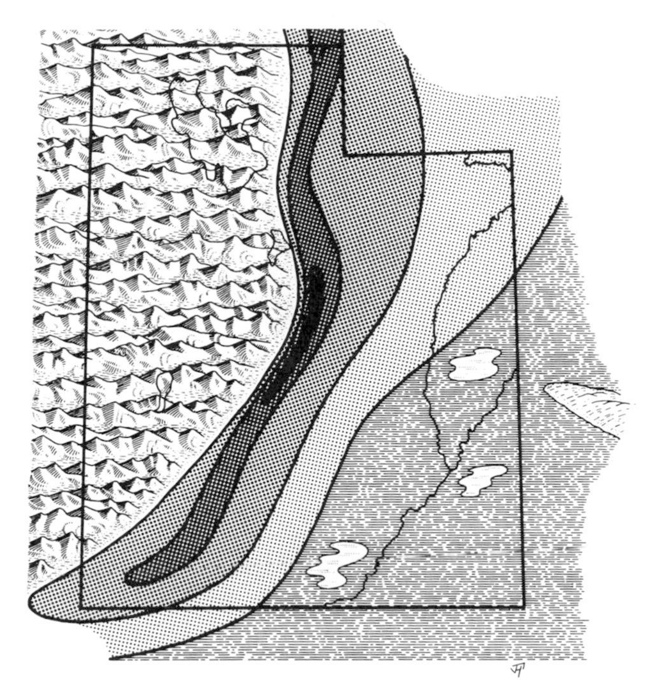

Figure 13-3b. Paleogeography of Utah and vicinity during Middle and early Late Jurassic time. Darkest pattern indicates thickest and probably most complete sedimentary accumulation. Successively lighter belts have correspondingly thinner and less complete sections. Horizontal cross-lined pattern indicates chiefly marginal marine mud flats. Note the eroded remnant of the Uncompahgre Uplift in western Colorado.

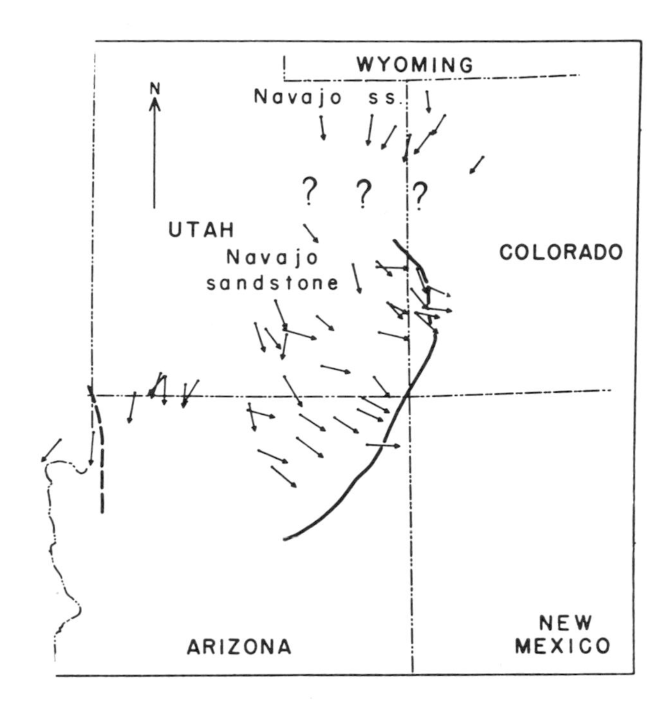

Figure 13-4. Wind directions in Utah during deposition of the Navajo and Nugget Sandstones as determined by studies of cross-bedding. Arrows fly with the wind. From Stewart, Pool and Wilson (1957).

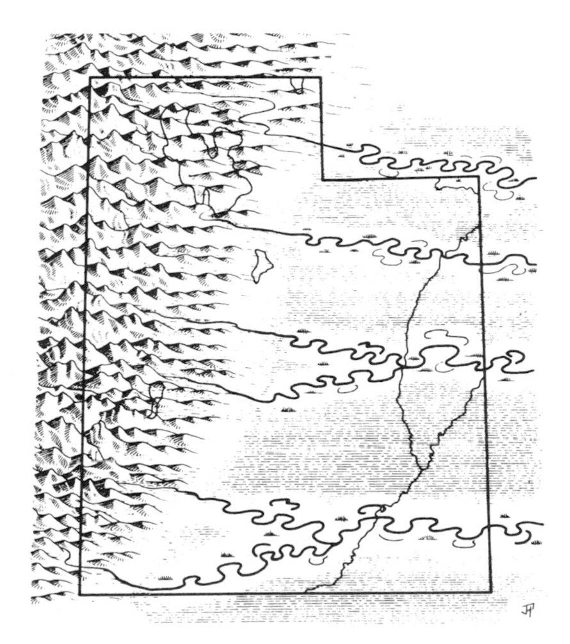

Figure 13-3c. Paleogeography of Utah during deposition of the upper part of the Morrison Formation. Rivers running from the Mesocordilleran Highlands to the east deposited fine-grained sediment over most of the western interior. At this time the remains of dinosaurs were buried here in large numbers.

The truth may lie between these two extremes. Water may have been involved in the deposition of certain restricted units. Perhaps one or several large rivers entered the dune field from the eastern uplands but were lost or literally soaked into the sand. Numerous parallel planes within the Navajo, Entrada, and other sandy formations could not have formed unless the underlying sand was saturated with water. There is virtually no evidence as to whether or not the water was salt or fresh, but there is no salt or gypsum either in beds or as single crystals, evidence which favors the fresh-water theory.

The unanswered question remains whether or not the sand body as a whole and the individual dunes within it were moved chiefly by wind or by water. Figure 13-7 shows a typical cross-bedded exposure. Most geologists vote for wind and refer to the Navajo Sandstone as a desert aeolian deposit. One definition of a desert is that it is essentially barren of life; the presence or absence of water is not the only criterion.

Any reconstruction of the second Jurassic environment must take into account extensive lateral transitions from marine to non-marine conditions (see fig. 13-3b). Shallow seas entered from Canada and spread over wide areas of Montana, Wyoming, and Utah. The Mesocordilleran High acted as a barrier in Nevada and southern Idaho. Insofar as Utah is concerned, the Colorado River marks the approximate eastern limit of actual marine waters although a band as wide as 100 miles exists between deposits with marine fossils and deposits of non-marine cross-bedded sand. The

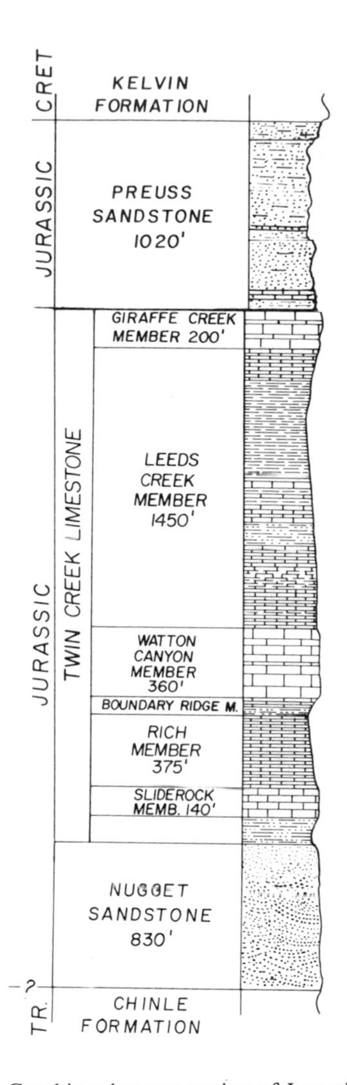

Figure 13-5a. Graphic columnar section of Jurassic formations in the Wasatch Range near Salt Lake City.

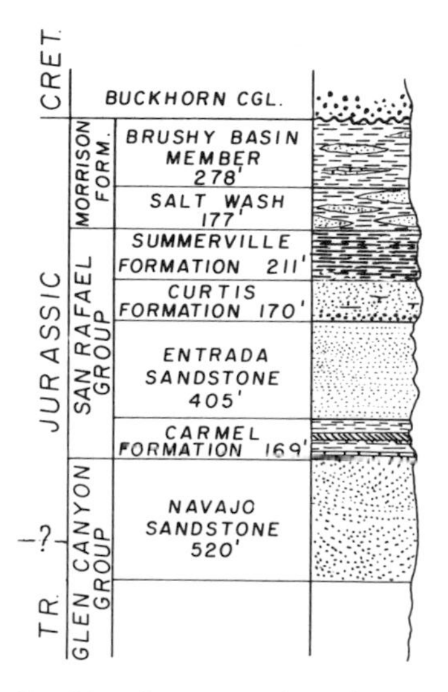

Figure 13-5b. Graphic columnar section of Jurassic formations of the northern San Rafael Swell.

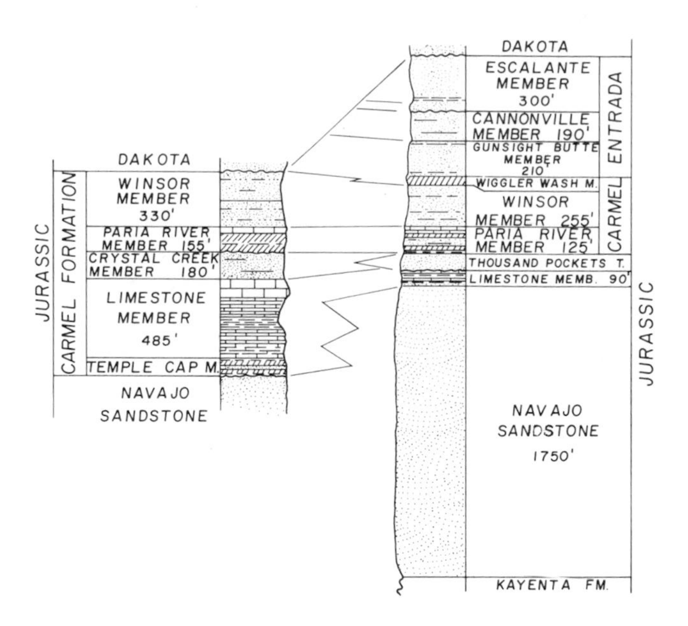

Figure 13-5c. Graphic columnar section of Jurassic rocks in south-central Utah. At left is the Cannonville area and to the right is the Zion Park area.

presence of abundant fossil organisms indicates water deep enough and permanent enough to support life, but from time to time the sea may have extended across flats many miles wide that were subject to frequent exposure to the air and dilution by fresh water, forming a marginal zone where life was not possible. Also compatible with this setting are dune fields built up by wind and later flooded and smoothed over by water.

The marine formations of central Utah contain unknown, but apparently large, amounts of salt and gypsum. The volume is uncertain because most deposits are now deeply buried under the Wasatch Plateau or have been intensely deformed by the mountain building episodes in the Sanpete-Sevier Valley area. Rocks rich in salt or gypsum usually accumulate in basins where the flow of sea water is restricted or periodically cut off. Climates with high evaporation rates naturally speed up the process of deposition.

Salt appears at the surface in several small areas near Redmond, Sevier County, and thicknesses of as much as 10,000 feet have been postulated to underlie the Sanpete-Wasatch transition area. Based on much detailed work by petroleum geologists, it is believed the salt was being deposited in a narrow down-faulted basin under the Sanpete-Sevier area while the gypsiferous Carmel Formation accumulated in the San Rafael Swell. No good explanation has been put forth as to why a fault-bounded trough should have formed in central Utah at this time.

The last environment of the Jurassic was dominated by river action (see fig. 13-3c). It is well represented by the Morrison Formation that once covered an estimated 750,000 square miles in the western United States. Two subdivisions are usually recognized, the Salt Wash Sand-

Figure 13-6. Jurassic rocks exposed on roadcut for Interstate 70, west flank San Rafael Swell. The light-colored, cross-bedded Navajo Sandstone is overlain by the darker, thin-bedded Carmel Formation. The contact representing a lengthly period of non-deposition and radical change in environments is exceptionally well exposed. Photo: Harry D. Goode.

Figure 13-7. Weathered surface of highly cross-bedded Navajo Sandstone, Escalante-Boulder Road, Garfield County. Photo: W. Forrest Johnson.

stone Member below and the Brushy Basin Shale Member above (figs. 13-8 and 13-9).

The Salt Wash Member is a major uranium producer in the Colorado Plateau and has been studied in great detail by hundreds of geologists who agree that it was produced by rivers spreading fanlike from an area near what is now the western Grand Canyon. In spite of intensive study, the sediments and environments of the Morrison Formation are not yet fully understood. This may be because few places on Earth today furnish comparable examples of large river systems spreading out and depositing sediment deep within a continent. The Salt Wash has the form of a huge delta but, inasmuch as it did not push forward into a sea or ocean, it has been referred to as a delta fan. Any one exposure shows cliff-forming lenses of sandstone alternating with mudstone slopes to produce a succession of low "rims." The sandstone bodies are the remnants of stream channels and the mudstone represents flood plain material.

The Brushy Basin Member is much more extensive than the Salt Wash and, although it too must have been built up by river action, it covers a much wider territory and has not been related to any specific river or river system. Figure 13-9 shows a typical outcrop. Apparently Brushy Basin streams carried much less sand than those of Salt Wash time and much more volcanic ash. Some ash fell directly on the Morrison plain and some came in by stream action. Shallow, temporary lakes left thin lenses of fresh-water limestone. The only known Jurassic rocks within the Great Basin are several small remnants of non-marine formations, including the Navajo sandstone, preserved under slices of overthrust Paleozoic rocks in the Wah Wah Mountains. More extensive outcrops in the transition zone of central Utah suggest great thicknesses of Jurassic rocks at depth.

Figure 13-8. Outcrop of Salt Wash Sandstone Member of Morrison Formation (Late Jurassic), Yellowcat Mining District, Grand County.

Figure 13-9. Typical exposure of the Brushy Basin Shale Member of the Morrison Formation, eastern flank of the Henry Mountains.

For instance, drill-hole data show that much of the Sanpete-Sevier Valley is underlain by several Jurassic formations.

In contrast to the limited outcrops in the western part of the state, those of the eastern part are very extensive. Insofar as surface exposure is concerned, the Navajo Sandstone is one of the most important formations in southeastern Utah. Exposures of the Navajo Sandstone exceed those of the slope-forming San Rafael Group and Morrison Formation combined.

Jurassic rocks underlie the entire Uinta Basin at depths of as much as 20,000 feet. Essentially the same formations that are seen in the San Rafael Swell also crop out along the northeast, southeast and southwest flanks of the Uinta Mountains. Jurassic formations are also found along the back slopes of the southern Wasatch Range in the drainage of Salt Creek and Diamond Fork and farther north in the canyon of the Weber River near Croyden, Morgan County. Striking exposures overlook Salt Lake City in the central Wasatch Range where they make up the front of the mountains from Red Butte Canyon to Parleys Canyon. As a rough estimate, possibly about half of the Jurassic sediment originally deposited in Utah is still preserved in its original form.

IGNEOUS CONTRIBUTIONS

Evidence for the first intrusive igneous activity within the confines of western Utah since the Precambrian consists of several igneous intrusions in western Utah: the Notch Peak intrusion in the House Range, dated at 148 million years (fig. 13-10); an unnamed intrusion in the Silver Island Mountains in Box Elder County, dated at 140 million years; an intrusion in the Gold Hill area dated at 152 million years; and the Newfoundland stock in the Newfoundland Mountains dated at 153 million years. These bodies are unusual in being located in an extensive sedimentary basin. There are no associated extrusive rocks although it is probable that they were once present and have been eroded away. Deposits of tungsten are associated with the Newfoundland stock and the Notch Peak intrusion. Small amounts of placer gold occur in the sand and gravel derived from the Notch Peak intrusion.

FOSSILS

Jurassic rocks in Utah range from almost barren to richly fossiliferous. In a general way, the older formations yield the fewest remains and the younger formations increasingly more (fig. 13-11). The Jurassic was a time of transition in the world of life. Old forms were dying out, new forms were spreading; dinosaurs and pterosaurs ruled, but birds and mammals were gaining. Even more significant were gradual alterations in the plant world. The Jurassic was an age of gymnosperms typified by cone-bearing trees and cycads. Angiosperms, dominant plants in the next period, were scarce.

The fossil record relates closely and directly to the succession of the depositional environments mentioned earlier. The first two-thirds of Jurassic time was apparently dominated by an arid, desert-like climate favorable only for the deposition of wind-blown sand and little else. As might be expected, under those conditions life was sparse, the only fossils of any consequence so far discovered in the Navajo-Nugget Sandstone are a few animal tracks, including: a lizard-like species; small, two-legged, stub-toed forms; yard-long, heavy-bodied, short-tailed species; fairly large dinosaurs and, most amazing of all, those of flying reptiles (pterosaurs). Tracks give little aid in resolving the age of the Navajo-Nugget, but bones and perhaps even complete skeletons may yet be discovered. Several fairly good dinosaur skeletons have been found in the Navajo Sandstone in northern Arizona.

The invasion of the sea in late Middle Jurassic time brought representative samples of contemporary marine life. Molluscs dominated; pelecypods and gastropods make up all but a small part of the total aggregation. Primitive oysters, scallop-like forms, and a variety of small bivalve species, many related to living shellfish, were abundant. Cephalopods are rare but significant for correlations with the rest of the Jurassic world. The best specimens come from Dinosaur National Monument in Uintah County.

It will be recalled that there were two marine invasions: the first produced the Carmel and Twin Creek Formations; the second left the Curtis and Stump Formations. Differences between the fossil assemblages of the two seaways are slight but the crinoid, *Pentacrinus*, with star-shaped plates is virtually confined to the earlier invasion while the "cigar-fossil", *Pachyteuthis densus*, is a guide to the later one. Fragments of bone belonging to ichthyosaurs and pieces of petrified wood are occasionally found in the Curtis Formation.

It is in the final deposit of the Jurassic, the Morrison Formation, that fossils reached their greatest variety and importance. The Morrison is said to be the most studied formation on Earth because of its unique fossils and uranium deposits. The formation is mostly fluvial and has not been traced into marine beds in any direction. The climate, in contrast to that of earlier Jurassic time, was obviously favorable for a great variety of life forms, including the largest known dinosaurs.

The plants and animals of the Morrison must have constituted a self-supporting system. Good examples of all the essential links in the ecological chain have been found as fossils. Abundant plant life included large trees such as the earliest known *Sequoia.* Lower forms of plant life, represented by the charophytes, thrived in shallow lakes and slow-flowing streams. Fresh-water molluscs (clams and snails) and ostracodes were locally abundant and there were even simple fresh-water sponges. The basic forms of life supported a great variety of vertebrates including fish, amphibians, reptiles, birds, and mammals. Of these, only fish and reptiles have been found in Utah although mammals have been collected from the Morrison Formation at nearby localities in Wyoming and Colorado.

The Morrison Formation is unsurpassed for its abundance of dinosaur remains. Two great quarries have contributed near-perfect skeletons for study and display. The first quarry, at Dinosaur National Monument, ranks as one of the great scientific and tourist attractions in the United States. It lies athwart the Utah-Colorado state line and covers more than 300 square miles of diverse formations and topography; the actual fossil quarry is not more than an acre in extent.

The great graveyard of bones uncovered at the quarry is a death assemblage accumulated by a powerful stream and left stranded as a sand-bar deposit. Subsequent to deposition and lithification the area was uplifted as part of the Uinta Mountains. This occurred about 55 million years ago, during the Paleocene Epoch. Since then erosion has eaten the Uintas to the core and great canyons have been carved by the Green and Yampa Rivers. By what can be termed a geologic accident, erosion reached the bone deposit just at the right time for it to be discovered by modern man.

Figure 13-10. Near view of the Notch Peak intrusion, House Range, Millard County. A thin offshoot of granitic rock, originating from a larger mass above is seen penetrating into thin-bedded sediments of Cambrian age below. The intrusion has been dated as Late Jurassic in age. Photo: Peter Varney.

Fossil bones had been noted in the area by early settlers and probably even earlier by native Americans. O. A. Peterson first identified them as pertaining to dinosaurs in 1893. Bones in place at the actual site of the future quarry were discovered by Earl Douglass in 1909 and, with money supplied by Andrew Carnegie through the Carnegie Museum of Pittsburgh, Pennsylvania, excavation began (fig. 13-12). Success was immediate and impressive; a veritable Noah's Ark of dinosaurs was unearthed. During the next 13 years, 350 tons of bones and protective matrix were shipped to the Carnegie Museum in Pittsburgh. Of an estimated 300 individual dinosaurs excavated, 24 were complete enough for mounting and exhibition.

The Carnegie Museum had all the specimens they wanted by 1922. There had been considerable apprehension among Utah citizens that all their dinosaurs would be lost to other areas. Under the direction of Dr. F.J. Pack, the University of Utah obtained funds to work at the quarry and procured a number of excellent specimens during 1923 and 1924 (figs. 13-13a, 13-13b, 13-13c, and 13-13d). One outstanding specimen was an almost complete *Allosaurus* which, when mounted, became the centerpiece of the old Department of Geology Museum at the University and the only dinosaur skeleton on exhibit between Denver and the Pacific Coast. The quarry yielded other specimens to the Museum of Natural History in New York City, New York, and the U.S. National Museum in Washington, D.C., and even then the limits of the bone bed had not been reached.

With the cessation of work at the site, the dangers of vandalism and natural disintegration were acute. Under the provisions of the Antiquities Act, the dinosaur quarry site and 80 acres of surrounding land were declared a National Monument on October 4, 1915. Soon it became a unit of the National Park Service, but full development of the site was slow in coming. Not until 1953 was work finally undertaken to expose enough of the remaining quarry face for an *in situ* exhibit suitable for public viewing and instruction (fig. 13-14). The bone deposit fortunately continued beyond the old working site and, in 1958, a Visitor Center, the first of its kind, was opened to the public. In it one can view many exhibits including the remains of large and small dinosaurs partly freed from the rocky matrix. As of 1980, the quarry had yielded 12 genera of dinosaurs, two genera of crocodiles, two genera of turtles, one rhynchocephalian genus, one frog genus, and one mollusc genus.

The story of Utah's second great bonebed, at the Cleveland-Lloyd Quarry in Emery County, is similar. It has also yielded a great number and variety of dinosaur bones and is developed as a tourist attraction in a minor way. It was designated as a National Landmark in 1967 and a small Visitor Center has been erected. Bones *in situ* are exposed for public viewing. No one knows the true discoverer of the

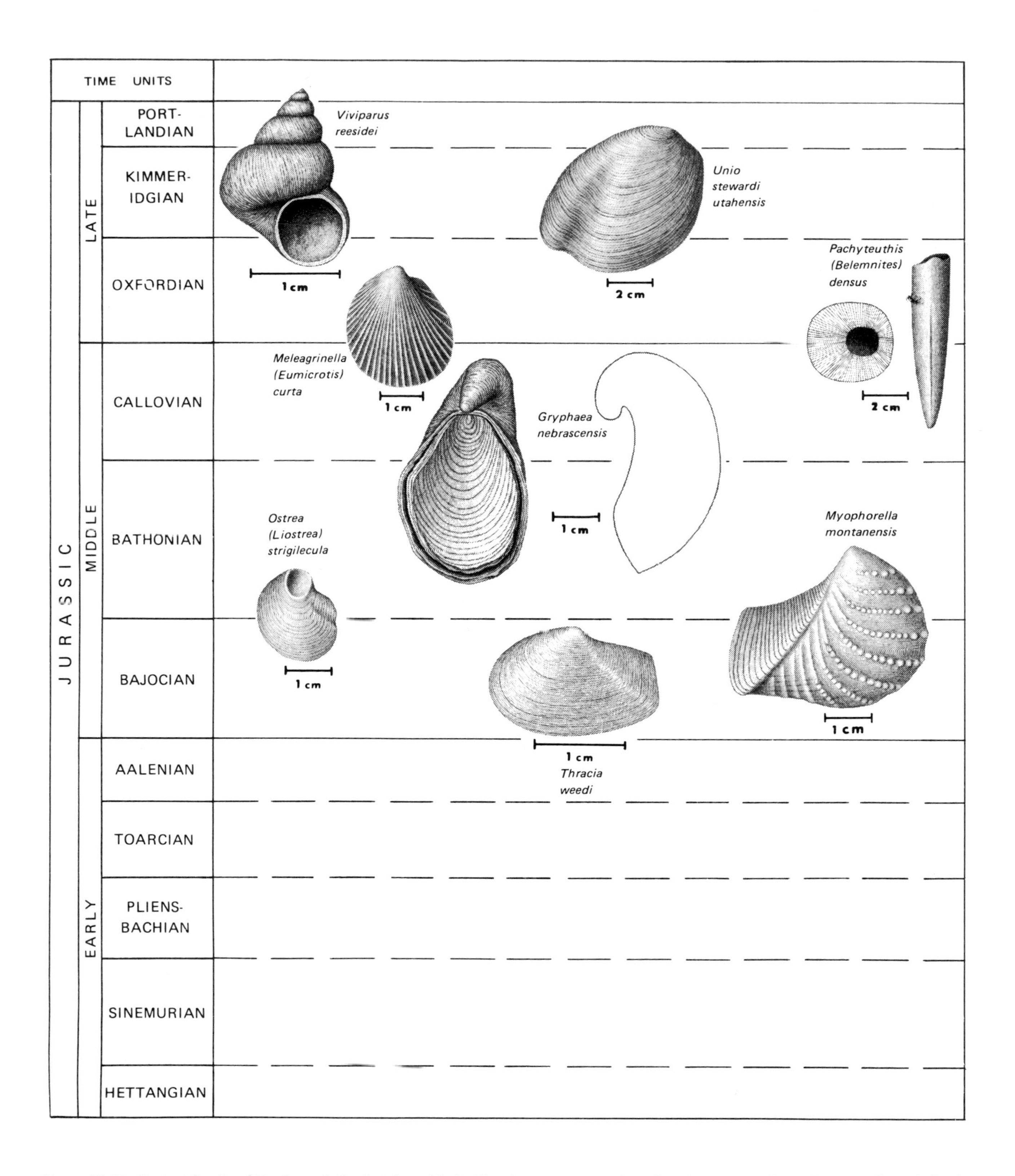

Figure 13-11. Typical fossils of the Jurassic Period from Utah. Sketches are arranged so that the center of any given specimen is in the zone of which it is typical. No fossils of value in correlation have yet been identified in the Early Jurassic non-marine sandstones. Sketches: John B. Balsley.

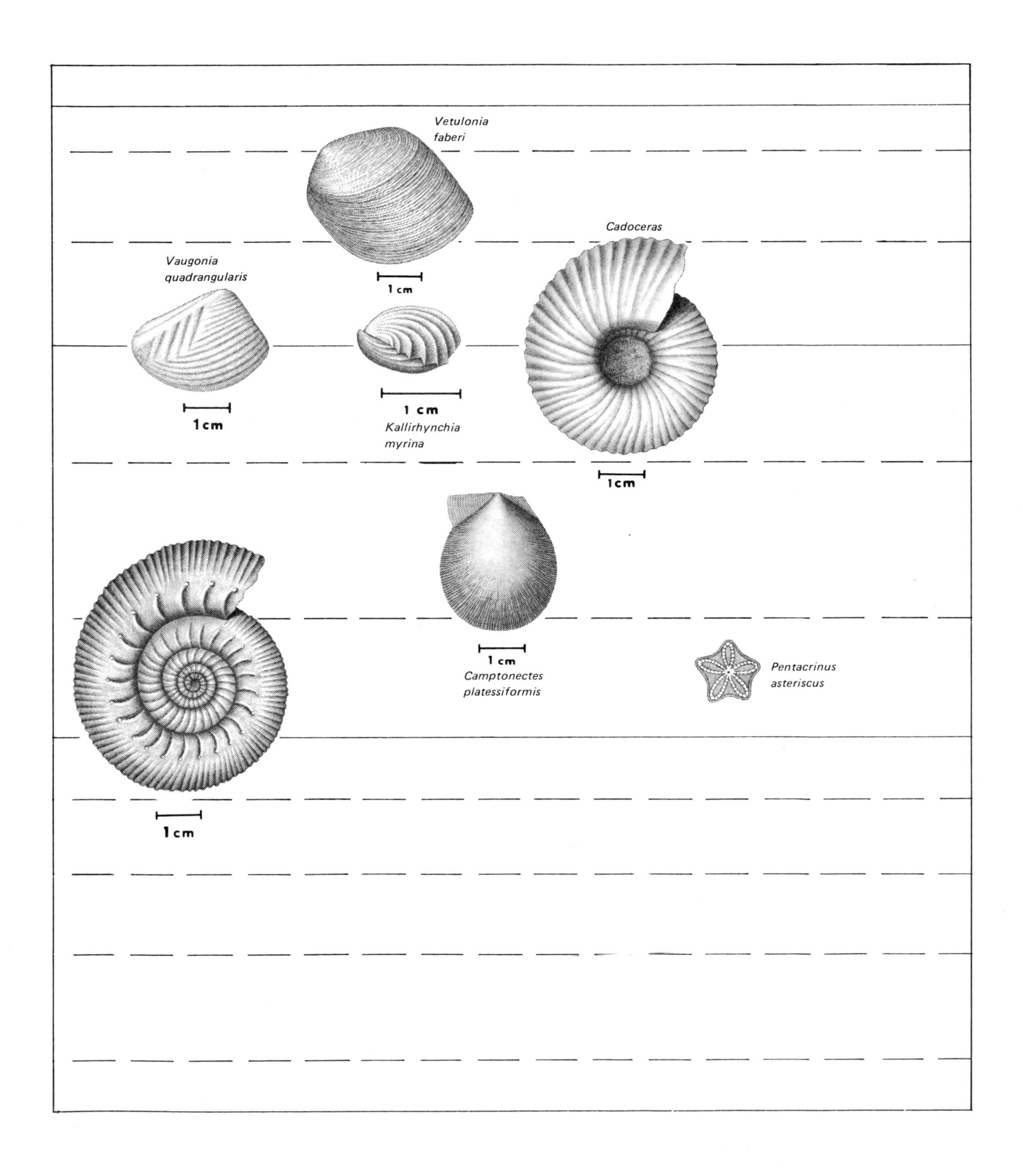

Figure 13-11. Continued.

Figure 13-12. An early stage in the development of the quarry at what is now Dinosaur National Monument. The bone-bearing sandstone forms the ragged ledge on the right. Specimens obtained from the sandstone are being transported down a steep trail in large crates as the first stage to a destination at the Carnegie Museum, Pittsburgh. The Lower Cretaceous Cedar Mountain Formation forms the ridge at the left, the quarry is in the upper Jurassic Morrison Formation.

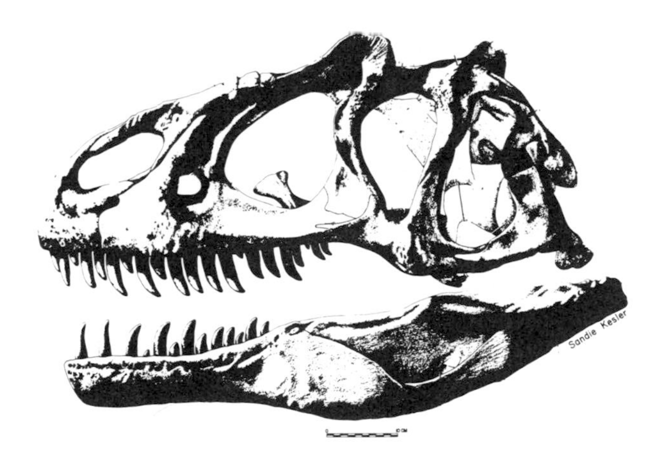

Figure 13-13a. Reconstructed skull of the common Jurassic carnivorous dinosaur *Allosaurus*. Length about 24 inches. Sketch: Sandi Kesler under the direction of James H. Madsen, Jr..

Figure 13-13b. Skeleton of *Allosaurus* from the Cleveland-Lloyd quarry, as mounted from display, Milano, Italy. Photo: James H. Madsen, Jr.

Figure 13-13c. Skeleton of juvenile *Camarosaurus* from the Dinosaur National Monument as mounted in partial relief, Carnegie Museum, Pittsburg, Pennsylvania. The specimen is unusually complete and is considered to be one of the most significant sauropods in existence. The skeleton is mounted in the pose in which it was found. Length about 15 feet. Photo: Carnegie Museum of Natural History.

Cleveland-Lloyd deposit but parties from the University of Utah made preliminary excavations in the early 1930s and removed several hundred bones. The quarry was again opened up and worked by parties from Princeton University from 1937 to 1939 under the direction of William Lee Stokes, a resident of nearby Cleveland, Utah, and a graduate student at Princeton. There was a lull in activity until 1960 when Stokes, then on the University of Utah's geology department staff, reopened the diggings with funds from the University's Cooperative Dinosaur Project, a self-supporting program by which any museum or college desiring a specimen contributed cash and received in return a mountable specimen, usually a composite of actual bones with whatever reproductions might be needed to make a complete skeleton.

The name, Cleveland-Lloyd, is a combination of the name of the nearby town of Cleveland and the surname of Malcolm Lloyd, Jr., a Philadelphia, Pennsylvania, lawyer who generously funded the early work by Princeton University. This quarry has furnished material for more mountable skeletons than any other deposit. Local prepara-

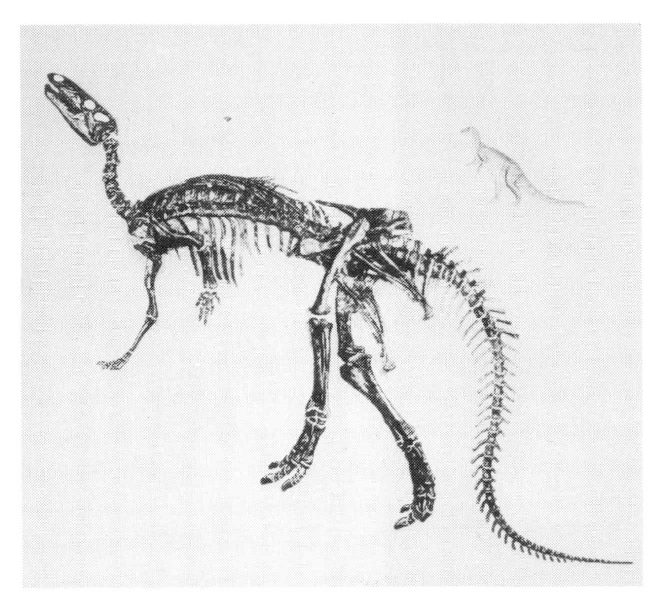

Figure 13-13d. Skeleton of the herbivorous, ornithopod dinosaur *Camptosaurus* also from the Dinosaur National Monument. Length about 10 feet. Photo: Carnegie Museum of Natural History.

Figure 13-14. View of dinosaur bones exposed in their places of burial on the quarry face at Dinosaur National Monument. The matrix, which is very hard sandstone, has been chipped away. The large femur bone in the foreground is about 5 feet long. A section of tail is seen lower left and a neck upper left. Photo: U.S. National Park Service.

tors, James H. Madsen, Jr. of the University of Utah and James Jensen of Brigham Young University, have put together many of the skeletons. As a result of this work, *Allosaurus* has become probably the best known of all carnivorous dinosaurs.

Interesting comparisons and contrasts are evident now that these two great quarries have been extensively worked. Both are in the Morrison Formation in strata deposited on an extensive, level, interior plain about 140 to 150 million years ago. The Morrison is made up of two types of deposits, elongate bodies of sand representing filled river channels, and extensive layers of clay and mud representing flood plains between the rivers. The Dinosaur National Monument bone bed is a river-channel or sand-bar death assemblage. The specimens are encased in coarse sand along with fresh-water clams, tree-trunks and small reptiles such as turtles. Evidence of strong current action is present everywhere and, as a rule, only the larger bones and skeletons remain. Smaller specimens, particularly skull fragments, are rare. The matrix has become very hard, almost like concrete and the bones can be freed only by careful, forceful application of hammer and chisel.

In contrast, the Cleveland-Lloyd deposit is of flood plain origin. The matrix is clay, once mud, and ice-picks and knife blades are sufficient for excavation. There are no signs of rigorous current action and even the smallest bones are preserved (fig. 13-15). The theory that this was an ancient bog, fed by ground water, seems to explain the observed content and preservation of the bones. Fresh-water algae, called charophytes, and turtles were entombed with the dinosaurs.

Figure 13-15. Dinosaur bones as they appear in process of excavation, Cleveland-Lloyd quarry, Emery County. Photo: Allan Staker.

The two quarries seem to have trapped different types of dinosaurs representative of the different environments (see table 13-1). Dinosaur Monument is dominated by the large, long-necked, four-legged, plant-eating sauropods plus stegosaurs and camptosaurs. Carnivores are rare. At the Cleveland-Lloyd quarry carnivores outnumber herbivores 10 to 1. At least 50 allosaurs of different sizes are represented but there are few herbivorous stegosaurs, camptosaurs, and sauropods. The assemblage of fossils at the La Brea Tar Pits near Los Angeles, though millions of years younger in age, is similar in representing an entire ecological chain for a given time period. The La Brea deposits are Pleistocene in age and the top carnivore, the most common fossil found there, is represented by *Smilodon*, a huge saber-toothed cat.

Table 13-1. Different types of dinosaurs representative of different types of environments of the two quarries.

Genus	Author, year	Suborder	Age	Formation	Utah Occurrence
Allosaurus	Marsh, 1877	Theropod	L. Jur.	Mor.	C-LDQ, DNM
Barosaurus	Marsh, 1890	Sauropod	L. Jur.	Mor.	C-LDQ(?),DNM
Brachiosaurus	Riggs, 1903	Sauropod	L. Jur.	Mor.	DNM
Brontosaurus(s)	Marsh, 1879	Sauropod	L. Jur.	Mor.	DNM
Camarasaurus	Cope, 1877	Sauropod	L. Jur.	Mor.	C-LDQ,DNM
Camptosaurus	Marsh, 1885	Ornithopod	L. Jur.	Mor.	C-LDQ,DNM
Ceratosaurus	Marsh, 1884	Theropod	L. Jur.	Mor.	C-LDQ,DNM
Coelurus(?)	Marsh, 1879	Theropod	L. Jur.	Mor.	DNM
Diplodocus	Marsh, 1878	Sauropod	L. Jur.	Mor.	DNM
Dryosaurus	Marsh, 1894	Ornithopod	L. Jur.	Mor.	DNM
Dystrophaeus(?)	Cope, 1877	Sauropod	L. Jur.	Mor.	Misc.
Hoplitosaurus(?)	Lucas, 1902	Ankylosaurid	L. Cret.	Cdr. Mtn.	Misc.
Hypsilophodon	Huxley, 1870	Ornithopod	L. Jur.	Mor.	Misc.
Iguanodon	Mantell, 1825	Ornithopod	L. Cret.	Cdr. Mtn.	Misc.
Iliosuchus(?)	Huene, 1932	Theropod	L. Jur.	Mor.	C-LDQ(?)
Laosaurus(?)	Marsh, 1878	Ornithopod	L. Jur.	Mor.	DNM
Marshosaurus	Madsen, 1976	Theropod	L. Jur.	Mor.	C-LDQ
Nanosaurus	Marsh, 1877	Ornithopod	L. Jur.	Mor.	DNM
Ornitholestes(?)	Osborn, 1903	Theropod	L. Jur.	Mor.	C-LDQ(?)
Pleurocoelus(?)	Marsh, 1888	Sauropod	L. Jur.	Mor.	DNM
Stegosaurus	Marsh, 1877	Stegosaurid	L. Jur.	Mor.	C-LDQ,DNM
Stokesosaurus	Madsen, 1974	Theropod	L. Jur.	Mor.	C-LDQ
Triceratops	Marsh, 1889	Ceratopsid	L. Cret.	No. Horn	No. Horn Mtn.
Uintasaurus(s)	Holland, 1924	Sauropod	L. Jur.	Mor.	DNM

This list does not include taxa named on the basis of footprints
C-LDQ = Cleveland-Lloyd Dinosaur Quarry; DNM = Dinosaur National Monument

SCENERY

One formation stands out as the greatest scene-maker of the western United States, the Navajo Sandstone. To list the scenic spots where the Navajo forms the chief attraction is to name many of the important parks and monuments of the southwest: Zion National Park (fig. 13-16a), Canyonlands National Park, Capitol Reef National Park, Rainbow Bridge National Monument (fig. 13-16b), and Lake Powell National Recreation Area. In the system of Utah State Parks, Dixie and Dead Horse Point also display the light-colored white or pink Navajo Sandstone.

This star attraction of geologic formations is usually accompanied by a strong supporting cast of the Triassic Kayenta and Wingate Sandstones. Together they comprise the Glen Canyon Group. When conditions are right, they may join in a solid vertical cliff 2,000 feet or more high. When appearing separately the Navajo tends to form rounded hummocks, domes, or "beehives," clustered or scattered like gigantic Navajo hogans over the landscape. The Kayenta is a bench former, somewhat more resistant to erosion than the other two. It remains as the bedrock surface across wide areas after the Navajo has been stripped away. It also protects the prominant underlying Wingate cliff, especially in the more eastern exposures where the Navajo is thin and less prominent.

What is it about these formations that makes them so fascinating to the viewer? It must be that they represent the rare and unusual in nature. Bare rock is less common than covered rock, smooth rocks rarer than rough rocks and light-colored rocks rarer than dark-colored ones. Both the Navajo and Wingate are relatively homogeneous and weather to uniform surfaces and forms. The Navajo gives rise to smooth, unbroken cliffs and also to more or less isolated remnants such as the Great White Throne in Zion National Park, one of the world's best known monoliths (fig. 13-17).

Figure 13-16a. Narrows of the North Fork of the Virgin River. Vertical walls are in the Navajo Sandstone. Photo: U.S. National Park Service.

Figure 13-16b. Rainbow Natural Bridge formed in the Navajo Sandstone. Figures on top of arch give scale. Photo taken before water from Lake Powell entered the gorge in left foreground. Photo: U.S. National Park Service.

Figure 13-17. Great White Throne monolith cut entirely in Navajo Sandstone. Photo: Hal Rumel.

Higher in the stratigraphic section and younger in geologic time is another scene-maker, the Entrada Sandstone (fig. 13-18). This unit forms the chief attractions in Arches National Park (fig. 13-19) and in Goblin Valley State Park (fig. 13-20). Much of what has been said of the attractiveness of the Navajo could be repeated about the Entrada. It too is homogeneous, light colored, and smooth weathering, especially in Arches National Park. The Entrada changes appearance and composition across eastern Utah, passing from a soft, predominantly silty condition in Emery County (see fig. 13-20) to a harder, predominantly sandy phase in Grand County (see fig. 13-19). This change is a good example of what geologists call a "facies change" within a formation.

Two other scenic attractions in Jurassic rocks were discussed earlier in the section on fossils: the Dinosaur National Monument and the Cleveland-Lloyd Dinosaur Quarry.

ECONOMIC

Jurassic rocks contain many valuable metallic and nonmetallic commodities. The important deposits of iron ore mined near Cedar City (fig. 13-21) that give Iron County its name are chiefly replacements of limestone beds in the Homestake Limestone Member of the Carmel Formation. Iron is thought to have entered the host rocks in hot solutions and vapors from middle Tertiary igneous rocks. The Iron Springs district was intensively mined between 1924 and 1982 to supply blast furnaces at Ironton (now abandoned) and U.S. Steel's Geneva Mill near Provo, Utah County.

Figure 13-18. Fluted stationary cliffs of Entrada Sandstone capped by small remnants of Curtis Formation, northwest Wayne County. Photo: Utah State Historical Society.

Figure 13-20. Goblin Valley, nodular weathering Entrada Sandstone, Emery County. Photo: Utah Tourist and Publicity Council.

Figure 13-19. Delicate Arch, Arches National Park, in its setting among other erosional features. All are carved from the sandy phase of the Jurassic Entrada Sandstone. Photo: Ward Roylance.

Figure 13-21. Operations at the Comstock mine, Iron Mountain, Iron County. The ore minerals have replaced large masses of the Jurassic Homestake Member of the Carmel Formation. Photo: Kenneth C. Bullock.

Other metallic elements produced from Jurassic rocks are copper, vanadium and uranium. Although ores of these metals were also introduced after the host rocks were in place, they are not considered to be of hydrothermal origin. Rather, they are classed as low-temperature (roughly less than 100°C; 212°F) deposits or as deposits of lateral secretion. This last term means that the elements making up the ore did not come from below or at depth, but from the surrounding sediments, those lateral to the final ore bodies. They are also referred to as sandstone uranium deposits from the host rocks with which they are associated.

It became known rather early that ores of uranium, radium, vanadium, and copper are closely associated in sediments of the Colorado Plateau. No less than 80 different formations are known to carry one or more of these elements in excess of normal concentrations. Historically, the ores were first mined in the 1880s for radium when it was much needed for research. During World War II the same ore was mined for vanadium which was in short supply. Lastly, with the dawn of the atomic age and the need for raw material for nuclear arms and reactors, interest shifted to uranium. The copper content is seldom high enough for separate mining but it is a valuable by-product that some mills can recover.

Many hundreds of vanadium-uranium ore deposits are known in the Salt Wash Sandstone Member of the Morrison Formation (fig. 13-22). They range from a few hundred pounds to huge ore bodies containing thousands of tons. Deposits have been mined in Garfield, San Juan, Emery, and Grand Counties. A few minor deposits are known in the Brushy Basin Member in Emery County and in the Wingate Sandstone (Triassic) of Castle Valley, Grand County.

Figure 13-22. Small uranium-vanadium mine in Salt Wash Member of the Morrison Formation, Cottonwood Creek, San Juan County.

Jurassic rocks contain a variety of construction minerals, chiefly cement rock, gypsum, and building stone. Certain parts of the Twin Creek Limestone have natural proportions of calcium carbonate ($CaCO_3$) and clay that are well suited for cement making. Raw material for Portland cement is mined from this unit in Parleys Canyon a few miles east of Salt Lake City and at Croyden on the Weber River, Morgan County. Gypsum, raw material for plaster board (drywall), is mined from the Arapien Shale and processed at Sigurd, Sevier County (fig. 13-23). Salt has been mined intermittently from quarries in the Arapien Shale near Redmond, Sevier County. Other Jurassic salt deposits are known but not exploited. The Nugget Sandstone has been a popular building material for more than a century and large quarries were opened in Red Butte Canyon near Salt Lake City as early as 1851. Active quarries are operating near Heber City and Peoa, Summit County. Reserves of all these materials are, for practical purposes, unlimited, and other quarries will be opened from time to time.

Jurassic formations have recently become important oil producers and potential targets for additional drilling in the Overthrust Belt of northeastern Utah. In 1975 oil was discovered in both the Nugget Sandstone and the Twin Creek Limestone in Summit County at depths of from 9,205 to 9,680 feet. The name "Pineview" has been applied to this field which currently is in an intensive stage of development.

Figure 13-23. Hills of soft, light-colored Arapien Shale (Jurassic), near Sigurd, Sevier County. Salt occurs in large quantities in this formation.

For additional reading about the topics discussed in Chapter 13, see the following list of authors:

Armstrong and Suppe, 1973
Baker, 1947
Baker and others, 1936
Bullock, 1973
Coffin, 1954
Cohenour, 1967a, 1967b
Conner and Colvin, 1977
Craig and others, 1955
Crawford and Tuttle, 1964
Dowler and Dowler, 1977
Eardley, 1944
Eardley and Schaack, 1971
Finch, 1960, 1967
Fischer, 1942, 1944, 1950, 1959
Fischer and Hilpert, 1952
Fischer and Vine, 1969
Freeman and Visher, 1975
Gehman, 1958
Gilliland, 1963
Goode and others, 1961
Granger, 1953
Granger and Sharp, 1952
Gregory, 1940, 1950b (1952)
Gregory and Anderson, 1939
Hagood, 1967
Hansen, W.R., 1964, 1969a, 1969c, 1976
Harshberger and others, 1957
Hite, R.J., 1964
Imlay, 1949, 1957, 1964, 1967

Johnson, H.S., 1957
Johnson, K.D., 1959
Lohman, 1974, 1975
Lupton, 1913
McKee, 1956
McKee and others, 1956
Mackin, 1947
Madsen, 1974, 1976a, 1976b
Maher, 1976
Marzolf, 1970
Miller, G.M., 1966
Morris, 1964
Moulton, 1976
Mullens and Freeman, 1957
Newberry, 1876
Otto, 1973
Peck, 1957
Petersen, D.W., 1976
Peterson, J.A., 1954, 1957
Phoenix, 1963
Poole, 1962
Pratt and Callaghan, 1970
Pratt and others, 1966
Schick, 1955
Smith, J.F., and others, 1963
Sohl, 1965
Spieker, 1949
Stacey and Zartman, 1978
Stokes, 1944, 1945, 1958, 1960, 1961, 1967, 1968, 1978
Stokes and Madsen, 1967
Stone and Lupton, 1920
Tanner, 1969
Thompson and Stokes, 1970
Tidwell, 1975
Untermann and Untermann, 1954, 1969
Utah Geological and Mineral Survey, 1966
Visher, 1971
Visher and Freeman, 1977
Waters and Granger, 1953
White, T.E., 1964, 1968
Withington, 1964
Wright and Dickey, 1963
Wright and others, 1962
Yen, 1952

For complete bibliographic citations, please see List of References.

Figure 13-24. The White Cliffs, mainly Navajo Sandstone, east of Kanab. Photo: Herbert E. Gregory.

14 THE CRETACEOUS PERIOD

The Cretaceous Period began about 144 million years ago and lasted an estimated 78 million years, making it one of the longer geologic periods. In 1882 geologist J. J. d'Omalius d'Halloy named the Cretaceous after *creta*, the Latin word for chalk. The type section is the famous White Cliffs of Dover, England.

Cretaceous rocks are abundant on all the great land masses and are also found in deep sea deposits and on a few oceanic islands. Many maps would have to be drawn to trace the stages of development of western North America during Cretaceous time. Figure 14-1 is a simplified map representing the time of greatest marine flooding. Most of Utah's Cretaceous rocks were deposited in the last half of the period. The amount of material deposited during this interval may have been greater than that of any equivalent time interval. Outcrops are extensive and about 100 Cretaceous formations are found partly or entirely in the state (see fig. 14-2). The more significant formations are listed with brief explanatory notations at the end of the book.

PALEOGEOGRAPHY

In terms of actual time, the Early Cretaceous is longer than one-half of the entire period. In Utah it is represented by a relatively small volume of rock. Lower Cretaceous strata resemble those of the upper part of the preceding Morrison Formation. As a matter of fact, Lower Cretaceous formations are so much like the Morrison Formation in physical appearance that they are frequently mapped together. Mild erosion seems to have prevailed over eastern Utah for an interval of perhaps 10 million years during the latest Jurassic and earliest Cretaceous and that part of the rock record appears to be absent. Subsequently, the Lower Cretaceous Cedar Mountain and Burro Canyon Formations were spread out east of the Mesocordilleran High on broad flood plains laced by channels of sand and gravel and inhabited by a variety of plant and animal species. The topography was so flat and nicely adjusted to the river systems flowing across it that deposition and erosions were at a minimum. The widespread Buckhorn Conglomerate and the irregular surface below may represent this state of near-equilibrium (fig. 14-3a). Fossils suitable for precise dating of the lowermost units have not yet been found but fossiliferous deposits of corresponding age are found in eastern New Mexico, Oklahoma, and throughout much of west Texas where marine beds demonstrate the extent of the ocean during Early Cretaceous time. The non-marine beds of the Rocky Mountains can be traced into that area in a fairly satisfactory way.

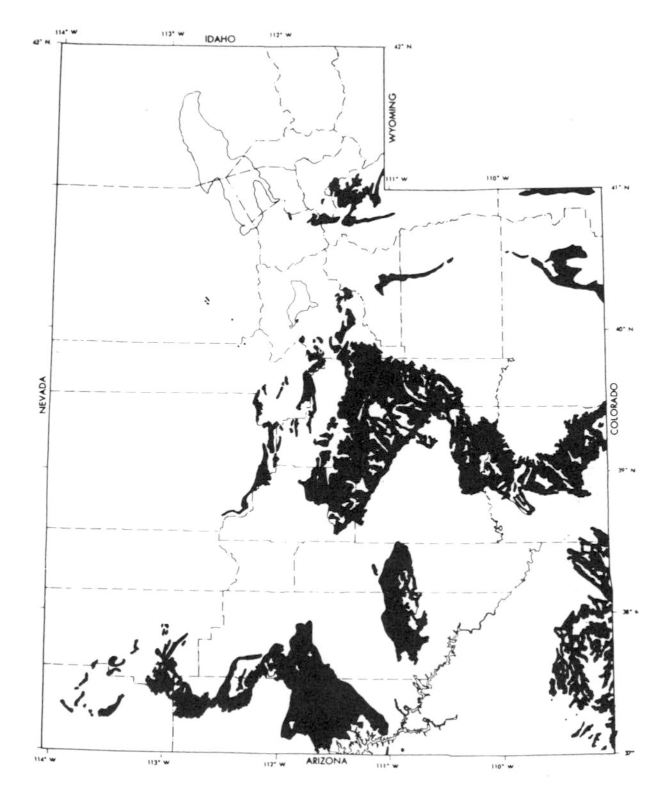

Figure 14-1. Outcrops of Cretaceous rocks in Utah.

The second distinct phase of Cretaceous history includes one of the great marine floods of all time. Seas spread inward from north and south to divide North America into two large islands. By then the Ancestral Rockies were

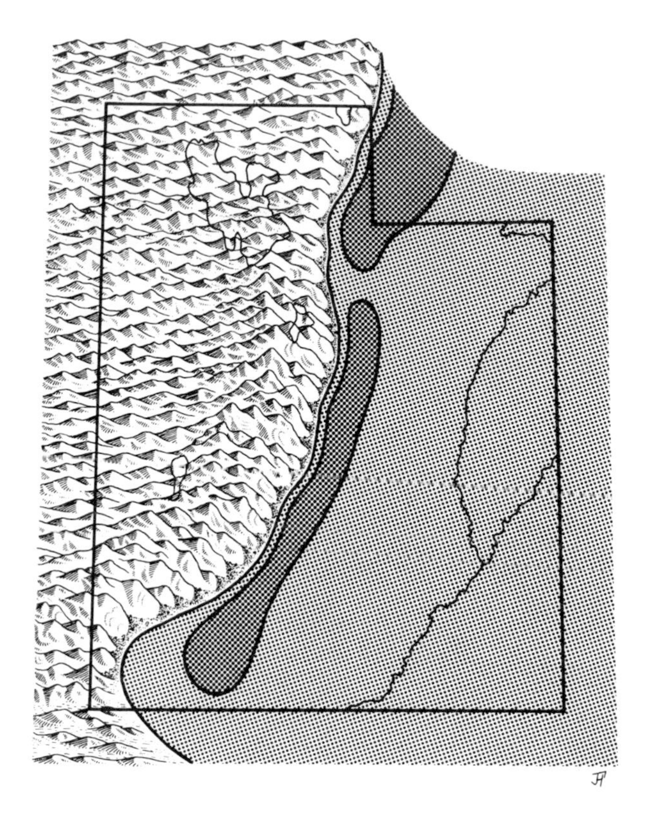

Figure 14-2. Generalized paleogeography of Late Cretaceous time in Utah. Darker pattern represents areas of thicker sediments in the transition belt between the Mesocordilleran Highland to the west and the interior of the continent to the east.

eroded and buried, allowing the sea to flood into Utah chiefly from the east. The westward shoreline followed the foothills of the Mesocordilleran High which was destined to become higher and wider as one of the great mountain ranges of North America. A cause and effect mechanism seems to have operated: As the region east of the Wasatch Line sank, that to the west rose. Both subsidence and uplift were extreme, a condition that produced great quantities of sediment, rapid transport by energetic streams, and voluminous deposition in the basins. The spectacular upward rise of the region that had once been the Cordilleran geosyncline and that would eventually become the Great Basin occurred between about 100 and 80 million years ago. This episode has been called the Sevier Orogeny, named after the Sevier Desert area where ancient mountains seem to have reached their greatest heights.

Near the close of the Cretaceous Period, the oceans withdrew from the continental interior. Both local and worldwide geologic influences seem to have been operating. Local influences are indicated by the belt of deltas and nearshore deposits that migrated progressively eastward with time so that earlier marine deposits are overlain by nonmarine varieties. Global influences are indicated by the fact that interior seas withdrew from all of the great continents about the same time. A reconstruction showing eastern Utah occupied by shifting river systems, swamps and alluvial plains at the end of the Cretaceous cannot be far wrong.

ORIGIN AND NATURE OF CRETACEOUS ROCKS

Lower Cretaceous sediments are of non-marine origin but geologists differ in their interpretations of specific environments. The physical appearance over practically all of the western interior is surprisingly uniform, suggesting a lack of varied climatic influences. The formations are mostly faintly colored in purple or lavender tones and contain many irregular calcareous cobble- and pebble-sized nodules (fig. 14-3b). Such features suggest soils of a semiarid climate in which calcareous material was carried by ground water and deposited beneath the surface like modern caliche or "hardpan." A minor mystery that has been discussed endlessly by professionals and amateurs is

Figure 14-3a. Lower Cretaceous non-marine formation, the Buckhorn Conglomerate at the type locality near the Buckhorn Reservoir, Emery County. It is composed chiefly of chert pebbles derived from the west and appears in patches at the base of the Cedar Mountain Formation.

Figure 14-3b. The Cedar Mountain Formation near the San Rafael River, southwest of Green River, Emery County, is another Lower Cretaceous non-marine formation. Abundant limy nodules, characteristic of the formation are weathering out on the surface.

the meaning of the so-called "stomach stones" or gastroliths found scattered in random fashion in all types of matrix including shale, sandstone, limestone, and conglomerate (fig. 14-4).

Early Cretaceous formations were deposited in interior environments hundreds of miles from the ocean. The great mass of marine Cretaceous rock in Utah is a soft, drab, gray siltstone known as the Mancos Shale (named after Mancos, Colorado; figs. 14-5 and 14-6). It averages considerably more than a mile in thickness and extends far beyond Utah into the interior of North America. The wide valleys that are significant portions of Emery, Grand, and Carbon Counties are carved from it (see physiographic and geologic maps).

The greatest problem presented by Cretaceous marine sediments is their place of origin. The questions to be answered can be stated more specifically: From which direction did the sediments come, from what land or lands, and from what type of rocks were they eroded? We know some of the answers and, strange as it seems, it is the answers that make the problem more difficult. The direction of sediment transport is not in doubt; it was from west to east. Primary structures such as cross bedding and channeling, exposed in thousands of outcrops, indicate eastward transport. Just as diagnostic is the transition in sediment size from coarse conglomerate in the west to fine silt and clay in the east. Only one conclusion seems possible: the Late Cretaceous seaways were filled with sediments from a large, island-like region that remained above sea level when North America was divided by the great flooding of Late Cretaceous time. When the outlines of this highland are drawn, and the volume of sediment derived from it is calculated, the problem becomes clear; the land mass was entirely too small and narrow to have produced the surrounding sedimentary blanket. It has been estimated that the total Late Cretaceous sediment is equal to a block 100 miles wide and 25,000 feet high along the site of the Rocky Mountains. The estimate that 1 million cubic miles of sediment must have been derived from an area of only 160,000 square miles emphasizes the problem in a different way.

Figure 14-4. Selected "gastroliths" from the Lower Cretaceous Cedar Mountain Formation. Evidence that pebbles such as these were rounded and polished in dinosaur stomachs is accepted as valid by many geologists. Note the single specimen embedded in limestone. It is difficult to explain such isolated occurrences except by the theory that the stones were carried and dropped by animals. Photo: Jim Howell.

Figure 14-5. Cretaceous formations in and near the Blue Gate, near Cainville, Wayne County, Fremont River, middle lowland. This is the type locality for the Blue Gate Shale. Photo: U.S. National Park Service.

Another aspect of the problem has to do with the nature of the source rocks. The partial answer only seems to raise more questions. The composition of the Cretaceous Mesocordilleran High can be reconstructed with some assurance from knowledge of the sedimentary rocks that filled the Paleozoic Cordilleran geosyncline. Those sediments, accumulated during 300 million years of subsidence along the edge of the continent, were mainly marine limestone and dolomite. In contrast, Cretaceous seas received a mile-thick accumulation of siltstone and medium-grained sandstone, rock types that seem to be incompatible with parent rocks of the source area. There may have been a great many volcanoes on the western land mass but, again, Cretaceous sediments are not of types produced by volcanic flows or fine material. This is not to deny the presence of numerous ash beds (now bentonite) but such units make up only a small part of the total volume of rock and can be disregarded as major contributions.

The depth at which most of the marine formations accumulated was less than a few hundred feet, possibly at times a few thousand feet, but certainly never as great as that found on the continental slopes around the present continent. Although there may be many similarities between Cretaceous environments and those along present-day shores of the Gulf of Mexico and the North Atlantic Ocean, there are still notable differences between interior or epicontinental seas of the past and the continental oceanic shelves of the present.

Interior seas are not as strongly stirred by waves and currents as are continental shelves fronting open oceans. This

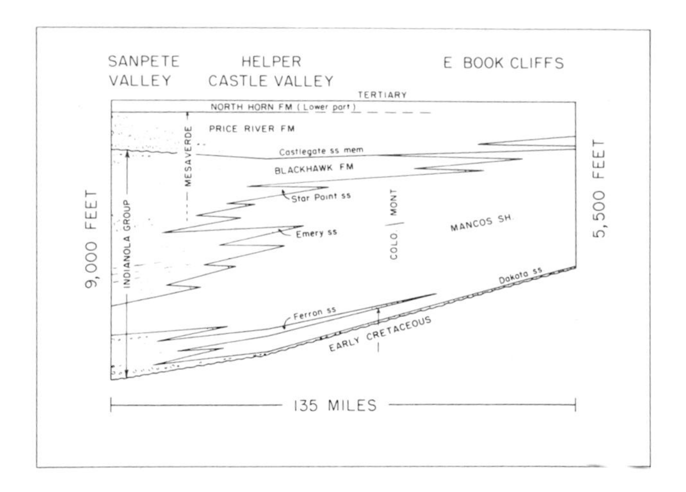

Figure 14-6. Diagrammatic cross-section of Cretaceous rocks from central to eastern Utah along the Book Cliffs. From Stokes and Heylmun, 1957.

is not to say that interior waterways are not agitated by powerful water movements, but the sediments deposited in them are laid down in less disturbed condition. For example, certain thin beds of volcanic ash that settled into the Cretaceous seaway are found to be present continuously over thousands of square miles. These volcanic derivatives, called bentonites, are probably the most consistently reliable key beds to be found in sedimentary deposits. Key beds, together with distinctive fossils, have permitted the marine Cretaceous rocks of the western interior to be divided into intervals of 750,000 years or even less. In other words, if the right fossils and bentonite beds are present, it is possible to correlate widely separated deposits that are within 750,000 years of each other in age.

Several very small outcrops of supposed Cretaceous rocks are known in the Great Basin but positive confirmation of their ages has not been made. This general lack of deposits agrees with other lines of evidence that the western part of the state was being eroded during this period. In contrast, Cretaceous rocks appear at the surface over thousands of square miles in the eastern part of the state (see geologic map and also figs. 14-7a and 14-7b). The most extensive outcrops form a broad S-shaped belt from eastern Sevier County across Emery, Carbon, and Grand Counties into Colorado (see fig. 14-2). Another line of outcrops follows the southern rims of the Markagunt, Paunsagunt, and Table Cliffs Plateaus. It is fairly certain that this belt continues under deep cover northward around the Aquarius Plateau. An extensive isolated patch of Cretaceous rocks occupies the central axis of the Henry Mountain Syncline and a much thinner remnant caps the Great Sage Plain in San Juan County. Thick sections of Cretaceous rocks make up much of the northeastern, southeastern, and southwestern foothills of the Uinta Mountains. Several formations occur in Parleys Syncline east of Salt Lake City.

It is obvious that great volumes of Cretaceous sediments have been removed from the Colorado Plateau and Uinta Mountains (fig. 14-8). Perhaps half the material deposited in Utah during the period has been eroded. Much Cretaceous sediment, deposited in subsiding basins, has been buried to depths of 18,000 feet or more. The Uinta Basin is such a repository; included in its contents is one of the deepest and largest coal reserves of North America.

FOSSILS

Insofar as the Utah rock record is concerned, the Cretaceous probably contains a greater number of fossil species than any other system. Both marine and non-marine types are well represented. The plant record is particularly rich and varied and a great number of microfossils, both plant and animal, are preserved. In order of decreasing abundance, marine fossils are: molluscs, protozoans, arthropods, worms, brachiopods, bryozoans, echinoderms, coelenterates, and sponges (fig. 14-9).

Pelecypods are numerically the most common fossils. Most plentiful, in number of species, are the Inocerami, extinct mud-tolerant bivalves. Banks consisting of millions of heavy-shelled oysters, *Gryphaea* and *Exogyra*, occur at certain stratigraphic levels (fig. 14-10). Many other species are found in less plentiful quantities. Gastropods are the next most numerous. More spectacular than either pelecypods

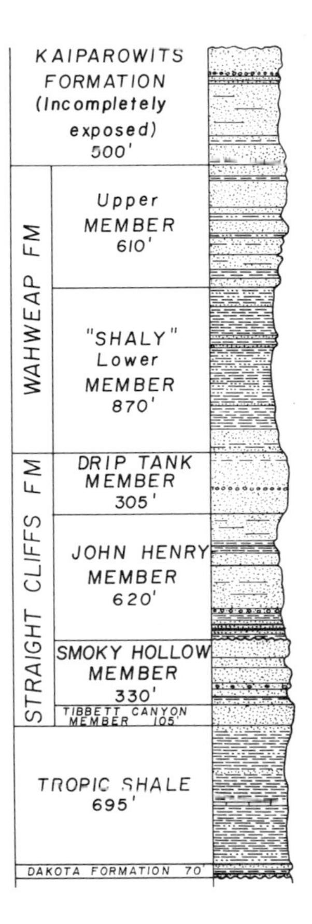

Figure 14-7a. Graphic columnar section of Cretaceous formations of the Kaiparowits Plateau.

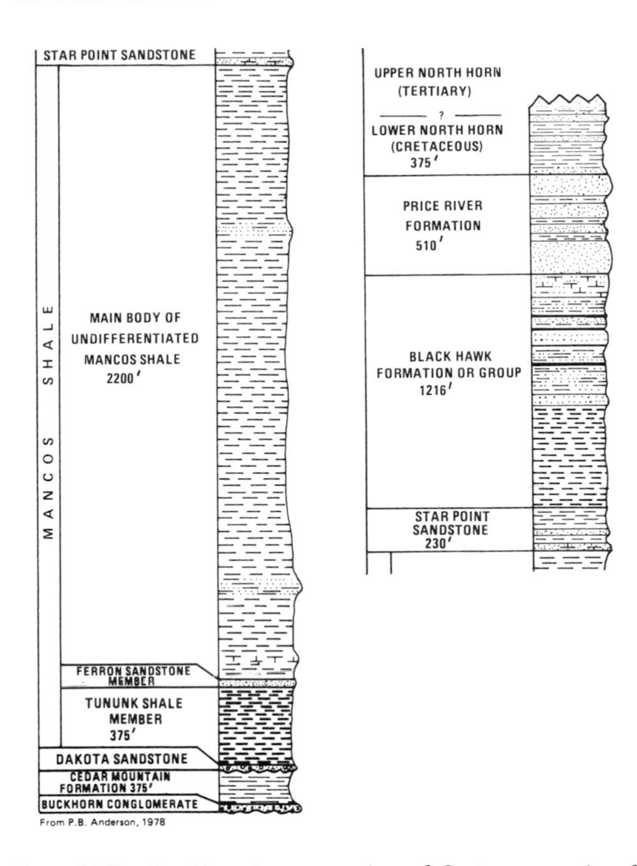

Figure 14-7b. Graphic columnar section of Cretaceous rocks of the northern San Rafael Swell-Book Cliffs area.

Figure 14-8. Cliff of Tununk Shale with cap of Garley Canyon Sandstone, near Carbonville, Carbon County.

or gastropods are the ammonites (extinct cephalopods; fig. 14-11). Hundreds of species are known, displaying practically all the possible shell shapes. Dozens of species based on differences in the suture lines, external ribs, and overall shell shape have been recognized, each characteristic of only a small segment of time and thickness of sediment. Two types are particularly plentiful and long-lasting: the scaphites and the baculites. Scaphites are boat-shaped with the earlier part of the shell in several close coils and the latter part drawn out and not touching the earlier coils (see fig. 14-9). Baculites have straight tapering shells as long as several feet. Other ammonites found in the Cretaceous include *Proplacenticeras*, *Placenticeras*, *Metoicoceras*, and *Neogastroplites*. Specimens of the last named genus as large as 25 in. across have been collected.

Protozoans of many types can be extracted from almost any of the fine-grained marine sediments. Although the Cretaceous of the western North American interior is far from being as calcareous as the White Cliffs of Dover, it does have some of the same calcite-secreting fossil foraminifera including *Stephanolithion* (figs. 14-12a and 14-12b). A single thin bed in the Frontier Formation has yielded 20 species of foraminifera belonging to 10 genera. Also present are species such as *Cretarhabdus* and *Watznaneria*, lime-secreting algae representing the group called coccoliths.

Phyla other than molluscs and protozoans are represented by only rare or specialized species. The only coelenterates known are a few small corals, none larger than an inch across. Bryozoans have been found but none so far have been described. The only brachiopod mentioned in the literature is *Lingula*, a long-lived, mud-tolerant type. Borings of a sulfur sponge in the shells of oysters are the only evidence of sponges so far reported and the best evidence of worms are small winding calcareous tubes attached to shells of pelecypods. Arthropods are represented by ostracodes, locally almost as abundant as the foraminifera.

Lime-secreting animal phyla are almost totally lacking, and those which are present lived either above the bottom in open water or could tolerate muddy bottom conditions. Taking into account the prevailing silty sedimentary environment, it is obvious why organisms needing calcium carbonate and clear seas could not thrive in the Late Cretaceous waters.

The Cretaceous rocks yield a notable record of both continental and marine vertebrates. Fish are represented chiefly by scales and teeth. The most extensive and prolific scale-bearing formation known anywhere is the Aspen Shale that crops out around the Uinta Mountains. Almost every square foot of bedding plane bears scattered scales that can be identified as having come from a half-dozen different species of medium-sized marine fish. Sharks' teeth may be encountered at almost any stratigraphic level but are particularly abundant in certain members of the Mancos Shale from which eight different species are known. Amphibians have not been positively identified in Cretaceous rocks but were almost certainly present in the marshy and swampy environments of the coal forests.

In Utah, Cretaceous fossils fully justify including the period in the Age of Reptiles. Remains of lizards have been reported from Late Cretaceous rocks as well as turtles, crocodiles, and dinosaurs—many undescribed. Not to be overlooked are numerous dinosaur tracks found in the coal mines of Carbon, Emery, and Grand Counties (fig. 14-13).

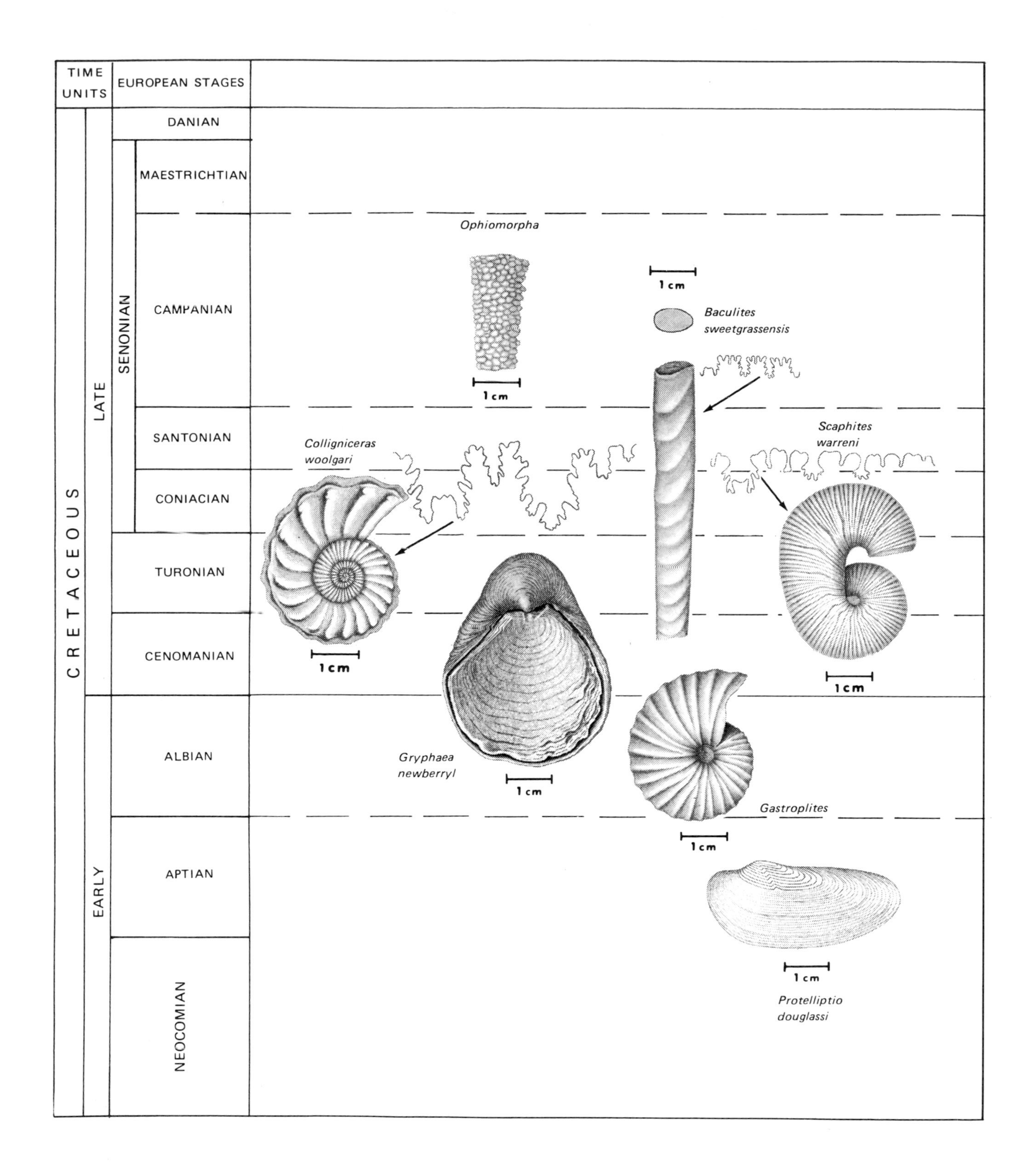

Figure 14-9. Characteristic invertebrate Cretaceous fossils of Utah. Chart is arranged so that centers of each specimen is in the zone of which it is a guide fossil. Sketches: John K. Balsley.

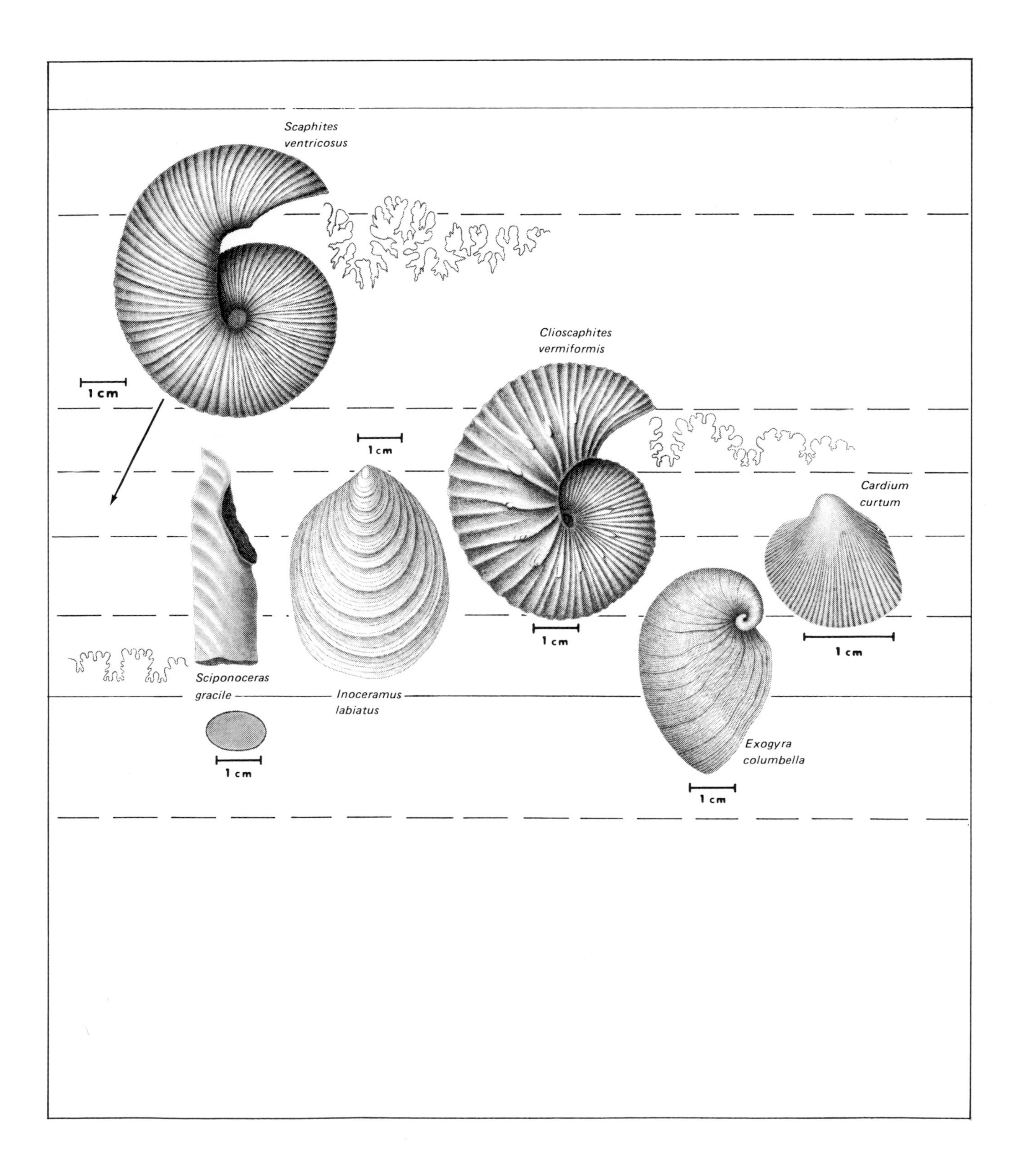

Figure 14-9. Continued.

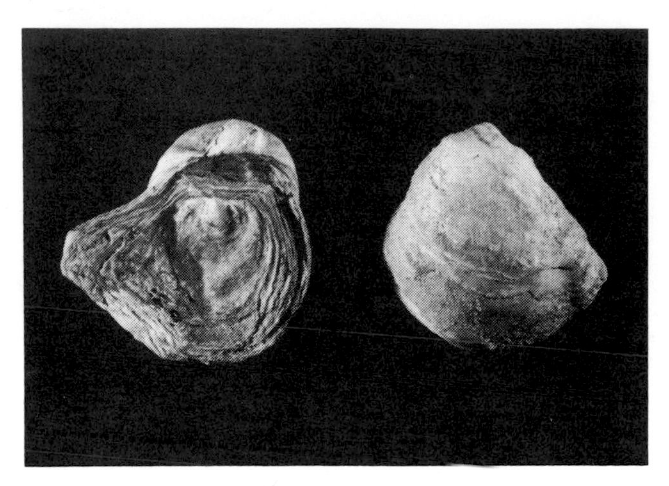

Figure 14-10. Fossil shells of the oyster-like pelecypod, *Gryphaea newberyii*, from the Mancos Shale near Hanksville. Shells average about 1 1/2 inches across. Both lower and upper valves are shown. Photo: Jim Howell.

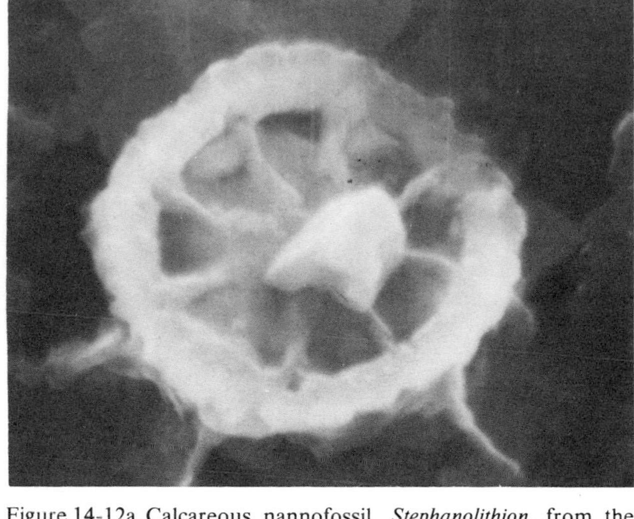

Figure 14-12a. Calcareous nannofossil, *Stephanolithion*, from the Mancos Shale of eastern Utah, enlarged 10,000 times. Electron micrographs by J. L. Bowdler and P. H. Roth.

Figure 14-11. Fossil cephalopod shells from the Mancos Shale near Mounds, Carbon County. Species represented are *Collignoniceras* and *Prionocyclus*. Twenty-five cent coin gives scale. Photo: Jim Howell.

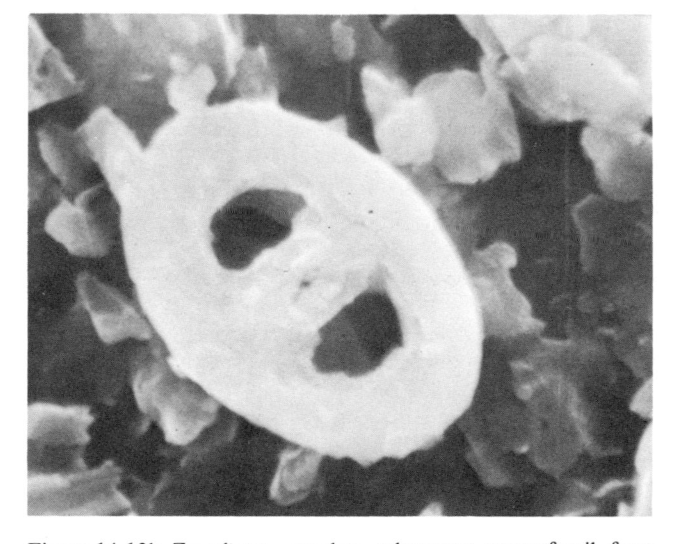

Figure 14-12b. *Zygodiscus*, another calcareous nannofossil from the Mancos Shale of eastern Utah, enlarged 10,000 times. Electron micrographs by J. L. Bowdler and P. H. Roth.

At least a dozen species, none positively known from skeletons, are represented. From Grand County come the largest tracks known, those of a two-legged monster with a foot 4.5 feet long and a stride of 14 feet. Among the last dinosaurs to tread the Earth were the sauropods found fossilized in the North Horn Formation of the Wasatch Plateau. Horned and duck-billed species accompany the sauropods. The North Horn locality is also an important collecting site for dinosaur eggs.

An extensive record of plant life is preserved in Cretaceous rocks. Three types of remains, each requiring study by special techniques, are plentiful. Spores and pollen constitute a class of remains studied by palynologists. Petrified wood requires the attention of wood anatomists and leaves are studied by the more commonplace comparative methods of botanical identification. A large flora of early angiosperms, represented by petrified wood, has been discovered in the Cedar Mountain Formation of Emery County. Mingled with them are abundant specimens of a curious

Figure 14-13. Dinosaur tracks in an abandoned coal mine, Carbon County. Stages in formation include: deposition of peat, making of tracks on upper surface of peat, flooding of the area and filling of the tracks with clean sand, conversion of peat to coal and sand to sandstone, uplift of region, and mining of coal from below tracks. These tracks have not been painted. The coaly film has been brushed away to reveal the natural white sandstone beneath. Several varieties of dinosaurs are represented. Photo: John K. Balsley.

fern, *Tempskya*, one of the best index fossils for Albian (late Early Cretaceous) time.

Spores and pollen are common in many Cretaceous marine and non-marine rocks. These minute objects are broadcast by the wind and may fall into sediment of almost any kind. They are remarkably durable and large numbers can be obtained from suitable sediments. As might be expected, they are most common in coal-bearing rocks. Floras represented chiefly by leaves are also best preserved in association with coal. Common genera which have plainly contributed to Utah coal are sequoia (fig. 14-14), palm, waterlily, fig, cypress, and magnolia. The most comprehensive study to date is that of Parker (1976). His study of the flora of the Blackhawk Formation revealed one liverwort, one lycopsid, 14 ferns, two cycad-like forms, 12 conifers and 86 angiosperms.

SCENERY

Marine rocks are mostly drab and dull colored, not only because they lack the colorful iron oxides that usually form in non-marine sediments, but also because they retain a

Figure 14-14. Fossil leaf of *Sequoia coneata* from the Blackhawk Formation. Sequoias were major contributors to Utah coal beds. This specimen is about 4 inches long. Photo: Lee R. Parker.

great deal of dark carbonaceous residue. This is well illustrated in the rock record where gray and light-brown marine strata of the Cretaceous are sandwiched between colorful Jurassic and Tertiary continental beds. In the Grand Staircase of southern Utah, the Cretaceous units form the Gray Cliffs. They are often ignored by map makers and lose out scenically in competition with their more colorful neighbors above and below. If the Mancos Shale were red instead of gray, it would be a world-famous attraction.

Another reason why the Cretaceous system is not productive of scenic spots is the lack of massive sandstone formations suitable for the formation of deep steep-sided canyons, arches, and bridges. One scenic feature of the Cretaceous is well known, however. The great 200-mile-long escarpment known as the Book Cliffs (fig. 14-15) extends practically unbroken from Price, Carbon County, Utah, to Palisade, Mesa County, Colorado. The cliffs are formed of one, two, or three ledge-forming sandstones, the most striking of which is the Castle Gate Sandstone, named from a configuration resembling a huge gate in lower Price Canyon, Carbon County (fig. 14-16). Unfortunately, the specific formation known as Castle Gate has been half destroyed by widening the highway. The sandstone ledges of the Book Cliffs rise above a slope of soft Mancos Shale and the combination of ledges and slopes constitutes an almost impassable barrier to travel. When and why the Book Cliffs received their peculiar name is not positively known. One version is that the successive ledges, cut in places by numerous vertical fractures, gave the appearance of shelves of gigantic books with their backs facing outward toward the valleys (see fig. 14-15).

Figure 14-15. View of the Book Cliffs near Green River, Utah. Sandstone ledges of the Mesa Verde Group make up the cliffs. The Mancos Shale forms the gullied slope and foreground flats.

Landmarks such as Castle Gate in Price Canyon; Brigham's Thumb near Green River, Emery County; and Pinnacle Peak near Price, Carbon County; are residual monuments of Cretaceous sandstone resting on pedestals of softer material. The Mancos Shale may not be scenic according to standards set by the National Parks and Monuments, but the badland slopes with sweeping lines like huge curtains and folded draperies have their own unique attractiveness.

ECONOMIC

Hydrocarbons in the form of coal, oil, and gas are the chief economic products of Cretaceous rocks. Of the three, coal is by far the most important and no sedimentary rock has received greater attention from geologists and engineers. Interest in coal has increased over the decades and will probably continue to increase for years to come. Geologists must find it, engineers must devise ways to mine it, and chemists must put it to use. In these practical pursuits, the subject of origin may not seem to be important, but a study of how coal came into being is of great assistance in determining the shape and size of beds, the quantity and quality of reserves, and the best methods for planning mines. It is known, for example, that in some areas the coal is in long narrow belts, in others it is in irregular plate-like deposits. In some fields there may be a dozen or more beds, one above the other; in other fields one bed may dominate. It is helpful to know the habits of the coal formation before expensive mining is undertaken.

Figure 14-16. Castle Gate Sandstone, type locality at Castle Gate, Carbon County. This is the north "pillar" of the gate. Photo: John A. Burger.

Eighteen coal fields are recognized (fig. 14-17) containing an estimated 39 billion tons of coal. Only reserves less than 3,000 feet below the surface and in beds more than 4 feet thick are included in this calculation. Nearly all of Utah's coal must be mined by underground methods. The Book Cliffs and Wasatch Plateau coal fields are the two most important. The Book Cliffs field yields coal from several zones in Blackhawk Formation strata and has a total production of about 225 million tons. An estimated 1 billion tons of recoverable coal remain in the field and the limit of mineable depth may be extended further under the Uinta Basin in the future. The Wasatch Plateau field may soon become the state's number one producer with the building of great coal-fired generating plants at several locations in Emery County. Recoverable reserves are estimated at more than 3.2 billion tons. A third field of potential major importance is the Kaiparowits field in Garfield and Kane Counties. Mining is being delayed because of environmen-

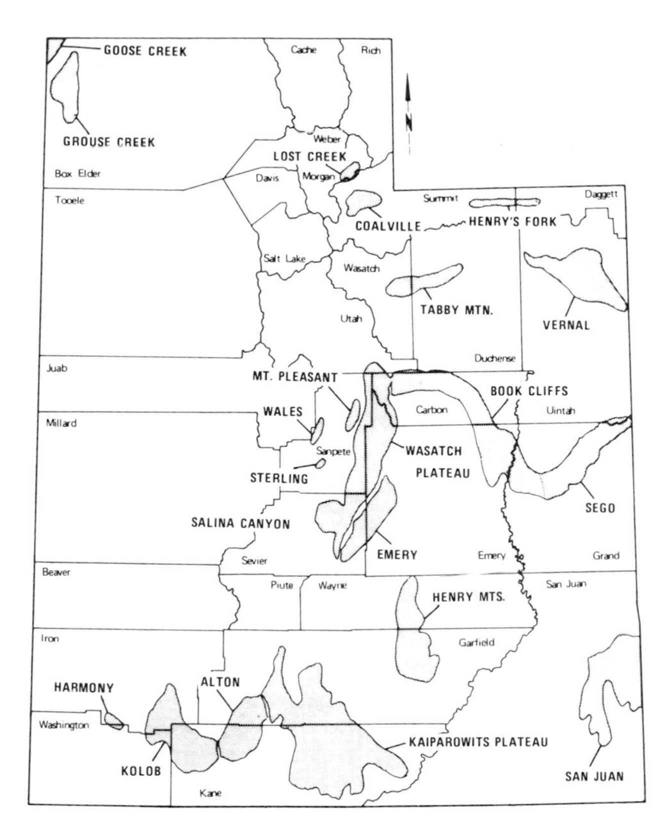

Figure 14-17. Index map to Utah coal fields. See text for explanation. From Doelling, 1972.

tal concerns but exploitation seems to be only a matter of time. Reserves of between 3 and 7 billion tons have been estimated. Other fields, not given in order of importance, are Emery, Henry Mountain, Alton, Goose Creek, Lost Creek, Salina Canyon, Wales, Mt. Pleasant, Tabby Mountain, Coalville, Henrys Fork, Kolob-Harmony and Vernal. More information can be obtained from suitable references given in various papers by Doelling and others. Information from drill holes is constantly being added and reserve figures are subject to refinement.

Limited coal deposition began about the middle of the Cretaceous Period, gradually increased to a maximum late in the period, and then declined near its close. A number of favorable circumstances coincided to produce and preserve organic material on a huge scale. They include: 1) luxuriant plant growth; 2) favorable climate; 3) low-lying coastal areas; and 4) relative subsidence of the entire region. The climate was warm temperate to sub-tropical and plant life was correspondingly abundant. In general, coal formation was localized in low-lying swampy tracts between the shallow interior sea to the east and the highlands to the west. The zone was constantly changing as the shoreline transgressed or regressed due to changes in the rate of subsidence of the basin as a whole or to variations in the amount of silt brought in by large rivers from adjacent highlands.

The coal deposits are of two principal types: 1) those laid down on extensive delta plains adjacent to large rivers which maintained fairly stable courses; and 2) those deposited along alluvial coastal plains where numbers of smaller rivers constantly shifted their courses and built deposits oceanward across the sites of successive swamps. The delta-plain coal beds are as wide as 20 miles across and 15 to 18 feet thick. Deposits in the Blackhawk-Sunnyside area are of this type (figs. 14-18 and 14-19). The alluvial coastal-plain deposits are smaller, 3 to 4 miles across and 5 to 6 feet thick. The higher coal beds of the Wasatch Plateau, the Emery field, and almost all others of southern Utah are of this type.

Most Utah coal is of bituminous rank and relatively high in potential heat production (BTUs); very small amounts are of sub-bituminous or anthracite ranks. Coal is classified by rank and grade but the two are not necessarily related. Rank signifies the percentage of fixed carbon and heat value. Lowest in rank is lignite, highest is anthracite. Any deposit could theoretically pass through the successive ranks in the normal processes of burial and heating. Grade is a measure of the purity and any rank may be of high or low grade.

Figure 14-18 Outcrop of upper part of Blackhawk Formation in deep road cut near Castle Gate, Carbon County. Coal bed near base is about 5 feet thick. Photo: John K. Balsley.

Figure 14-19. Coal bed uncovered for measurement and study, Wasatch Plateau coal field. Coal, being relatively soft, is usually not well exposed. The thickness of this seam is about 15 feet. Photo: Hildred G. Bucurel.

Exceptionally valuable coal deposits are found in the Sunnyside area of the Book Cliffs field where the coal is not only of high-volatile bituminous A rank, but it is also amenable to coke conversion. It is blended with small amounts of low-volatile coal and used in the manufacture of coke for the iron and steel industry of Utah, California, and Japan.

The Cretaceous is a noteworthy oil and gas producer, particularly in the Book Cliffs (or Uncompahgre Uplift) area, Grand County, where 20 to 25 small fields draw oil from the Cedar Mountain and Dakota Formations. In the Wasatch Plateau-Castle Valley area, four fields produce gas from the Ferron Sandstone. An important gas field, Clay Basin field in Daggett County, produces from the Dakota and Frontier Sandstones. Many Dakota gas wells in Clay Basin field have produced continuously for more than 30 years with a cumulative yield of approximately 12.5 billion cubic feet. As of December, 1977, the field had produced about 133 trillion cubic feet. Wells between 15,000 and 16,000 feet deep produce oil from the Dakota Sandstone in the Bridger Lake field on the northern flanks of the Uinta Mountains, Summit County. The field was discovered in 1966 and its presence has stimulated hope for other fields in near proximity to the mountains, perhaps even beneath associated thrust plates.

One other hydrocarbon of note is found in Cretaceous rocks. The famous Asphalt Ridge deposit of tar sand near Vernal, Uintah County, is partly in the Mesaverde Sandstone. The inert oil in this deposit is calculated at 1.0 to 1.2 billion barrels.

For additional reading about the topics discussed in Chapter 14, see the following list of authors:

Armstrong, 1968a, 1968b
Ash and Read, 1976
Averitt, 1969
Bodily, 1970
Clark, F.R., 1914, 1918, 1928
Cobban, 1951, 1976
Covington, 1957
Cross and Maxfield (eds.), 1976
Doelling, 1975
Doelling, and Graham, 1972a, 1972b
Doelling and others, 1972
Duncan, 1944
Fisher, 1936
Garvin, 1969
Gilluly, 1963
Gilmore, 1940, 1946
Gregory and Moore, 1931
Hamblin (ed.), 1975
Harris, 1958
Hummel, 1969
Hunt, 1953
Jensen, J.A., 1966, 1967
Kauffman, 1977a, 1977b
Kayser, 1967
Kinney, 1956
Lee, 1907
Lupton, 1916
McGookey, 1972
Marsell and Threet, 1964
Parker, L.R., 1976
Peck, 1941
Peterson, William, 1924
Peterson, F., and Ryder, 1975
Peterson, R.H., and others, 1953
Preston, 1960, 1961, 1973
Reeside, 1957
Shepardson, 1973
Spieker, 1931, 1949
Spieker and Baker, 1926
Stanton, 1893
Stokes, 1952, 1978
Stowe, 1972
Tidwell, 1975, 1976
Tidwell and others, 1976
Untermann and Untermann, 1954
Utah Geological and Mineral Survey, 1966
Wegemann, 1915
Young, R.G., 1955, 1960, 1973

For complete bibliographic citations, please see List of References.

15 DISTURBANCES GREAT AND SMALL

When confronted with the fact that mountains exist and that strata composing them are commonly contorted and shattered, it is only natural that geologists frequently employ terms such as upheavals, convulsions, and disturbances. They have even given somewhat formal meaning to several of these terms. A "revolution" refers to a time of unusually strong activity resulting in significant mountain systems or uplifts. Revolutions are usually named after the mountains they produce; thus, the Rocky Mountain Revolution, the Appalachian Revolution, and so on. Perhaps because it is shorter, the word "orogeny", from the Greek word for mountain, seems to be replacing the word revolutions; hence, the Rocky Mountain Orogeny, etc. The term diastrophy may be appropriate for disturbances in which no uplift takes place.

Geologists once believed that mountain-building episodes were separated by much longer periods of comparative quiet. Mountain-building was considered as having created convenient breaks between major chapters of Earth's history. North American geologists generally regarded the Appalachian Mountains as having been uplifted quite rapidly at the end of the Paleozoic Era and the Rocky Mountains in a similar way at the end of the Mesozoic Era. Nothing is fundamentally wrong with this concept, except that it must be modified to give proper perspective to other important disturbances.

Just as human history includes upheavals ranging from global wars to tavern brawls, geologic history includes disturbances of graded importance. Hard and fast distinctions are not possible but only the greatest events are referred to as orogenies or revolutions. There are relatively few great mountain systems, therefore not many major geologic orogenies.

Mountains, in the popular view, are "upthrust" from formerly low-lying regions. Geologically this is essentially true and mountains are referred to as being upthrust, uplifted, or merely elevated. In any extensive and complicated mountain system, certain sections will be found that have obviously been elevated by local folding, others by faulting, and still others by intrusion of magma from beneath or by extrusion of lava on the surface. In describing what is seen in any great mountain system, interrelated structural, igneous and metamorphic effects must be given the relative importance they locally deserve. Some mountains are strongly folded (Appalachian), others are highly faulted (Ouachitas, in Oklahoma), others are mostly intrusive (Sierras), while others are strongly volcanic (Andes). Much study is required to understand how a complex range relates to fundamental events such as deep-seated movements in or below the crust, the internal heat of the Earth, the varying pull of gravity, and changes in the Earth's rotation.

Utah bears the imprint of several major mountain-building episodes, the strongest of which occurred during the past 100 million years. In describing them it may be best to begin with conditions before mountains existed. At the beginning of the Mesozoic Era, 245 million years go, erosion and deposition had nearly leveled what is now the western United States. Although something happened in Middle Triassic time to drive out the shallow sea, it is difficult to prove any associated mountain building. The region west of the Wasatch Line may have been slightly uplifted, but not high enough to supply either erosional products or running water to the eastern part of the state.

JURASSIC DISTURBANCES

A few positive evidences of unrest in Late Jurassic time are documented in western Utah. Igneous intrusions at Gold Hill, Newfoundland Mountains, Notch Peak and Silver Island Mountains have been dated as 152, 149, 143, and 140 million years old, respectively. These intrusions originated approximately during the time of deposition of the Morrison Formation in the Rocky Mountain region to the east. This formation is composed of many cubic miles of material, including much conglomerate, derived from western sources. Fossil and rock fragments in the Morrison Formation can be identified as having originated in what is now the Great Basin. Slightly older Curtis Formation conglomerates in the San Rafael Swell also document higher land and minor unrest toward the west. These evidences coincide with what geologists usually call the Nevadan Orogeny, a time of intensive activity at the location of the Sierra Nevada. It is probably not justified to say that the

Figure 15-1. Maple Canyon, east side of Gunnison Plateau, Sanpete County. The Indianola Conglomerate of Cretaceous-Tertiary age forms steep cliffs and a narrow canyon. Photo: U.S. Forest Service.

topography of Utah was significantly influenced by this diastrophy.

SEVIER OROGENY

Early Cretaceous formations such as the Kelvin, Cedar Mountain, and lower part of the Dakota Formation provide evidence for increased geologic activity in western Utah. Conglomerates with fragments of Paleozoic formations of the Great Basin make up significant, but not dominant, components of these formations. If the conglomerates are orogenic in the sense of being derived from newly created uplifts, the Sevier Orogeny had a beginning in the Albian (late Early Cretaceous) about 105 million years ago. Evidence for full-scale orogeny becomes indisputable when great floods of coarse material, for which a nearby source cannot be doubted, appear in central Utah. The first really massive conglomerate deposits occur in the Indianola Group that is as much as 16,000 feet thick in the Cedar Hills. Fossils, though scarce, prove an early Late Cretaceous age. The Ferron Sandstone, exposed east of the Wasatch Plateau, is regarded as a marine expression of massive conglomerates farther to the west.

The Indianola Conglomerate (fig. 15-1) was eroded from a highland composed of a series of large eastward-moving plates brought up along thrust faults rising out of the Cordilleran geosyncline along the Wasatch Line transition zone. The distribution and history of the great thrust faults (fig. 15-2) define and localize the Sevier Orogeny. Although the dislocations are now exposed in discontinuous and offset segments, they all seem to belong to a single deep-seated system.

All Late Cretaceous thrust faults and the folding and erosional effects that accompanied their movements fall within a fairly narrow belt called the Sevier orogenic belt that trends diagonally across Utah from western Iron County to the vicinity of Cache Valley in Cache County (fig. 15-3). This belt is composed of five segments: 1) the southern Nevada-southwest Utah sector; 2) the Wah Wah Mountains-Canyon Range sector; 3) the Charleston-Nebo sector; 4) the Salt Lake sector; and 5) the northern Utah

Figure 15-2. Canyon Range, Juab and Millard Counties, looking west. Shows darker Precambrian quartzite series forming skyline that have been thrust eastward upon the lighter-colored Devonian carbonate Paleozoic rocks of the slopes. This is one of the best exposures of a thrust fault to be found in Utah. Photo: Harold J. Bissell.

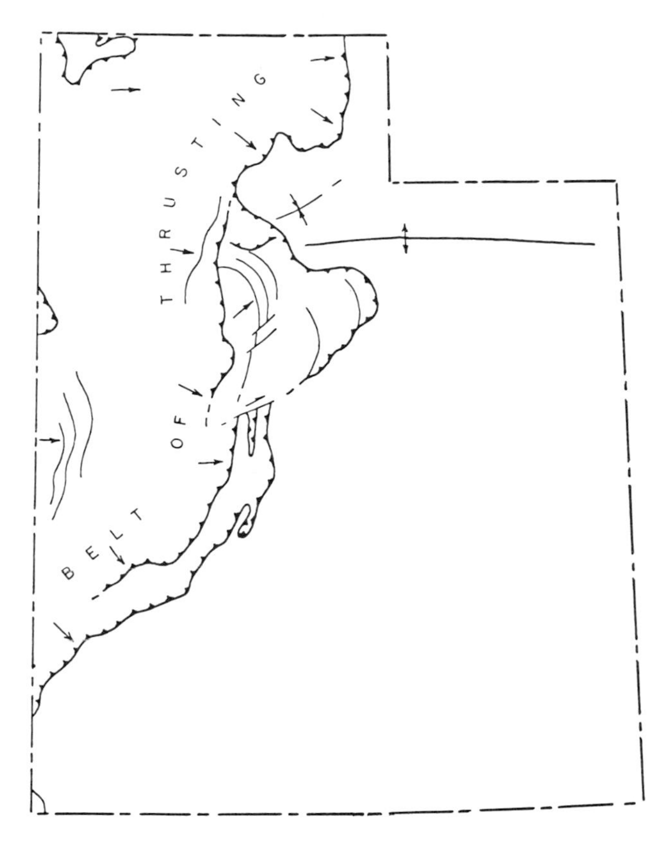

Figure 15-3. Thrust structures of central and western Utah according to Crittenden, 1964, and Eardley.

sector. Eastward movement on the Wah Wah Mountains-Canyon Range sector has been well documented. Large folds broke the surface west of what is now the High Plateaus and were eroded to produce large volumes of coarse sediment in what is now Sanpete and Sevier Counties. The thickest Cretaceous deposits of Utah are in that vicinity.

In contrast, the thrust sheets of the Charleston-Nebo sector seem to have encountered less resistance and traveled well onto the flanks of the Uinta Basin, 30 miles farther east than the Wah Wah Mountains-Canyon Range sector. To the north, roughly on line with the Uinta Mountains, the fault system again met an obstacle in the ancient highlands of the Salt Lake sector. The trace cuts sharply westward around Antelope Island in the Great Salt Lake. The northern Utah sector again penetrated to the east, curving far into Wyoming.

Evidence indicates the various great thrust sheets had ceased to move by the close of Cretaceous time or very shortly thereafter. Segments of the Charleston-Nebo plate are partly buried by the Price River Formation of latest Cretaceous age, a relationship not possible if the thrusts were post-Cretaceous. Cretaceous fossils are found in conglomerates that were deposited upon thrust blocks in northern Utah, proving the same sequence of events. Thus, the Sevier Orogeny reached its maximum intensity during Late, but not latest, Cretaceous time and had maximum effects west of or along the Wasatch Line (fig. 15-4).

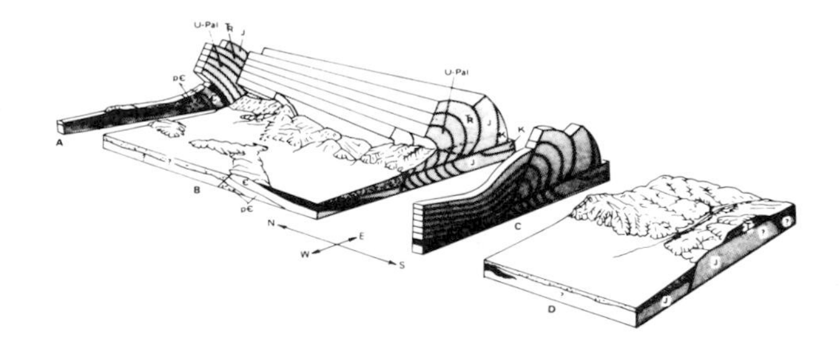

Figure 15-4. Diagram showing geologic deformation of the southern Wasatch Range. Block B represents the eastward movement, folding, and overturning of a thick section of Carboniferous, Triassic, and Jurassic strata above the Charleston-Nebo thrust fault. Mount Nebo, represented at the southern end of the block, is carved from thousands of feet of Carboniferous, Triassic, and Jurassic formations - all of which are overturned. Block D is the Salt Creek Canyon area as it is today. The four blocks should be imagined as pushed together for a composite representation. As currently understood, the movement depicted here took place in very latest Cretaceous time as part of the Sevier Orogeny. Diagram: A.J. Eardley, 1933.

THE LARAMIDE (ROCKY MOUNTAIN) OROGENY

The Laramide, or Rocky Mountain, Orogeny followed close on the heels of the Sevier Orogeny and affected territory mostly east of the Wasatch Line. This event has been defined to include disturbances (fig. 15-5) that took place between about 80 and 40 million years ago. In geologic terms, this is between mid-Late Cretaceous (Campanian) and early Eocene time, 84 to 66 million years ago. Geologists differ in their terminology; some prefer the term "Laramide Orogeny" others refer to the same event as the "Rocky Mountain Orogeny." In the matter of geologic his-

Figure 15-5. Highly disturbed strata at the Palisades, Daggett County, record uplift of the Uinta Mountains. Rocks of the darker Uinta Mountain Group, lower left, are separated by the Uinta fault from the steeply dipping Madison Limestone on the right. Photo: M. Dane Picard.

tory, it may be good procedure to leave the term "Rocky Mountains" to geographers and the term "Laramide" to geologists. In geographic terms the Uinta Mountains and Wasatch Range generally belong to the southern Rockies but in some writings they are included in the Laramide Wyoming Rockies.

The uplift of the Uinta Mountains is the most obvious result of the Laramide Orogeny. They are basically a great east-trending anticlinal fold 160 miles long and about 30 miles wide with numerous secondary structures extending outward in all directions (fig. 15-7). For example, effects can be recognized transecting the Wasatch Range 30 miles west of the Uinta foothills. There are, in effect, two segments to the Uintas, both large oval-shaped elongate domes aligned along the major east-west axis. The East Dome and the West Dome merge at a saddlelike constriction roughly between the towns of Roosevelt, Duchesne County, and Manila, Daggett County. The West Dome is highest near Gilbert Peak. The East Dome has collapsed (fig. 15-6) so that its former high point is now the vicinity of Browns Park. The anticlinal form is markedly asymmetrical. The crestline is much nearer the north flank than the south flank. Strata of the north flank dip at 45° or more while dips on the south flank seldom reach 30°.

The mountainous core of the range is nearly enclosed by faults (fig. 15-7). The North Flank Fault and the South Flank Fault parallel each other and roughly separate the mountains from the flanking foothills. It is known from drilling that the North Flank Fault is mainly a thrust plane along which rocks of the mountain have pushed north onto sediments of the Green River Basin. Faults on the south side are mostly of the normal variety, but there are minor exceptions to this general statement and it is argued by some that a hidden fault parallel to the southern margin is also a major overthrust. If this is so, the structure of the range is that of a giant elongate mushroom partially buried in its own debris.

The structural complexities of the Uinta Mountains are the outcome of a long series of events spread over the past 60 million years of geologic time. The flanking structures and sediments tell the tale of the Uinta uplift and its subsequent development into full-scale mountains. The record along the northeast margin is especially clear. In this area uplift began after the deposition of the highly deformed, Late Cretaceous Erickson Sandstone but before deposition of the overlying Paleocene Fort Union Formation that is little deformed and contains fragments from older formations that were concurrently exposed in the nearby uplift. The time span between the two formations, on the conventional geologic time scale, is 20 million years, from Late Cretaceous Campanian (84 to 74 million years ago) to Paleocene (65 to 58 million years ago). It is reported that

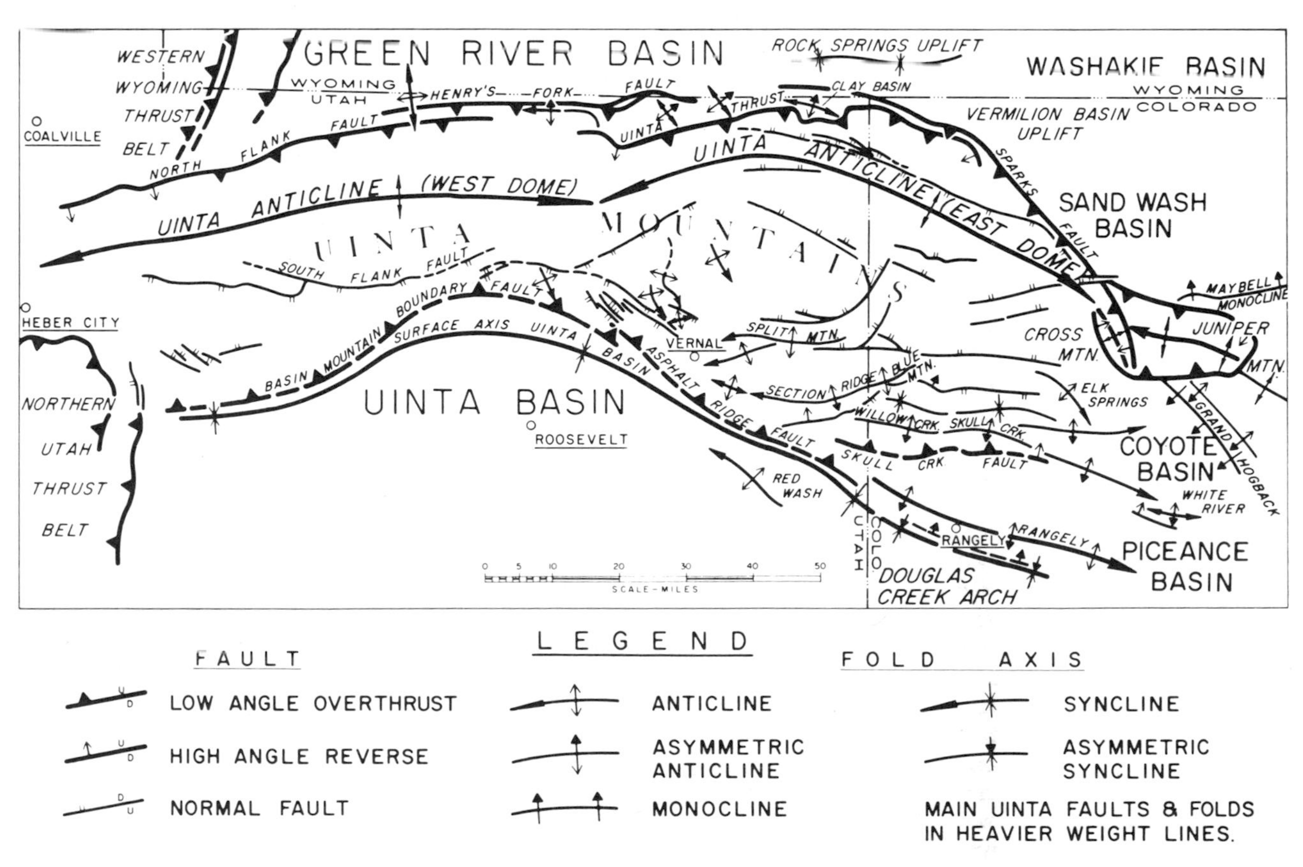

Figure 15-6. Generalized tectonic features of the Uinta Range. See legend or explantion. Diagram: Howard R. Ritzma, 1969.

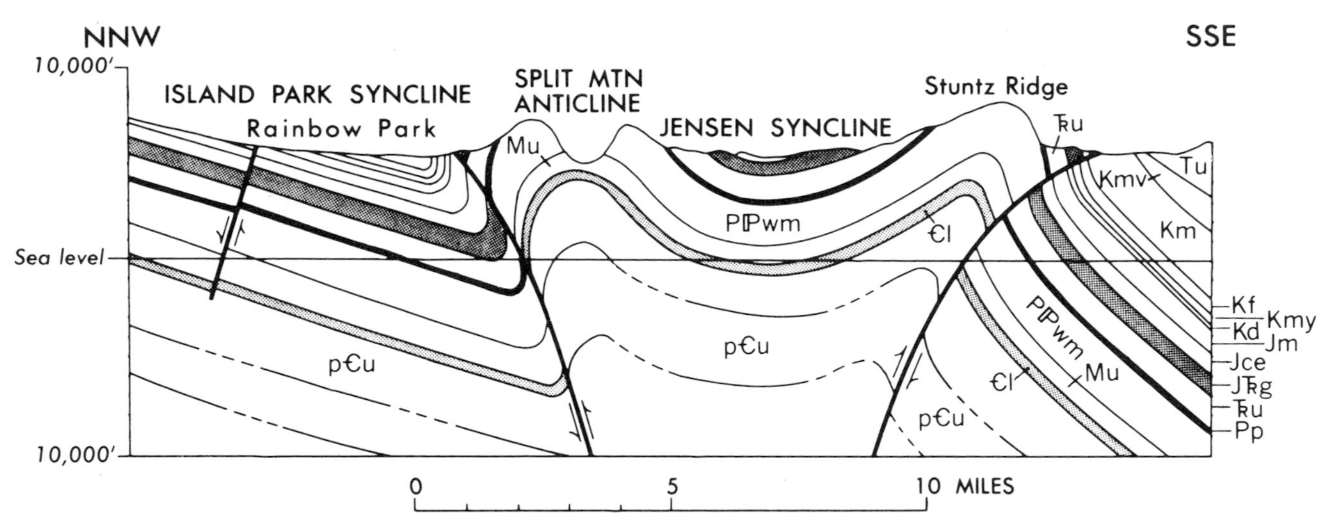

Figure 15-7. Cross-section of the eastern Uinta Mountains showing structure and stratigraphic units. The collapsed segment between two inward dipping faults is emphasized. Explanation of symbols: pꞒu, upper Precambrian; Ꞓl, Cambrian Lodore Formation; Mu, undifferentiated Mississippian; PⱣwm, Pennsylvanian-Permian Morgan and Weber Formations; Pp, Park City Formation; Ꞧu, undifferentiated Triassic; JꞦg, Triassic-Jurassic Glen Canyon Formation; Jce, Carmel and Entrada Formations; Jm, Morrison Formation; Kd, Cretaceous Dakota Sandstone; Kmy, Mowry Shale; Kf, Frontier Sandstone; Km, Mancos Shale; Kmv, Mesaverde Sandstone; Tu, Tertiary Uinta Formation. Diagram: Hansen,USGS Bulletin 1291, 1969.

the Fort Union Formation near Flaming Gorge Reservoir contains pieces of material that were originally buried at least 8,000 feet deep in the core of the Uinta Mountains. This gives a clue as to the amount of uplift and erosion that was accomplished in the first 5 to 10 million years. The Wasatch Formation, which overlies the Fort Union, contains diagnostic cobbles and pebbles from the Precambrian core of the Uinta Mountains, indicating removal of at least 10,000 feet of additional cover. Fragments identified as Madison Limestone (Mississippian) have been identified in Paleocene strata south of the range.

Other, less positive, evidences of the emergence of the Uinta Mountains are found in deposits along the northwest flanks near the southwestern corner of Wyoming. Here the highly conglomeratic Evanston Formation has been dated, by a number of methods, as bridging the Cretaceous-Paleocene boundary (66.4 million years). Opinions differ as to the source of the fragments in this formation; some say they have a western source, some an eastern source. There is the strong probability that much of the Evanston Formation was derived from the pre-existing Echo Canyon Conglomerate (Upper Cretaceous) (fig. 15-8) and not from primary bedrock sources. One thing is certain; an angular unconformity indicates uplift on the flanks of the Uinta Mountains in the interval between deposition of the Cretaceous Echo Canyon Conglomerate and the essentially flat-lying Paleocene Evanston Formation above it.

The Currant Creek Conglomerate, exposed on the south flank of the Uinta Mountains between Currant Creek and the Duchesne River, clearly records the presence of nearby uplifts but its relationship to the Uinta Mountains is not as clear as might be desired. It contains boulders of fossiliferous Frontier Sandstone resembling that in place near Coalville, Summit County, rather than that exposed nearby along the south flank of the Uinta Mountains. Rocks ranging in age from 360 to 100 million years old must have been exposed in the area drained by the Currant Creek streams because it contains Weber Quartzite and black Paleozoic chert (Mississippian to Permian?); however, Nugget Sandstone and granitic rocks, such as might be expected from erosion of the Wasatch Range, are not present. Also, there are no fragments of extrusive igneous rocks which would

Figure 15-8. Historically famous Echo Canyon. Strata in the foreground are in the Cretaceous Echo Canyon Formation. Those capping the ridge on the left are in the Cretaceous-Tertiary Evanston Formation. The lower beds are truncated by the upper ones at an angle of 5° to 15° indicating uplift of the Uinta Mountains area to the south in the Laramide Revolution.

scarcely escape being included if the Park City volcanic field were then in existence. The Park City (or Keetley) volcanic field is dated as 32.35 million years old and the Cottonwood intrusion as 24.33 million years old. Even though this is not much to go on, it seems safe to say that early Late Cretaceous rocks were being eroded but older rocks were not yet exposed. Obviously, much remains to be done before the complicated history of the Uinta Mountains is understood. In the meantime, the "maverick range" may be regarded as a product of the early Tertiary Laramide Orogeny.

MINOR LARAMIDE UPLIFTS

There are Laramide uplifts in eastern Utah other than the Uinta Mountains, but they are minor by comparison (fig. 15-9). They include the San Rafael Swell (figs. 15-10 and 15-11), Circle Cliffs, Monument, Kaibab, and Uncompahgre Uplifts. All are bounded on at least one side by a deep-seated basement fault. In shape and surface area affected they are not significantly different from the truly mountainous uplifts of the Laramide Rockies. They were simply not sufficiently elevated to become full-scale mountains. No ready explanation for this arrested development is evident, but the reason is undoubtedly related to the generally mild geologic reactions that characterize the Colorado Plateau as a whole.

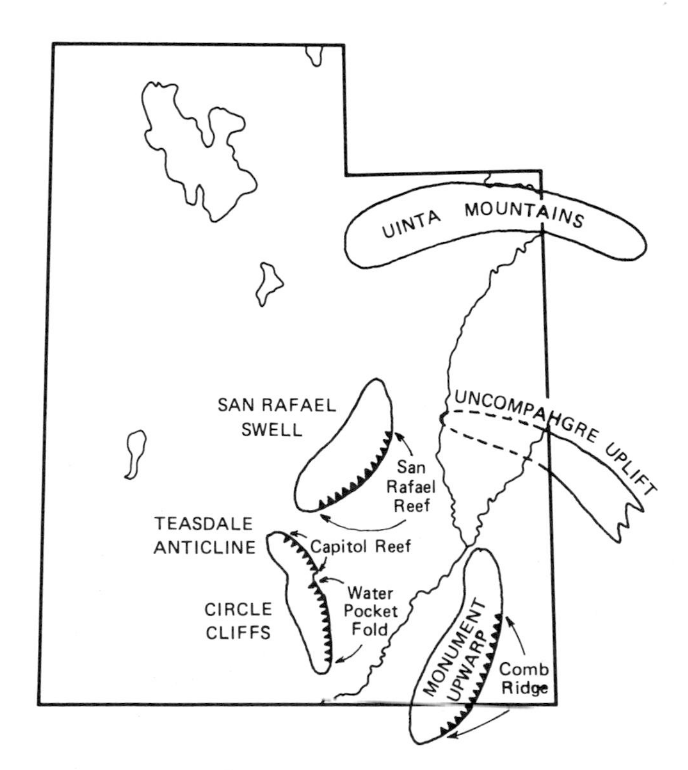

Figure 15-9. Uplifts of eastern Utah. Not all of these have been accurately dated but they are usually regarded as products of the Laramide Orogeny. Steeply dipping monoclinal folds associated with the Colorado Plateau structures are named and indicated by barbed lines.

Figure 15-10. Middle section of the San Rafael Reef, Emery County, looking south. Early Triassic-Jurassic rocks are to the right, Triassic-Jurassic rocks are in the Reef, and Late Jurassic rocks are to the left. This and similar monoclines are regarded as surface expressions of deep-seated faults that cut and displace the crystalline basement several thousand feet below. Still deeper, in the basement, the faults are probable low angle thrusts dipping to the west. Photo: Donald A. Preston.

It has been postulated that a large mobile intrusion underlies each of the Laramide uplifts. That the uplifts should thus be related to the expansive and weakening effects of heat is logical when previous zones of orogeny lying to the west are considered. Local pockets of magma that failed to break to the surface could have caused the overlying blocks to rise and tilt in various configurations. Comparisons with the Ancestral Rockies uplifts come to mind.

Little direct geologic evidence exists on which dating of uplifts in the Colorado Plateau can be based. Their arrangement in relation to the contents of adjacent downwarps such as the Uinta Basin shows that they were supplying sediment by at least middle Paleocene time. The San Rafael Swell must have been uplifted and deeply eroded during an interval 65 to 60 million years ago. The present Uncompah-

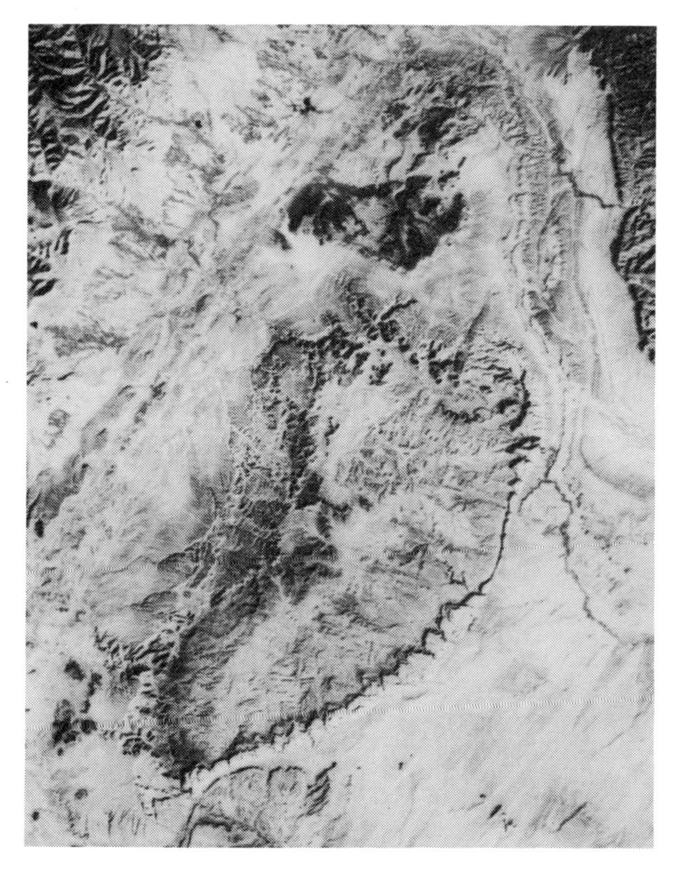

Figure 15-11. Space view of the entire San Rafael Swell about 80 miles long and 30 miles wide. Dips on the east reach 80° and on the west they range from 5° to 15°. The area enclosed by prominent sandstone cliffs is called Sinbad. Cedar Mountain is the dark tree-covered area in the upper center. The anticlinal structure goes beyond this almost to the edge of the photograph. Photo: U.S. Department of Agriculture.

gre Plateau was clearly rejuvenated along the same lines as its Pennsylvanian predecessor; the present south-facing scarp follows virtually the same line as that of 300 million years ago.

THE WASATCH RANGE

Little has been said to this point about the place of the Wasatch Range in the story of mountain-building in Utah. The Wasatch does not fit into either of the major orogenic episodes just described and yet its presence as a Tertiary mountain range cannot be ignored. The following facts seem to bear on its history. The southern Wasatch, from Salt Creek to American Fork Canyon, is made up of a portion of the great Charleston-Nebo thrust plate uplifted relative to other parts of the same plate that are west of the Wasatch Line. Similarly the higher parts of the Wasatch Range east of Ogden are composed of multiple thrust slices that are dated as having moved in very Late Cretaceous time (fig. 15-12). They too have been cut and dismembered by the Wasatch and associated faults. The Wasatch Range therefore, must have originated after the Sevier Orogeny, even though that event was an essential step in its evolution.

During Late Cretaceous time, the site of most of the Wasatch Range was lower, topographically, than the region to the west from which the thrusts came. Nearby conglomerates offer significant clues. The range is partly buried in thick, coarse deposits, some of which still occupy fairly high positions and cover a previously existing, rugged topography. For example, the high ground north of Parleys Summit east of Salt Lake City is covered by a coarse deposit called Conglomerate No. 1 by Granger (1953). Boulders of Precambrian quartzite, Tintic Quartzite, and Paleozoic limestone are abundant constituents. This conglomerate overlies folded beds of older formations and is obviously derived in part from higher exposures of the same forma-

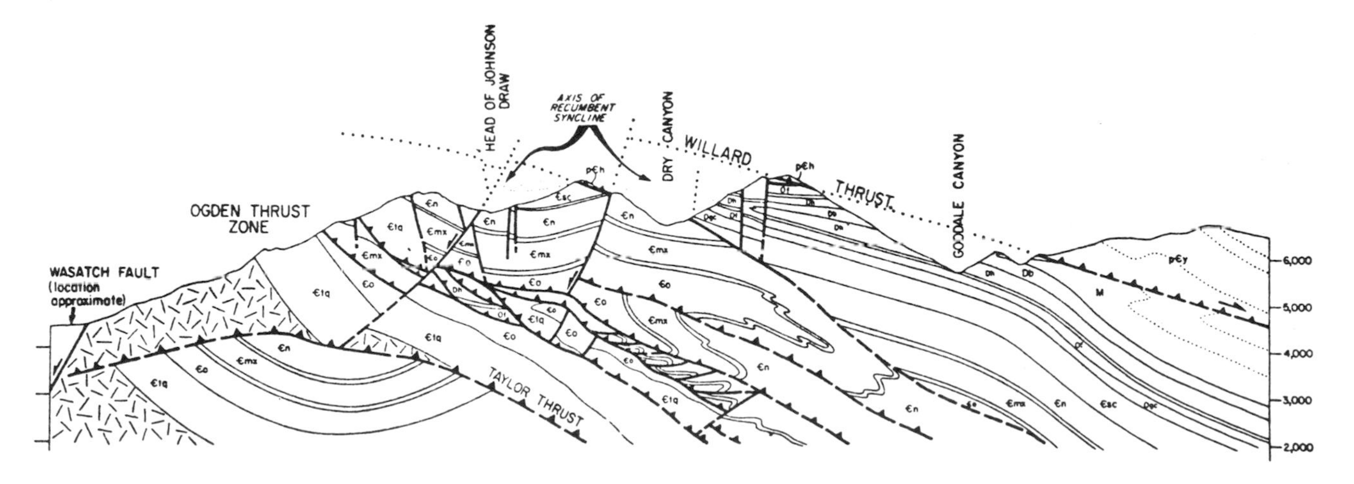

Figure 15-12. Geologic cross-section of the Wasatch Range east of Ogden. Explanation: dash pattern, crystalline Farmington Canyon Complex; p€y, rocks between 900 and 1000 million years old; p€h, Huntsville sequence; €tq, Tintic Quartzite; €o, Ophir Shale; €mx, Maxfield Limestone; €n, Nounan Formation; €sc, Saint Charles Formation; Oqc, Garden City Formation; Of, Fish Haven Dolomite; Dh, Hyrum Dolomite; Db, Beirdneau Sandstone; M, Mississippian formations. Length of section is 52 miles. Diagram: M.D. Crittenden.

tions. It contains no rocks from nearby portions of the Wasatch Range such as granite from the Cottonwood stock that, therefore, was probably not in existence when Conglomerate No. 1 originated.

The internal evidence for an eastward source of this conglomerate is not as strong as for a western or northwestern one. Regardless of their sources, streams flowing from nearby high areas, such as would have existed either east or west of what is now the Wasatch Range, occupied wide valleys rather than deep canyons and flowed through areas of low to moderate relief. Whatever structural elements lay between the Uinta uplift on the east and the Great Basin to the west might be called the Ancestral Wasatch. Pre-Miocene topography, including both valleys and interstream areas, was carved from a variety of rocks including those now making up Parleys Syncline, the Late Cretaceous thrust sheets, and the old Northern Utah highland. The trend of the Ancestral Wasatch was probably not as strongly north-south as is the trend of the present mountains; in fact, east-west topographic configurations created by streams flowing into low areas east of the Wasatch Line probably dominated the landscape.

The important point is that areas east and west of the Wasatch Line (future Wasatch Range) may have had nearly the same elevation and the drainage may have been sluggish or even locally ponded on a structural divide. However, the Uinta Mountains continued to rise, the Great Basin began to subside, and a point was reached when drainage from the east spilled westward across the site of the Wasatch Range. This was when the Spanish Fork, Provo, and Weber Rivers established their seemingly impossible courses across the now lofty obstruction of the Wasatch Range. It is not necessary that those rivers should have deposited sheets of sediment to record their original diversion. For a time there probably were ponds and lakes against the east flanks of the Ancestral Wasatch. The first westward-flowing streams originated when the water bodies overflowed the lowest passes of the surrounding uplands. Under such conditions no great beds of sediment need to have been produced. Tracts to the west were subsiding and eventually became the lowest areas of the landscape. Exits in other directions were blocked and so it was only natural that the rivers took a westward course.

This raises the interesting probability that the passes across the range now occupied by westward-flowing rivers were formerly the valleys of eastward-flowing drainage (fig. 15-13). Once settled in their reversed courses the Spanish Fork, Provo, and Weber Rivers were able to cut downward and extend their headwater tributaries east of the range. It is difficult to judge the time of drainage reversal, but it was certainly after the creation of the Uinta Mountains, and after the collapse of the Great Basin was well under way. A date of middle or late Oligocene, 30 to 25 million years ago, is suggested.

The final destination of present-day rivers that cross the Wasatch Range (fig. 15-14) is the Great Salt Lake. Possibly there were other, older depressions or lakes west of the Wasatch into which these rivers emptied. Evidence is, however, that the great system of down-faulted trenches, or grabens, that parallels the front of the range is at least as old as Miocene and has been filling with sediment since that time.

Figure 15-13. View looking west across Heber Valley through Provo Canyon in the Wasatch Range. Many geologists consider that the higher part of this canyon was cut by east-flowing streams when territory to the west was higher than that to the east. Later, it is supposed, that west-flowing streams occupied the canyon and deepened it to the present levels. Photo: A.J. Eardley.

EPEIROGENY

Previous paragraphs have emphasized the uplifts in Utah created by the Sevier and Laramide mountain-building movements. To leave the subject at this point without mention of other effects of Late Cretaceous-early Tertiary disturbances would give a very incomplete view of the development of the western United States. A new term must be introduced: epeirogeny, meaning broad or regional uplift rather than localized mountain building or orogeny. Consider the fact that the intensive folding of the Sevier Orogeny occurred at or near sea level, but the affected territory is now a mile or more above that plane. Consider also the downwarped areas. A careful review of the life and climate under which the extensive Eocene Green River Formation accumulated leads to the conclusion that the lake surface was less than 1,000 feet above sea level. Green River deposits are now found in extensive outcrops 6,000 feet or more in elevation.

Tertiary uplift must have affected much of North America. The Cretaceous seas withdrew on all sides but the effects were clearly greater in the western mountains, basins, and plains, than elsewhere. Special attention has been paid to the Tertiary uplift of the Colorado Plateau where evidence of elevation became apparent at a very early stage of geologic exploration. The most obvious clue is the almost unbelievable erosional display in the Grand Canyon of Arizona

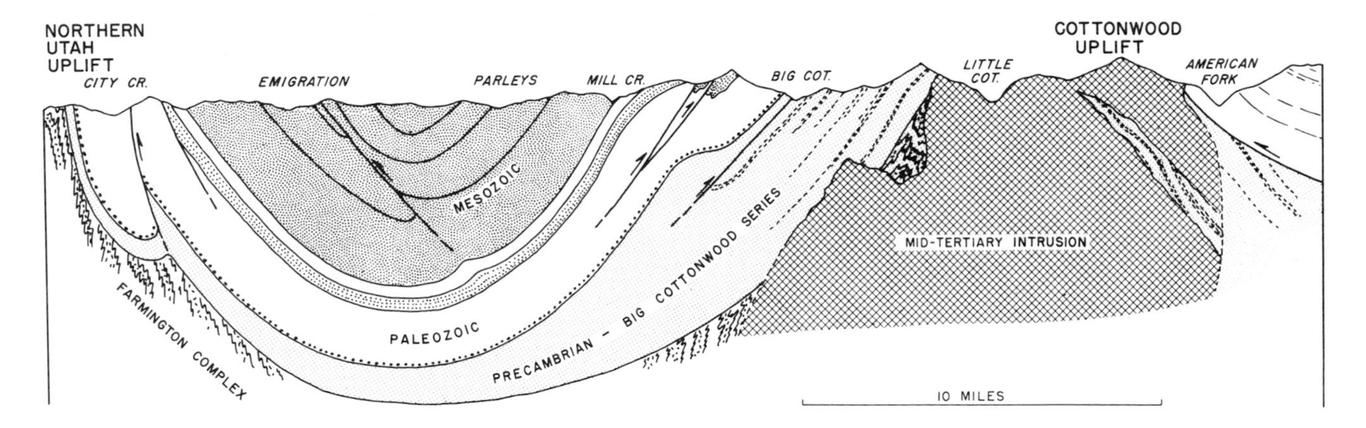

Figure 15-14. Cross-section parallel with the front of the Wasatch Range near Salt Lake City showing synclinal structure and major canyons. Only the upper one-fifth of the section is exposed. Diagram: A.J. Eardley.

and the Colorado River system generally. Perfectly level and undisturbed marine beds thousands of feet above sea level are still being dissected by present-day erosion and can have no other explanation than that there has been great regional uplift.

Part of the explanation is tied to the great fault systems along the southwestern margin of the Colorado Plateau and their relationships with igneous rocks and other deposits. The Plateau side has clearly been elevated with respect to the Basin and Range side. This is true of each of the great faults of the area. The cumulative effect amounts to several thousand feet. Other margins of the Plateau do not show this relative upward movement. As a matter of fact, higher ground surrounds it on the south, east, and north. The conclusion seems inescapable: although the entire intermountain area has been uplifted, there have been unequal internal effects. Some areas have had orogeny added to epeirogeny, some have had epeirogeny only and thus express an average uplift, and others must have subsidence subtracted from orogeny and epeirogeny and have dry-land deposits well below sea level. Even though the Great Basin has clearly subsided or collapsed, it nevertheless had a net upward gain in elevation during the Tertiary. The faults separating the Basin and Range Province to the west and the Colorado Plateau Province to the east seem to represent a subsidence of the western side more than an uplift of the eastern side. The lowering of the Great Basin and contemporaneous igneous events is the topic of the next chapter.

For additional reading on the topic discussed in Chapter 15, see the following list of authors:

Armstrong, 1968a, 1968b
Armstrong and Suppe, 1973
Astin, 1977
Averitt, 1964
Baker, 1959
Bradley, 1936
Campbell, J.A., 1975
Christiansen, 1951c
Craig and others, 1955
Crittenden, 1972a, 1972b, 1975
Eardley, 1933, 1949, 1963, 1968, 1969
Forrester, 1937
Garvin, 1967, 1969
Gilluly, 1949
Granger, 1953
Hamblin, 1963
Hansen, W.R., 1965
Harris, 1958
Hunt, C.B., 1956, 1974
Kelley, 1955, 1960
Lindsay, 1969
McGookey, 1972
Madsen, 1959
Mann, 1974
Mullens, 1971
Osmond, 1964, 1965
Powell, 1874
Ritzma, 1969, 1971
Rowley and others, 1978
Schoff, 1951
Stacey and Zartman, 1975
Stokes, 1960, 1964, 1973, 1979
Threet, 1959
Untermann, 1969
Walton, 1964
Williams, N.C., 1955

For complete bibliographic citations, please see List of References.

Figure 15-15. The Hurricane fault scarp at Cedar City. Early Tertiary sediments, well exposed in the Cedar Breaks badlands make up the surface of Markagunt Plateau on the skyline. Cretaceous, Jurassic, and Triassic displacement of the entire region west of the fault amounts to more than the 2,000 feet. The history of movements on the fault is complex but the net effect has been to elevate the plateau section relative to the Great Basin. It is recognized, however, that both provinces have been uplifted since deposition of the marine Cretaceous which is 9,000 feet above sea level in this view and 6,000 feet above the same datum a few miles west of it. See cross-section figure 15-14. Photo: Ward Roylance.

16 THE EARLY TERTIARY

The Tertiary Period is the first, or earliest, major subdivision of the Cenozoic Era or Time of Modern Life. It commenced about 65 million years ago and ended about 2 million years ago. It is divided into five epochs, mostly named from outcrops in the Paris Basin, France. These epochs, together with their estimated lengths, are: Paleocene (oldest), 9 million years; Eocene, 21 million years; Oligocene, 13 million years; Miocene, 18 million years; and Pliocene, 3.7 million years. Each epoch is represented by both marine and non-marine formations, not only on all continents, but also in the major ocean basins; however, in localities that lie far from the ocean only non-marine deposits are found. More than 160 non-marine formations, most of which are of igneous origin, occur partly or entirely in Utah. The sedimentary rock record of the two earlier epochs, the Paleocene and Eocene, is much more extensive than that of later time. The Paleocene and Eocene Epochs constitute the subject of this chapter. An annotated list of Tertiary stratigraphic units named or recognized in Utah is presented at the end of the book, and a diagrammatic representation of events and conditions is portrayed inside the cover of the book.

PALEOGEOGRAPHY

The shallow seas that occupied Utah during much of the Cretaceous drained away a few million years before the end of the period. This event is indicative of uplift and was merely an early expression of progressive disturbances that had already affected broad belts to the west.

The cause of this creeping unrest was the westward movement of the North American continent and its violent reactions with the margin of the Pacific Basin. The massive collision of lithospheric plates had already brought about drastic effects in Nevada and western Utah during the Triassic, Jurassic, and Cretaceous Periods as expressed in the Nevadan and Sevier Orogenies described in the previous chapter. A definite eastward shifting of geologic events is apparent on the overriding continental block, and the Laramide Orogeny marks the last and most easterly disturbance of the series. The Laramide phase is geologically different because of the nature of the rocks involved. Previously the forces of continental movement were spent on the thick but relatively weak pile of sedimentary rocks of the Cordilleran geosyncline. East of the geosynclinal belt, the continent is underlain by a more solid, thick, and resistant crystalline basement, the eroded roots of the ancient transcontinental mountains. This interior region tended to remain intact or to break up in massive blocks that tilted, tipped, and shattered with much less folding and thrusting than had been the case in the area to the west. This is not to say that there is no folding and thrusting in the Rocky Mountains. There is, but much of it is superficial and can be explained satisfactorily as a reaction to vertical movements of the great blocks that make up the solid continental crust.

This brief digression into tectonic geology explains the type of scene that must be imagined for the early Tertiary Paleocene Epoch. Highlands undergoing erosion still dominated western Utah but there is evidence that subsidence had begun. The Uinta Mountains had, by then, almost suddenly became a prominent feature of the landscape and were contributing sediment to lowlands on their flanks. Lesser uplifts marking the San Rafael Swell, Circle Cliffs-Teasdale Anticline, and Monument Upwarp were also in existence. Occupying at least one of the major lowland areas between these uplifts was an extensive body of fresh water, Flagstaff Lake. It was long and relatively narrow, bounded on the west by uplifts of the Sevier Orogeny and on the east by the San Rafael Swell and Circle Cliffs Uplift. To the north an arm or bay may have expanded slightly into what is now the Uinta Basin, its extent is uncertain. If there were other similar bodies of water farther east in the central Colorado Plateau, their deposits have been completely destroyed. Although the record of a connection is not preserved, the same body of water in which the Flagstaff Formation was deposited probably continued southward and was responsible for the Claron Formation that covered the area of the southern High Plateaus and much of Washington County as well. For this bay or extension the name Lake Claron is proposed (fig. 16-1).

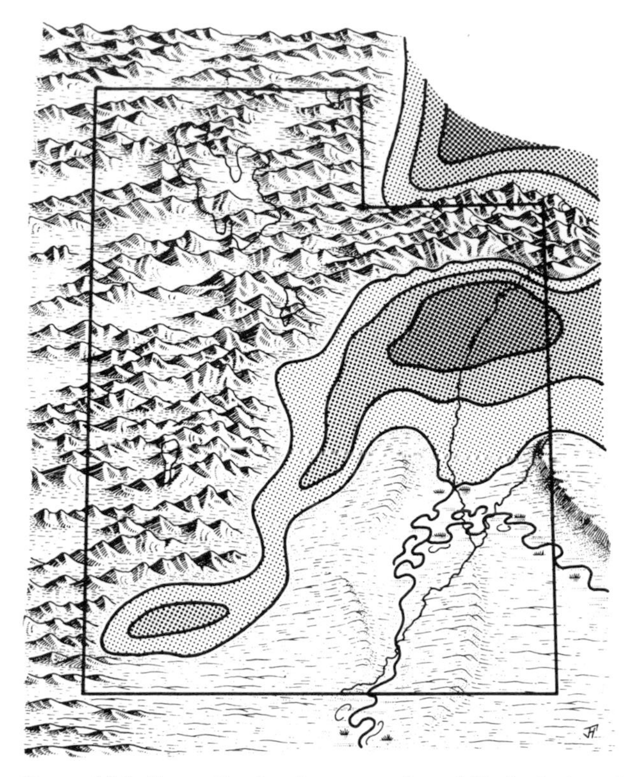

Figure 16-1. Generalized paleogeography of Utah during the early Tertiary. The darker the pattern, the thicker the deposits of lake sediment. Chief site of deposition was the Uinta Basin; the southwestern extension into central Utah was the site of deposition of the Flagstaff Formation and southwestern Utah received the Claron Formation.

The most notable development of Eocene time was the expansion of fresh-water lakes. This was not confined to Utah; there were large water bodies in Colorado and Wyoming as well. The entire interconnected aggregation is called the Green River Lake (or Lakes). The portion in Utah is referred to as Lake Uinta. It is probable that the later history of Lake Flagstaff overlapped the early history of Lake Uinta; in fact, they may have been one body during the late Paleocene and early Eocene. Later in the middle Eocene, Lake Flagstaff disappeared. A generalized paleogeographic map of the Eocene must show a large elongate to oval body of water in the Uinta Basin with a fingerlike bay extending into central Utah slightly west of the main body of the previous Flagstaff Lake. An unsolved problem is the route taken by the drainage of all these ancient lakes. As a preliminary guess it may have been to the southwest and more or less southward into the Pacific Ocean. The lake system contracted and expanded in a complex way in response to climate, to crowding by incoming sediment, and to deep-seated changes in the shape of the basins. One thing is certain: there had to be continual subsidence of the Uinta Basin to accommodate the thousands of feet of sediment that eventually accumulated (fig. 16-2).

As happens to all lakes, the Eocene water bodies of the Rocky Mountains eventually disappeared. Again the causes are complex but the rock record proves that the area occupied by water gradually contracted and was eventually taken over by river deposits. The history is told in broad outline by the sediments of four great formations that occupy the Uinta Basin (fig. 16-3. At the base is the Wasatch Formation, locally subdivided into the North Horn (lowest), Flagstaff, and Colton Formations (figs. 16-4a, 16-4b, and 16-4c) (pending agreement on the complex relations among these units, geologists are here using formations as subdivisions of a formation). The North Horn and Colton are river deposits derived from nearby higher ground. They surround and enclose the Flagstaff Lake beds that represent the water body into which the rivers drained.

Next above the Wasatch is the lacustrine Green River Formation (figs. 16-5a, 16-5b, and 16-5c). This is possibly the most complex body of sediment in Utah, being composed of a great variety of rock types that interfinger with each other across wide transitional zones. The comprehensive study of Ryder and others (1976) points out that the Green River contains claystone, sandstone, and carbonate beds and that each type shows, by its composition and position, all stages from deep water to marginal alluvial conditions. Colors include red, green, gray, brown, and black, the last being appropriately applied to very dark organic-rich oil shale.

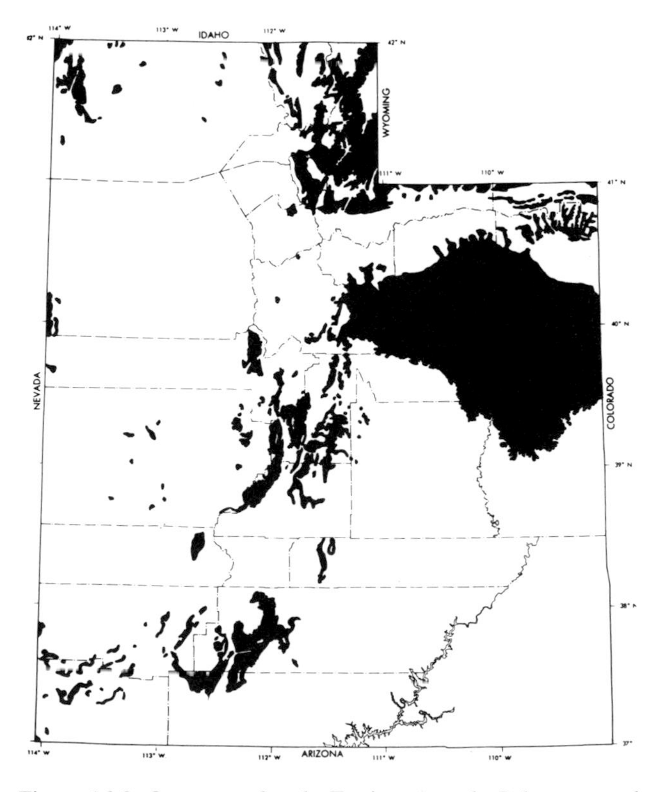

Figure 16-2. Outcrops of early Tertiary (mostly Paleocene and Eocene) sediments in Utah. Rocks of younger age are probably present in outcrops west of the Wasatch Line.

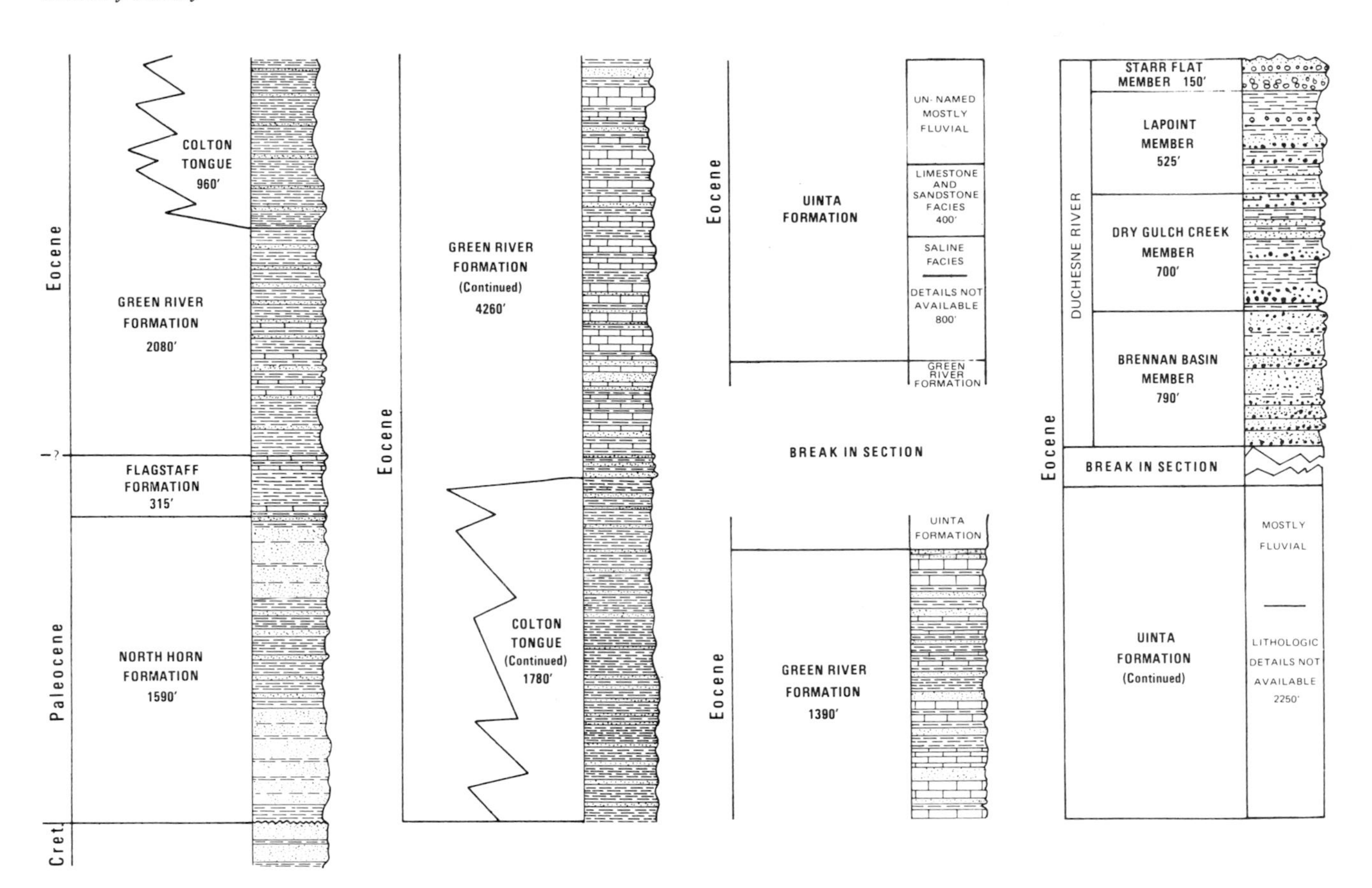

Figure 16-3. Graphic columnar section of Paleocene and Eocene strata of the Uinta Basin. Note breaks in section.

The third great deposit of the Uinta Basin is the Uinta Formation (figs. 16-6a and 16-6b). No clear-cut contact with the Green River can be drawn but the base of the Uinta may be regarded as marking the time when river deposition became dominant in the area. An ever-contracting body of water continued to occupy the center of the Uinta Basin but the bulk of sediment deposited was laid down in the channels and on the flood plains of sluggish rivers that entered the basin from the north and east. The Uinta Formation shows rapid lateral variations as it is traced across the region. In the western part of the basin it consists of sandstone, shale, siltstone, conglomerate, and minor limestone, mainly in shades of red. Eastward there is more limy siltstone and finer grades of shale. A so-called "saline facies" in the south central part of the basin consists of brown shale with a high lime content and abundant salt-crystal molds. Most of the gilsonite "veins" of the Uinta Basin reach the surface and are mined in the Uinta Formation but their origin is deeper in the upper Green River Formation.

Final filling of the Uinta Basin came with deposition of the Duchesne River Formation (fig. 16-7). It consists of more than 3,000 feet of river-deposited conglomerate, sandstone, and fine-grained rocks; lake beds are absent. The source of sediment was clearly the ancient Uinta Mountains and the depositing streams were flowing almost due south to unknown destinations beyond the eroded edges of the present outcrops. Anderson (1972) recognized four subdivisions, from oldest to youngest: the Brennan Basin, Dry Gulch Creek, Lapoint, and Starr Flat Members. The important tar-sand deposit on Asphalt Ridge near Vernal, Uintah County, is partly in the Brennan Basin Member. The Duchesne River Formation is also the bedrock for most of the northern Uinta Basin and, as such, provides the soil on which the settlements, ranches, and rangelands in that area are situated.

The great tectonic features that governed the original distribution of early Tertiary sediments are still in existence or can be easily reconstructed. It is clear that most Paleocene and Eocene sediments were laid down in one great center of deposition, the Uinta Basin. Although erosion has removed a great deal of the southern margin of the deposits and probably as much as several thousand feet from the central area, most of what was originally there still remains. As a rough guess, perhaps 70 percent of the early Tertiary sediments of Utah still remain where they were deposited.

FOSSILS

The fossil record of early Tertiary time is entirely nonmarine and is exceptionally rich in plants and animals of lake and river environments (fig. 16-8). The earliest Terti-

Figure 16-4a. Deer Point, Roan Cliffs, Uintah County. Arrows point to the Deer Point Conglomerate, the lower contact of which marks the Cretaceous-Tertiary boundary over a wide area in eastern Utah. Rocks above are undifferentiated Wasatch Formation. Photo: Gordon Blair.

Figure 16-4b. Wasatch (Colton) Formation in cliffs and slopes overlying light-colored limy beds in North Horn Formation. The limy bed is probably an eastward extension of the Flagstaff Limestone. Spring Wash, east of Green River, Grand County. These deposits are mostly above those in Figure 16-4a. Photo: Gordon Blair.

ary rocks of the region, comprising the upper part of the North Horn Formation, have yielded a fauna of small placental mammals with many important links in the early evolution of the group. This fauna has been given the name Dragonian which designates one of the recognized stages of the Paleocene. The name is from Black Dragon Creek, a locality in the North Horn Formation of the Wasatch Plateau. Lizards are an important component of the North Horn fauna (fig. 16-9).

Figure 16-4c. Patmos Head, 8 miles southeast of Dragerton, Carbon County. Rocks exposed here are classed as undifferentiated Wasatch and Green River Formations of Eocene age. These are above the outcrops shown in Figure 16-4b. Photo: Ward Roylance.

The Flagstaff Limestone fauna that follows the North Horn has been studied by LaRoche (1960). He identified five species of pelecypods and 32 species of gastropods (fig. 16-10). Based on ostracodes, F.M. Swain designated six zones in the early Tertiary of the Uinta Basin. Bones of fish are not uncommon. From the so-called Manti beds of central Utah, which are a local phase of the Flagstaff Formation, very fine complete specimens of ganoid fish were described as early as 1880 by the pioneer vertebrate paleontologist E. D. Cope. Many specimens were found while quarrying stone for the Manti Mormon Temple. Recently a complete skeleton of a champsosaur was discovered near Soldier Summit and a single mammal jaw has been described by Rich and Collinson (1973). Other interesting specimens of Paleocene life may be expected as the formation is studied in greater detail.

The Colton Formation, lying between the Flagstaff and Green River Formations along the southwestern margin of the Uinta Basin, has so far yielded few fossils. In contrast, the succeeding Green River Formation, more than 6,000 feet thick along its exposed southern margin, contains a unique assemblage of fossils including many plants, nonmarine invertebrates, bird feathers, insects, fish, and lizard-skin impressions. Most unusual are the tracks of insects, annelid worms, birds, and mammals that have been collected in great numbers but not yet fully studied and described (figs. 16-11a, 16-11b, and 16-11c). Since many of the re-

Figure 16-5a. Green River flowing through the lower part of the Green River Formation in Desolation Canyon, Uintah-Carbon Counties. Photo: U.S. Bureau of Reclamation.

Figure 16-5b. Outcrops of the middle part of the Green River Formation, southeastern Uinta Basin. Dark ledge in the middle of the slope is the kerogen-rich (oil shale) Mahogany Member. Photo: Bryant Kimball.

Figure 16-5c. Nine-mile Canyon, Carbon County. Walls of the upper Green River Formation (Eocene) rise above the alluvial valley. Photo: Utah State Historical Society.

Figure 16-6a. Uinta Formation, near Highway 40, Uintah County. Shows irregular lensing of channel sandstone bodies and thin-bedded flood plain deposits. Photo: M. Dane Picard.

Figure 16-6b. The Duchesne River Formation (ledgy sandstone) overlying the Uinta Formation (smooth shale slopes), eastern Uinta Basin. Photo David W. Anderson.

Figure 16-7. Typical outcrop of Duchesne River Formation (Brennan Basin Member) in the western Uinta Basin. Photo: David W. Anderson.

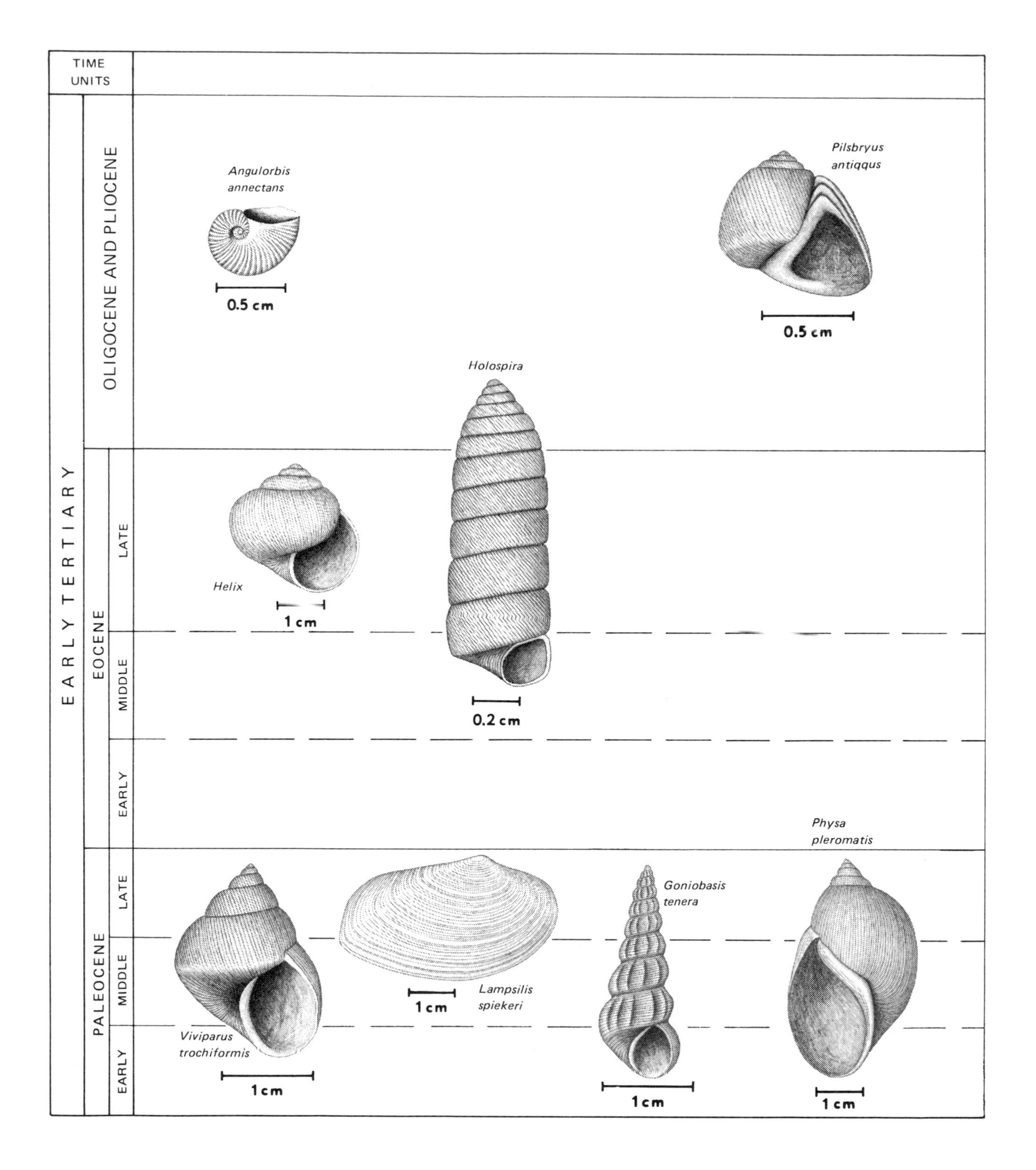

Figure 16-8. Representative fresh-water molluscs of early Tertiary age. Most fresh-water molluscs are long ranging and of limited value as guide fossils. Sketches: John K. Balsley.

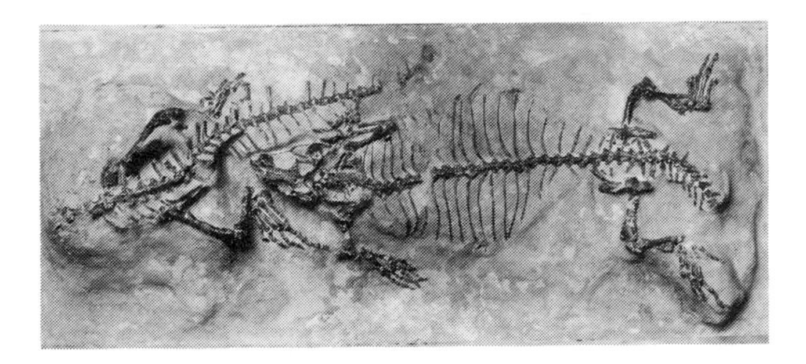

Figure 16-9. Fossil lizard skeletons, *Polyglyphanadon*, from the North Horn Formation, Emery County. Specimens are in the U.S. National Museum. The length is about 15 inches. Photo: Smithsonian Institution.

Figure 16-10. Specimens of the common fresh-water gastropod, *Viviparus*, from the Flagstaff Formation, Wasatch Plateau. Photo: Jim Howell.

Figure 16-11a. A fossil leaf, *Aralia*, from the Green River Formation, Uintah County. Photo: Jim Howell.

Figure 16-11b. A fossil feather, Green River Formation. White spots are ostracod shells. Photo: Jim Howell.

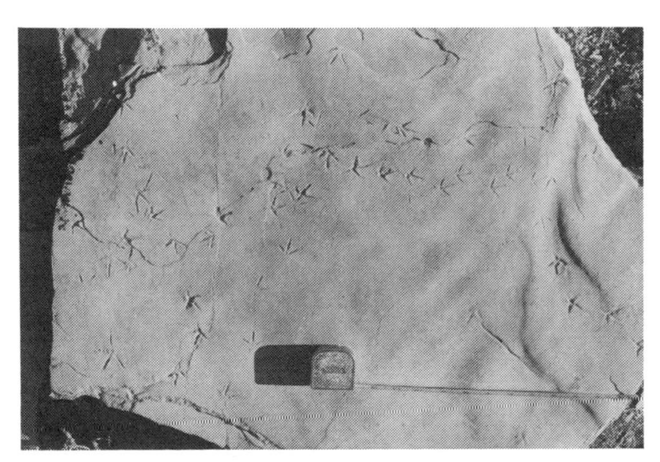

Figure 16-11c. Fossil bird tracks, Green River Formation (Eocene), near Soldier Summit, Utah County. Photo: H.D. Curry.

mains are of types that could have been picked up and carried by wind it is suggested that they were air-borne to their places of deposition.

Structures produced by fresh-water algae were sufficiently massive and prolific to contribute large volumes of rock in certain marginal areas of the Flagstaff and Green River Formations. Remains include bodies ranging from microscopic size to "reefs" many feet across. Rounded algal bodies, called oncolites, characterize the "birdseye marble" beds of the Flagstaff (figs. 16-12a, 16-12b, and 16-12c). They indicate well oxygenated water of fairly uniform and stable depth.

As the Green River Lake was destroyed by sedimentation and climatic changes, the Uinta Basin became a flood plain traversed by sluggish westward-flowing streams rising in the Uinta Mountains and the Rocky Mountains of Colorado. In this semi-tropical environment lived a variegated

Figure 16-12a. Algal growth from early Tertiary rocks. Polished specimen of "Birdseye Marble" from the Flagstaff Formation, Birdseye, Utah County. The circular concentrically banded objects are oncolites formed by lime-secreting algae. The matrix is fine-grained limestone. This rock was once quarried and used as a decorative stone. Photo: Jim Howell.

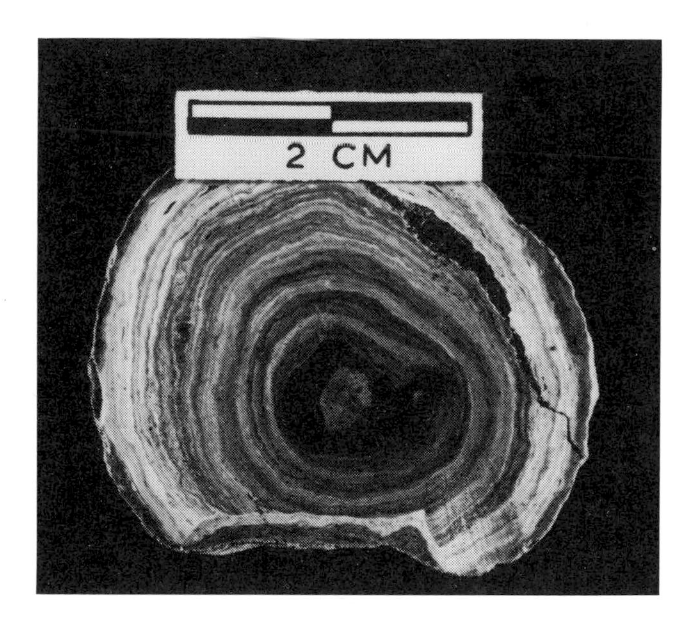

Figure 16-12b. A single large oncolite cut and polished to show concentric layering and nodule forming the nucleus. Specimens up to 6 inches in diameter have been collected. Photo: Jim Howell.

and abundant fauna of vertebrate animals including both reptiles and mammals. Early collectors found abundant bones and teeth (fig. 16-13) weathered out on the surface at a number of localities which they referred to as "pockets." Best known is the Myton pocket. Now, after years of collecting, not much can be found, but that which was previously salvaged is safely preserved in collections of the

Figure 16-12c. Core obtained by drilling of Green River Formation, southern flank of the Uinta Basin. The layered structure is part of a colony of fresh-water algae. The rock has been impregnanted with asphaltic material. Photo: Jim Howell.

American Museum of Natural History, the U.S. National Museum, Carnegie Museum in Pittsburgh, and other institutions.

A compilation by J. LeRoy Kay, a devoted student of Uinta Basin geology, includes 23 turtles, one fish, one lizard, and one crocodile. Mammals include 42 species of perissodactyls, 37 artiodactyls, 14 carnivores, 11 rodents, two insectivores, and one amblypod.

The last significantly large deposit of the Uinta Basin is the Duchesne River Formation. It was first included in the Uinta Formation but later separated on the basis of significant age differences discussed by Peterson and Kay (1931). The fauna is much less abundant than that of the Uinta. A list of described species, also compiled by Kay (1957), includes 10 species of artiodactyls, seven perissodactyls, five rodents, four carnivores, one insectivore, one lizard, and one crocodile. It is thought that the Duchesne River Formation contains the latest Eocene fauna of North America; however, some paleontologists believe it to be Oligocene.

Although there are Tertiary deposits in and near the Uinta Basin younger than the Duchesne River, they have yielded no diagnostic fossils and probably won't because they are chiefly coarse conglomerates unfavorable for the preservation of organic remains.

Figure 16-13. Upper cheek teeth of *Telodus*, a large herbivorous mammal of the Eocene. This specimen was found in lake deposits near Spring City, Sanpete County, and is important in correctly dating the beds in which it was found. Photo: Michael E. Nelson.

SCENERY

Lower Tertiary rocks cap the Wasatch Plateau, the southern rim of the High Plateaus, and the highest surfaces of the Roan Plateau on the southern margin of the Uinta Basin (see geologic map). As such they constitute the topmost tread of the Grand Staircase of plateau geology that has been described step by step in previous pages. Even before National Parks and Monuments were designated, outcrops of these rocks had received such names as Pink Cliffs, Cedar Breaks, Table Cliffs, Sunset Cliffs, Roan Cliffs, and Badland Cliffs, all descriptive of something outstanding in form or color.

Many stratigraphic names have been applied to these rocks and study still continues to yield new classifications. A recent interpretation of the Table Cliffs region suggests the following divisions: Canaan Peak Formation (Late Cretaceous and Paleocene?) at the base, Pine Hollow Formation (Paleocene?) and Wasatch Formation (Eocene). The Wasatch Formation makes up the greater part of the Pink Cliffs. Approximately equivalent strata have been called the Claron Formation as far west as the Iron Springs mining district. The name Cedar Breaks Formation has also been suggested for the High Plateaus generally, but Wasatch is an old name and was established in the area almost 50 years ago. Originally it included what is now the Canaan Peak and Pine Hollow Formations.

Regardless of names, the early Tertiary strata of the high plateaus form several major scenic attractions. Two particularly striking areas have been officially designated: Cedar Breaks National Monument at the headwaters of Coal Creek in the Markagunt Plateau (fig. 16-14) and Bryce Canyon National Park on the east face of the Paunsaugunt Plateau about 35 miles to the east (figs. 16-15 and 16-16). Even the most untrained eye must observe that these two areas are similar and represent the same formation. It (Wasatch, Claron, or Cedar Breaks Formation) was originally a continuous unbroken desposit that covered not only the area between Bryce and Cedar Breaks, but also extensive territory on all sides. Today the continuity is broken chiefly by the great Paunsaugunt fault on the east and by erosion on the south (see geologic map).

In the language of the western pioneer or outdoorsman, a "breaks" is the edge of an upland where it begins to descend or break down in eroding to a lower erosional level. The term is correctly applied to Cedar Breaks. Bryce is cer-

Figure 16-14. Cedar Breaks, looking north along western edge of the Markagunt Plateau, Iron County. Early Tertiary (Paleocene-Eocene) strata variously termed Wasatch, Claron, or Cedar Breaks, make up the striking badland topography. Photo: U.S. National Park Service.

Figure 16-15. Near view of a wall in Bryce Canyon National Park. Varying degrees of resistance to weathering has given rise to the prominent grooves and protrusions. The more resistant layers have been found to contain relatively more dolomite. Photo: Robert C. Lindquist.

Figure 16-16. Regional setting of Bryce Canyon on the rim of the Paunsaugunt Plateau. Headwater erosion by tributaries of the Paria River drain southeasterly and is creating the amphitheaters that constitute the so-called "Canyon." Photo: Robert C. Lindquist.

tainly not a canyon; it is more correctly described as a series of breaks or headwater amphitheatres of the Paria River. However, the term "canyon" puts it in the company of its two great scenic companions: Grand Canyon and Zion Canyon. The three together certainly form a magnificent, unparalleled display of much of the Earth's history.

In the eyes of the geomorphologist, Bryce Canyon and Cedar Breaks are well developed badlands of barren cliffs and slopes with little soil, vegetation, or surface debris (fig. 16-17). They are situated on a plateau edge where water runs downward with greatest velocity and erosive effect and protective cover is at a minimum. Once erosion broke through the soil and destroyed the vegetation that may have once been there, the bedrock was laid bare in its true colors and structure. Many badlands are entirely slopes, but Bryce and Cedar Breaks display a combination of both slopes and cliffs, a compromise between the erosion of material too soft to form uniform cliffs and too hard to form uniform slopes.

The Wasatch Formation of southwestern Utah was laid down in a shallow, oscillating lake. At times silty sediment covered the bottom and at other times limy components were included. Lime-rich rocks are more resistant than lime-poor rocks in arid situations. This explains the horizontal parallel groovings that are so characteristic of the scene. The deeper indentations follow less resistant lime-poor layers, the protrusions follow lime-rich ones.

Water may be supplied by either rain or snow, but it trickles downward over the cliff faces where it tends to be drawn by surface tension across the surfaces where it loosens and removes the constituents according to their solubility. Water that reaches the base is either soaked up by the porous rubble or gathered into streams that carry away all loose material. It seems unlikely that this type of weathering could occur under conditions of either greater or lesser humidity. There is moderate precipitation but it is so unevenly distributed in time that it creates many cycles of alternate drying and wetting of the cliff walls (see fig. 16-15).

Those who know the region are aware that the same types of colorful eroded badlands occur outside the official parks in other stretches of the plateau rims such as Sunset Cliffs and Strawberry Cliffs (elevation 9,400 feet). Farther north, in east-central Utah, are other cliffs of Tertiary rocks. Little known and almost hidden from the view of travelers are the Roan Cliffs in Carbon and Grand Counties. Again the Wasatch Formation is the basic cliff maker, but in this area the formation is less colorful but of more varied composition than in southern Utah. No scenic areas have been officially designated in the Roan Cliffs, but it is through this somber succession of strata that Desolation Canyon of the Green River has been cut. Other, more eye-catching, scenes of the early Tertiary include the higher levels of the often-portrayed cliffs of Echo Canyon, route of transcontinental travel since the middle of the 19th century.

ECONOMIC

The early Tertiary rocks of Utah constitute a vast storehouse of hydrocarbons including oil, gas, oil shale, oil or tar sands, gilsonite, and other solid hydrocarbons. Practically all are localized in Tertiary rocks of the Uinta Basin. The classification of hydrocarbons into gaseous, liquid, and

Figure 16-17. Erosional details, chiefly badland slopes, stationary cliffs and pinnacles cut in the Claron (Bryce Canyon) Formation. Photo: Utah Tourist and Publicity Council.

solid types is helpful and appropriate. Gaseous and liquid hydrocarbons rarely make their presence known at the surface but a few oil seeps and gas emanations have been known in the Uinta Basin since prehistoric time. In contrast, solid hydrocarbons are well known from surface exposures. This is particularly true of the Uinta Basin where oil shale and tar sands are exposed throughout hundreds of miles of continuous outcrops and in many isolated spots. Vertical veins of gilsonite, a variety of solid petroleum residue, are unique to Utah (figs. 16-18, 16-19).

Oil shale is a fairly common rock type and has been found interbedded with other sediments of many geologic ages. It may be of fresh water or marine origin. The common distinguishing characteristic is not age or origin, but content of a peculiar mixture of organic mineral material called kerogen (figs. 16-20 and 16-21). Kerogen is not oil, it is the little-altered remains of fossil algae; in fact, some refer to it as algal coal. A temperature of 900° F is required to "crack" the kerogen and produce oil. After the oil is removed there is a large residue of mineral matter that must be discarded.

The Green River Formation is regarded as perhaps the world's greatest repository of oil shale (fig. 16-22). Outcrops and vast subsurface reserves are found in Colorado, Wyoming, and Utah. Total area underlain by oil shale in Utah is about 5,400 mi^2. The economic importance is not entirely dependent on extent or volume; the grade, or relative kerogen content, is of more practical importance. All things considered the exact amount of oil present in this reserve is very difficult to estimate. Most of the richer material is buried at depths of several thousand feet and relatively few holes have been drilled to sample it. The best current estimate, based on all available information, is that Utah reserves total 7,500 million barrels of oil in raw material containing a yield of 20 gal/bbl or better. Lower grade reserves are even greater.

Many deposits of oil or tar sand are also known in early Tertiary rocks. Information has been summarized by Utah Geological and Mineral Survey Map 33 (1973). Twenty-two deposits are listed for the Uinta Basin. Those considered to be of major or giant proportions, together with estimated content in millions of barrels of oil are: Asphalt Ridge

Figure 16-18. Gilsonite mine following the Harrison Dike, Uintah County. Photo: Donald Preston.

Figure 16-19. Specimen of gilsonite from a "vein" in the Green River Basin. Photo: Jim Howell.

Figure 16-20. Looking north along Hells Hole. The Mahogany Ledge, richest kerogen zone in the Green River Formation, forms dark cliff. Photo: Bryant Kimball.

Figure 16-21. Near view of oil shale in the Green River Formation. Note thin bedding and range in color depending on kerogen content.

(partly in Cretaceous rocks) 1,05 billion barrels; P.R. Spring, 4 billion barrels, and Hill Creek (Douglas Creek Member of the Green River Formation), 1.2 billion barrels. The Sunnyside deposit, chiefly in the Wasatch Formation, in the Book Cliffs is estimated to contain 4 billion barrels. Total potential yield of oil-impregnated rocks in the Uinta Basin is estimated at 2,500 billion barrels at 42 gal/bbl.

Figure 16-22. Rich oil shale from the Green River Formation. Specimen is cut and polished to show fine laminations (varves) produced by differences in organic content and presumed to be of seasonal origin. Specimen about 2 inches across. Photo: Jim Howell.

Utah's most important oil- and gas-producing strata are of early Tertiary age. Of approximately 75 producing fields, about 35 are in the Wasatch, Green River, or Uinta Formations of the Uinta Basin. Two fields, or trends, are particularly outstanding: the Greater Red Wash and the Altamont-Bluebell. The Red Wash field was discovered in 1951 and, as of 1982, has produced 1.25 billion barrels of oil and 330.2 billion cubic feet of gas. The chief productive zones are in the lower part of the Green River Formation at depths of from 4,735 to 5,864 feet. The oil and gas is trapped in a network of lenticular river-deposited sandstones on a small anticline.

The Bluebell field was discovered in 1967 and the Altamont field in 1970. Production is from transitional beds between the Green River and Wasatch Formations at depths ranging from 8,000 to 18,000 feet. Fracturing has created an extensive and exceptionally thick trap for oil and gas. Since the Altamont field was discovered, the 9 miles that separate it from the nearest Bluebell well have been drilled and found to be highly productive. To 1982 cumulative production is 148+ million barrels of oil and 199+ billion cubic feet of gas. Other important fields include the Natural Buttes field which produced gas from the Green River Formation and Mesaverde Formation (Cretaceous) and oil and gas from the Wasatch Formation. The Monument Butte field, discovered in 1964, produces oil and gas from the Green River Formation. There are numerous smaller fields. As of 1982, the cumulative production of Uinta Basin fields is 156 million barrels of oil and 482 billion cubic feet of gas.

The Evanston Formation of late Paleocene age contains coal in the Lost Creek coal field, Morgan County. In the early part of the century seams as thick as 6 feet were mined for local use, but all mines are now abandoned.

For additional reading on the topics discussed in Chapter 16, please see the following list of authors:

Anderson, D.W., 1972, 1973
Armstrong, 1968a, 1968b
Atwater, 1970
Bradley, 1963
Bradley, 1929, 1931
Borchell, 1974
Bowers, W.E., 1972
Brox, 1961
Campbell, J.A., 1975
Campbell and Bacon, 1976
Cashion, 1959, 1961, 1964, 1967
Chatfield, 1972
Christiansen and others, 1972
Clark, F.R., 1918
Coney, 1972
Cook, E.F., 1957
Cope, 1880
Covington, 1963, 1964
Crawford and Pruitt, 1963
Currey, 1957
Dane, 1955a, 1955b
Eardley, 1968, 1969
Garvin, 1967
Gazin, 1938, 1941
Gregory, 1940, 1949, 1951, 1970
Hansen, A.R., 1963
Hintze, L.F., 1973
Hunt, C.B., 1956
Hunt, D.M., and others, 1954
Hunt, J.M., 1963
Jaffe, 1962a, 1962b
Jones, 1957
Kay, J.L., 1953, 1957
Kayser, 1957
Knowlton, 1923
LaRoche, 1960
LaRocque, 1956
Leith and Harder, 1908
Linford, 1979
Lipman and others, 1972
Loring, 1976
MacGintie, 1969
McDonald, 1972
McGookey, 1972
Mackin, 1947
Madsen, 1959
Moussa, 1968, 1970
Osmond, 1964, 1965
Peterson, P.R., 1973
Peterson and Kay, 1931
Phillips and Forsythe, 1972
Picard, 1957, 1959, 1962
Preston, 1961
Pruitt, 1961

Quigley and Price, 1963
Rich and Collinson, 1973
Ridd, 1960
Ritzma, 1972
Ritzma and Seeley, 1969
Ryder and others, 1976
Sabatka, 1964
Schneider, 1967
Scudder, 1877, 1890
Spieker, 1931, 1946
Stokes, 1969, 1977, 1978, 1980
Swain, 1956, 1964a, 1964b
Thorpe, 1938
U.S. Geological Survey, 1974
Utah Geological and Mineral Survey, 1973
Utah Geological Association, 1974
Walton, 1964
Warner, M.A., 1966
Weber, 1964
Winkler, 1970

For complete bibliographic citations, please see List of References.

Figure 16-23. Table Cliff Plateau with the bordering Pink Cliffs as seen from Bryce Canyon National Park. Town of Tropic appears in the lowland which is carved in soft Cretaceous shale. Photo: Herbert E. Gregory.

17 MIDDLE TERTIARY IGNEOUS AND METALLOGENIC INTERVAL

After the early Tertiary lakes disappeared and thc high land areas of the western interior had been lowered by erosion, a period of intensive igneous activity began. For about 25 million years, chiefly during the Oligocene and Miocene Epochs, both intrusive and extrusive igneous rocks were produced on an unprecedented scale. As incidental by-products, most of the great metallic mineral deposits of the western United States also came into being at this time

Igneous rocks originate and behave very differently from sedimentary rocks. Although many extrusive varieties are deposited in layers on the surface, the intrusive varieties solidify beneath the surface where they usually cut across or push aside the surrounding rocks. More commonly than not, igneous rocks tend to pile up in irregular lumpy masses that do not fit neatly into the "layer cake" scheme of stratified sedimentary rocks. Then too, igneous rocks are usually accompanied by hot gases and solutions that cause extensive alteration over wide areas, even to the point that the original rocks are practically unrecognizable.

For these reasons, igenous rocks may be somewhat exasperating to the average geologist. In many cases, diverse kinds have been lumped together on geologic maps with little or nothing to indicate their proper ages or positions in the time scale.

New techniques and discoveries are rapidly shedding new light on the origin of igneous rocks. Many varieties are amenable to age-dating by radiometric methods and satisfactory age assignments are being made at an accelerated rate. Such determinations are expensive but results are well worth the cost, not only scientifically but in practical ways as well. Without a framework of age dates a coherent story of what happened in Utah during the mid-Tertiary would be mostly speculation.

Igneous rocks have been subjects of chemical study ever since chemistry came of age but only within the past 25 years have extremely precise analyses become possible. Wet chemical tests yield the best results for major elements such as silicon, aluminum, iron, manganese, magnesium, calcium, sodium, potassium, and thorium. Chemical tests give results accurate to 0.1 percent. For trace elements that exist in very small amounts, but tell much about the origin and relationships of igneous magmas, several new techniques including X-ray fluorescence, atomic absorption, and neutron activation have come into use. The last-named technique is capable of detecting trace elements in parts per billion.

A very brief digression into the classification of igneous rocks may be helpful here. Needless to say, a distinction is always drawn between extrusive varieties, those cooled on the surface, and their intrusive equivalents cooled beneath the surface (figs. 17-1 and 17-2).

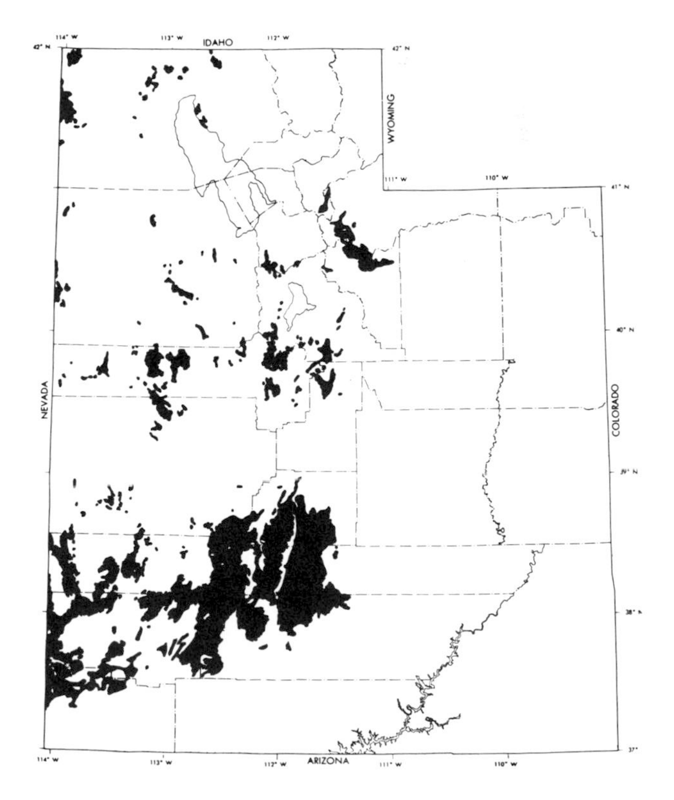

Figure 17-1. Extrusive rocks of Utah. Major aggregations are described in the text.

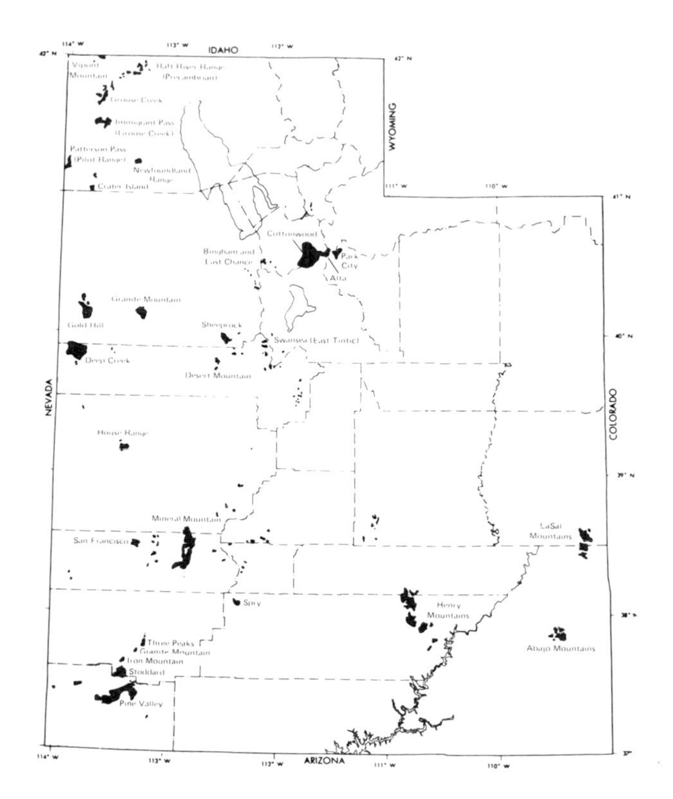

Figure 17-2. Exposed intrusive rocks of Utah. The chief groups or individual bodies are named.

Figure 17-3a. Pressure dome in basaltic lava flow, Tabernacle Butte field, Millard County. Pressure of liquid lava from below is responsible for such blister-like features.

EXTRUSIVE ROCKS

Extrusive igneous rocks are usually classified according to the forms they take upon arrival at the surface. Lava is the general term for fluid, or once fluid, rock that reaches the surface through vents or fissures. If lava is able to spread widely under the influence of gravity, it is called a flow (fig. 17-3a). If the ejected material piles up near the place of origin, a cone or dome results. Flows and cones are usually intermingled in any large volcanic field. For material such as ash that settles out of the atmosphere, terms such as bed, layer, or blanket are appropriate.

Small popcorn-like pieces, usually making up cones, are called cinders; smaller pulverized material is called dust or ash. Broken angular pieces held together more or less firmly so as to make up coherent bodies of appreciable size are called breccia (fig. 17-3b). If large angular blocks are dominant features, the mass may be called an agglomerate. Tuff (fig. 17 3c) is a general term for fragments of different size brought together by any or all of the agencies that operate during an eruption. The term "tephra" applies to all solid, air-borne material ejected by volcanoes.

A relatively new term in the classification of extrusive igneous rocks, and one of special significance in Utah, is ignimbrite or ash-flow tuff (fig. 17-4). Ash-flow is a more general term designating not only material that is welded or fused, but also material that is not welded.

Figure 17-3b. Volcanic breccia of the Markagunt Plateau. Photo: Herbert E. Gregory.

The special significance of ash-flow tuffs is that they were deposited in layers covering immense areas and can be recognized from place to place by distinctive physical and chemical characteristics. They are being mapped, correlated, and named over extensive areas. In this regard they are much more like sedimentary formations than igneous flows (fig. 17-4). It is customary to refer to ignimbrites in terms of cooling units, single falls of heated material that fused and solidified before the next blanket of similar material descended. Some volcanic formations consist of one cooling unit, others have a half-dozen or more. One ignimbrite, the Needles Range Formation, had an original areal extent of at least 10,000 square miles in southwestern Utah.

Figure 17-3c. Near view of the Racer Canyon Tuff showing unusual weathering and coarse texture, northwestern Washington County. Photo: U.S. Forest Service.

Figure 17-4. Erosional forms in the Racer Canyon Tuff, northwestern Washington County. This unit is nonwelded to moderately welded. The age is about 18 million years. Photo: U.S. Forest Service.

INTRUSIVE ROCKS

Intrusive rocks, like their extrusive counterparts, occur in bodies that are classified by form and mutual relationships. Intrusive bodies include batholiths, sills, dikes (fig. 17-5), stocks, plugs (figs. 17-6 and 17-7), domes and laccoliths. Most are well represented in Utah. Laccoliths are of special significance; the first described examples are in the Henry Mountains.

Neither the manner of origin nor the shape of an intrusive or extrusive body directly reveals the fundamental chemical or mineralogic nature of the consituent material; however, most igneous rock types have names that tell something about their megascopic or microscopic appearance and chemical composition. Some of the more common igneous rocks are andesite, basalt, dacite, granite, quartz monzonite, latite, rhyolite, syenite, and trachyte (figs. 17-8 through 17-11). These rocks types are distinguished by the percentage of silica and/or the sodium/calcium ratio of their feldspars.

GENERAL NATURE OF MIDDLE TERTIARY IGNEOUS ACTION

The intense mid-Tertiary igneous activity of the eastern Great Basin has been related to the westward movement of the North American lithospheric plate and its collision with the various plates of the Pacific Basin. Evidence of an

Figure 17-5. Dark dike of igneous rock cutting Jurassic sediments, southern end of San Rafael Swell. Photo: Phillip Howland.

eastward-moving wave of volcanic action and intense deformation beginning along the western edge of the continent and moving gradually eastward had long been accepted as a matter of fact. A satisfactory explanation came with the realization that westward motion of the American plate has carried it over the East Pacific Rise and that thermal energy from lower levels is entirely sufficient to generate igneous action in and on the overriding plate.

Composition of igneous rocks adds confirmation to plate tectonics concepts. Those associated with colliding oceanic and continental plates are relatively rich in silica, potassium, and calcium. The general term is calc-alkalic and andesite is an example. Basalt, rich in iron and magnesium, has an origin from shallower sources. Calc-alkalic material, when mobile, reaches the surface to become part of the lighter, outer crust of the Earth. The ultimate source of the silicic material for mid-Tertiary volcanism of western North America is thought to be at depths ranging from 70 to 90 miles. This is in agreement with many lines of geophysical evidence that place an important discontinuity at this level.

Figure 17-6. Crystal Peak, famous landmark of intrusive rhyolite in the Confusion Basin, Millard County. It is one of the few igneous bodies of Utah classified as a plug dome. Photo: Utah State Historical Society.

Figure 17-7. Plug of soda trachyte in the center of Castle Valley, Grand County. This body is unusual in having been intruded through a thick salt bed. Photo: Bureau of Land Management.

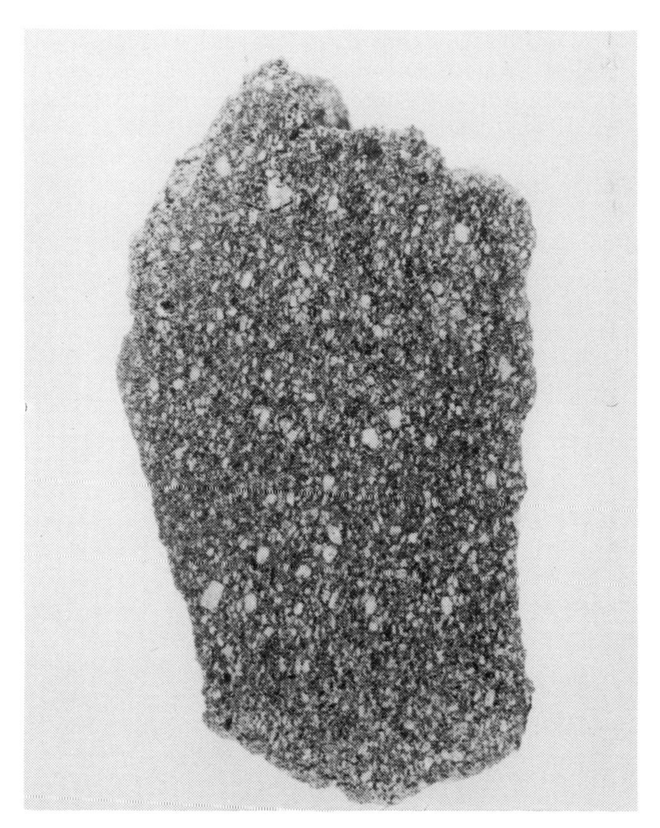

Figure 17-8. Specimen of andesite about 4 inches long. Photo: Jim Howell.

Figure 17-9. Specimen of basaltic lava from near Fillmore. Long dimension of specimen is 4 1/4 inches. Photo: Glen Ungerman.

Figure 17-10a. Cut and polished specimen of quartz monzonite from the Cottonwood stock. This is the so-called Temple Granite, granitic only in texture. Photo: Jim Howell.

Figure 17-10b. Polished specimen of diorite porphyry, Henry Mountains. Photo: Jim Howell.

IGNEOUS CENTERS AND MINERALIZED DISTRICTS

Utah has many famous and highly productive mining areas. Almost without exception they are genetically related to igneous activity (fig. 17-12), shown mainly by the proximity of the valuable mineral deposits to intrusive and extrusive rocks (fig. 17-13). The association is not invariable, however. Although most metallic mineral deposits do accompany igneous rocks, most igneous bodies are barren of such deposits. It has been one of the intriguing problems for economic geologists to discover what it is that relates ore deposits to certain conditions of heat and pressure such as exist in connection with igneous activity.

In view of their close relationships, it is convenient to discuss the intrusive rocks, the extrusive rocks, and the ore deposits on a district-by-district basis. The Oquirrh Mountains and associated mining districts will serve as a starting point, then the other districts will be considered in a rough clock-wise fashion as they occur in western Utah (fig. 17-14). Space permits only brief mention of many important matters that the reader can pursue by consulting the references.

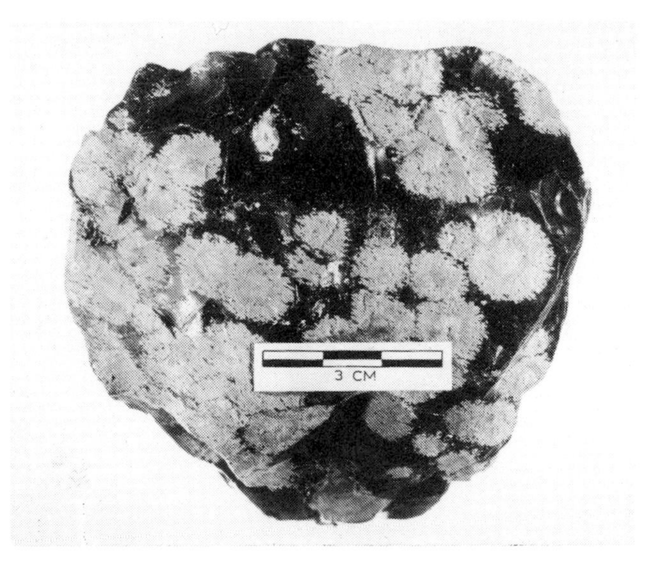

Figure 17-11. Specimen of "snowflake" obsidian. The spherical areas are made of crystals of cristobalite. The black glassy portion is more typical of obsidian. The chemical composition is that of rhyolite. Photo: Jim Howell.

Oquirrh Mountains Igneous Bodies and Mining Districts

The Oquirrh Mountains are the site of the Bingham, or West Mountain, mining district, the richest in Utah (fig. 17-15). The chief mine is a great open pit but many underground workings penetrate the adjacent rocks. The Mercur and Ophir mining districts are located diagonally across the mountains to the southwest. The Oquirrh Mountains are good contenders for the title of "richest mountains on Earth."

The Bingham and Last Chance stocks constitute the heart of the Bingham mining area. Most of the ore is associated with the Bingham stock; the Last Chance stock is essentially barren. The chief rock of the Bingham intrusion is medium-gray quartz monzonite composed of equigranular crystals averaging 0.01 inch in size. Associated rock containing large crystals of pink orthoclase feldspar is classed as quartz monzonite porphyry. Minor rock types are latite and latite porphyry. Potassium-argon age dates place the time of intrusion of both stocks at between 39 and 36 million years ago.

Ore deposits of the Bingham district are found in five over-lapping zones: barren core, molybdenum, copper, iron, and lead-zinc-silver. Copper exceeds all other metals in value and is found mainly as small disseminated grains or in veinlets pervading the outer shell of the intrusion and, to

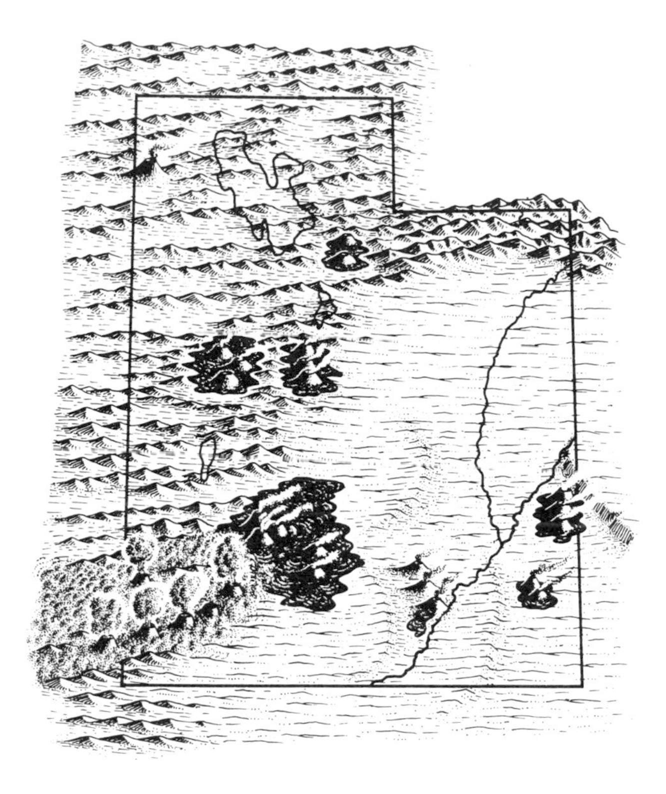

Figure 17-12. Sketch map showing distribution of mid-Tertiary igneous centers. See text for discussion.

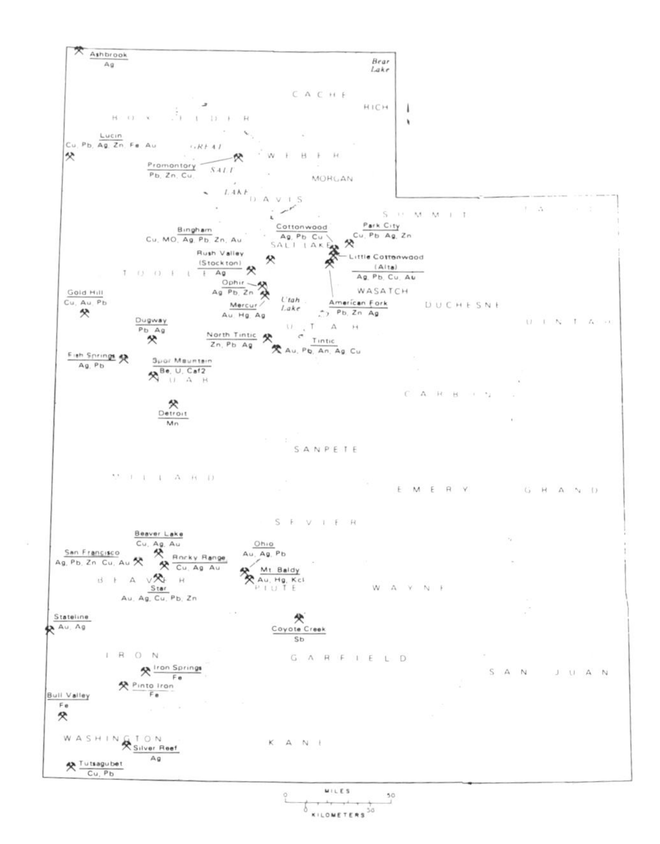

Figure 17-14. Chief metal producing districts of western Utah. Formal names are underlined and metallic products are identified by their chemical symbols.

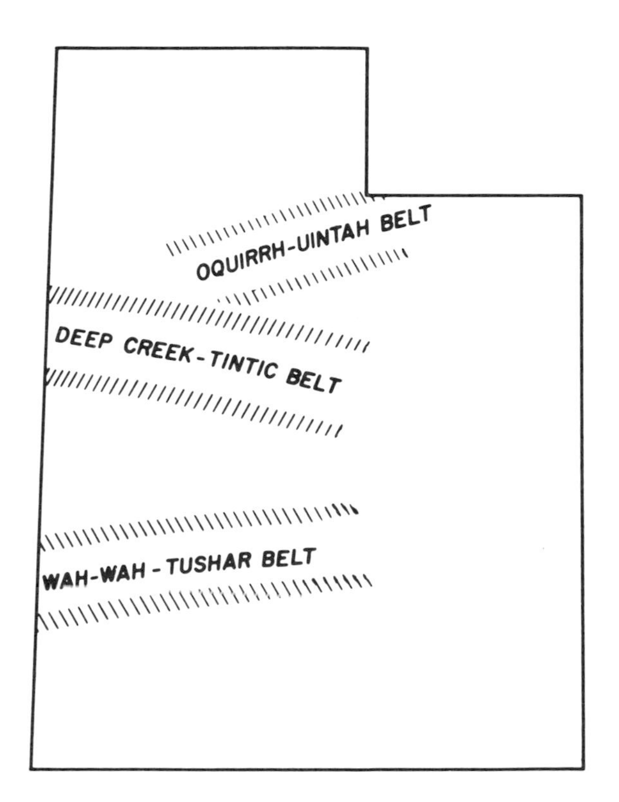

Figure 17-13. Mineral belts of Utah. See text for discussion.

Figure 17-15. Aerial view looking up Bingham Canyon into the Bingham open-pit copper mine and the Oquirrh Range beyond. Photo: Utah Historical Society.

a lesser extent, the nearby sediments. The zones are neither uniform nor continuous, the entire assemblage belongs to a class known as zoned porphyry-ore deposits. A major development in the district was the opening of the Carr Fork Mine by the Anaconda Company in 1980. Workings lie beneath the crest of the range west of the open-pit Bingham Mine. The Carr Fork ore deposits are replacements of favorable strata in the Oquirrh Formation; the chief product is copper and there are significant amounts of gold, silver, and molybdenum. The ore bodies are estimated to contain 60 million tons of ore.

Total production and value of metals produced from the Bingham district are said to exceed those of any other district in the world. Metal production through 1960, as compiled by the U.S. Bureau of Mines, is given:

Copper	15,863,594,000 lbs
Lead	3,954,480,000 lbs
Zinc	1,556,508,000 lbs
Molybdenum	451,086,517 lbs
Silver	205,041,444 ozs
Gold	10,971,041 ozs

Total combined value by today's standards exceeds $10 billion.

Volcanic rocks crop out along the foothills of the Oquirrh Mountains near the Bingham Mine and in the western Traverse Mountains to the south. They lie upon the older Paleozoic and Tertiary rocks to the west and pass under valley alluvium to the east. Flows and breccias are represented. The most abundant flow rock is latite; one small andesite flow is known. Latitic breccia is the most common rock of the volcanic sequence and reaches a thickness of several thousand feet in places. Included are water-deposited tuffs, sandstone, and gravel. Age dates ranging from 38.8 to 20.7 million years have been reported for rocks of the volcanic sequence.

The Mercur-Ophir mining area (fig. 17-16) is also associated with a variety of igneous rocks. Relatively small stocks, sills, and dikes of granitic rock classified as monzonite porphyry, diorite, diorite porphyry, and granodiorite cut the sedimentary rocks. Stocks, necks and dikes of intrusive rhyolite are also fairly common. At least 62 sills are known in the Ophir district. No extrusive rocks are reported. Compared to the Tintic and Bingham area, the igneous bodies of the Mercur-Ophir area are small and the number of ore bodies relatively great.

The Mercur district has produced more than $25 million in gold and silver, much of it coming from reworking older tailings for gold. Currently (1985) the entire mineralized area is being mined in an open-pit operation. Plans call for removal and milling of 3,000 tons of low-grade ore per day. A production of about 80,000 ounces of gold a year for 14 to 17 years is anticipated. The Ophir district is essentially a lead-silver producer but it has also contributed gold, copper, and zinc. Total production from the Ophir-Rush Valley districts has been about $92 million.

Figure 17-16. Mine dumps and surface installations at Mercur when it was being actively mined. Photo: Utah Historical Society.

Cottonwood-Park City Mining Districts and Igneous Rocks

The large intrusions, rich mining districts, and volcanic fields that trend in an east-northeasterly direction from Little Cottonwood Canyon near Salt Lake City almost to the Uinta Mountains can conveniently be discussed under one heading (see geologic map). The component features are definitely aligned in an east-west direction and their common axis is in line with the crest of the Uinta Mountains and with the intrusions and volcanic fields of the Oquirrh Mountains across Salt Lake Valley to the west. The significance of this unmistakeable alignment has not been fully explained.

Three great intrusions that are probably connected at depth trend about N. 70° E. across the widest part of the Wasatch Range (fig. 17-17). These are the Little Cottonwood stock, transected and well exposed by Little Cottonwood Canyon; the Alta stock (fig. 17-18), chiefly between Alta and Brighton; and the Clayton Peak stock, physically in contact with, and east of, the Alta stock. The Clayton Peak stock forms the high divide between the headwaters of Big Cottonwood Creek on the west and Pine Creek on the east. All three are prominently exposed in well known local landmarks. The Alta stock has been carved by Pleistocene glaciation into three horn-shaped peaks, Mt. Millicent, Mt. Wolverine, and Mt. Tuscarora. Five cirque lakes in the area make important contributions to Salt Lake City's water supply. The Clayton Peak stock takes its name from Clayton Peak (Mt. Majestic). Good exposures are seen in road cuts at Guardsmans Pass between Brighton and Midway. A rather wide range of age dates have been obtained from these intrusions. Estimates of about 38 million years for the Alta stock and about 26 million years for the Little Cottonwood stock may be taken as good approximations.

In the Park City district (fig. 17-19), ores of silver, lead, and zinc occur as bedded replacements and as veins in Paleozoic and Mesozoic sedimentary formations. The most important host rocks are in the Park City (Permian),

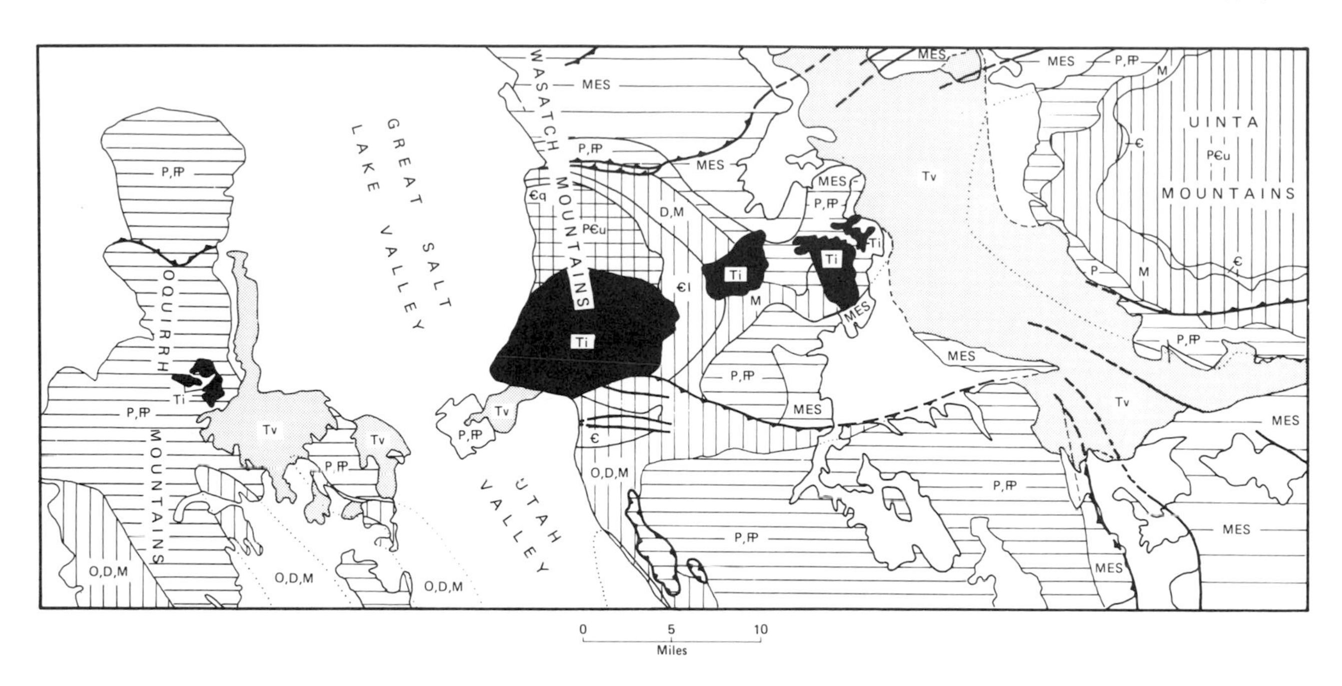

Figure 17-17. General geology of the Oquirrhs and central Wasatch Range area. Tertiary stocks (Ti) are emphasized. P€u, Precambrian; € and €I, Cambrian; O, D, M, Ordovician, Devonian, and Mississippian; PIP, Pennsylvanian and Permian; MES, Mesozoic; Tv, Tertiary volcanics. See text for details. Diagram: A.J. Eardley.

Figure 17-18. Twin Lakes, near Brighton and the head of Big Cottonwood Canyon, Salt Lake County. Surrounding rock is graniodiorite of the Alta Stock. Photo: Utah State Historical Society.

Figure 17-19. Underground workings in the Ontario Mine, Park City District. Photo taken late in the nineteenth century. Note the vein behind the miners. Photo: Utah Historical Society.

Humbug (Mississippian), and Thaynes (Triassic) Formations. These are characterized by alteration of carbonate and sandy beds, an arrangement which seems especially favorable to ore formation. Vein deposits are found cutting nearly all the sedimentary formations of the area and contained in Tertiary intrusives as well (fig. 17-20). The replacement bodies are relatively richer in lead and zinc while the veins are richer in silver. Galena, sphalerite, and tetrahedrite are the most important primary ore minerals. Native gold is present in small amounts. Total production since 1869 amounts to more than $500 million.

Figure 17-20. Contact of Tertiary quartz monzonite intrusive rock of the Cottonwood Stock on the left and Precambrian sediments of the Little Willow Formation on the right. Photo: Thomas R. Neff.

A large, crescent-shaped mass of volcanic rocks occupies much of the territory between the Uinta Mountains and Wasatch Range. It has been called the Park City, or Keetley, Volcanics from the village of Keetley, Summit County. Included in this complex assemblage are flows, tuffs, and volcanic breccias. The rock types are chiefly andesites and rhyodacites. The Keetley Volcanics, as fixed by radiometric dating, originated in the early Oligocene, 35 to 32 million years ago. The igneous rocks rest on an irregular surface of older sedimentary rocks ranging from Pennsylvanian to Early Triassic in age and must have been extruded quite rapidly onto a somewhat rugged surface, perhaps into a river valley that once traversed the area. Portions of the mass have been highly altered but are not known to carry valuable ore deposits.

Tintic Mountains and Vicinity

The Tintic Mountains are world famous for the rich ore deposits that were discovered and mined there (fig. 17-21). The mountains are a north-trending fault-block range near the eastern edge of the Great Basin. More than 10,000 feet of sedimentary rocks, ranging in age from Late Precambrian to Late Mississippian, are exposed. The ore occurs chiefly in large, irregular bodies that have replaced folded and faulted limestone and dolomite strata. The deposits are clearly associated with igneous activity that produced abundant extrusive and intrusive rocks. No district in Utah reveals the various geologic factors that influence the localization of replacement-type ore bodies better than those of the East Tintic Mountains. A list of geologists who have studied this area reads like a "Who's Who" of western geology. Much attention has been given to understanding the relation of alteration products and patterns in finding hidden ore bodies.

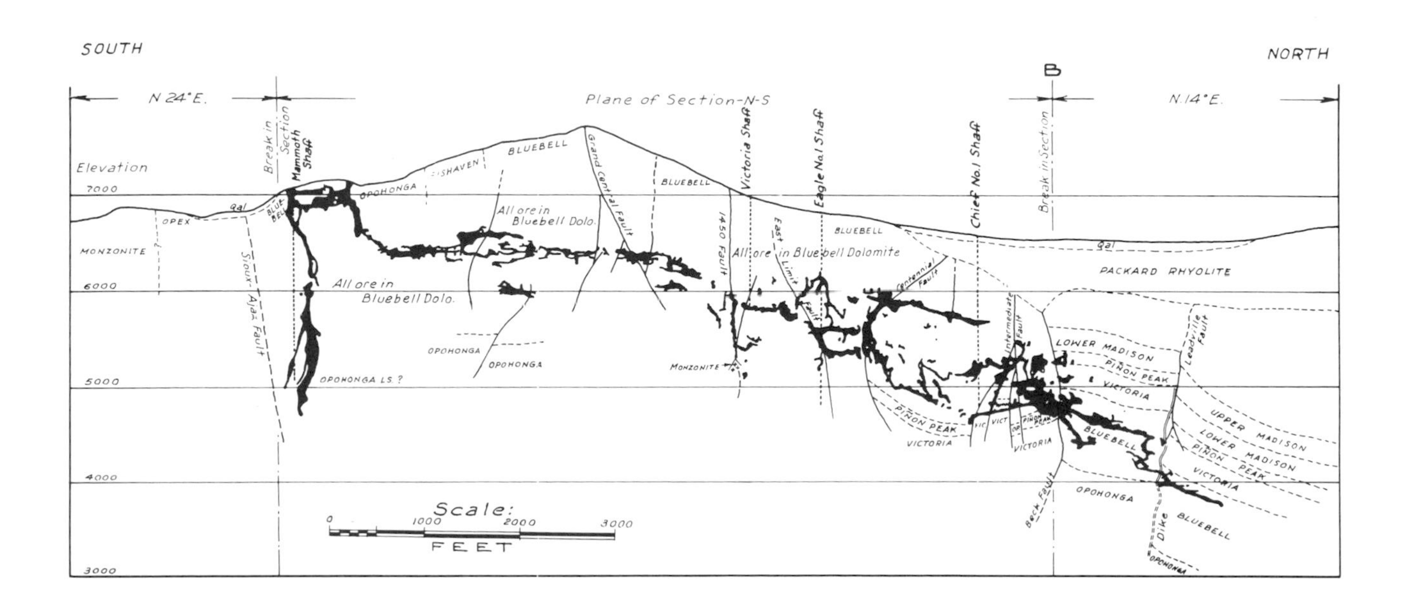

Figure 17-21. Longitudinal cross-section emphasizing ore bodies in the Chief ore zone, Tintic Mining District. Diagram: D.R. Cook, 1957.

There are three mining districts, East, Main and West Tintic. The Main and East Tintic districts, which include most of the range, have yielded approximately 17.3 million tons of silver, lead, gold, copper, zinc and other ores with a value of more than $440 million.

The East Tintic Mountains may be thought of as the eroded remnants of a large composite volcano. The eruptions buried a pre-existing, structurally complex mountain range that is now being reexposed by erosion. The possible centers of eruption are exposed in the form of a number of stocks, plugs, and dikes in the approximate center of the range. Much of the extrusive rock has been eroded, but large patches still exist, especially in the more southerly section.

The intrusive rocks are mainly quartz monzonite, the largest body of which is the Swansea stock. There are associated bodies of monzonite, monzonite porphyry, lamprophyre, latite porphyry, and diabase; the last three are of minor importance and are found chiefly in dikes, sills, and plugs.

Extrusive rocks consist of a sequence that has been divided into three successive groups: 1) lower flows and tuff beds of quartz latite; 2) intermediate tuffs, flows, and agglomerates of latite and possibly andesite; and 3) basalt flows of relatively late origin. The early series of flows is termed the Packard Volcanics and is the most extensive of the extrusive rocks. It reaches a thickness of several thousand feet and shows abrupt changes in thickness resulting from having been deposited on an uneven surface. It is significant that the Packard quartz latite and the Swansea stock quartz monzonite have nearly identical chemical and mineralogic compositions, emphasizing their origin from a common magma.

The Tushar Mountains Mineral Deposits and Igneous Rocks

The Tushar Mountains are fairly compact in form and rise to 12,173 feet elevation, 6,300 feet above the valleys on either side. Most, but not all, of the well known Marysvale mining region is in these mountains. Here is the most concentrated and varied assemblage of igneous rocks known in the state and a record of volcanic action longer than that of any other center (fig. 17-22). Extrusive rocks from the Tushar Mountains interfinger with and were produced at the same time as other volcanic rocks to the south and east, but the evidence is clear that the present Tushar Mountains are what remain of a long succession of volcanoes that began to erupt about 30 million years ago and continued active until 4 or 5 million years ago.

Seven major groups of igneous rocks are recognized, from oldest to youngest: 1) Mount Dutton Group (fig. 17-23), consisting of latite and andesite flows and breccias; 2) intrusions of monzonite; 3) Dry Hollow-Roger Park Group, consisting of latite tuff, andesite porphyry, basaltic breccia, and other complex rocks; 4) intrusions of granite; 5) older basalt flows; 6) Mount Belknap Group, consisting of flows, tuffs, obsidian, and ignimbrites of mainly rhyolitic composition; and 7) basalt of fairly late origin. Total thickness exceeds 10,000 feet and there were periods of deep erosion between eruptive events.

The Tushar Mountains have produced significant quantities of gold, silver, mercury, copper, lead, zinc, uranium, manganese, iron, and alunite. Six mining districts are recognized. In the Gold Hill district, the Annie Laurie Mine has been the chief producer and gold the chief commodity. In the Mt. Baldy district, the chief producer is the Deer Trail Mine that has yielded ores of lead, zinc, silver, and gold. Alunite occurs chiefly in the Henry district, shared with the Sevier Plateau to the east. Alunite has been mined for both potash and sulfur, but only under wartime emergencies. At the present time it cannot compete with foreign bauxite as an aluminum source or with domestic sedimentary salt deposits as a source of potash. Reserves of 3.75 million tons of alunite, containing 19 percent alumina are calculated for all deposits.

Uranium occurs in all the districts but major production has been from the Antelope Mountains in the Henry district. Ore is found chiefly in the quartz monzonite intrusive and adjacent rhyolite. At present (1985) the known uranium deposits are worked out to their economic limits.

Production of mineral commodities other than those mentioned above has been minor. Total past production of the Tushar Mountains may never be accurately known. A recent compilation credits the Gold Mountain district with a total output of $3.83 million of copper, lead, zinc, gold, and silver from 1892 to 1961. Callaghan (1973) credits the Deer Trail Mine with $4.03 million production for the same metals during the periods 1960-1962 and 1964-1971. Detailed investigation of the surface and present mine workings has convinced geologists of the U.S. Geological Survey that at least three areas in the Tushar Mountains contain major undiscovered deposits of uranium and other metals. Exploratory drilling on the basis of predicted mineralization began in 1981.

Figure 17-22. Volcanic rock, Bullion Canyon Formation, Marysvale Canyon, Sevier County. The exposed rocks are tuffs and breccias.

Figure 17-23. "Big Rock Candy Mountain" near Marysvale, Piute County. A brilliantly colored area of altered volcanic rock in the Mount Dutton Formation. Pyrite has been oxidized causing yellow color and forming selenite.

The Volcanic High Plateaus and Their Mineral Deposits

Volcanic rocks form the protective cover of most of the High Plateaus (fig. 17-24), including the Sevier, Awapa, Fish Lake, northern Paunsaugunt, and northern Markagunt. There is complex interfingering of formations into the Marysvale volcanic pile to the northwest and between the western plateaus and the Great Basin to the west. Because of the transitional relationships along the margins, it is not possible to draw clear-cut boundaries on the basis of rock types alone. Physiographic and structural considerations are helpful; the Hurricane Fault serves as a western boundary to the plateaus as far north as a line connecting Fremont Wash and Spry, Garfield County. This line, in turn, gives a rough but adequate dividing line between the Markagunt Plateau and the Marysvale volcanic pile. From Spry northward, the Sevier River continues as a satisfactory western boundary to the plateaus section.

The complex and varied Mount Dutton Formation, that seems to have originated in the Marysvale center where it is represented by the so-called vent facies, is also recognized as the dominant formation of the Sevier, Awapa, and Fish Lake Plateaus, where the so-called alluvial facies prevails. Great volumes of volcanic breccias are widespread; they reach southward into the Markagunt Plateau as well as far to the north and east. As a rule the volume of tuff, especially the welded varieties, decreases eastward across the plateaus section; thus, the center of production of these rocks was definitely to the west in the Great Basin Province. On the other hand, there is a marked eastward increase in flow rocks (fig. 17-25), especially basalt, across the plateaus. The cap rocks of Sevier Plateau, Awapa Plateau, Fish Lake Plateau, eastern Aquarius Plateau, Table Mountain, and Thousand Lake Mountain are practically all flow rocks (see geologic map).

Relatively few valuable metallic mineral deposits are associated with the volcanic rocks of the High Plateaus; however, there are extensive deposits of alunite on both sides of the Sevier River valley in the vicinity of Marysvale. Following usual custom, they are described in connection with the Marysvale mining district even though, by the scheme used in this book, many belong with the Sevier Plateau. The only other metallic commodity of significance is antimony, once mined from a concentrated area in Antimony Canyon (fig. 17-26) near the town of Antimony, Garfield County, on the western margin of the Awapa Plateau. Relatively small, high-grade pockets were taken from sedimentary beds of the Flagstaff Formation. Ore formation is undoubtedly related to the general igneous activity. There is little mining at present.

Various sedimentary products, such as bentonite, diatomite, and building stone have been taken from the volcanic sequence at scattered localities, and large reserves remain.

Figure 17-24. Brian Head, famous landmark of the western Markagunt Plateau, carved from middle Tertiary volcanic rocks. The elevation is 11,307 feet. Photo: Herbert E. Gregory.

Figure 17-25. Dark-colored Miocene lava flows at mouth of Monroe Canyon, Sevier County. Photo: Ward Roylance.

Figure 17-26. View looking north across Antimony (Coyote) Canyon, Garfield County. Note unconformity between sedimentary and igneous rocks cutting across the view from the left middle border. Antimony is present and has been mined from the sediments about 600 feet below the unconformity. Summit of Awapa Plateau is on the skyline. Photo: Hellmut H. Doelling.

Tonoquints Volcanic Province

One of the major igneous fields of the United States occupies much of the southeastern Great Basin (see geologic map). It is comparable in size and complexity to the San Francisco field of Arizona, the Absaroka field of Wyoming, and the San Juan field of Colorado. It extends roughly from near Richfield, Sevier County, across southern Nevada. The Utah portion has an area of approximately 7,500 square miles. No entirely satisfactory name seems to be available because the field is not centered on any dominating geographic feature. For present descriptive purposes, the term Tonoquints Volcanic Province is suggested (see chap. 21). This huge field is not a fortuitous juxtaposition of separate volcanic centers nor are the exposed rocks products of unrelated events. The rocks that compose it originated during a short span of geologic time, had similar modes of formation, and have much the same chemical characteristics. Under no classification system can this region be divided into more than one clear-cut igneous province.

The three manifestations of igneous activity, plutonic or intrusive rocks, extrusive rocks, and hydrothermal mineral deposits, are all found within the area in close, unmistakable genetic associations. The volcanic rocks were not built up from any dominating center as were those of the Marysvale pile, but occur in widespread continuous sheets. There appear to have been many eruptive centers. The rock units are varied in composition and there is a preponderance of ignimbrites almost everywhere.

Structural conditions are also diverse, mainly because the province lies across the Basin and Range-Colorado Plateau transition zone. On the north, igneous rocks rest upon faulted Paleozoic formations while to the south they are on fairly flat-lying Mesozoic strata. The broad, low area known as the Escalante Desert breaks the continuity of the bedrock outcrops but it is fairly certain that igneous rocks similar to those of adjacent mountains lie under the cover of unconsolidated sediments.

The impressive Pine Valley Mountains are of laccolithic origin (fig. 17-27). They were formed after a long period of volcanic activity had already produced several thousand feet of rhyolite and dacite ignimbrites; flows and breccias of andesite, latite, and dacite; mudflow deposits; and minor air-fall tuffs. The chemical composition of these igneous rocks seems to be reflected in their modes of occurrence; the basalts, andesites, and latites are flows; the dacites are found as ignimbrites and flows; and the rhyolites are all ignimbrites. Eight subdivisions of the extrusive section were mapped and described by E. F. Cook, a leading student of ignimbrites and of the area.

The Pine Valley magma rose and spread laterally between the pre-existing volcanic rocks and the underlying Eocene Claron Formation. At the time of its implacement, the magma is described as being "mush-like" in consistency. The solidified rock, which appears in five large exposures, is classed as monzonite porphyry. Apparently no significant ore deposits are genetically related to the intrusion.

Several major and many minor mining districts are located in the ignimbrite section. As a matter of fact, the rather well defined Wah Wah-Tushar mineral belt, trending N. 82° E. lies mostly within the volcanic field, slightly north of and parallel to its axis. The shorter, less well defined Iron Springs mineral belt lies somewhat further north and includes the mineral deposits of the Iron Springs district.

The iron ore bodies of the Iron Springs (fig. 17-28) district are replacements of the Jurassic Homestake Limestone around the borders of three intrusions of quartz monzonite porphyry. The chief minerals are magnetite, limonite, goethite, apatite, amethyst, and diopside. Total production

Figure 17-27. Pine Valley Mountain, carved from a large Tertiary intrusion, looking north. Triassic and Jurassic rocks are in the foreground. Photo: Utah Historical Society.

through the 42-year period 1923 to 1965 was 72.14 million tons, with a reported value of $340 million. Mining was discontinued in 1982.

The iron-bearing Three Peaks intrusion is 22 million years old by lead-alpha dating and 24 (+4 or -2) million years old by the K/Ar method. Direct and indirect means of dating place the time of formation of the first post-intrusion tuffs at 19 million years. These dates agree well with the growing evidence that most of the igneous activity of southern Utah occurred from 20 to 25 million years ago. Ore deposition was a late phase of the solidification of the associated igneous bodies; the date of mineralization coincides essentially with the cooling of the intrusion.

Figure 17-28. Exposure of quartz monzonite-porphyry, Three Peaks intrusion, Iron Springs District. The numerous dark layers are selvage joints filled with iron minerals. The intrusion is dated as having originated 22 to 24 million years ago. Photo: Kenneth C. Bullock.

Wah Wah-Tushar Mineral Belt

Although the meaning of the association is not clear, the Wah Wah-Tushar mineral belt coincides with the northern edge of the ignimbrite field. The axis of volcanic deposition curves to the left from southwestern Iron County toward central Piute County and the axis of the mineral belt is almost straight from the center of the western boundary of Beaver County to central Piute County. In other words, the two features converge but do not cross. The mineral belt seems to end near Marysvale but the volcanic field continues 30 to 40 miles further east into the High Plateaus.

A variety of intrusive and extrusive igneous rocks are found within the mineral belt that are not greatly different from those of the main Tonoquints field to the south. According to M.P. Erickson (1973), the dominant volcanic rocks of the Milford district, typical of the mineral belt, are ignimbrite sheets of dacitic or rhyolitic composition. They thin to the north so as to cover progressively less of the pre-volcanic topography in that direction. Flows of andesite, rhyolite, and basalt are present but of small extent. Except for the more recent basalt and rhyolite flows, the igneous rocks were produced in the interval from 19 to 35 million years ago.

Several dozen intrusive bodies are exposed along the Wah Wah-Tushar belt. The largest is the Mineral Mountains pluton (fig. 17-29), of which about 100 square miles are exposed. This is the largest exposure of intrusive igneous rocks in Utah and it has yielded an average K/Ar age date of 11 million years. The rock has been called a granite, but quartz monzonite is probably a more precise designation. Practically all intrusions along the Wah Wah-Tushar belt are of this type, a few are granodiorite.

The mineral products of the Wah Wah-Tushar belt, exclusive of those of the Marysvale region, include copper, silver, gold, lead, zinc, tungsten, fluorite, uranium, and perlite. Major deposits have been mined in the Rocky Range, Beaver Mountains, Lake Mountains, Star Range, and San Francisco Mountains. During the early nineteeth century the chief producers of copper, silver, lead, zinc, and gold were the bonanza ore bodies of the Cactus and Horn Silver Mines in the San Francisco Mountains (fig. 17-30). A major molybdenum deposit has been discovered and outlined by drilling in the central Wah Wah Mountains. Development awaits better market conditions. A large silver-bearing ore body near Beryl, Iron County, is currently in production. There are dozens of less productive mines in the belt. Production of tungsten, fluorite, and uranium has been small.

Thomas Range-Keg Mountain-Desert Mountain Volcanic Rocks and Mineral Deposits

A number of relatively low, barren ranges in the approximate center of Juab County constitute a separate and distinct volcanic center with a number of unusual mineral deposits. The only intrusive rocks are bodies of quartz monzonite in Desert Mountain. The oldest group of extrusive

Figure 17-29. Igneous rocks of the Mineral Mountains, Millard County. The massive white exposures are quartz monzonite dated at 11 million years. The heavily vegetated hills on the skyline are rhyolite extrusions dated at about 400,000 years old. Photo: U.S. Bureau of Land Management.

Figure 17-30. San Francisco Mountains, Beaver County, from the west. Rocks on skyline are Precambrian quartzite thrust from the west upon Ordovician rocks seen in the foothills. The rich ore bodies for which the range is famous are on the opposite side.

Figure 17-31. Crystal of topaz in rhyolite, Thomas Range, Juab County. Photo: Ann Staub.

rocks consists of dark lavas, tuffs and agglomerates of andesite basalt, andesite, latite, and rhyodacite. They have been dated about 39 to 38 million years old. An intermediate group consisting chiefly of rhyolitic ash-flow tuff has been dated as 32 to 30 million years old. Rocks believed to be of this group are cut by the Desert Mountain intrusion, dated as being 30 to 27 million years old. The youngest group of igneous rocks did not appear until much later and consists of rhyolite 8 to 10 million years old at Keg Mountain. There are similar rocks in the Thomas Range.

Economic deposits of beryllium, fluorspar, manganese and uranium occur in intimate association with the volcanic rocks. Topaz, the state gemstone, is found in the younger rhyolite flows (figs. 17-31 and 17-32) and has been the subject of much study for almost a century. Other minerals in this flow include garnet, beryl, bixbyite, pseudobrookite, and specularite. The fluorspar deposits are believed to have formed by reactions between dolomite and fluorine-rich fluids accompanying the younger extrusions. Fluorspar is mined chiefly from pipe-like bodies on Spor Mountain. Uranium ores occur on the east and west flanks of the Thomas Range; they are found as veinlets in rhyolite and tuff and also disseminated in tuffaceous sandstone. This area has the world's largest known beryllium deposits (fig. 17-33). Beryllium minerals that replaced certain favorable tuff beds were probably introduced when the younger rhyolites were extruded about 6 million years ago.

The Sheeprock Mountains in Tooele and Juab Counties are mainly sedimentary rocks, but a 12-square-mile outcrop of granite (fig. 17-34) makes up part of the southwestern flank. An age of approximately 19 million years has been determined by radiometric dating. Small bodies of extrusive rock, andesite and rhyolite, make insignificant contributions to the total area. Several mining districts have been established; there has been much prospecting and small shipments of lead and zinc ore are recorded. Efforts to develop the small deposits of manganese, copper, fluorite, and beryllium have been disappointing.

Figure 17-32. "Rock hounds" searching for topaz crystals, Thomas Range, Juab County. Well-formed crystals are found in cavities in the rhyolite and also in the stream beds where they have accumulated by weathering. Photo: U.S. Bureau of Land Management.

Granite Mountains

The Granite Mountains are located entirely within the Dugway Proving Grounds (U.S. Department of Defense) and are almost completely surrounded by silty or muddy lake beds (fig. 17-35). Light-colored granitic rocks (quartz monozonite and quartz diorite), together with biotite-granite gneiss and pegmatites, are the major rock-forming units. A small area of metamorphic rocks of unknown age laps up on the southern end but no extrusive or sedimen-

Figure 17-33. Air view of the Blue Chalk open-pit mine of Brush Wellman, Inc., Topaz Mountain District. Beryllium ore is being mined from volcanic rocks in the Spor Mountain Formation, which is 21 million years old. Paleozoic strata of Spor Mountain appear in ridges in the background. Photo: Brush Wellman, Inc.

Figure 17-34. Specimen of granite from the Sheeprock intrusion with a rosette of beryl crystals. Width of specimen is about 7 inches. Photo: Robert E. Cohenour.

tary rocks are known. The age cannot be determined by geologic association but a sample of pegmatitic mica has yielded a K/Ar date of about 30 million years.

Ibapah Stock (Deep Creek Range)

One of the largest intrusive bodies in Utah with which no extrusive rocks are directly associated is the Ibapah stock with a surface outcrop of about 40 square miles and occupies the entire width of the Deep Creek Range (fig. 17-36). The intrusion also forms the highest peaks of the range and has been deeply eroded on all sides. The constituent rock is classified by some as granodiorite and by others as quartz monzonite, the whole being described as remarkably homogeneous in appearance and composition. It is generally coarse grained and many parts have a porphyritic texture. A number of dikes, one more than 100 feet thick, have been described. No significant extrusive rocks are associated. A K/Ar age of 18.7 (± 0.4) million years has been obtained.

The Deep Creek Range is a potential producer of gold, silver, copper, tungsten, beryllium, and mercury. There has been a great deal of prospecting and exploration in the

Figure 17-35. North end of Granite Mountains, Tooele County. The range is almost entirely granitic and is surrounded by the barren to sparsely vegetated Great Salt Lake Desert. Photo: U.S Army.

Figure 17-36. Granite Canyon with Ibapah Peak in the background, Deep Creek Range, Tooele County. The intrusion making up much of this range is one of the largest in Utah. Photo: Arthur C. King.

Figure 17-37. Gold Hill, Tooele County, August, 1981. The town has experienced several boom periods. During the last, which occurred in the middle 1940's, the population was about three thousand.

area, but to date production has been minor. Mines in the Reilly-Goshute Canyons area are reported to have produced nearly $700,000 worth of gold during the period from 1934 to 1954.

Gold Hill Area

The Gold Hill area is located in the southwestern corner of Tooele County, a few miles from the Nevada border (fig. 17-37). Mines in the area have produced gold, silver, copper, lead, zinc, tungsten, arsenic, and bismuth valued at more than $3 million. There were several boom periods but Gold Hill is now little more than a ghost town. Intrusive and extrusive rocks appear to be intimately related to the ore deposits. An intrusive quartz monzonite stock and associated projections with a total surface area of about 24 square miles makes up most of the east-central part of the mountains. The Gold Hill intrusive is a composite stock; the older component is Jurassic (152 million years) in age and the younger is middle Tertiary (38 million years). A great many porphyry dikes cut the stock and enclosing sediments, and strong metamorphism has affected the intrusion and its surroundings. Small patches of extrusive rock that are clearly remnants of once larger bodies are preserved in the area. Both flows and agglomerates can be identified; they are chiefly latite or trachyte with minor basalt and rhyolite.

The valuable mineral constituents are found in pipe-like deposits, veins, and replacement bodies. The replacement bodies, chiefly in limestone, have yielded copper-lead-silver ores and small quantities of tungsten and the veins have been mined for moderate amounts of tungsten, copper, and gold. More than 100 minerals have been recognized in the ore bodies and metamorphic rocks. Many Gold Hill area minerals are relatively rare and much sought after by collectors. The town of Gold Hill is one of Utah's best preserved ghost towns.

Silver Island Mountains Igneous Rocks and Mineral Deposits

The Silver Island Mountains (fig. 17-38) consist of the Leppy Hills, Silver Island Mountains, and Crater Island. The three components are aligned northeastly from Wendover, Tooele County, into Box Elder County. The geology and geography have been described by Schaeffer and Anderson (1960) and the mineral deposits of the northern part by Campbell and others (1980). A variety of extrusive and intrusive igneous rocks are present. Five small stocks of quartz monzonite, syenite, and granodiorite are reported. One of them has been dated at 140 million years old (Late Jurassic). Dikes of andesite, rhyodacite, lamphrophyre, and aplite are unusually abundant. Extrusive rocks are mainly lavas and breccias; seven flows of andesite and rhyolite were mapped in the Leppy Hills. Many of the flow rocks are porphyritic. A date of 11.6 million years has been obtained from one of the extrusive bodies.

The Silver Island area has been well prospected. Small deposits of silver, gold, copper, and lead have been mined in a minor way in the Crater Island section. Total production from 1908 to 1913 was valued at less than $100,000.

Pilot Range Igneous Rocks and Mineral Deposits

The Pilot Range (fig. 17-39) lies partly in Utah, partly in Nevada. The only intrusive body is a monzonite/quartz monzonite stock underlying Patterson Pass north of Pilot Peak. It is cut by a large dike of diabase, a relatively rare rock in the Great Basin. Small flows of rhyolite and basalt are also present at the north end of the range. A date of 8.4 million years has been obtained for a vitrophyre from this locality.

The Lucin mining district at the north end of the range is chiefly in Utah. Deposits of copper, silver, gold, lead, and zinc have been exploited. The reported value of these metals from 1870 to 1917, the period of most intensive mining, is $3,256,200. Several million dollars' worth of ore may have been extracted since then; iron joined the list of commodities and was mined in a small way in the 1950s.

Figure 17-38. The southern Silver Island Mountains consist of a mixture of igneous and sedimentary rocks. Volcano Peak, in the center of this view, is rhyolite porphyry. Lower ridges on either side are Paleozoic marine sediments.

Figure 17-39. Igneous rocks at the northern end of the Pilot Range near the Utah-Nevada boundary. The flat-topped feature on the left is capped by rhyolite. A smaller basalt-capped hill lies to the right. The rhyolite rests on soft sediments of the Salt Lake Group. Photo: Hellmut H. Doelling.

The semi-precious gemstone variscite was discovered in 1902 a few miles north of Lucin. While of great interest to lapidarists and mineralogists, the total value of mined material is small.

Raft River-Goose Creek-Grouse Creek Mountains Igneous Rocks and Mineral Deposits

Extrusive rocks make up much of the southern and northern Goose Creek Range and there are smaller exposures in nearby uplifts. The larger exposures are rhyolitic flows that have been dated as 4 million years old. In addition, there are extensive surface exposures of the Payette(?) and Salt Lake Formations that are chiefly bedded sediments with a large volcanic ash and tuff component. What is seen at the surface is obviously only a small indication of what is probably a very large body of volcanic-rich sediment in the down-faulted valley areas. In this connection, a significant contribution is that of Nash and Smith (1977) who correlated ash beds from 12 widely separated localities in northern Utah and adjacent parts of Idaho and Nevada. They concluded that large-scale production of ash was a major episode in the history of the region. Unfortunately, exact dates have not been obtained that would place this event in its proper time frame.

The Raft River and Grouse Creek Mountains (fig. 17-40), together with the nearby Albion Range in Idaho, constitute one of a series of unusual configurations extending from Mexico to Canada that are designated as metamorphic core complexes. These are characterized by roughly dome-shaped uplifts of metamorphic rocks separated from overlying, strongly disturbed, non-metamorphosed rocks by extensive, almost flat-lying faults. Detailed study

Figure 17-40. Outcrop of volcanic ash, Salt Lake Group, Grouse Creek Mountains. Photo: Hellmut H. Doelling.

Figure 17-41. Part of the Ashbrook Mining District, Goose Creek Mountains, showing soil-covered topography, mines, and prospect pits. Photo: Hellmut H. Doelling.

indicates that these areas were heated from below and uplifted by resulting expansion of the affected rock column. Subsequent severe stretching and sliding of the uppermost layers has exposed the central cores in uplifts of moderate elevation.

The Raft River-Grouse Creek-Albion core complex consists of late Precambrian metamorphic and igneous rocks. Separated from the core by a complex fault zone are patches of detached, late Paleozoic rocks, chiefly the Oquirrh Formation. An unusual feature is the presence of displaced Paleozoic blocks upon flanking mid-Tertiary sediments. The thermal event that produced the core complex is judged to have occurred between 20 and 55 million years

Figure 17-42. One of many outcrops of the Immigrant Pass intrusion, south end of the Grouse Creek Range. The intrusion is mainly biotite graniodiorite. Photo: Hellmut H. Doelling.

ago, between the Laramide Orogeny and the initiation of Basin and Range faulting. Although a geologic connection is not obvious, it is thought that the formation of core complexes coincided with the widespread extrusion of ignimbrites.

The Ashbrook mining district on the west side of the northern Goose Creek Range (fig. 17-41) has yielded about $400 million worth of silver ore, mainly from replacement bodies in limestone thought to be of Paleozoic age. The area is one of complex thrusting, and the extrusive rocks in the vicinity are chiefly rhyolite porphyry. The Park Valley district on the south flank of the Raft River Mountains is reported to have yielded about $500,000 worth of gold ore. The deposits are in Precambrian rocks but the age of mineralization is unknown.

Intrusive rocks in this region (fig. 17-42) are chiefly of Precambrian age. An irregularly shaped outcrop of quartz monzonite and quartz diorite about 10 miles square makes up the southern Grouse Creek Mountains, Box Elder County. Although there is considerable alteration of bordering rocks the only mineral commodity so far discovered in possible commercial quantities is tungsten. An age date of 23.3 (±0.5) million years has been obtained.

Newfoundland Mountains

The Newfoundland intrusion, about 6 miles square, makes up the highest part of the Newfoundland Mountains (fig. 17-43). The rock is chiefly porphyritic quartz monzonite. It cuts Cambrian and Ordovician sedimentary rocks and has been dated as Jurassic in age. The intrusion is accompanied by small deposits of metals that have been extensively prospected and worked in a sporadic fashion. The chief product has been tungsten ore but there has been

Figure 17-43. The Newfoundland Range, looking southeasterly. An igneous intrusion makes up much of the range north of the pointed peak which is Silurian dolomite. Photo: Hellmut H. Doelling.

minor interest in copper, lead, gold, and silver. No extrusive igneous rocks are present.

LACCOLITHS AND STOCKS OF EASTERN UTAH

Although igneous rocks are rare in eastern Utah, the few that are present are of unusual interest and importance. A study by G. K. Gilbert in 1875 and 1876, based on a trip to the Henry Mountains (fig. 17-44), produced the first irrefutable proof that igneous rocks can deform and push aside the sedimentary strata they penetrate. Gilbert proposed the name laccolites (later modified to laccoliths) for igneous bodies like those he thought responsible for the Henry Mountains. A laccolith, as he envisioned it, is a fairly large body of igneous rock forceably injected between sedimentary strata so as to arch the beds above into domelike form while leaving those below relatively flat. It is now known that the five central peaks of the Henry Mountains are not laccoliths at all but should be classified as stocks (fig 17-45). A stock is a more or less cylindrical, moderate-sized mass rising vertically from depth; however, each of the central stocks of the Henry Mountains (Mt. Ellen, Mt. Pennell, Mt. Hillers, Mt. Holmes, and Mt. Ellsworth) is a source of branching offshoots that are true laccoliths as Gilbert defined them. These radiating laccoliths penetrate into surrounding rocks at various levels. Some are highly eroded, others less so, and many must still be completely buried. The entire aggregation has been aptly called a "Christmas tree" intrusion. The Henry Mountains are the largest of the seven laccolithic mountain groups of the Colorado Plateau. The five high peaks form a chain-like north-south aggregation about 40 miles long in Wayne and Garfield Counties.

The Henry Mountain intrusions consist of diorite porphyry with small amounts of monzonite porphyry in Mt. Pennell and a few scattered dikes and sills of basalt and aplite. There are differences in texture from locality to locality but no great variations in chemical composition. This indicates that a common magma chamber must have supplied all the intrusive material. No extrusive rocks are found but it is

Figure 17-44. The Henry Mountains, looking northwesterly across the Colorado River. At the left margin is Mount Holmes and near the center is Mt. Hillers. The pointed peak at far center is Mt. Pennell and the distant snow-capped peak is Mt. Ellen. Photo: U.S. Bureau of Reclamation.

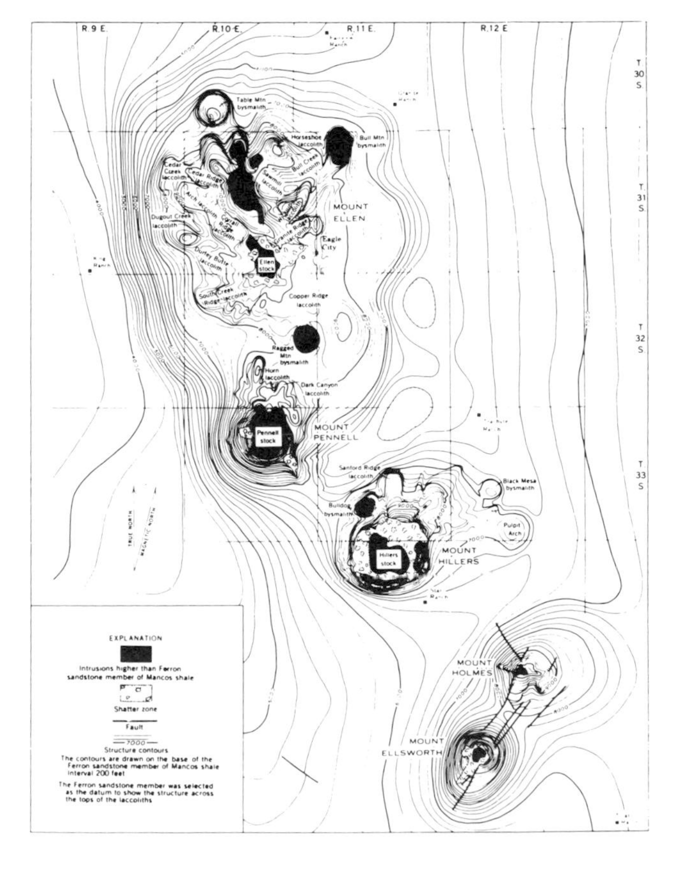

Figure 17-45. Structure contour map of the Henry Mountains showing distribution of inferred and exposed intrusions. From Hunt, 1953.

likely that magmas originally reached the surface to produce volcanic rocks.

A small amount of gold, associated with copper, has been produced from fissures on Mt. Ellen and Mt. Pennell and a little placer gold has been obtained from gravels derived from the mountains. The uranium and vanadium ores in flanking sedimentary rocks were already in existence before the intrusions and seem to have no connection with igneous activity.

Across the Colorado River from the Henry Mountains, in San Juan County, is the Abajo (or the Blue Mountain) group (fig. 17-46). This is also an aggregation of peaks, but the group is much more compact. Four igneous centers are present including 33 laccoliths. The dominant rock types are identified as diorite porphyry and quartz diorite porphyry (fig. 17-47).

Figure 17-46. Aerial view of the Abajo (Blue) Mountains, looking west. Flat-lying Jurassic and Cretaceous formations make up the foreground. Photo: Sherman A. Wengerd.

The Abajo Mountains have been intensively prospected and a few small gold-bearing deposits have been mined, usually at a loss. A small amount of placer gold, evidently from sources associated with the intrusions, has been taken from gravel along Johnson Creek. No extrusive rocks are present.

About 50 miles north of the Abajo Mountains, in southeastern Grand County, are the LaSal Mountains (fig. 17-48). Intrusions occur in three distinct groups; northern, central, and southern, aligned in a north-south direction with the long axis of the northern and southern groups each trending northwesterly in conformance with the major faults and salt anticlines in the general region (see physiographic and geologic maps). The northern group has an elliptical shape similar to that of several nearby salt structures and is directly in line with the Paradox Valley to the east. The central group is roughly tri-radiate with Mt. Peale (nearly 13,000 feet) as the highest point. The southern group is in line with salt structures to the southeast and northwest. The alignment suggests some degree of intrusive control by deep-seated regional fractures which also determined the trend of large faults and anticlines.

The chief rock type is diorite porphyry, with minor bodies of aegirine granite porphyry and soda rhyolite porphyry also present. No extrusive rocks occur but it is thought that the northern group preserves the roots of once-active volcanoes, the upper levels of which have been destroyed by erosion. Small amounts of copper, lead, zinc, selenium, silver, and gold are associated with the intrusions. Placer gold, evidently derived from the igneous rocks, has been taken from several gravel deposits on the mountain flanks.

Mineral dating of the three major laccolithic groups place the formation of the Henrys at 44 million years, the Abajos at 28 million years and the LaSals at 24 million years.

Solitary, dome-shaped Navajo Mountain (fig. 17-49) rises above a wilderness of eroded sandstone formations

Figure 17-47. Summit of Abajo (Blue) Mountains, San Juan County, Utah. Abundant rubble is weathering from the latite porphyry which forms the central igneous intrusion. Photo: Herbert E. Gregory.

Figure 17-48. Summit area of the LaSal Mountains. The peaks consist almost entirely of diorite porphyry. Glaciation has sharpened the profiles of the higher elevations that are well above the timber line. Photo: Ward Roylance.

near the Utah-Arizona line in Kane County. A body of igneous rock is possibly concealed within the shell of sediments. This is a sacred mountain to the Navajo Indians. Fortunately, no mineral deposits have been found which would lead to mining or road building.

Figure 17-49. Navajo Mountain, looking southeast. The light colored ridges on the slope are Navajo Sandstone. The upper slopes and summit are younger formations including the Dakota Sandstone. A dome-like intrusion of igneous rock almost certainly lies within the shell of sediments. Photo: U.S. Bureau of Reclamation.

Discussions of mid-Tertiary igneous rocks of Utah would be incomplete without mention of the peculiar features called diatremes. There are many in nearby Arizona. Two examples, in Utah, are the Mule Ear diatreme near Mexican Hat, San Juan, County, and Alhambra Rock. Alhambra Rock is shown in figure 17-50. The matrix is basic rock intruded from great depths, but there are pieces of younger rocks, even some from much higher than any formations seen in the surrounding countryside, that have been mixed into a jumbled mass, probably by the churning action of hot vapors and solutions. An age of about 30 million years has been determined for the date of intrusion.

Figure 17-50. Aerial view of Alhambra Rock, San Juan County. As seen in this view, the protruding well-like intrusion is the thicker part of a dike that extends away from it in both directions. Photo: Peter Winn.

For additional reading on the topics discussed in Chapter 17, please see the following list of authors:

Anderson, W.L., 1960
Armstrong, 1963, 1969, 1970, 1973
Armstrong and Suppe, 1973
Armstrong and others, 1969
Atwater, 1970
Baker, W.H., 1959
Beeson, 1927
Best, 1969, 1970
Best and Brimhall, 1974
Best and others, 1973
Bick, 1958, 1966
Blue, 1960
Boutwell, 1912, 1933
Bowers, D., 1978
Bray and Wilson, 1975
Bullock, K.C., 1970, 1973, 1976
Bullock, K.D., and Proctor, 1949
Butler, 1913
Butler and others, 1920
Calkins and others, 1943
Callaghan, 1939, 1973
Campbell and others, 1980
Christiansen and Lipman, 1972
Cohenour, 1959, 1963
Compton and others, 1977
Condie, 1973
Cook, D.R., 1957
Cook, E.F., 1957, 1960a, 1960b, 1963

Crittenden and others, 1952
Crosby, 1972, 1973
Cross, Whitman, 1886
Dane, 1935
Dasch, 1974
Doelling, 1975
Dutton, 1880
Erickson, A.J., 1968
Erickson, M.P., 1973
Everett, 1961
Everden and James, 1964
Everden and others, 1964
Felix, 1956
Gilbert, 1877
Gilluly, 1927, 1929, 1932
Graff, 1959
Granger, 1963
Gregory, 1938
Griffitts, 1964, 1969
Griffitts and Rader, 1963
Hamblin, 1970
Hammond, 1961
Hanley, 1950
Hausel and Nash, 1977
Hewitt, 1968
Hilpert, 1964
Hintze and Whelan, 1973
Hodge and others, 1968
Hunt, C.B., 1953, 1954
Hunt and others, 1953
James and others, 1969
Kerr, 1957, 1963, 1968
Lindgren and Loughlin, 1919
Lindsey and others, 1975
Lipman and others, 1972, 1978
Lovering, 1949
Lovering and Morris, 1960
McKee, E.H., 1971
Mackin, 1947, 1960, 1963
Mardirosian, 1977
Meeves and others, 1966
Menard, 1960
Moore, 1973a, 1973b
Moore and others, 1972, 1973a, 1973b
Morris, 1968
Morris and Lovering, 1962
Nash and Smith, 1977
Nolan, 1935
O'Toole, 1951
Paddock, 1956
Park, 1970
Patton, 1908
Peterson, V.E., 1942
Proctor 1959a, 1959b
Proctor and Bullock, 1963
Rowley and others, 1965, 1975, 1978
Schaeffer and Anderson, 1960
Shawe and others, 1972
Shepard and others, 1968
Staatz and Carr, 1964, 1974
Staatz and Osterwald, 1959
Stacey and Zartman, 1978
Stokes, 1968
Stowe, 1975
Stringham, 1942
Stuart-Alexander and others, 1972
Thomson, 1973
Thorpe, 1919
Traver, 1949
U.S. Bureau of Mines, 1961
Utah Geological and Mineral Survey, 1942
Utah Historical Society, 1963
Utah Mining Association, 1959, 1967
Wells, 1938
Wender, 1976
Whelan, 1970
Williams, N.C., 1963, 1964
Witkind, 1975
Woodward, 1965, 1967

For complete bibliographic citations, please see List of References.

18 THE LANDSCAPE TAKES FORM

In allusion to its sedimentary layered structure, the Earth is frequently compared to a gigantic layer cake. The successive, superimposed rock strata not only constitute a record of past geologic history but also provide raw material from which sucessive landscapes have been carved. Thus, the cake analogy may be extended from the concept of original layering to the point where cakes and rocks are cut or crumble away. What has been learned about past geologic periods from the rock record has already been outlined. How the present landscape came to be is the theme of the present chapter.

After Middle Triassic time, uplift and erosion affected ever expanding regions of western North America. The Nevadan and Sevier Orogenies, described in chapter 15, elevated the Great Basin, including western Utah, to the extent that it was never again flooded by the ocean. Later, during the Laramide Orogeny, the seas were expelled from eastern Utah as well. For another 12 million years the area remained not far above sea level and deposition continued in the extensive Green River and Flagstaff fresh-water lakes and other smaller ones (fig. 18-1). Eventually they also disappeared, leaving only low-lying flood plains to receive permanent sedimentary deposits.

The most recent significant sedimentary formation of eastern Utah is the Duchesne River Formation of late Eocene age. It was deposited in a semi-tropical climate by sluggish streams running southward from the Uinta Mountains across the Uinta Basin. If there were lakes farther south in the Colorado Plateau all evidence has been eroded. Clearly there were no deep structural basins and any water bodies would have been shallow. After active deposition ceased in the late Eocene a condition of near equilibrium may have prevailed over most of Utah for additional millions of years. Erosion and deposition proceeded at a slow pace and produced open valleys and low uplands, all deeply weathered under the more humid climate that seems to have prevailed during the Oligocene and Miocene. This placid scene was eventually disrupted by several events which imparted vast additional energy to the stream systems and initiated a long period of intense erosion. Most important mid-Tertiary events were regional uplift of the entire western United States and the capture of the upper Green River by the Colorado River.

It is an oddity of geography that most of southwestern Wyoming should drain into the Pacific Ocean by way of the Green and Colorado Rivers. How this drainage found its way across the great obstacle of the Uinta Range is a story pieced together from a variety of clues (fig. 18-2). Our account must be short and generalized. Until about 30 million years ago, the upper Green River was a tributary of the Platt River and its waters eventually reached the Gulf of Mexico. This pattern was upset by the relatively sudden collapse and subsidence of the east end of the Uinta Mountains. How and why the crest of a previously high mountain should sink below the general level of the surrounding country is not fully understood but there appears to have been a keystone effect as what is now Browns Park settled to form an elongate trough that roughly follows the crest of the East Dome of the Uinta Mountains. It is tempting to relate this event to other happenings that occurred at a time when compression lessened against the western margin of the United States and the oblique motion of the San Andreas Fault system began.

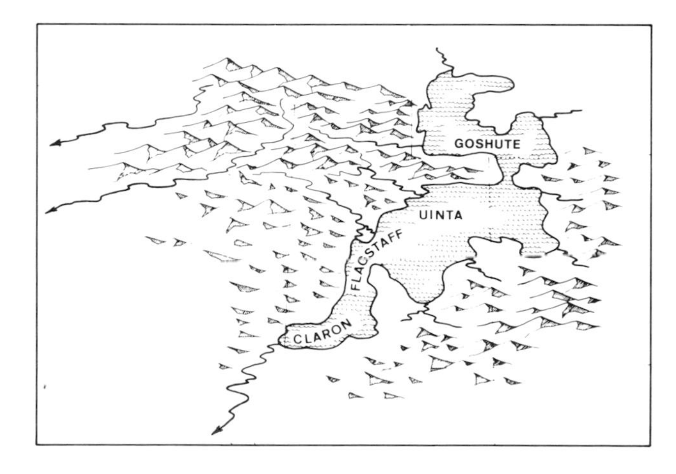

Figure 18-1. Generalized paleogeography of Utah and adjacent areas during the Eocene Epoch. The chief lakes are named. It is doubtful that all of these were contemporaneous and had their maximum extent at the same time. Courses of rivers are highly conjectural. From Stokes, 1979.

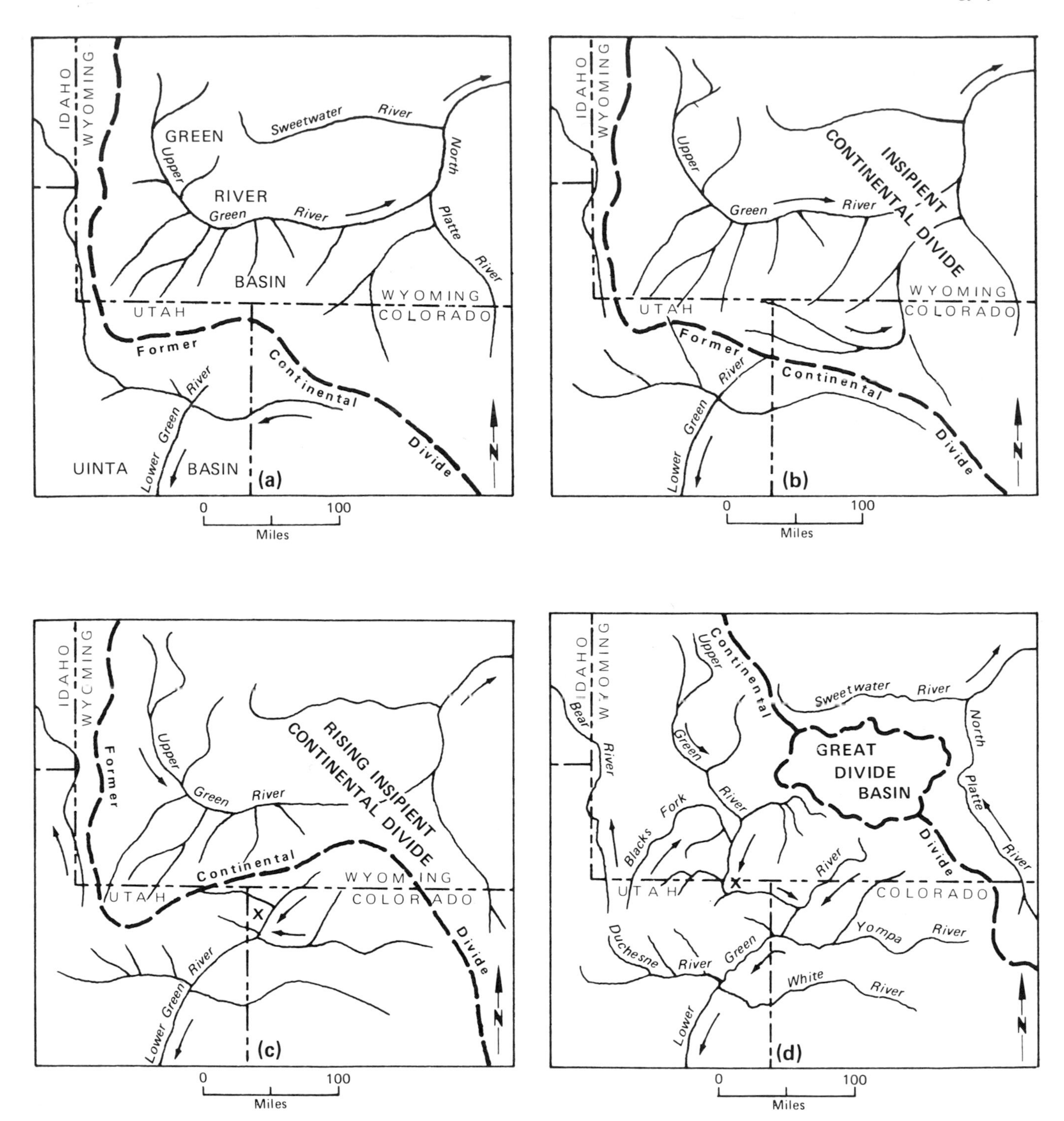

Figure 18-2. Capture and diversion of the Upper Green River. (a) Drainage pattern in the middle Tertiary (early Miocene). The Continental Divide is in western Wyoming and along Uinta Mountains. The Upper Green River joins the Platte and drains to the Atlantic. (b) Collapse of eastern Uinta Range creates Browns Park graben and an east-flowing stream parallel to the Continental Divide. (c) Headward erosion of Green River tributaries and filling of Browns Park graben allows capture of eastern Uinta drainage at X. Continental Divide shifts northeastward. (d) Headward erosion of east-flowing Browns Park drainage captures some of the streams of the north Uinta slope at point X and eventually taps the Green River, which may have been ponded in the Green River Basin at this time. With this final diversion, the entire Upper Green River was diverted to the Colorado system and the Continental divide shifted to its present position in central Wyoming. The Great Divide Basin sits on the divide with no external drainage. Modified from Hansen, USGS Bulletin 1291, 1969.

One drastic effect of the depression of Browns Park was the ponding of an extensive body of water within it and the diversion of the upper Green River to become its largest tributary. As the lake rose within the irregularly shaped basin it eventually reached the lowest point in the rim which happened to be a low pass leading southward into the Uinta Basin. Once it reached the outlet the water spilled out and energetically began to cut what today is the Canyon of Lodore. Through this canyon passed not only the lake waters and much of the sediment of the lake bottom but eventually the drainage of most of southwestern Wyoming. Quite suddenly the former drainage of the Colorado River almost doubled and the stage was set for drastic changes along the entire system. Although the capture of the Green River is well documented geologically, what happened downstream remains conjectural. It may be that the newly added runoff only enlarged existing downstream lakes in Utah and Arizona or it may have over-filled the southernmost lake and diverted the entire system to the Pacific drainage (fig. 18-3).

At this point something more may be said about the history of the Colorado River. The Green River could not have been in existence when the great Uinta Lake was at full stage but it was flowing by Pliocene time, 30 million years later. Much happened during this interval that is now difficult to reconstruct. Many investigators believe that for much of this time drainage from the Colorado Plateau was into the Atlantic by way of the Rio Grande system. This might be expected from what is known about the eastward shift of the continental divide. During the Cretaceous, the divide was somewhere in Nevada, today it crosses Colorado. During intervening time there was obviously a drastic eastward shift and a diversion of drainage into the Pacific Ocean. At some time during the shifting process there may have been a ponding of water in a large lake, possibly located in northern Arizona. This hypothetical lake may have been the one that was filled to overflowing by the diversion of the Green River in Miocene time.

In any event, the Colorado River did establish a route to the Pacific Ocean and became one of the most erosive streams on Earth. Its waters, no longer ponded, could now cut rapidly downward into valley fill, lake bed sediments, and solid bedrock. Tributaries also were charged with heightened, erosive energy as they cut ever deeper to keep pace with the master stream (fig. 18-4). Even small contributing gullies in distant highlands were eventually affected and cut not only downward, but headward into higher ground.

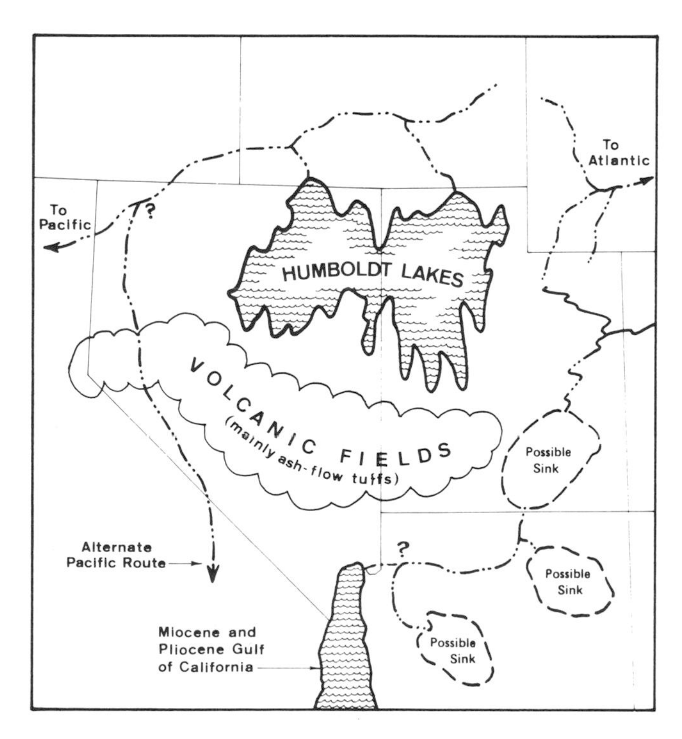

Figure 18-3. Hypothetical hydrologic features of Utah and vicinity during middle Tertiary time. Adapted from Stokes, 1979.

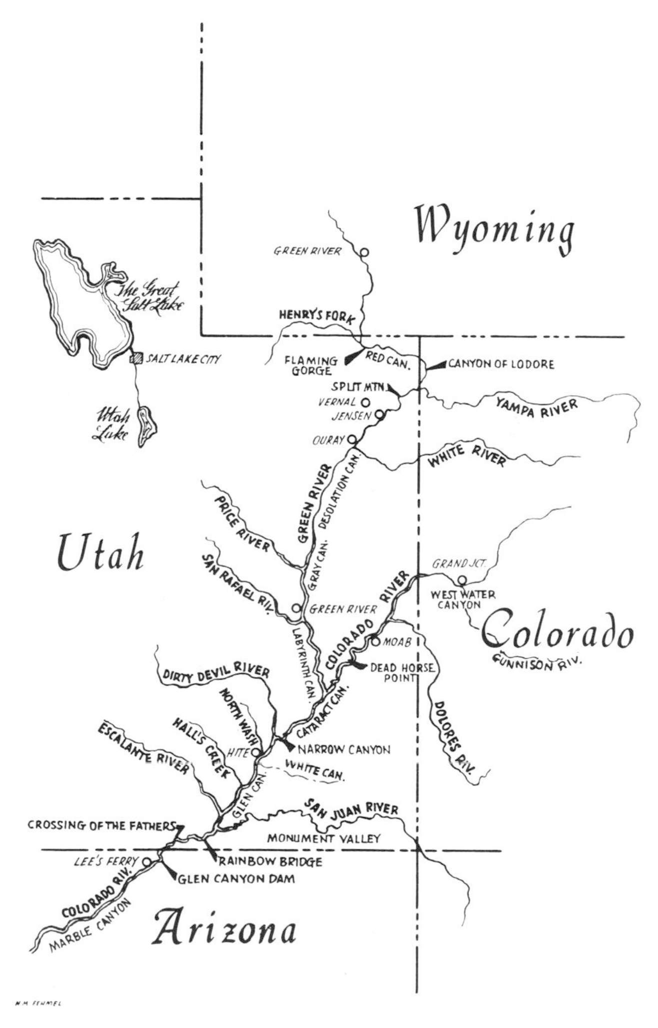

Figure 18-4. The upper Colorado and its major tributaries. The great canyons, a few of the scenic attractions, and settlements near the river are noted. Diagram: Utah Historical Society.

Estimates of the amount of erosion on the Colorado Plateau have been made by various geologists. Based on the sediment load carried by the Colorado River today, the drainage basin is being lowered about 6.5 in. per 1,000 years, or about a mile every 10 million years. Certainly there have been times less favorable to erosion than the present, but probably not many that were more favorable. At the present rate, about all the material available to be removed could be removed in 20 million years or so.

DEVELOPMENT OF THE GREAT BASIN

While eastern Utah lay under the ocean until near the close of the Cretaceous Period, western Utah was elevated and being eroded. This is proved not so much by what is found in the Great Basin itself, but by the evidence from the adjoining territory to the east where there are many cubic miles of coarse debris, all clearly derived and transported from the west. The earliest identifiable fragments are found in the Late Jurassic Curtis Formation. Sediments from the west reached a flood stage in the Late Cretaceous when great conglomeratic deposits spread eastward across much of central and northern Utah, declined in the early Tertiary and ceased near the close of the Eocene 40 million years ago. By then much of the higher ground had been effectively erased by erosion.

Since the Great Basin today is mostly lower than the Colorado Plateau, there has obviously been a great reversal in relative position since the middle Tertiary. One geologist refers to a decline of the Great Basin; others describe the event as a great collapse or subsidence. No matter how it is viewed, it was certainly a major event in shaping the western United States.

It bears emphasis that although the Great Basin declined or collapsed by sagging or bending of subcrustal material the surface expression was subsidence along literally hundreds of normal faults, most of which trend in northerly directions. Erosion has modified the structural blocks to produce the distinctive basin-and-range topography.

The arrangement of geologic features within the Great Basin section of the Basin and Range Province is not entirely haphazard. A crude, but unmistakable, symmetry is seen when the locations of the great Ice Age lakes, Bonneville and Lahontan, are considered. Lake Bonneville was crowded toward the eastern edge, Lake Lahontan toward the west. Between them, in east-central Nevada, is a crude divide or low barrier. A degree of symmetry around this axis has been noted in connection with Tertiary volcanism and several other features. Contrary to several theories, the faulting that accompanied the collapse shows no clear symmetry in either distribution or in time of origin. Faulting began in the late Mesozoic and is still continuing along much the same lines and in the same areas (fig. 18-5). There does seem to have been a marked acceleration during mid-Tertiary time. In practical terms this means that basins exist in which sediments might be of any age from Late Cretaceous to Quaternary; adjacent basins might have different histories and different rock records.

Figure 18-5. West-facing front of the Wasatch Range near Nephi, Juab County. A fault scarp of fairly recent origin follows the foot of the range and is a reminder of the process by which the Great Basin has been lowered with respect to its surroundings. Photo: Ward Roylance.

The effects of subsidence are obvious but the causes are still being debated. Early ideas called on the withdrawal of lava from deeper levels and on effects of cooling of the mantle below the crust. As might be expected, the theory of plate tectonics has generated many new ideas. The geologic history of western North America between the Triassic and the middle Tertiary must be considered as background. During this interval, the Cordilleran region experienced mountain building and volcanic activity on a vast scale. North America was actively moving westward to collide with and override the margin of the Pacific basin. Effects were compressional and it is only to be expected that sedimentary rocks of the former Cordilleran geosyncline were folded and uplifted into several great mountain systems. As long as active pressure was exerted against the continental margin, mountain building continued and rocks of the Great Basin were elevated, perhaps to spectacular heights.

In the middle Tertiary, about 40 to 30 million years ago, the Pacific Plate began to move northwesterly while the American plate slowed down or came to a halt. This was a great and fundamental change and it left a record of widespread effects. It was a time of reorganization of many interlocking plates, the full effects of which are still being analyzed. In western North America it marked the beginning of the San Andreas Fault system which is still carrying the Pacific Plate away from North America on an oblique path. It is the timing that is important. The change in direction of plate motion, the beginning of movement on the San Andreas Fault and the intensification of the collapse of the Great Basin are all closely associated events of the middle Tertiary. This in itself hints at a common cause.

Geologists are using the terms extensional tectonics or extensional faulting to describe what has happened in the Great Basin. Normal faults are extensional features because two points originally in contact become farther apart horizontally (a measurement called the heave) as faulting progresses. By adding up the estimated horizontal displacements on all normal faults between the Sierra Nevada and Wasatch Ranges, an extension of between 60 and 100 miles has been calculated. Gravity then becomes the force responsible for dragging down the crust of the Great Basin but the splintering into narrow blocks is a modifying effect that is not fully understood. The creation of eroded ranges and alluvial valleys followed as a consequence of the surficial activity of wind and water.

The exposed mountain ranges are long, narrow and, for the most part, they trend in northerly directions. Most geologists in the past and many today regard each valley and each mountain as a separate block separated by steeply dipping normal faults. In contrast, the view seems to be gaining ground that the whole aggregation is a series of tilted blocks, the upper edge of which constitutes the ranges, and the lower parts, mostly covered by alluvium, the valleys. This theory, in effect, reduces the number of faults and makes half-grabens out of the depressions (fig. 18-6). Both arrangements can be explained by stretching the substratum and allowing the blocks to settle. The configuration of the faults becomes the critical clue. If the arrangement is a horst-and-graben system, the faults should be steeply dipping and should continue downward until absorbed into the mantle below. If the blocks are tilted, the faults should flatten gradually and eventually become horizontal at the top of a less brittle layer (such faults are called listric faults). The structure is a large-scale duplicate of surficial landslide blocks which can be seen and studied in their entireties.

Much attention has been focused on the structure and stratigraphy of the individual ranges of western Utah (fig. 18-7), particularly those with major mineral deposits. The deposition of ore, formation of igneous bodies and, to a lesser extent, the internal structure of the ranges were mostly determined before the collapse of the region - that is, before about 30 million years ago. In contrast, the arrangement of the ranges with respect to one another, the sizes of the blocks composing them, and the position of each block as a whole would seem to have been determined largely at the time of collapse. If these assumptions are true, it is possible to learn a great deal about the past few million years from studies of the existing internal structure and stratigraphy of the ranges. Evidence from the igneous deposits, such as ash beds and lava that originated during or after collapse, is very significant in working out the history.

EMERGENCE OF LANDFORMS

A brief summary of middle Tertiary events will justify and clarify the title of this chapter which implies that this was the time when the present landscape took form. Many basic geologic concepts are involved. First, the ideas of planation and peneplanation. That rivers cannot cut below sea level is obvious. When a region is near sea level streams can erode only from side to side, slowly and gradually removing existing elevations. Given time an essentially featureless peneplain (almost a plain) will theoretically be produced. What happened in eastern Utah and much of the western United States during the Oligocene illustrates this. Wide areas of formerly rugged and uneven topography had been eroded to an almost uniform plain. Possibly, for a short period, the only identifiable feature in eastern Utah, in terms of present topography, were the Uinta Mountains and they were evident only as a spine of relatively low, rounded hills.

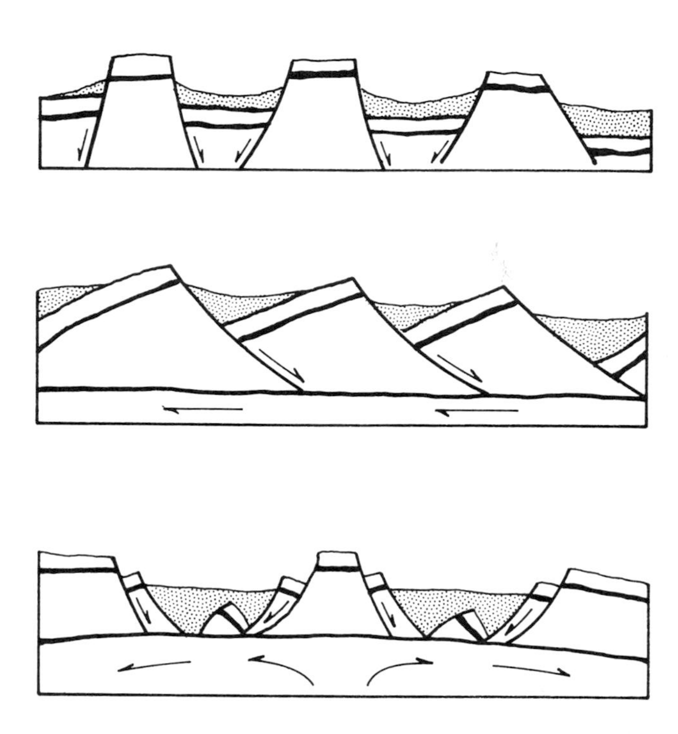

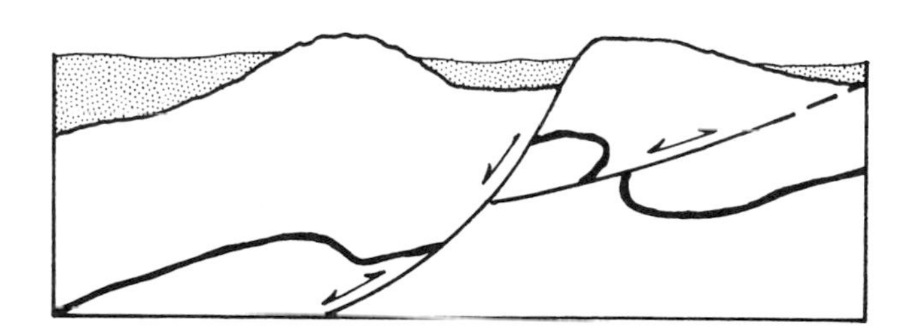

Figure 18-6. Explanations for the basin-and-range structure of the Great Basin. First cross-section illustrates the horst-and-graben theory, each mountain bounded by high-angle normal faults on each side. Second section shows the mountains as tilted blocks with bounding faults merging with horizontal master displacement at depth. Third section illustrates expansion of an underlying plastic layer with downward displacement of overlying rocks. Fourth section illustrates reversal of movement along planes of thrust faulting to create normal faults. Arrows show direction of movement in corresponding blocks.

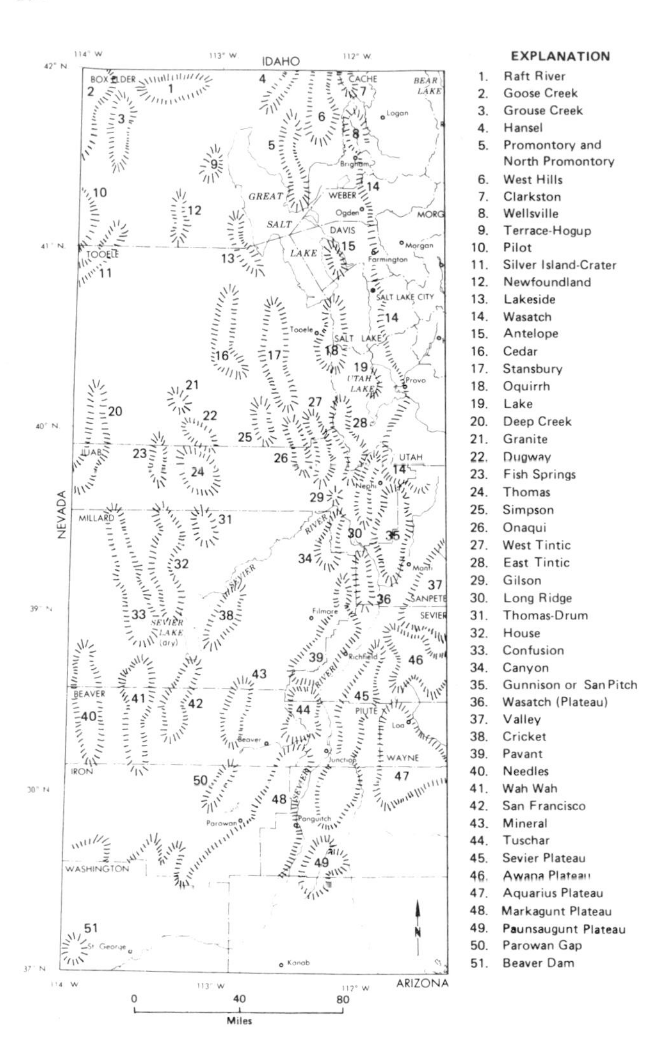

Figure 18-7. Diagrammatic map of ranges of the eastern Great Basin, western Utah. Names listed on right are numbered to correspond with localities shown on the left.

What is now the central Colorado Plateau and Four Corners region was probably occupied by several large shallow lakes, each with its individual drainage and low marginal divides. There was, as yet, no Colorado River. Although the San Rafael Swell, Circle Cliffs, and Monument Uplifts had been formed long before in the Laramide Orogeny, they had been worn down and perhaps covered by sediment to the extent that they had no surface expression.

The mountains and plateaus that now constitute the north-south backbone of the state were not prominant. Western, central, and eastern Utah were nearly at the same elevation, the whole being possibly less than 1,000 feet above sea level. Sizeable rivers drained from west to east across what would become the Wasatch Range, and almost surely, much of south-central Utah drained westward to the vicinity of what is now Sevier Lake (or sink).

Several volcanic centers were intermittently active in what would become the Tushar, Pine Valley, Thomas, and Tintic Ranges. Lava, ash, and breccia clogged, ponded, and diverted drainage in ways that are now impossible to reconstruct. When volcanism was at its height, the process of faulting that would eventually divide the Great Basin into prominent north-trending basins and mountains was getting under way.

A hypothetical space view of Utah several million years after erosion became dominant would reveal important alterations in the landscape. Most of the changes in eastern Utah were due to integration of the Colorado drainage system. As a result of the capture of the upper Green River and its diversion from the north to the south side of the Uinta Mountains, the lower Green River (in Utah) became the dominating stream and gathered tributary after tributary across eastern Utah. Clearly, the course of the Colorado River (as distinct from the Green) was determined by a diagonal zone of crustal weakness that had its beginning in Precambrian time and is now called the Colorado River Lineament.

The integration of river systems in the western United States is usually regarded as a consequence of regional uplift. Energy imparted to streams that were forced to follow steeper courses intensified erosion and led to the cutting of canyons and lengthening of tributaries on all sides. The Colorado Plateau presents world-famous proof of the process in the form of deep canyons (fig. 18-8) and especially in the meander patterns (fig. 18-9) that characterize stretches of both large and small streams. Meandering courses, such as that followed by the present-day Mississippi River, are formed on level flood plains where streams unconfined by valley walls obey the laws that govern freely flowing water. In order for a curving meander pattern to

Figure 18-8. Powerful erosive action of the Colorado River is manifested in the Big Drop, a major rapids in Cataract Canyon. Walls are chiefly the Hermosa Formation (Pennsylvanian).

Figure 18-9. Goosenecks of the San Juan River, San Juan County are possibly the best known meanders in North America. Pennsylvanian Hermosa Formation makes up lower two-thirds of canyon walls. The upper canyon walls up to the bare and level surface above the rims are Permian and are variously mapped as Rico or Goodrich. Note view area at left center. Photo: U.S. Bureau of Reclamation.

become incised below the surface, the river must somehow gain enough energy to cut rapidly downward (fig. 18-10). The process may be complex, but incised meanders seen along the Colorado River and its tributaries are regarded by most geologists as evidence of regional mid-Tertiary uplift.

Whether the larger rivers maintained their courses during uplift and once in a certain pattern could not turn aside to easier routes or, by contact, they worked their way downward into and across pre-existing topographic features is a basic geomorphic problem.

The facts to be considered in choosing between antecedence (rivers maintaining their courses during uplift) and superposition (rivers eroding downward into buried structures during uplift) are evident in the space photographs of representative parts of the Colorado Plateau. For example, three permanent rivers, the Price, San Rafael, and Muddy cross the kidney-shaped San Rafael Swell almost at right angles. The Swell is a prominent topographic feature that rises 2,000 feet above lower ground on all sides. If the rivers were to take what are now easier courses they would avoid the Swell entirely and follow the valleys that encircle it to the north and south. How then did the rivers take up courses into, across, and out of this uplift as though it did

Figure 18-10. Escalante River gorge, looking north. Partly filled with water of Lake Powell, the remarkable meandering canyon is nevertheless well shown. It has been called the crookedest river on earth. Slickrock benches on either side are Navajo Sandstone. Photo: U.S. Bureau of Reclamation.

not exist? Under the antecedence theory the rivers were running along their southeasterly courses when the rocks were undeformed and the Swell did not exist. When it did begin to bow upward the swelling action was so slow that the rivers were powerful enough to maintain their courses across the obstacle.

According to the superposition theory, the drainage history is somewhat more complex (fig. 18-11). The Swell was folded and uplifted before the rivers existed. It was then planed off to at least the highest levels that now exist and had little or no surface expression. At that time the entire Colorado Plateau may have been an extensive low-lying plain with thin sedimentary deposits and perhaps even shallow lakes. It was on this plain that the rivers originated. Following the slope of the land they flowed, on gentle gradients, from high ground to the northwest toward the youthful Colorado River on the east. As they cut downward their tributaries first uncovered and later etched out the pre-existing structures. The process is easily visualized; it is still going on at the present time.

C. B. Hunt (1956) has proposed a hypothesis combining features of both superposition and antecedence, quite properly called anteposition. It follows the concept of superposition to the extent that a river is able to maintain its course only up to a certain point in time, after which its waters are ponded behind the growing barrier. The river may fail to keep pace for several reasons: The volume of water may decline, uplift might speed up, or territory behind the barrier might actively subside. Even without overflowing, the resulting lake need not grow indefinitely; it need expand only to the point where evaporation equals inflow. However, incoming sediment usually fills such basins until the water level reaches a low point in the barrier, usually the level of the former channel. After the river reoccupies the abandoned channel the process of downcutting is now superposition. Eventually the sedimentary contents of the lake may be entirely removed and the river will begin to trench the bedrock upstream of the barrier. Thus, according to the anteposition concept, an entire river system, trunk streams, and major tributaries, might eventually cut a succession of canyons across alternating structural uplifts and depressions (fig. 18-12). This is apparently what is seen in the Colorado River system today, but even Hunt admits that the cutting of the Grand Canyon across the last great barrier "is one of the major problems of Cenozoic history."

Several additional factors have possibly been given insufficent attention in the history of the Colorado Plateau. One is regional tilting. During much of the Tertiary and perhaps even some of the Mesozoic, southwestern Utah and adjacent Arizona tilted slowly to the northeast. This effect has

Figure 18-11. The Green River crossing Split Mountain anticline. The problem of choosing between the theories of superposition and antecedence is well illustrated here. The Green River, after flowing between low banks in the open valley of Island Park, upper left, plunges directly into the anticline. It emerges from Split Mountain between walls of the Weber Sandstone, right center, and again flows through open country into the Uinta Basin. On the theory of antecedence the river has maintained its course during uplift of the anticline across its path; on the superposition theory the river once ran on a level, featureless plain as high or higher than the crest of the anticline as expressed in the hard rocks that now outline it. The basic anticline structure, formed millions of years earlier, lay below the higher surface. By cutting downward and by sending out tributaries that have removed the softer formations on the flanks of the anticline the river has carved the entire landscape on an essentially static crustal block. The superposition model is favored. In fact, a considerable tract of the original pre-canyon surface is preserved in the rolling, heavily vegetated territory in the background. This surface may have formed in the Miocene as much as 10 million years ago. Photo: Hal Rumel.

Figure 18-12. Looking west through Provo Canyon with the slopes of Mt. Timpanogos on the right and Cascade Mountain on the left. Note that the canyon consists of a more steep-sided inner gorge and a broader more valley-like upper part. The older upper profile may have been cut by an east flowing stream at a time when the Great Basin was topographically higher. See text for explanation. Photo: A.J. Eardley.

forced the Colorado River to run "against the grain," cutting successively deeper canyons from north to south. That it has been able to do so without being ponded more than it has is a tribute to its great erosive power.

Another poorly understood factor is wind erosion. This might seem at first glance to have had no effect on the river and an insignificant role in erosion. Evidence is hard to obtain because wind action is sheetlike and not confined to definite channels. Rock fragments moved by wind will probably leave the area entirely and settle to become unrecognizable components of formations in distant localities. In Utah, southwesterly winds have been generally prevailing for a very long time (figs. 18-13a and 18-13b). Any material removed has traveled northeasterly in a direction exactly opposite that carried by the Colorado River. It is within the realm of possibility that wind has removed as much or more material than the river. This interesting topic is clearly worthy of future attention.

The establishment of the major outlines of a river system such as the Colorado is only preliminary to creation of landforms within it. Like a vine sending out branches and tendrils, a master river generates a system of subdividing tributaries that play dominant roles in creating details in interstream areas (fig. 18-14). Tributaries that originate after the main system are guided by inequalities in the bedrock rather than by the orginal slope of the land. The key concept, demonstrated with great clarity in the Colorado Plateau, is "differential erosion" (fig. 18-15). Simply stated, differential erosion means that under given conditions of climate, hard rocks will stand higher or protrude farther than soft rocks (fig. 18-16). This might even be called the first law of scenery. In specific terms, streams operating on a diverse aggregation of hard and soft strata will eventually remove softer layers and leave the harder ones in relief. A valley cut for a considerable distance along the outcrop of a soft layer is called a strike valley. Typically strike valleys are

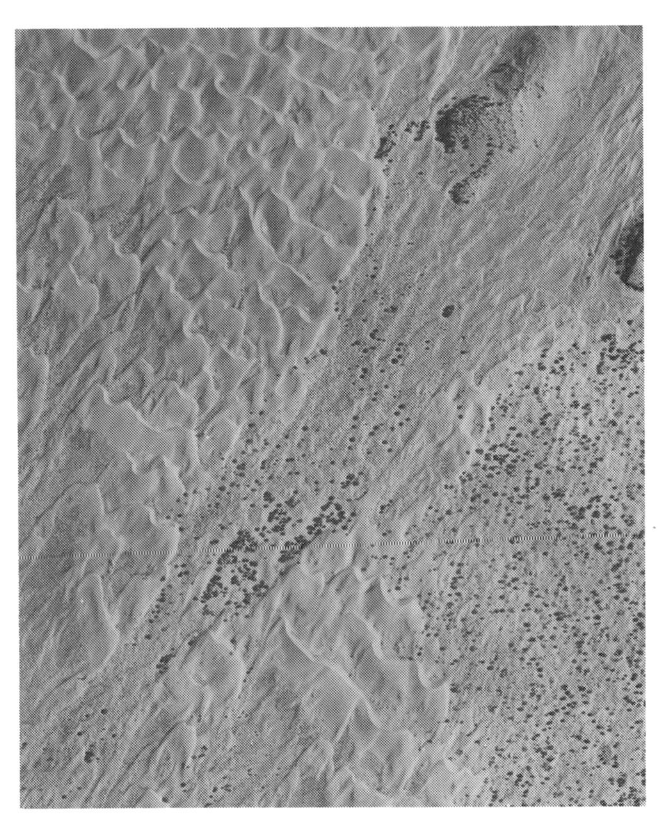

Figure 18-13a. Part of the dune field near Jerico, Juab County. Called Little Sahara by the U.S. Bureau of Reclamation, this is a popular recreation area. These dunes are moving actively in a north by northeast direction. Compare with Figure 18-13b.

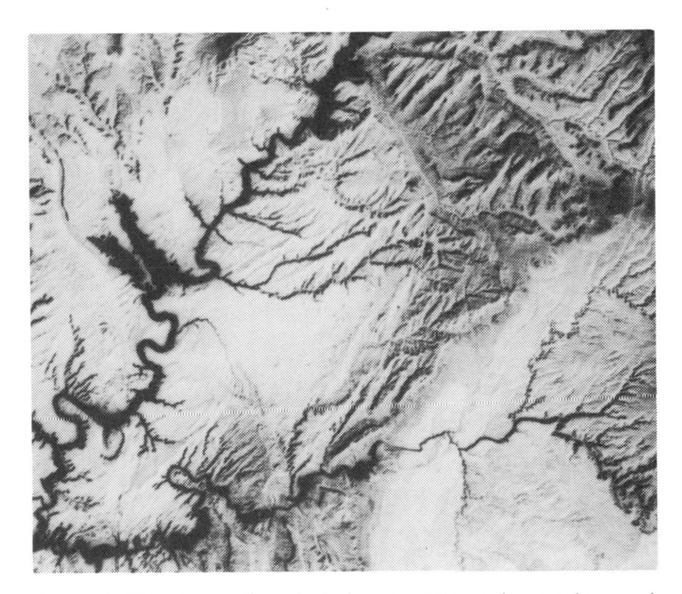

Figure 18-13b. Wind-aligned drainage patterns in south-central Utah adjacent to the Colorado and San Juan Rivers. The many northeast trending canyons are thought to have originated by downcutting of streams that were originally confined between longitudinal dunes that trended in the direction of the prevailing northeasterly winds.

Figure 18-14. Dendritic tributaries of the Colorado River system eroding headward into the relatively non-resistant Mancos Shale near Price. Distance across view is about four miles. Photo: U.S. Department of Agriculture.

bounded by hogback ridges. Consider again any of the great monoclines which show many water courses following strike valleys and many third-order tributaries in the process of stripping away softer formations to create hogbacks and dip slopes in profusion.

The San Rafael Swell is only one of several uplifts that dominate the Utah portion of the Colorado Plateau. Others are the Circle Cliffs-Teasdale Anticline, Monument Upwarp, and the Uncompahgre Uplift (in part). Each has a core and rim of harder rocks surrounded by belts of softer ones. It goes without saying that the laccolithic mountains - the Henrys, LaSals, and Abajos - consist of hard, igneous rocks and stand higher because they are surrounded by relatively soft, sedimentary formations. The distribution of groups of hard and soft sedimentary rocks explains most of the landforms and scenic details of eastern Utah.

To summarize: The major physiographic features of Utah were outlined in recognizable form in middle Tertiary time. The critical point was the establishment of the present-day major rivers. This means that recognizable direct ancestors of present mountains, basins, volcanic centers, and uplifts were in existence as long ago as 30 million years. Outlines in most cases were vague and subdued. There was a San Rafael Swell, but no Buckhorn Draw; a Wasatch Range, but no Parleys Canyon; a Uinta Basin, but no Myton Bench; a Colorado River, but no Glen Canyon, and so on.

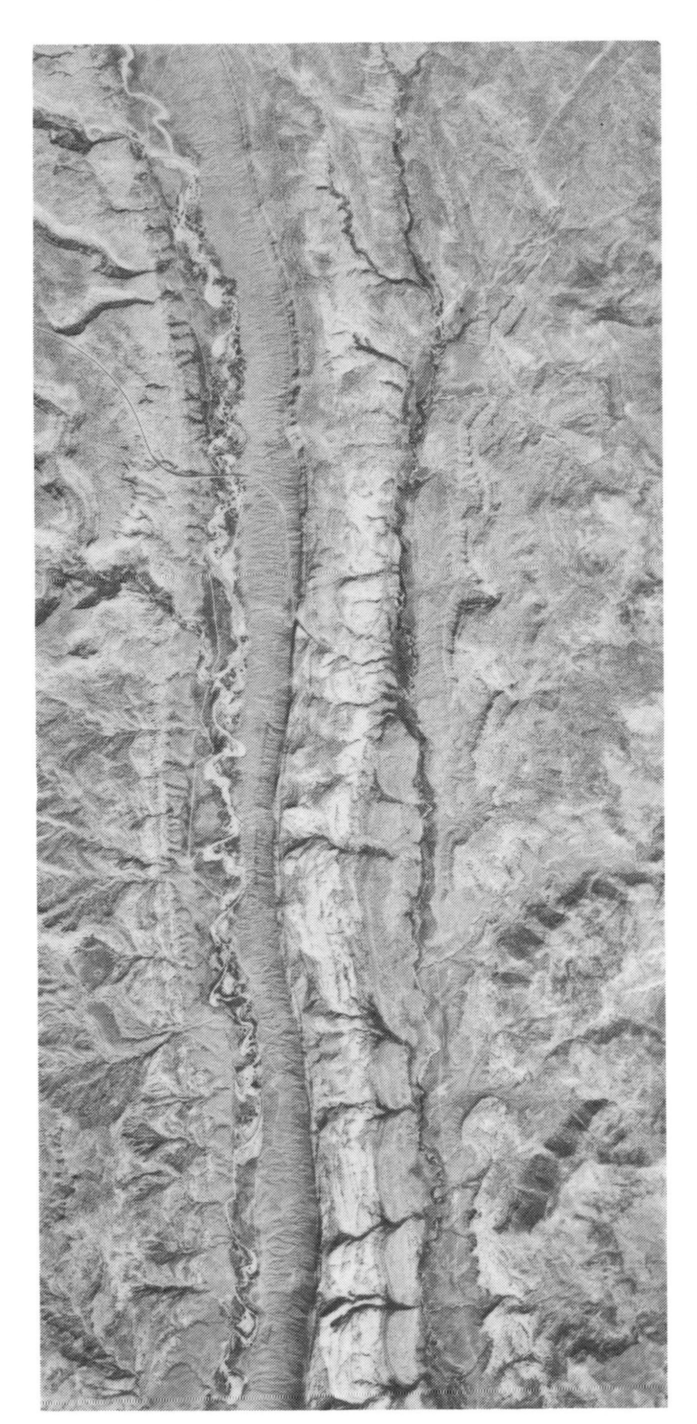

Figure 18-15. Aerial view of Comb Ridge, San Juan County. Differential erosion and the production of strike valleys is well shown. Cottonwood Wash, running west (left) of the light-colored sandstone formations that make up the ridge, is eroding its valley in the relatively soft Moenkopi Shale. East of the ridge (right), Butler Wash is eroding a smaller parallel valley in a stratigraphically higher zone of soft sandstone at the San Rafael Group. Length of this view is about six miles. Photo: U. S. Department of Agriculture.

Figure 18-16. Differential erosion demonstrated in the Waterpocket Fold. The various sedimentary units stand in relief according to their resistance to erosion. The Navajo Sandstone forms the highest ridge and the Brushy Basin Shale forms the lowest valley. Photo: Bureau of Land Management.

The same was true of western Utah. Modifications of the basic units to produce present scenery will be described in chapter 20.

For additional reading on the topics discussed in Chapter 18, please see the following list of authors.

Anderson, D.W., 1973
Armstrong, 1969
Atwater, 1970
Atwater and Molnar, 1973
Best and Hamblin, 1978
Blackwelder, 1934
Blakey, 1979
Bradley, 1936
Breed, 1969, 1971
Butler and others, 1920
Christiansen and McKee, 1978
Coney, 1972, 1978
Cook, H.J., 1960
Crosby, 1972, 1973
Eardley, 1966
Eaton and others, 1978
Gilbert, 1928
Gilluly, 1965
Hamilton and Myers, 1966
Hansen, W.R., 1969a, 1969b
Harris, 1958, 1959
Hunt, C.B., 1956, 1967, 1969, 1974
Lachenbruch and Sess, 1978
Larson and others, 1975
Longwell, 1950
Loring, 1976
McKee, 1959
McKee, E.D., and others, 1967
Mackin, 1960

Osmond, 1960
Rowley and others, 1978
Stewart, 1971, 1978
Stokes, 1960, 1064, 1968
Warner, L.A., 1978
Warner, M.A., 1966

For complete bibliographic citations, please see List of References.

Figure 18-17. Vertical view of The Loop, an incised meander of the Colorado River, Grand County. Various members of the Permian Cutler Formation form the canyon walls and surfaces between the loops. Photo: U.S. Geological Survey.

19

LATE CENOZOIC VOLCANISM

Although there have been no volcanic eruptions in Utah within historic time, the well-preserved cinder cones and fresh-looking flows of dark lava have been known for what they are since the earliest exploration of the region. Many cones show practically no erosion and attendant flows follow existing drainage lines so closely that it is evident they flowed onto essentially the present surface. Successively older volcanic features show increasing effects of erosion and the oldest accumulations preserve little of their original topographic forms. Aside from differences in degree of erosion that are obvious to any observant person, many other age-related characteristics are coming to light.

Practically all volcanic rocks of Utah were produced during the past 45 million years. Within this interval there are two well-marked episodes with notable variations in the type and volume of material produced as well as shifts in eruptive centers. The first episode, of mid-Cenozoic age, is briefly described in chapter 17; the second, of late Cenozoic time, is described in this chapter. Figure 19-1 shows the general outlines of the older and younger centers. Earlier, or mid-Cenozoic, effects are recognized in: 1) the Bingham-Park City field, 2) the Thomas Range-Tintic field, 3) the Tushar-northern High Plateaus field, and 4) the Tonoquints-Markagunt field.

Later volcanism was much less extensive and the flows and cones produced fall into in two natural groups: the St. George Basin-southern High Plateaus field and the Sevier Desert field. Not enough is known about the scattered volcanic outcrops of northwestern Utah to assign specific ages; they are shown on figure 19-1 as outliers of the great lava fields of the Snake River Plain in adjacent Idaho.

It should be pointed out that all Utah volcanic fields are shared with adjacent states. The St. George area is a minor extension of the western Grand Canyon field of Arizona where there are dozens of cones and many extensive flows. Likewise the Tonoquints-High Plateaus field is continuous with a larger territory of similar rocks in southern Nevada. Although the total area of late Cenozoic volcanic rocks within Utah is relatively small, the diversity of material produced, in terms of igneous petrology, is unusally great.

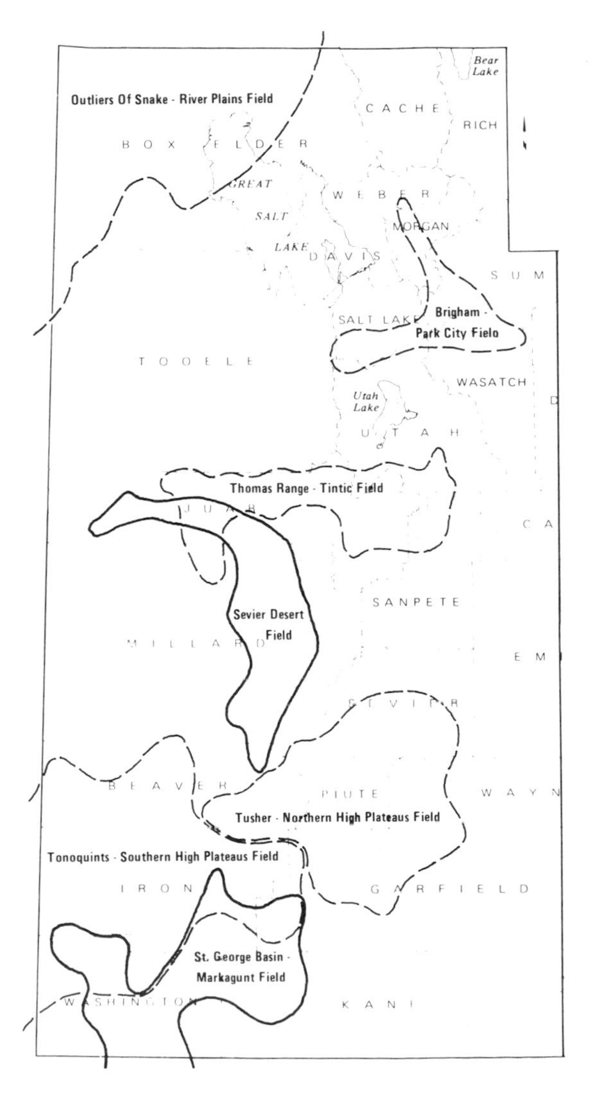

Figure 19-1. Map of western Utah showing volcanic fields. Dashed lines enclose mostly older, mid-Cenozoic fields and solid lines enclose younger, generally late Cenozoic fields.

ROCK TYPES

Due chiefly to application of refined chemical analyses, the study of volcanic rocks is in a state of rapid evolution, a fact that must be taken into account in regional surveys such as this. Information ranges from very precise and detailed for some centers and some individual flows to only the most general observations for others.

Middle Tertiary volcanic rocks have been designated broadly as silicic in recognition of the relatively high silica content. They are also referred to as intermediate or calc-alkalic (see chap. 17). In contrast, late Cenozoic products are distinctly mafic, being relatively high in iron and magnesium. Late Tertiary volcanism is also referred to as bimodal, signifying the close association of rhyolite and basalt in many centers. Since basalt generally predominates, the term "basaltic" is also used by some investigators to designate the entire aggregation of late Cenozoic volcanic products.

Based purely on megascopic characteristics, all varieties of basalt are dark in color; dark gray, dark green, dark red, or black. Due to high iron and magnesium contents they are also dense and relatively heavy. They are, by definition, fine grained but this does not exclude varieties that contain scattered large-size crystals (phenocrysts). Basaltic lava may show a variety of surface features described as jagged, ropy, smooth, or brecciated, depending on the appearance when final cooling occurred. Internally many flows are dense and uniform; other varieties have bubble-like cavities or cells (vesicules) and a texture not unlike that of lighter varieties of pastry. If molten basaltic material is thrown out in small hot fragments the result is cinders that fall in the vicinity of the vents to build cinder cones. Cones and flows commonly form simultaneously, but loosely constructed cones are soon destroyed by erosion, whereas associated flows may exist as surface features for millions of years (fig. 19-2).

On the basis of chemical composition many varieties of basalt have been recognized and a number of them have been identified in Utah. The dominant variety in the southwestern part of the state is Hawaiite; it commonly contains the minerals olivine and andesine. The soda-potash (K_2/Na_20) ratio is greater than 2:1. Another less common variety is tholeiite, a silica-rich type characteristic of ocean basins. Its presence is somewhat anomalous. Basanite is present, but relatively rare. Basalt grades into andesite with increasing silica content; basaltic andesite, a rock showing transitional characteristics, has been mapped in several centers. The deep-seated intrusive equivalent of basalt, gabbro, is extremely rare in surface outcrops. Of course, it is abundant at depths far below the present level of erosion.

Rhyolite (fig. 19-3), like basalt, is a group name, but the varieties are less numerous and areas covered much less extensive. Colors range from light gray to pink to red and brown. Flow textures due to the alignment of large megascopic mineral grains such as crystals of quartz and feldspar are characteristic. The intrusive equivalent is granite. Rhyolite grades into rhyodacite with decreasing content of alkali feldspar and into trachyte with decreasing quartz content.

LATE CENOZOIC VOLCANIC FIELDS

St. George Basin-Southern High Plateaus

About 70 individual late Cenozoic lava flows have been mapped in southwestern Utah south of the latitude of Parowan, Iron County, and west of the longitude of Red Canyon near Panguitch, Garfield County. For descriptive purposes they are grouped together as the St. George Basin-southern High Plateaus field. Most of the individual flows have not been studied in detail but valid generalizations are possible. Dark-gray to light-gray basalt with visible crystals of olivine is the most common variety. According to Lowder (1973), "Other rock types include an intermediate

Figure 19-2. Cinder cone and basalt flow, Diamond (Damron) Valley, Washington County.

Figure 19-3. Honeycomb Hill, west-central Juab County. This hill illustrates the tendency of rhyolite to pile up in dome-like forms. Compare with the flows of less viscous basalt. Photo: Arthur C. King.

variety rich in amphibole phenocrysts, a basic variety rich in olivine and pyroxene but lacking feldspar, a very light-gray aphanitic rock and varieties containing conspicuous quartz crystals."

At least two dozen individual lava flows and a dozen recognizable cinder cones make up the St. George Basin sub-field. The ages of the dated flows average slightly more than 2 million years. The relation to topography, as determined by erosion, has been found to be the best basis for classifying these flows. When basaltic lava emerges in a molten condition it is almost as fluid as water and flows downhill along available drainage ways and slopes until it solidifies, sometimes many miles from its place of origin. Basaltic lava, once cooled, is an extremely resistant rock, generally less easily eroded than the formations making up the valley or canyon walls against which it comes to rest.

Lava flows of the St. George Basin illustrate what happens when eruptions take place in a fairly rugged, rapidly eroding terrain. The basin drains into the Colorado River, 75 miles away in Nevada, by way of the Virgin River. The Virgin descends about 200 feet between St. George, Washington County, and the Utah-Arizona line. As a result of the steep gradient, all tributaries are highly energetic and erosion is rapid. Lava flows spilling onto this terrain had not far to go before entering a valley or canyon. Results were undoubtedly dramatic as molten lava ejected the streams from their courses.

Water flowing into a typical V-shaped valley or a canyon already partly filled by a lava stream will establish two parallel courses, one on either side between the flow and the valley wall. As the streams erode downward the mid-valley flow between them takes the form of an elevated ridge that becomes more prominent with the passage of time. As demonstrated in the vicinity of St. George, mid-valley lava streams have become the highest elevations in the vicinity. The common result is a long, sloping, flat-topped mesa or bench, capped with dark basalt and fringed with rough boulder-strewn slopes. The whole process is called topographic reversal from the fact that valley bottoms become ridges and mesas while divides are lowered and become valleys (fig. 19-4).

Following the concept of topographic reversal, W. K. Hamblin (1963) has classified the flows of the Grand Canyon region, including those of the St. George Basin, into four stages or groups. Stage I is oldest and was deposited on a surface that now stands about 1,000 feet above the adjacent lowlands; Stage II flows were deposited on an erosional surface that now stands 200 to 500 feet above present drainage; Stage III flows were deposited 20 to 100 feet above present streams; and Stage IV flows are on essentially the present surface. Of the four groups, Stage II is most abundantly represented in the St. George Basin.

Twelve or more basaltic flows are intimately associated with the Hurricane Fault and constitute a link between the St. George Basin and the southern High Plateaus centers. Many have been dated radiometrically with results that are important in understanding the history of the associated Hurricane Fault. Dates range from slightly more than 21

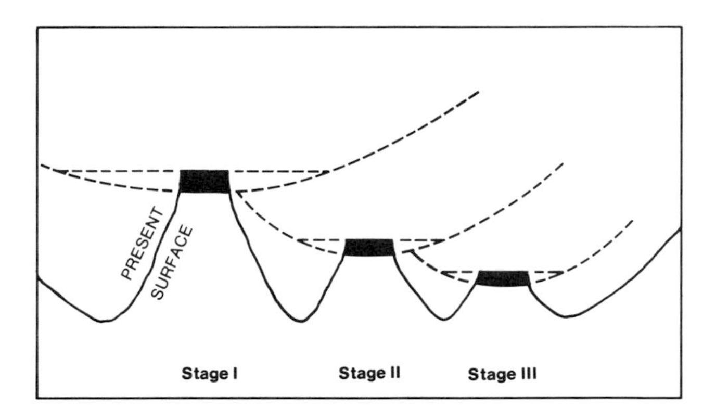

Figure 19-4. Lava flows of the St. George area. Remnants of oldest (Stage I) cap buttes near Hurricane. Stage II lavas dominate as sinuous mesas. Stage II flows overlie Stage III, partly fill present drainages, and are associated with extant cinder cones. Erosion of lava and underlying surfaces occurred between flow cycles.

million to 8 million years; most of the flows evidently originated about 10 million years ago. From measurements between segments of dated flows separated by displacement on the Hurricane Fault, a rate of movement ranging from about 1,000 to 1,500 ft/million years has been determined. Since total displacement is 2,000 to 2,800 feet, it is concluded that the Hurricane Fault came into existence in the Quaternary or late Pliocene.

Basalt flows and associated cones are scattered over the surface and flanks of the southern Markagunt Plateau (fig. 19-5), including part of Zion National Park. As many as 29 identifiable cones have been mapped. Those on the Kolob terrace are prominent landmarks and have received names such as Black Mountain, Square Mountain, and Three Knolls. Lava extruded into Duck Creek dammed the stream and created picturesque Navajo Lake on the southern margin of the plateau. Hancock Mountain and Houston Mountain are centers on the plateau's surface.

High Plateaus flows and clusters have not been studied in detail, but from their fresh appearance and relation to topography, it may be assumed that they are essentially contemporaneous with flows of the St. George Basin and the Hurricane Cliffs.

Sevier Desert Volcanic Field

Most of the remaining late Cenozoic flows and cinder cones are centered about 100 miles north of St. George in the Sevier Desert field, Beaver and Millard Counties. Except for the Thomas Range, the igneous rocks of this field have an average age of between 1.3 and 0.9 million years. The presence of considerable rhyolite in association with basalt contrasts with the St. George Basin-southern High Plateaus centers.

Also in contrast to the flows of southwestern Utah that occupy relatively narrow, well-marked drainage ways, those of the Sevier Desert were mostly free to spread out on flat surfaces in all directions (fig. 19-6). They are conse-

Figure 19-5. View northward across the Markagunt Plateau from the vicinity of Cedar Breaks. Volcanic centers rise above the general surface which is blanketed by flows of basaltic lava. The Sevier Plateau is dimly visible on the distant skyline. Photo: U.S. Department of Agriculture.

quently found in gently sloping pancake-like sheets surrounding the vents from which they originated. No obvious relationships between topographic elevation and age have been observed. To a minor extent some of the flows are buried by sand dunes, lake and/or river sediments, or by succeeding flows from the same centers.

The topographic forms assumed by rhyolite deserve separate mention. Because of its high silica content (as much as 75 percent), rhyolite has much greater viscosity and flows less readily than basalt. It tends to pile up near the point of origin to produce blister-like or domelike forms (see fig. 19-3). Extrusions of rhyolite remain as elevated hills for lengthy periods and may be identified in bimodal volcanic fields by their topographic prominence. The term "rhyolite domes" is commonly used in describing the external forms produced by rhyolitic lava.

Obsidian from the Mineral Mountains was considered to be a valued resource by native Americans as indicated by primitive mines and by the wide distribution of artifacts made from it. This is the only major source of implement-grade obsidian in the southwest between eastern California and northern New Mexico. The best material is found in the basal few feet of several flows in the central part of the field.

Many geologists have contributed to an understanding of volcanism in and adjacent to the Sevier Desert field. Important studies have been conducted on individual flows and centers including (commencing with the northwest sector of the field and proceeding clockwise) Honeycomb Hills, Thomas Range, Fumarole Butte, Smelter Knolls, Black Rock Desert or Fillmore, Cove Creek Domes or Twin Peaks, and the Mineral Mountains (see authors cited at the end of this chapter).

Sevier Desert volcanic centers and flows (fig. 19-7) show a wide range in complexity and volume of material produced, but not all are well enough known to be described in detail in this brief summary. From an economic viewpoint, the Thomas Range-Spor Mountain area is by far the most important. According to radiometric dating, volcanism commenced 42 million years ago and there were important high points at 32 to 30, 21, and 7 to 6 million years ago. Only the very latest event that produced tuff and rhyolite is considered as late Cenozoic. No basalt is present. Important deposits of uranium, beryllium, and fluorite occur in the older volcanic tuffs.

Six separate centers, each with a number of flows, are recognized in the Black Rock Desert. Condie and Barsky (1972) dated two as pre-Lake Bonneville, 970,000 to 250,000 years old, and two that are post-Bonneville, about 5,000 years old, demonstrated by the fact that they overlie the lake terraces.

Hoover (1973) recognized three primary eruptive episodes in the Black Rock area. Episode one occurred between 920,000 to 536,000 years ago and Episode two produced lavas 128,000 to 75,000 years ago. Episode three, which produced the Tabernacle Volcanics field, erupted

Figure 19-6. Fumarole Butte (called Hot Plug by some) from the west, Millard County. The central volcanic neck seen in profile in the distance is surrounded by outward spreading basalt flows of geologically recent age. Photo: Ward Roylance.

Figure 19-7. Basaltic lava flow and cinders of Ice Spring volcanic field, a few miles west of Fillmore, Millard County. Photo: Arthur C. King.

into waning Lake Bonneville 24,000 to 10,000 years ago and produced the Ice Springs field, dated by Carbon-14 analysis of a plant root beneath the flow as only 600 years old. The Black Rock lavas are classified by Hoover as transitional between the lehiites and hawaiites. He concludes that the periodic arrival of lava is related to normal faulting that attended the widening of the Great Basin in the late Cenozoic. Most Black Rock lava flows are localized along fault traces and many are furrowed by tension-crack zones coinciding with regional fault patterns. The rate of expansion across the area is calculated roughly at about 0.01 inch/year.

Rocks of the Twin Peaks volcanic complex, centered about 20 miles southwest of the Black Rock Desert cluster, southeast Millard County, have been studied by Crecraft, Nash, and Evans (1981). They mapped nine igneous units; four basalts, four rhyolites, and one rhyodacite. Active extrusion ranged from 2.7 to 1 million years ago. Two sequences are recognized: one is chiefly rhyolitic and erupted 2.7 to 2.5 million years ago, the other postdates the rhyolite and is mainly basaltic.

The Mineral Mountains and vicinity have been intensively studied by scientists from the University of Utah in connection with the geothermal energy potential of nearby Roosevelt Hot Springs. More than a dozen rhyolitic centers have been mapped in the range. All are dated at less than 1 million years and they all rest directly on a granitic batholith dated at 9 million years old. It is thought that the source rock of the relatively young rhyolite may still be hot enough to constitute a hydrothermal energy resource; the Roosevelt Hot Springs are about 1.5 miles west of the nearest exposed rhyolite.

AGE RELATIONSHIPS

The study of igneous rocks has been greatly accelerated by the application of recently developed age-dating techniques. The most reliable method is based on K/Ar (potassium-argon) ratios. The radioactive potassium isotope K^{40} is present in a number of common minerals found in both basalt and rhyolite. With a half-life of 1.31 billion years it converts to Ar^{40}. Potassium-bearing feldspar, orthoclase ($KAlSi_3O_8$, commonly referred to as K-feldspar) and biotite ($K(Mg,Fe_2)_3(Al,Fe_3)Si_3O_{10}(OH)_2$) are common datable minerals. Sanadine, a variety of orthoclase, is particularly characteristic of rhyolite. If the proper minerals are present, not only flows but also obsidian, ash, and tuff can be dated. Chief deterrent to age dating is the cost of analyses. Currently (1985) individual analyses of basalt and rhyolite cost from $400 to $600.

Several important compilations of radiometric dates should be noted. Everden and others (1964) published a list of ages associated with mammalian remains. The application of these dates to unfossiliferous igneous products in Great Basin localities is mostly indirect. Whelan (1970) assembled radioactive and isotopic age dates obtained by himself and others. Armstrong (1970) contributed a very important list of dates for the eastern Basin and Range Province that has been basic to determining a coherent chronology of geologic events in western Utah. Other important studies include that of Lemmon and others (1973) on 12 K/Ar dates of extrusive and intrusive rocks of the San Francisco and Wah Wah Mountains and that of Best and others (1980) contributing K/Ar dates for 68 Miocene and younger mafic flows of southwestern Utah and adjoining areas. Other dates are found scattered in studies of individual flows or centers. The papers referred to above have furnished most of the data shown on the map of late Cenozoic flows (see fig. 19-1).

IMPLICATIONS FOR REGIONAL GEOLOGIC HISTORY

Much has been learned from study of the relatively young volcanic rocks that is important to an understanding of the tectonic and thermal history of western Utah. Gross distribution alone shows that mafic flows are more abundant in the vicinity of the Wasatch Line than they are in the adjacent high plateaus and west-central Great Basin. Best and Hamblin (1980) report a wavelike progression of basaltic eruptions that produced successively younger lavas from southwest to northeast. Flows near the western Grand Canyon in Arizona are 7.5 million years old, those of the Shivwits Plateau 6.7 million years old, those of the St. George Basin 2.2 million years old, those of the Pavant area 15 miles north of Cedar City 1.3 million years old, and those near Fillmore 980,000 years old or less (fig. 19-8).

Rhyolite distribution also shows a definite pattern. It decreases in a general way from north to south across western Utah. The most extensive rhyolite outcrops are in the northwest corner of the state and are probably middle Tertiary in age. Mixed rhyolite-basalt flows characterize the Sevier Desert field. Large volumes of rhyolite have been mapped at Keg Mountain and the Thomas Range and minor amounts in the Honeycomb Hills and Smelter Knolls. Dates of eruption range from 42 to 3 million years ago. Continuing southward, basalt makes up the surficially extensive Black Rock Desert and Cove Fort (fig. 19-9) flows that were mostly produced within the past 1 million years. A northern basaltic outlier is Crater Springs, dated as 3.4 million years old. The Twin Peaks center is an excellent example of bimodal volcanism where four basalt units, four rhyolite units, and one rhyodacite unit have been mapped. Activity spans the period from 2.7 to less than 1 million years ago.

Rhyolite strongly dominates over basalt in the Mineral Mountains, Thermo, Blue Ribbon, and Cove Fort centers. With very minor exceptions rhyolite is absent south of 38° N. latitude. The St. George Basin field and minor satellites to the east and northeast are entirely basaltic. The line marking the southern limit of rhyolite extrusions coincides with the Las Vegas branch of the Wasatch Line, with a zone of geophysical anomalies interpreted by Halliday and Cook (1980) as a strong structural linement, and with the northern border of the Wah Wah-Tushar mineral belt.

Figure 19-8. Entrance of lava cave in basalt, Tabernacle volcanic field, near Fillmore, Millard County. Debris of collapsed section of cave is in foreground. Age of this field is determined at about 12,000 years.

Figure 19-9. The Cove Fort volcanic field looking southwest. The high point is a large cinder cone.

The existence of distinct stages of volcanism in the eastern Great Basin is now an established fact. Even though eruptions may not have ceased entirely and gradational rock types were produced in the transition, a lull between the older episode and the increased volcanic activity of a different sort about 13 million years ago is real. The first episode was silicic, calc-alkalic or intermediate; the second was basic, mafic, or bimodal.

SUBSURFACE CONTROLS

Modern techniques have added much important information to what may be learned from volcanic products. Analytical procedures are available to measure extremely small quantities of elements from which the eruptive and preeruptive history of lavas can be inferred. Individual volcanic fields or flows originate from specific subterranean pockets or magma chambers (fig. 19-10). One chamber, for example, has been estimated as having a diameter of about 7 miles and a depth of about 2 miles. Such sources are transitory because they result from heating and cooling influences that do not remain constant throughout long time periods.

A number of influences are known to govern the production of lava from magma chambers: 1) effective life of heat sources, 2) movements within chambers brought about by convection, lateral transport, and gravitational settling of component elements or minerals, and 3) contamination produced by melting of chamber or conduit walls during escape to the surface.

Magma that is liquid for extended periods tends to become stratified with regard to density of component elements. Roof zones become enriched in silicon, sodium and other light or chemically incompatible elements; lower zones are correspondingly enriched in magnesium, cobalt, iron, strontium and barium. Ratios between light and heavy isotopes of radioactive elements may change significantly with time and provide clues as to when and at what depths specific magmas are generated. Strontium for example. Due to radioactive decay of Rb^{87}, Sr^{87} has been increasing since the formation of the earth. This results in crustal rocks, forming at progressively later time, having generally higher Sr^{87}/Sr^{86} ratios.

Only a small fraction of the many flows and clusters of flows in Utah has been analyzed by precise geochemical, volumetric, and geothermal means. The Twin Peaks cluster, about 20 miles southwest of Fillmore, is an excellent example of a thoroughly investigated volcanic assemblage. According to Crecraft and others (1981) bimodal volcanism was active from about 2.7 to less than 1 million years ago and produced material with a volume of about 12km^3. Activity began with eruptions that produced rhyolitic lava and pyroclastics. Heat necessary to generate the rhyolite is

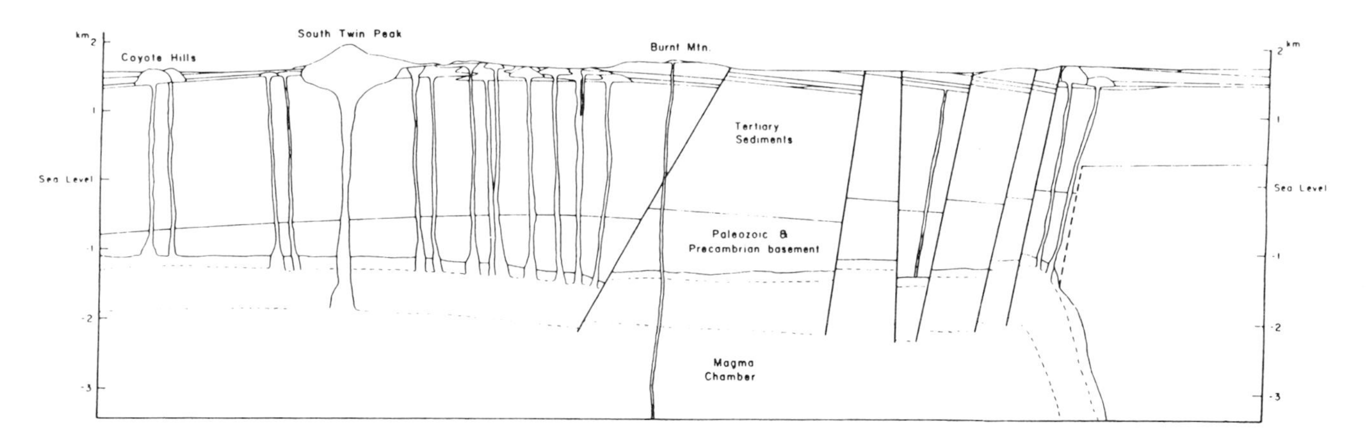

Figure 19-10. Cross-section showing inferred subsurface conditions. Twin Peaks volcanic field, near Fillmore, Millard County. Note magma chamber below a depth of about 1.2 miles. From Crecroft, Nash and Evans, 1981.

thought to have been supplied by injection of basalt from deeper levels of the crust. The SiO_2 content of the early rhyolite ranges from 70.9 to 71.6 percent and the temperature of the magma is estimated at 875° C (1,1527° F). Intermittent eruptions occurred throughout a period of from 100 to 200 thousand years with energy supplied from the basalt reservoir at depth. During that time, the magma separated into distinct zones, upper levels being enriched in silica, sodium, water, and other volatiles.

After rhyolite production waned, voluminous basalt flows dated at 2.5 million years were extruded. Immediately afterward, from 2.4 to 2.3 million years ago, rhyolite eruptions were resumed but the volume produced at various sites is relatively small. Silica content increased with time from 71.9 - 73.8 percent in earlier units to 76.2 percent in the latest. Heat input into the magma chamber apparently declined and the final eruptions were derived from the stagnant upper levels of the roof zone. This is shown by the presence of large crystals of a number of minerals that would have required rather stable conditions for growth. The last volcanic episode in the Twin Peaks area was another eruption of basalt that averages about 1 million years ago.

Study of igneous rocks is well begun but far from complete. To obtain age dates and chemical analyses of numerous unstudied flows, tuffs, and intrusions will be time consuming and expensive. Information from the igneous rocks is vital to solving broader problems of regional tectonics, particularly those having to do with the assembly and consolidation of the western United States.

For additional reading on the topics discussed in chapter 19, please consult the following references.

Anderson and Menhart, 1979
Armstrong, 1970
Best and Brimhall, 1974
Best and Hamblin, 1980
Best and others, 1980
Clark, E.F., 1977
Condie, 1972
Condie and Barsky, 1972
Crecraft and others, 1981
Doelling, 1975
Erickson, M.P., 1963
Evans and Nash, 1979
Evans and others, 1980
Everden and others, 1964
Gregory, 1950
Halliday and Cook, 1980
Hamblin, 1963, 1970
Haugh, 1978
Hoover, 1973
Lemmon and others, 1973
Lindsey, 1949
Lipman and others, 1978
Lowden, 1973
Lowder, 1973
Menhart and others, 1978
Nash and others, 1980
Peterson and Nash, 1980
Staatz and Carr, 1964
Turley and Nash, 1980
Whelan, 1970

For complete bibliographic citations, please see List of References.

Figure 19-11. View looking north near head of Snow Canyon. Relatively young basalt flows eminating from cones in the middle distance make up most of the lower left view. Older flows cap the benches on the right. Hills of Navajo Sandstone rise above the flows. Photo: W.K. Hamblin.

20 THE QUATERNARY PERIOD

The Quaternary Period is the current, or latest, period of geologic time, the one in which modern man exists. It is made up of two epochs, the Pleistocene and the Holocene, or Recent. The placement of a boundary between the Pleistocene and Recent, on one hand, and between the Pleistocene and Pliocene (the last epoch of the Tertiary Period) on the other are difficult problems. The term Pleistocene Epoch was an appropriate synonym for the Great Ice Ages when it was supposed that they were permanently over. Unfortunately, this is not the case; as demonstrated by the great Antarctic and Greenland glaciers, the ice ages still hold sway. Furthermore, the evidence is becoming more and more convincing that glaciation began in the Antarctic millions of years before Pleistocene time as it was originally defined in Europe and America. We are beginning to suspect that we may be merely enjoying a lull or, as climatologists would say, an interglacial stage between two full-fledged glacial stages. Most students of the subject believe that full glacial conditions must surely return. Until terminologies are clarified, about all we can state with certainty is that there was a maximum spread of continental glaciers in the northern hemisphere during the Quaternary.

On a somewhat arbitrary basis, the end of the Pleistocene and beginning of the Holocene is considered to have taken place 11,000 years ago. About this time there was a decided warming trend and glaciers disappeared from many higher latitudes and elevations. As to a more distant event, the beginning of the Ice Ages, we are much less certain since it is the habit of successive ice sheets to erase the evidences of their predecessors. Even though better records might be expected in oceans and deep lakes, geologists are having trouble correlating events from land to ocean. Apparently the onset of the Ice Ages was gradual and took effect at different places at different times. Climate appears to be only a rough guide to its beginning. Certain fossils that seem to appear or disappear about the right time may eventually serve to define the beginning of the Pleistocene, or enough actual dates based on radiometric measurements may be obtained to serve as a framework. Until more is known, the best that can be done is to follow current opinions that place the beginning of the Pleistocene (not necessarily the Ice Ages) at 1.8 million years ago. No actual placement of this important milepost has been determined from the rock record of Utah, but chances are good that needed information will come to light if the deep troughs of the Great Basin, where sediments have been accumulating without interruption for a very long time, are explored by drilling.

For purposes of the present discussion an attempt will be made to build upon previous chapters in which the evolution of the present arid and semi-arid landscape of the Basin and Range and Colorado Plateau Provinces are described. The encroachment of lake water across the lower levels of the landscape and of glaciers in its higher levels must mark the beginning of the Quaternary (fig. 20-1).

PALEOGEOGRAPHY

The average person finds no difficulty believing in the actuality of the Great Ice Ages; glaciers still thrive in frigid polar and alpine zones and evidence of their former presence is widespread far beyond the present remnants of ice. Residents of Utah can observe recently abandoned glaciated landscapes in the higher parts of the Wasatch Range or Uinta Mountains. Inhabitants of the lowlands know that the parallel level terraces, or benches, skirting the Wasatch foothills are shorelines of an ancient lake (fig. 20-2).

Both the wave-cut terraces and the glacial valleys represent relatively minor alterations of pre-existing topography. The glaciers widened and deepened valleys already in existence and the Bonneville terraces have created little more than shallow scratches along most of the slopes they cross; therefore, the geography of the region before the Pleistocene was not greatly different from what it is today. This does not deny that the addition of water to the basins and ice to the mountain uplands created a landscape fully as distinctive as any of the more distant periods (figs. 20-3 and 20-4). A paleogeographic map of conditions at the maximum extent of the lakes and glaciers is the last scene out of the past that is significantly different from the present (compare fig. 20-3 with the physiographic map inside the front cover of the book.)

Figure 20-1. Quaternary deposits of Utah. Dark areas are occupied by surface deposits that are mostly unconsolidated and in the same forms as when deposited. Those on the west are chiefly lake beds and alluvium; those of the Uinta Range are glacial till and outwash; those of southeastern Utah are pediments, alluvium, and sand. Much material deposited in the past few thousand years is not included.

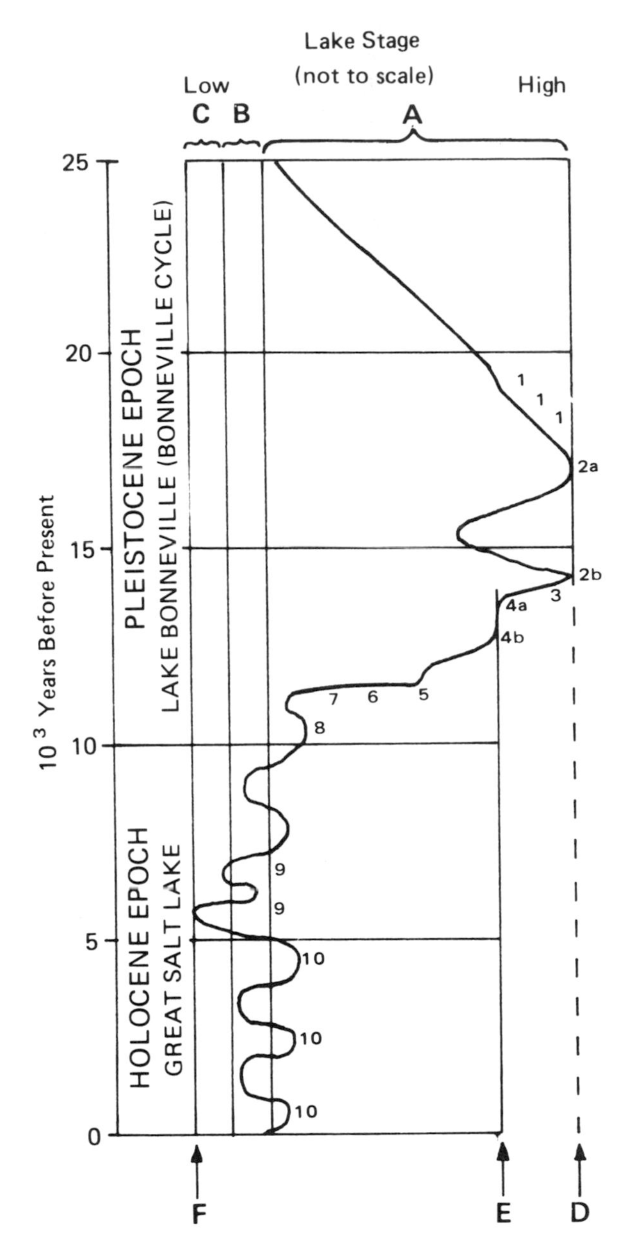

A. High shoreline zone
B. Historic shoreline zone
C. Submerged shoreline zone
D. Bonneville threshold
E. Provo threshold
F. Great Salt Lake Playa

1. Transgressive shorelines
2a. Earlier Bonneville shorelines
2b. Later Bonneville shoreline
3.. Bonneville Flood
4a. Earlier Provo shoreline
4b. Later Provo shoreline
5. Stansbury shoreline
6. Lake Puddle level
7 Danger Cave level
8. Gilbert shoreline
9. Mid-Holocene playa stage(s)
10. Late Holocene shorelines

Figure 20-2. Diagram showing fluctuations of Lake Bonneville and Great Salt Lake in relation to the Pleistocene and Holocene time scale. Adapted from Currey, 1980.

ONSET OF THE ICE AGES

The term ice age brings to mind a period of bitter cold long enough for glaciers to form and cover thousands of square miles, not only in northern latitudes but in places that are ordinarily temperate and ice-free. But it takes more than cold to make an ice age; the other essential ingredient is moisture. Even today many extensive tracts are cold enough for glaciers but they cannot form without greater precipitation. In thinking of local geologic history, it is well to bear in mind both the effects of lower temperature and of increased precipitation. The simultaneous formation of great interior fresh-water lakes and the growth of glaciers at higher elevations emphasizes this point. Since neither seems capable of causing the other, it seems logical to assume that both were due to some other cause or causes.

The depressions which were eventually filled with water already existed and had reached essentially their present forms long before the expansion of Pleistocene lakes. A distinction must be drawn between those water bodies, typified by Lake Bonneville, and an older series of lakes that occupied extensive areas in the Great Basin during the Miocene Epoch 5 to 20 million years earlier. The location,

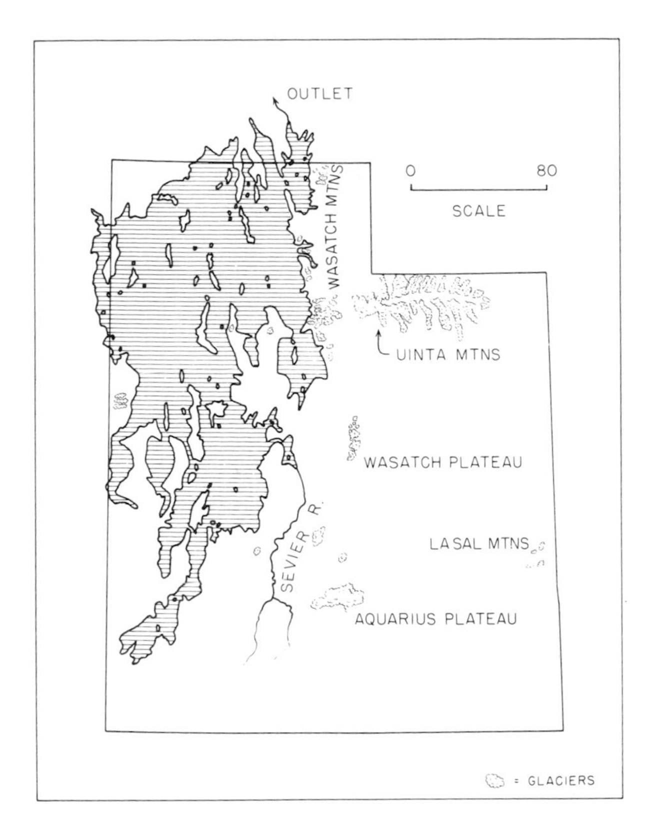

Figure 20-3. Quaternary paleogeography of Utah. Lined pattern indicates Lake Bonneville; irregular patterns associated with mountains and plateaus are glaciers. From Stokes and Heylmun, 1957.

Figure 20-4. Aerial photo of a tract in south-central Tooele County selected to show contrasting topography of area covered by Lake Bonneville, upper right, and areas shaped by ordinary subaerial processes. Note that the lake waters have done little more than smooth the pre-existing surface in a superficial way. Outlines of cultivated fields appear along eastern edge. Photo: U.S. Department of Agriculture.

shape and size of the Miocene lakes are largely unknown because their sediments are deeply buried under present lake and valley floors. Scattered deposits of Miocene water bodies, brought to the surface by localized earth movements, have been lumped under the general term Salt Lake Formation. Data from drilling in the bed of Great Salt Lake show deposits of pre-Bonneville lakes that exceed 10,000 feet in thickness. Evidence is that an interval of extreme aridity during the Pliocene Epoch intervened between the earlier and later lake episodes. Regardless of details, the chain of essential events leading to Ice Ages lakes began with the subsidence of elongate trenches and elevation of the intervening ranges that constituted the Basin and Range Province. Subsequently, the ranges were deeply weathered and eroded to provide material to fill the neighboring trenches.

No matter what else may be said about prehistoric water bodies of the interior basins, it is clear that they could not have formed unless more water was supplied than was removed. Two methods of increasing the supply are obvious; increased precipitation and diversion of streams from external sources. However, increased evaporation is the only method of water removal that can be imagined.

CLIMATIC OSCILLATION

A key chracteristic of ice ages is climatic oscillation; glaciers advance and withdraw, lakes expand and retreat, ocean levels rise and fall and life forms flourish and decline. Although all the effects are tied together by climate, not enough is known about the whole complex subject to present an acceptable explanation of what actually causes an ice age. The matter of cyclic or repetitive changes must be explained by any comprehensive solution to the problem. We know that repetitive changes occurred and would like to know if they were equally spaced, orderly, or mathematically progressive.

Consider the example of the Pleistocene lakes of the Great Basin. Any decision as to whether the contractions and expansions were or were not cyclic in nature depends on how and where the data are obtained. Maximum expansions are recorded only by the higher lake terraces (fig. 20-5) where successive studies have steadily increased the estimates of how many times the water reached those levels. Data from beneath Great Salt Lake could conceivably record lengthy unbroken submergence with no period of complete dryness. Between the Bonneville (highest) level and the center of the present-day Great Salt Lake the surface was obviously alternately exposed or submerged. This is illustrated by the amazing evidence of at least 80 separate wet/dry alternations recorded in a 1,065-foot core taken near Burmester, Tooele County (to be described more fully later in this chapter). Another excellent exposure recording only the higher lake levels was exposed in a large excavation in Little Valley on Promontary Point (fig. 20-6) where material was taken for constructing the causeway for the Southern Pacific Railroad.

By combining evidence from all sources the history of the Great Basin lakes is becoming better understood but in-

Figure 20-5. Terraces of Lake Bonneville in Cache Valley, Cache County. Sketch is reproduced from the classic work of G. K. Gilbert on Lake Bonneville, Monograph I of the U. S. Geological Survey.

Figure 20-6. Layers of gravel, sand, and silt exposed in the large excavation in Little Valley on Promontory Point from which fill material for the causeway across the Great Salt Lake was obtained. Important details of the history of Lake Bonneville were obtained from these sediments. Photo: A. J. Eardley.

vestigators are far from satisfied and are not fully in agreement among themselves. They realize that the Great Basin may contain the best record of climatic changes in North America for the past 700,000 years but additional strategically placed cores or surface excavations are necessary. Such operations are expensive and really large ones, such as those at Little Valley, are available only rarely.

ICE AGE LAKES

What is known about Pleistocene lakes can now be briefly outlined. Two sources of geologic evidence are available. One consists of shoreline features that can be seen and mapped on the surface and includes terraces, beach ridges, spits, bars, and deltas. The other is buried in the layered sedimentary deposits of the valley sides and floors. The visible record can be studied with little cost, except in time, but the subsurface evidence cannot be obtained without expensive drilling and sophisticated analyses.

It is not surprising that the first study of the ancient lakes was based almost entirely on surface evidence. In 1859, G.K. Gilbert set out in a horse-drawn buggy to trace the levels and chart the shoreline features of the ancient lake. The result was a truly monumental work, the first monograph of the U.S. Geological Survey, *Lake Bonneville*, published in 1890. Gilbert's conclusion was that there had been two high levels of the ancient lake. The first reached a point 75 to 90 feet below the highest level; Gilbert could not date it except to estimate that it was separated from the second, higher level, by a period five times longer than the elapsed time since the lake disappeared. The second rise, according to Gilbert, reached the highest level ever, the Bonneville

Figure 20-7a. Mouth of Logan River, showing present flood plain and terraces of Lake Bonneville. Photo: Clyde T. Hardy.

Figure 20-7b. South Mountain at southern end of Tooele Valley between the Oquirrh and Stansbury Ranges consists entirely of the Oquirrh Formation. Famous Stockton Bar built at the high stage of Lake Bonneville is at the right. Photo: Ward Roylance.

Figure 20-7c. Pavant Butte, a basaltic volcanic cone terraced by Lake Bonneville, near Holden, Millard County. Photo: Robert Q. Oaks, Jr.

Figure 20-7d. Eastern section of Traverse Range, southeast edge of Salt Lake Valley, shows broad terrace at the higher level of Lake Bonneville and the Wasatch Range in the background. Photo: A. J. Eardley.

level, after which the lake overflowed and dropped back quickly to the lower Provo level where it was held steady by a bedrock barrier at the outlet for an indefinite but lengthy period. It then receded gradually to below the lowest terrace, the Stansbury level, to which it rose again before dropping to its present elevation.

The fascination of Lake Bonnevile has continued to attract students ever since Gilbert's work. Most of the earlier students had to rely on surface features (figs. 20-7a, 20-7b, 20-7c, and 20-7d) but they also began to study deposits below the surface. Ives (1951) suggested that the lake had risen not twice, but three times, to high levels and that the last two rises were quite close together in time but still separated by a decline, perhaps to total dryness. Greater and greater attention was given to the lake deposits as large gravel pits, road cuts and excavations for foundations revealed more and more detail. Hunt (1953b) redefined Lake Bonneville as the body of water that existed only during the Wisconsinan, or last, glacial stage. He did not deal extensively with the older, pre-Wisconsin lakes. Hunt applied the name Lake Bonneville Group and subdivided it into the Alpine (oldest), Bonneville, and Provo (youngest) Formations. Williams (1962), Bissell (1963), and Morrison (1965a) used Hunt's division in mapping Lake Bonneville deposits in Cache Valley, Utah Valley, and the southern part of Jordan (Salt Lake) Valley. These workers did not deal extensively with older water bodies.

New techniques developed, one of which is paleopedology, the study of ancient soils. Soils form only under exposure to air, their presence proves that specific surfaces cannot have been under water. Morrison (1965a) has identified several distinct soils in the Bonneville record. The Dimple Dell soil was formed immediately before Lake Bonnevile (in Hunt's usage) came into existence. For all deposits above the Dimple Dell, including a second soil (the Promontory soil), Morrison used the term Alpine Formation. For deposits between the Promontory soil and a third, or Graniteville, soil he applied the term Bonneville Formation, and for the next set of deposits between the Graniteville and a fourth, Midvale, soil he used the term Draper Formation. Now, for the first time, the history of the Pleistocene lakes could be referred to in terms of sedimentary deposits rather than geomorphic features.

The soil horizons furnished good punctuation marks in Bonneville history but a lot of work still had to be done to understand the events between them. Other techniques developed and became widely applied, including radiometric dating, paleomagnetic chronology and study of key beds, particularly volcanic ash beds.

According to Morrison's latest analysis (1975), the main events that can be detected from all lines of evidence are: 1) three deep lake stages that cannot be exactly dated except as being early or middle Pleistocene, older than about 1 million years: 2) a period of oscillations during which the Bishop volcanic ash was deposited an estimated 800,000 to 700,000 years ago and the Pearlette "O" ash was deposited about 600,000 years ago (fig. 20-8); 3) a long, probably moist and warm, period in which several strong soils were formed between intervening shallow-lake stages; 4) another three or more deep-lake stages; 5) formation of the deep Dimple Dell soil; 6) five moderate- to deep-lake stages during which the Alpine Formation was deposited; 7) formation of the moderate to strong Promontory soil; 8) a final three deep-lake stages, the last of which reached and overflowed a short distance north of Red Rock Pass, Idaho, about 14,000 years ago; 9) formation of the moderately strong Graniteville soil; and 10) one or more moderate to shallow lakes leading to the present. Currey (1980) has refined some of these stages. He places the formation of the Stansbury Level before, rather than after, the Bonneville levels. Also, he believes that the lake may have evaporated to complete dryness one or several times between 8,000 and 3,000 years ago.

Figure 20-8. The Pearlette ash (white bed at level of person's head) in the excavation at Little Valley, Promontory Point. The age is estimated at 600,000 years. Photo: Harry D. Goode.

This abbreviated summary may be supplemented by reference to unfinished work on a 1,065-foot core taken near Burmester, Tooele County. Evidence of at least 17 lake stages are recognized in the upper 360 feet of the core. The 360-ft level is interpreted to coincide with the Jaramillo paleomagnetic event dated elsewhere as having occurred 860,000 20,000 years ago. Below this level approximately 68 additional wet/dry cycles are recognized beginning about 3.4 million years ago. The final several hundred feet of core is unstudied and could well represent late Pliocene lakes. Well known Lake Bonneville and its predecessor, Lake Alpine, as defined by Hunt and Morrison, are lakes I and II, respectively, in Eardley and others' (1973) nomenclature. Apparently all lakes before number VIII were shallow and exclusively fresh water; those afterward were salty.

Subtle features of lake cores, the meaning of which would have amazed earlier workers, include thin beds of volcanic ash and changes in magnetic polarity. Two important ash beds have been mentioned, the Bishop ash and the Pearlette "O" ash. They resulted from very powerful eruptions that blanketed wide areas with fine dust and provided precise datum planes for instants of geologic time. Ash falls can be distinguished from each other by chemical composition and physical characteristics. Many can also be dated by contained radioactive minerals. Thus, the Bishop ash is dated as between 700,000 and 800,000 years old and the Pearlette "O" ash as 600,000 years old. These same two ash beds have been found in other Salt Lake cores and in the excavations at Little Valley, Promontory Point. Both have been recognized throughout half a dozen states; the Pearlette "O" from Nevada to Kansas and the Bishop from California to Utah.

Magnetic stratigraphy is based on the discovery that the Earth's magnetic field has alternated between normal (present field) and reversed or opposite field many times in the past. It has been mostly normal since 740,000 years ago. Before then it was reversed for about 600,000 years. A very short period of reversed magnetism, called the Blake event, estimated at about 10,000 years' duration, interrupted the present normal interval about 111,000 years ago.

All these important time markers are found in the Burmester core: the Blake event (reversed polarity at 51 ft, return to normal polarity at 57 feet), the Pearlette ash (283 feet), and the Bishop ash (317 feet). Taking into account all well-dated events, it is evident that about 3.5 million years of history are recorded in 1,000 feet of lake sediment. The only breaks in the record may be in connection with beds of gravel at a depth of about 360 feet.

GLACIAL TOPOGRAPHY

Conditions favorable to the expansion of lakes in previously dry basins also produced snow fields and eventually glaciers at adjacent higher elevations. Rain filled the lakes; snow nourished the glaciers. A glacier is defined as a mass of ice that moves, by gravity, over the underlying surface; the ice or snow field on Mt. Timpanogos is not a glacier since it does not move (figs. 20-9a and 20-9b). Glaciers left distinct and unmistakable erosive effects on many mountains and plateaus during the Pleistocene (fig. 20-10). In rough order of decreasing size the major glaciated areas were: the Uinta Mountains, central Wasatch Range, Bear River Range, northern Wasatch Range, southern Wasatch Range, Aquarius Plateau, LaSal Mountains, Wasatch Plateau, Deep Creek Range, Sevier Plateau, Fish Lake Plateau, Stansbury Mountains, Raft River Mountains, and Tushar Mountains. Evidence suggestive of snow or ice fields, but not necessarily active glaciers, is found on such elevated areas as the Oquirrh Mountains and Navajo Mountain. Other evidences of ice action will undoubtedly be found.

Figure 20-9b. Southeastern slope and crest of Mt. Timpanogos. The high-walled, flat-bottomed cirque valley is a measure of ice action in this part of the Wasatch Range. A portion of Utah Lake appears in the upper left part of the view. Photo: U. S. Department of Agriculture.

Figure 20-9a. The permanent snow or ice field, miscalled a glacier by some, eastern side of Mt. Timpanogos. This is apparently the last lingering remnant of the ice age in Utah. Photo: Arthur C. King.

Figure 20-10. Mt. Nebo from the west, Long Ridge in middle distance. The three cirques of Mt. Nebo are well shown. Photo: Ward Roylance.

There are also many evidences of what are called periglacial effects - that is, manifestations of glacial climates that were not created by moving ice. Included are patterned ground, stone polygons, and stone stripes that are arrangements of loose stones created as water freezes and melts between blocks.

A typical glacial landscape is displayed in the western Uinta Mountains (figs. 20-11a, 20-11b, and 20-11c). According to Atwood (1909), a pioneer student on the subject, the total area covered by ice was more than 1,000 square miles and there were two distinct epochs of glaciation shown by two systems of moraines in each of the major canyons. During the earlier epoch there were 30 distinct glaciers or glacial systems. Glaciation was more extensive on the south slope where the area for collecting snow was larger. The glaciers reached a maximum length of 27.5 miles. An excellent map of Uinta Mountains glaciers is included in a popular account by Hansen (1969a).

Figure 20-11a. Headwater cirque of the East Fork of the Bear River, west-central Uinta Mountains.

Figure 20-11b. Part of a lateral moraine, East Fork of Black Fork, north-central Uinta Mountains. Photo: Paul K. Grogger.

Figure 20-11c. Lakes and moraines in the lower part of Ostler Basin, high Uintas Primitive Area. Photo: Paul K. Grogger.

A later study of glaciation in the High Uintas Primitive Area by P. K. Grogger (1974) distinguished four major glacial advances which he called the Little Dry, Blacks Fork, Smiths Fork, and Neoglacial. Each can be further subdivided into stages and substages, minor advances of the ice within periods of major activity. The existence of numerous divisions and subdivisions is based on recognition and evaluation of such features as the size of moraines, the degree to which they have been modified by later erosion; the weathering, angularity, and polish of stones within them; and by the growth of lichen and higher plants on areas free of ice at various times in the past. Needless to say, the older the moraines the greater various weathering, vegetative, and erosive effects have been.

Grogger was able to correlate glacial events in the Uinta Mountains with those of other western mountains. In an indirect way, the age of the earliest determinable glaciation (Little Dry) is set at probably more than 600,000 years ago and the beginning of the latest (Neoglacial) at less than 5,000 years ago. Evidences of the Neoglacial stage are very well displayed in the Uinta Mountains, probably because of the great piles of loose rock available to be shaped by even small bodies of ice.

Atwood (1909) also studied the glaciation of the Wasatch Range. He found that 50 Wasatch glaciers exceeded 1 mile and 10 exceeded 5 miles in length. Glaciers in Little Cottonwood Canyon (fig. 20-12) near Salt Lake City were 12 miles long and reached the shores of Lake Bonneville. Morrison (1965a, 1968) and Richmond (1964) have mapped and studied the relationship of lake and glacial deposits below the mouths of Little Cottonwood and Bells Canyons. It is concluded that the outer edges of the glacial tills were deposited in standing water and that the last high lake stage of Alpine time (5,280 ft?) correlates with a glacial maximum (late Smiths Fork glaciation? of Grogger). The time of this synchronous high lake level and glacial maximum is dated roughly as 45,000 to 40,000 years ago.

Figure 20-12. Looking west down Little Cottonwood Canyon, Wasatch Range, Salt Lake County. Shows the U-shaped profile typical of mountain glaciers. Oquirrh Mountains in the distance. Photo: Hal Rumel.

An interesting correlation was made possible by finding the distinctive ash bed called Pearlette "O" at Promontory Point between the older and younger pre-Lake Bonneville deposits and also in the Harpole Mesa Formation of the LaSal Mountains. The ash was also found 202 feet below the surface in the Burmester core, in what Eardley and others (1973) designated as Lake XII. To add to a somewhat roundabout series of correlation, Grogger (1974) regarded his Little Dry glaciation to be contemporaneous with the Harpole Mesa Formation. As stated, the age of the Pearlette "O" ash is calculated at close to 600,000 years and provides a most valuable datum for Pleistocene correlations in the west. From the position of the ash and other evidence it is tentatively concluded that the earliest glaciation capable of leaving strong evidence was under way some 600,000 years ago, but that there had been a number of large lakes and many small ones before then. This theory agrees with those who maintain that increasing precipitation triggers a glacial onset.

The High Plateaus were also glaciated. Boulder Mountain, the northeastern section of the Aquarius Plateau, exceeds 11,000 feet in elevation and supported an ice cap of more than 50 square miles (fig. 20-13). The ice draped over the edges of the plateau in several broad lobes as long as 9 miles and descended as low as 6,600 feet elevation. Two periods of ice formation have been detected. The earlier is correlated with the Blacks Fork and the second with the Smiths Fork glaciation of Grogger. After the ice cap melted, extensive rock glaciers were formed and there were many complex landslides along the plateau margins. The Fish Lake Plateau west of the Aquarius Plateau was also glaciated. As a general rule areas above 11,000 feet elevation were above the regional snow line and were glaciated, those below were not.

The LaSal Mountains, with an maximum elevation of 12,700 feet, were glaciated at least nine times, according to Richmond (1962). The earlier glaciations are recorded in the Harpole Mesa Formation and probably represent the Nebraskan, Kansan, and Illinoian stages of continental glacial history. The Pearlette "O" ash is preserved in the middle member of the Harpole Mesa Formation.

Many fossils soils are present in connection with the Quaternary deposits of the LaSal Mountains. On higher ridges and peaks a variety of features, composed of loose rock fragments, are abundantly represented. The loose material has been shaped, by frost action, into rubble rills, stripes and festoons, and large "rock glaciers" (fig. 20-14), some of which have been mistaken for moraines.

Figure 20-13. View from the Aquarius Plateau looking east to Boulder Mountain on the skyline. Boulder Mountain, 11,000 feet in elevation was covered by a Pleistocene ice cap. Photo: U.S. Forest Service.

Figure 20-14. Glacial effects in the LaSal Mountains. Stream-like accumulations of loose rock called "rock glaciers" are well shown in these mountains.

BEYOND THE LAKES AND GLACIERS
Surficial Deposits

Effects of the ice age are not confined to surfaces submerged by lakes or covered by ice. Climate, as an all encompassing influence, produces lasting and distinctive effects on the entire landscape. In Utah, significant imprints were superimposed upon a desert landscape that, almost as a geologic accident, had a few small elevated tracts high enough to be glaciated and a considerably lower enclosed basin where temporary lakes could form. After the ice melted and the lakes dried up the climate returned to its former condition and the area was again essentially a desert.

Climatic effects are superficial, and deposits influenced by climate are referred to as surficial. A great many familiar materials may be grouped under this heading. They occur mostly as loose and unconsolidated deposits covering the bedrock in localized areas. The most familiar is alluvium (fig. 20-15), material moved and deposited by running water, either by present-day streams or at some former time (even millions of years ago), then left stranded out of reach of later streams. Alluvium, therefore, comprises present-day stream beds and banks, high abandoned terraces, alluvial fans, and pediment surfaces. Closely related is colluvium, material moved chiefly by gravity, but not necessarily without the aid of water. Included are talus and scree, the former being generally in thick piles at the base of cliffs, the latter being loose and in more or less uniform layers on the bedrock that produced it.

Other extensive deposits of varied thickness were laid down in lake beds. It is difficult to draw a fine line between surficial lake deposits and those that are too deeply buried to be called surficial; nevertheless, numerous terraces, bars, spits, and thinner silt deposits of Lake Bonneville covering thousands of square miles are best considered as surficial deposits. Wind action also produces extensive surficial deposits such as dune fields (fig. 20-16) and accumulations of finer material, called loess or adobe, that cover wide areas in arid climates.

Figure 20-16. Coral Pink Sand Dunes State Park 10 miles west of Kanab, Kane County. Dunes are derived from disintegration of sandy Triassic and Jurassic formation to the southeast. Photo: Ward Roylance.

Figure 20-15. Alluvium exposed in uncovering an archaeological site near the eastern slopes of the Henry Mountains. Some of the finer silt has been deposited by wind, but coarser sand and gravel, including large stones visible in the distance, is the result of sporadic flooding. The log visible in the center has been dated at over 1,000 years old. This type of alluvium is typical of thousands of square miles of the semi-arid west. Photo: Archaeology Center, Dept. of Anthropology, University of Utah.

Glaciers create particularly characteristic surficial deposits. Outwash deposits, spread beyond the glacial front by melting ice water, are important around the Uinta Mountains. Various types of moraines, piled up at the ends or margins of glaciers or left in irregular patches as glaciers melted, are also common in areas of ice action.

Finally, the most widespread and important surficial material is soil. According to agricultural usage, soil is any earth material capable of supporting higher plants, meaning that it is composed of rock material significantly modified by weathering and organic activity (fig. 20-17). Soil forms not only on bedrock but also on all the varied surficial deposits mentioned previously. It is obvious that there is continuous gradation between solid bedrock and final well developed soil. In this day of increasing attention to open-cut mining, road building and other construction activities, much attention must be given to the material that lies below the soil (which may be roughly considered as the zone penetrated by plant roots) and above the solid bedrock. The term "overburden" is sometimes used if only material above bedrock is referred to, but in deep mining the overburden of an ore body may include great thickness of solid bedrock as well. There is another useful term "regolith" meaning all loose unconsolidated material above bedrock no matter what its origin or capabilities for supporting life may be. Regolith is the correct designation for the loose material making up the surface of any area of any planet or moon where solid bedrock is not actually at the surface.

Figure 20-17. Farmland on the southeast shore of Utah Lake. Only a small fraction of the former bed of Lake Bonneville is soil suitable for agriculture; most of it is poorly drained, impregnated with salt, or too rocky for farming. Photo: Ward Roylance.

Surfaces and their Interpretation

Even though surficial deposits are solid, three-dimensional bodies of rock-derived material, it is mostly only their upper surfaces that are visible and available for study. Only with the passage of time do earth movements and erosion eventually cut into surficial deposits to reveal details of their thickness and distribution. Because of obvious restrictions, students of Quaternary geology have become as expert on the interpretation of surfaces as they are on what underlies them. Two types of depositional surfaces predominate in desert regions: the alluvial fan and the pediment. Both result from erosion and deposition under arid to semi-arid conditions and both are well represented in Utah. The subject of alluvial fans and pediments is complex but they have similar external forms and gradients because both are shaped by powerful sheet floods. Pediments are well developed in eastern Utah, alluvial fans in the Great Basin.

Alluvial fans (figs. 20-18a and 20-18b) are generally composed of mixed coarse and fine material derived from nearby sources and spread out by floods resulting from desert thunderstorms. These have such large volume they immediately overflow any depressions or channels in their paths, fill them with mud and gravel, and quickly become sheet floods. It is the spreading of flash-flood waters over wide areas that ultimately produces the geometrically near-perfect fans or cones that surround desert ranges. Material worn from the isolated Great Basin ranges is not carried away by through-flowing steams because there are none, but ample depositional space is available in nearby down-faulted trenches and the alluvial material, representing

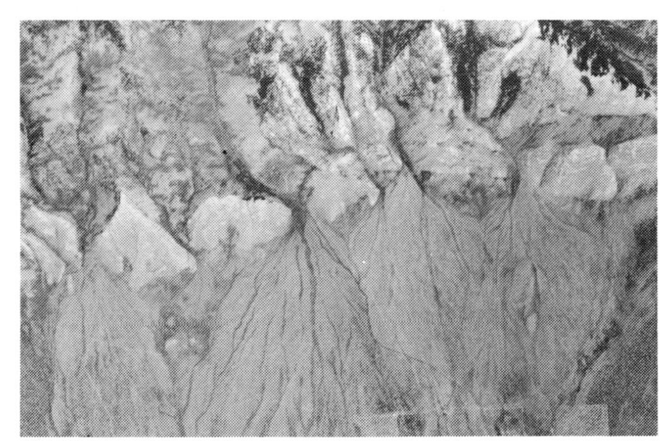

Figure 20-18a. Aerial view of a series of alluvial fans constructed by small ephemeral streams draining the southern slopes of the Raft River Mountains, Box Elder County, Utah. Width of view about 4 miles. Photo: U.S. Department of Agriculture.

Figure 20-18b. Sloping alluvial fans and east face of Fish Springs Range, Juab County. Formations of early Paleozoic age are exposed in the mountains. Photo: Ward Roylance.

numerous superimposed fans, may be thousands of feet thick. As long as there are mountains and valleys (or basins and ranges) situated side by side in a semi-arid climate, alluvial fans will be forming in the Great Basin. Permanent streams occupying permanent channels are not usually associated with alluvial fans.

Pediments closely resemble alluvial fans in outward appearance (figs. 20-19a and 20-19b). Only when their internal structures are known can the two be distinguished. The interior of an alluvial fan is crudely bedded, unsorted material that may be hundreds of feet thick, but a typical pediment has only a thin veneer or coating of such material. Bedrock, like that of nearby outcrops, is found at shallow depths below pediment surfaces. What is seen on the surface of an ordinary pediment is material that has been ar-

Figure 20-19a. Pediment undergoing erosion near Huntington, Emery County. The relatively smooth surface making up most of the photo is Mancos Shale covered by a thin (10′-15′) layer of gravel. This protective cover has been eroded and the shale is being converted to a badland in the upper right part of the view. The mesa-like remnant in the right upper center is over 600 feet high.

rested in a step-by-step movement from its source to a nearby stream channel.

Although the climate and rainfall of eastern and western Utah are not greatly different, there are significant geographic contrasts. Most of eastern Utah, where pediments dominate, is drained by the Colorado River. The products of erosion are just as prolific and varied as they are in the Great Basin, where alluvial fans dominate, but they are carried rapidly out of the region by the Colorado and its tributaries. Only in a very few places is space available for alluvial fans to develop. Erosional debris that coats the numerous pediments skirting the great lines of cliffs in the Colorado Plateau is, therefore, thin and transitory in a geologic sense. Even though rock debris is moved by floods in exactly the same way that it would be in western Utah, the form it takes is fundamentally different. The large rivers that are working to lower the Colorado Plateau are simultaneously constructing, dissecting and destroying the pediments. Remnants in all stages of erosion are easily found. Some of these pediments appear as broad, low mesas, some as irregular benches, some as buttes and some, in their final stages, as pointed pinnacles. Representatives of these shrinking land forms make up broad tracts in the great Mancos Shale lowlands of Emery, Carbon, and Grand Counties; other noteworthy examples characterize the northern Uinta Basin where sheets of gravel have spread outward from the Uinta Mountains.

Desert climates and erodable rocks combine to produce areas devoid of soil, rocky debris, and vegetation called badlands. Ragged, rugged, and virtually valueless, the badlands are, nevertheless, scenically attractive because of the intricate erosional forms and colorful strata exposed in many of them.

Not all areas of barren rock are called badlands; only if much of the surface is in the form of steep slopes is the

Figure 20-19b. Erosional edge of the pediment shown in 20-19a. The Mancos Shale appears in the light-colored badland hills and in the vertical cliff in deep shadow above them. Especially well shown is the gravel capping of the pediment above the vertical cliff. Similar semi-consolidated veneer covers many miles of the pediment shown in 20-19a. The source of the gravel is the Wasatch Plateau seen in the background.

name generally applied. Areas of cliff-forming rocks are not usually called badlands, no matter how rugged, barren, or intricately eroded they may be. The Canyonlands area, adjacent to the Green and Colorado Rivers, is of this type. Bryce Canyon displays both cliffs and slopes and might be called a modified badland. The best badland topography is associated with the Mancos Shale; areas adjacent to Factory Butte and the Cainville mesas in Wayne County are outstanding (figs. 20-20a and 20-20b). They illustrate the importance of loose debris and soil in shaping desert surfaces. Loose surficial material has a smoothing effect, as demonstrated by the common association of smooth debris-covered hills or benches side by side with debris-free badlands.

Mountain slopes show combinations of variously inclined surfaces and are difficult to describe in a few simple terms. Although details vary from range to range, a simple classification based on surficial characteristics is suggested. For surfaces consisting chiefly of bare bedrock, with insignificant cover of soil, loose rock, or plants, the term "skeletonized" has been proposed (fig. 20-21). In contrast, surfaces covered with soil, debris, and vegetation may be called non-skeletonized. Obviously, skeletonized mountains are rugged and barren, non-skeletonized equivalents are smoothed, rounded, and more or less vegetated. Both may form on identical bedrock formations; the controlling factor being climate. Moist climates produce non-skeletonized slopes (fig. 20-22a); arid conditions produce skeletonized slopes (fig. 20-22b).

Figure 20-20b. Ground level view of Mancos Shale badlands. Same area as shown in 20-20a.

Figure 20-20a. Badland topography cut in the Mancos Shale at the base of South Cainville Mesa, Wayne County. Note that the Mesaverde Sandstone capping the mesas provides practically no gravel to impede badland erosion. Photo: Herbert E. Gregory.

Humidity, as an all-pervasive meteorological element, is the key to much of what may be observed in areas subject to changeable ice age climates. Heightened precipitation favors lakes, glaciers at higher elevations, and accumulation of soil at lower elevations. Given time, enough moisture, and a mild climate, an entire landscape might become blanketed with thick soil. This process is responsible for obliterating most surface outcrops in humid regions as, for example, the mountainous part of the southeastern United States.

When the climate shifted from moist to arid, as it did when the last glacial stage ended, the blanket of previously formed soil became vulnerable to erosion. Vegetative cover dwindled, soil structure weakened, and rain fell directly on unprotected fragmental material that it could easily dislodge and remove. Climatic transition from humid to arid in the western United States was accompanied by an increase in the thunderstorm or "cloudburst" type of storm. Effects need not be imagined, they are seen in operation at the present time as a wetter climatic phase gives way to a drier one (fig. 20-23). Flash floods occur somewhere in Utah almost every year and the effects of the more violent ones contribute to the news of the day. Their devastating effects might be described as creating skeletonized mountains out of non-skeletonized ones. The debris removed in the process becomes another coating on nearby alluvial fans or makes a sudden contribution to the load of silt in the Colorado River. The creeping aridity of the southwest is working

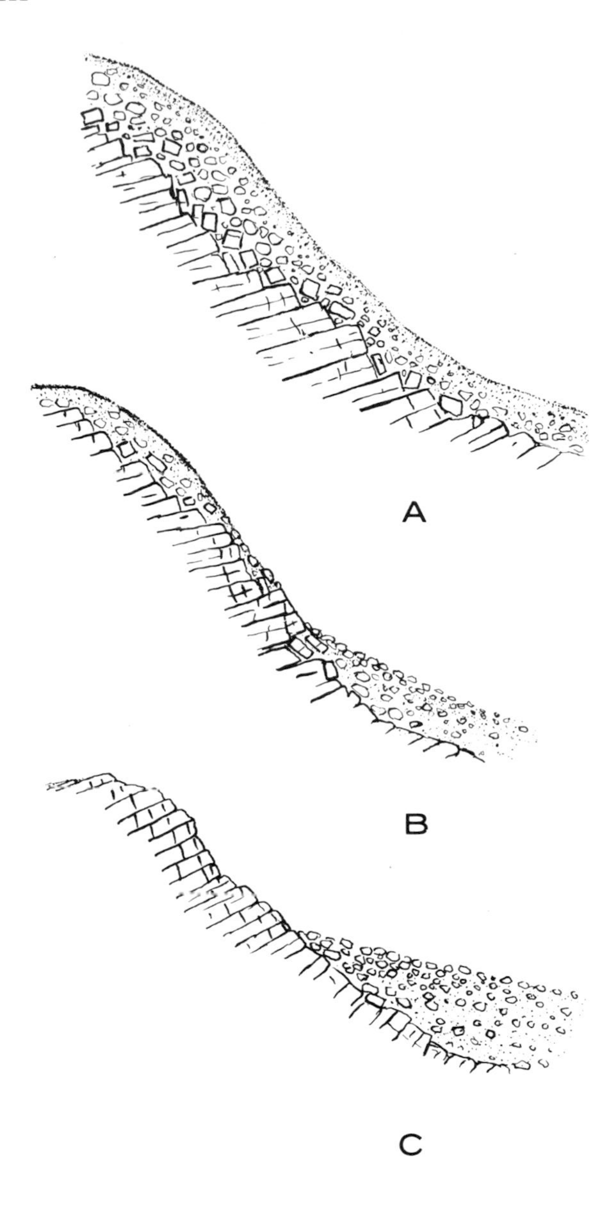

Figure 20-21. Diagram showing progressive changes during skeletonization of a typical mountain face as climate changes from humid to arid: A. Continuous soil and thick blanket of loosened bedrock fragments under humid conditions; B. Soil and regolith in process of rapid removal when moisture is insufficient to maintain a stable cover; C. Bare rock exposure with little or no cover under conditions of extreme aridity.

Figure 20-22a. Slopes of Twin Peaks, Grouse Creek Mountains are almost completely vegetated and have deep soil cover. A change of climate resulting in erosion might be expected to convert this area to bare bedrock. Photo: Hellmut H. Doelling.

Figure 20-22b. The rugged barren east face of the Fish Springs Range, western Juab County is typical of many skeletonized ranges in the Great Basin. Photo: Ward Roylance.

to remove a surficial protective cover built up thousands of years ago, some of it probably before the ice ages began.

Any discussion of surfaces would be incomplete without mention of what has been called "the flattest place on Earth." This is the Great Salt Lake Desert and its salt flats (fig. 20-24a). Although this vast area of more than 6,000 square miles was once under Lake Bonneville, it is not the surface that was left when the lake dried up; that surface has been planed away by the wind. The present salt flats are flat because they are saturated with water and the wind can pick up and carry away only those particles that are not tied together by water. The solution of salt by occasional rains also has a smoothing effect. The salty water seeks the lowest spots and evaporates, leaving a deposit of salt. With enough such deposits, the spots are filled and the water moves into other low areas. By a combination of wind action and salt solution the entire area has become almost as flat as the surface of a calm body of water.

The entirely barren salt pans are surrounded by zones progresssively more vegetated and well drained (fig. 20-24b). The surfaces that are mostly devoid of vegetation or have only scattered plants have little effect on erosion. Scattered salt-resistant plants characterize marginal areas of the Great Salt Lake Desert and a typical sagebrush associa-

Figure 20-23. Crest of the Wasatch Range near Provo. Shows contour trenches cut in vegetated slopes of the Oquirrh Formation to aid in control of erosion. Summit areas of many mountains in the semi-arid west are well vegetated and have deep soil cover. However, as climates shift toward dryness, vegetation is decreasing, soil structure is loosening and intense erosion is taking place. Lower slopes of these mountains are already skeletonized. Photo: U.S. Forest Service.

Figure 20-24a. The Salt Flats, western Tooele County. Photo: A. J. Eardley.

Figure 20-24b. Typical of the many flat-bottomed valleys of western Utah is Pine Valley shown here with the Wah Wah Mountains in the background. Valleys such as this, with external drainage, have not developed permanent salt deposits and support typical desert shrubs. Photo: U.S. Bureau of Reclamation.

tion occupies more distant valleys where drainage is good and humis can accumulate.

In ecologic terms Utah landscapes range from alpine to desert. Almost all details may be explained in terms of changes brought on by oscillations of ice age climate. Although the landscape appears essentially changeless in human terms the present is, in fact, one of rapid changes as unstable deposits built up under more humid conditions are being destroyed by the semi-arid climate.

PLEISTOCENE LIFE AND FOSSILS

One important difference between presently existing animal life and that of the ice ages is the absence of the giant mammals that died out within the past few thousand years. Although Utah has yielded nothing as rich as the famous LaBrea tar pits of Los Angeles County, California, a fairly complete record of the vertebrate life, contemporary with the great ice age lakes, has been gathered from scattered localities. A particularly significant discovery was made in 1965 at Silver Creek Junction, Summit County, on the Highway 40 right-of-way. In a small marshy spot that may once have been the outlet of an active spring, scattered bones of the following animal forms were found: frog, shrew, ground squirrel, chipmunk, pocket gopher, meadow mouse, deer mouse, muskrat, porcupine, rabbit, bison, mammoth, ground sloth, camel, horse, fox, and mink. The age as dated by Carbon-14 is more than 30,000 years old.

Excavations in lake deposits at lower elevations have uncovered bones of mammoths, native horses, bison, mountain sheep, native camels, pecarries, giant bears, and two varieties of musk-oxen (fig. 20-25). It is interesting to note that of these, the mammoth, native horse, native camel, giant bear, and the two so-called musk-oxen are extinct; the bison and peccaries no longer live in Utah and only the mountain sheep still exist in a wild state.

A tabulation of molluscs found in Lake Bonnevile sediments include 11 pelecypods, 55 aquatic gastropods and 13 land gastropods (fig. 20-26). A recent study of ostracodes lists 31 species in 13 genera from lake bed cores taken from the lake beds. An interesting discovery is that of fossil fish in Stansbury level sediments. The only life forms in Great Salt Lake today are adapted to its very saline waters.

Figure 20-25. Reconstruction of Pleistocene animal life of Utah. Shown are native horse, deer, camel, mountain sheep, musk-oxen, mammoth, and bobcat. Bones of all of these have been reported from deposits of Lake Bonneville. Painting by L. A. Ramsey.

SCENERY

The aim of this chapter is to describe the most recent chapter of geologic time. Geologists usually regard the Pleistocene Epoch as having ended 11,000 years ago, everything since then is assigned to the Recent, or Holocene, Epoch. The date of 11,000 years is, in many ways, a convenient termination to the present study. Although it does not end with the historic period, for which abundant written records exist, it does roughly coincide with the first evidences of human occupation in western North America. What has happened, geologically, in the few thousand years of Recent time is almost insignificant and is less than the proverbial drop in the bucket in comparison with preceding events.

A difficult decision must be made with regard to how much should be said at this point about scenery. In most definitions scenery is equated with landscape and landscape is that which a human eye perceives in any broad view of the natural surroundings. Scenery is the broad framework of the landscape but not its small details. Scenery is forests, not individual trees and certainly not leaves. Scenery is hills and mountains, not individual strata, and never gullies, ravines, washes, cliffs, natural bridges, caves, or holes in rocks., Not that these details are unimportant and uninteresting; they have significant and valuable things to contribute, not only to the casual observer who meets them face to face on hiking trails and roads, but also to the trained geologist who must integrate them into the history of that which he studies. Readers of this book must accept the omission of scenic details as a consequence of lack of space and the necessity of presenting at least an outline of the truly vast prehistory that lies behind the present landscape.

Significant sections of preceding chapters have already been devoted to scenery. Noteworthy features have been described in connection with the successive periods with which they are associated. Even though most scenic features were given final shape during the past few thousand years, they need not be re-described as products of the Quaternary Epoch. Only those scenic effects associated with ice action have been reserved for treatment in this chapter.

Glacial Scenery

Glacial scenery may be said to be concentrated just as ice is concentrated. Among the most spectacular scenes on

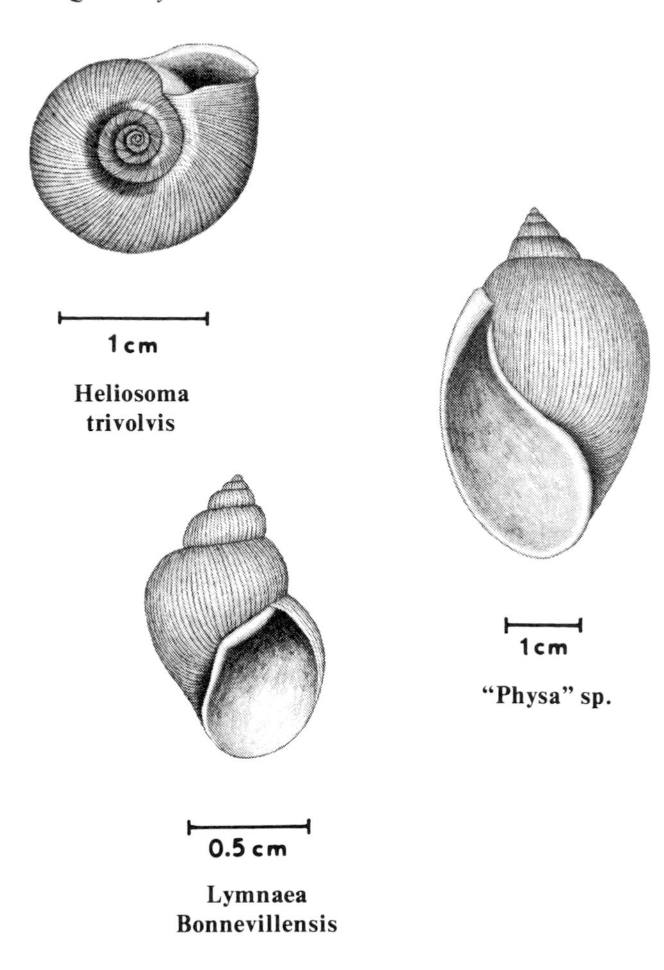

Figure 20-26. Common gastropods of Lake Bonneville. Almost unaltered shells of these and other species abound in Lake Bonneville sediments at some localities. Sketches by John K. Balsley.

Earth are those carved by mountain glaciers in the Alps, Himalayas, southern Andes, and Canadian Rockies. Utah was never under a major ice sheet, the nearest approach of a really large glacier was to the Yellowstone/Teton National Parks, Wyoming, area 350 miles away. Also, in comparison with those of higher latitudes and elevations, Utah's mountain glaciers were of relatively small extent and short duration. This is not to downgrade the glacial scenery, the Uinta Mountains are considered by many connoiseurs to be the most beautiful in North America (figs. 20-27a). In recognition of this assessment, a rather large area in the central, higher part, embracing most of what is commonly called the High Uintas, has been designated as an official Primitive Area.

By a somewhat unusual coincidence the glacial landscape of the high mountains (fig. 20-27b) has much in common with the landscapes of the better known and much lower desert areas. Both are characterized by an absence of soil and vegetation and a corresponding dominance of bare rock surfaces. In the high mountains, plant life is inhibited by low temperature, in desert areas it is sparse because of low precipitation. In both environments, nothing stands between the bare rocks and the agents of weathering and erosion.

The largest area of glacial scenery in Utah is the central Uinta Mountains. The dominant landform is the cirque, a semicircular, relatively wide, flat-bottomed valley, usually with high, steep, confining walls (fig. 20-28). Cirques may be thought of as branching headwater valleys which were originally outlined by stream erosion but later occupied and enlarged by ice. Cirques grow by the undermining and gnawing of ice around the margins so they become wider, deeper, and more nearly circular with time.

Cirques on opposite sides of a ridge commonly grow toward each other by destruction of the intervening divide. Original surfaces between the cirques are gradually eaten away until only sharp ridges, called aretes, remain. When a number of glaciers have taken large semi-circular bites out of the surface, the result is "biscuit-board topography." This was the stage reached by most Uinta glaciers before they ceased to be active. A long remnant of the original crest of the Uinta Mountains eaten into from both sides by great cirques constitutes a well-marked divide and trail for hikers. Attached to this central remnant and radiating outward and downward like the legs of a centipede are the divides between the stream courses, broad or narrow, according to how strong the adjacent glaciers were (fig. 20-29).

At the west end of the mountains, the original topography was mostly submerged as numerous glaciers merged into an unbroken ice sheet. Following the terminology of alpine geography, a sharp-edged divide where two cirques intersect is a col and a sharp-pointed peak left after numerous cirques have eroded away everything but a slender spire is a matterhorn. No real matterhorns are found in the Uinta Mountains. Their profile, from a distance, preserves much of the low, rolling character of the pre-glacial stage.

The descent from the aretes and cols to the floors of the cirques is steep and rocky. These slopes bear record of the plucking away of rock fragments by moving ice. A glacier almost literally digs itself into the Earth. Pieces of the wall rock, once they are embedded in ice, are carried away and may not touch bottom or be deposited until the glacier melts at its lower end. When it melts away, the vertical wall, recording the last line of attack, is left exposed to a new set of forces. This stage is an ideal time and place for the accumulation of loose rocks known as talus piles. Pieces loosened by the ice but not yet carried away fall or roll to the base of the cliffs where they are joined by subsequent pieces broken off by freezing ice, plant roots, or passing animals. The Uinta Quartzite is a very hard and much fractured rock, well suited for the production of loose pieces of moderate size. Talus, by the millions of tons, is accumulating around the edges of cliffs in cones and sheets waiting to be carried away if reached by running water. Once in streams, pieces are sorted, rounded, and smoothed so that when they arrive at the valley below they are mostly cobbles; streams draining the glaciated parts of the Uintas are cobble choked like no other streams.

Figure 20-27a. Glaciated High Uintas. (See Figure 20-27b for caption.)

Figure 20-27b. Glaciated central Wasatch. The two most heavily glaciated areas of Utah are the western Uinta Range (20-27a) and the central Wasatch (20-27b). The glaciated highlands are mostly above 11,000 feet elevation, are above present timberline, and were areas of heavy snowfall in the glacial period. View of the High Uintas is looking east along the north slope of the range. In the foreground glacial action has removed almost all of the higher strata. Remnants which were in the process of erosion when glaciation ceased make up the high peaks on the skyline. View in the Wasatch is looking into the headwaters of Big Cottonwood Creek and southward along the crest of the range. Twin Lakes Reservoir, middle right; Lake Mary, middle left. Glaciated area of the Wasatch is chiefly homogeneous igneous rock. In the Uinta Range, the surface is relatively undeformed stratified quartzite. This probably explains the somewhat chaotic topography of the Wasatch and the more ordered appearance of the Uintas. Photo: Hal Rumel.

Figure 20-28. Glacial erosion in the High Uintas. This view emphasizes a deep cirque with a cirque lake, the wide bedrock floor, and great talus piles that have accumulated since the glacier melted. The divide between this cirque and the one working from the opposite side has been reduced to a thin rock wall and pass. Photo: U.S. Forest Service.

Figure 20-29. Space view of the Uinta Range showing glacial valleys and cirques as dominant land forms. White areas are not snow, they are bare rocks above timberline. Glaciers occupied the wider areas between the bare divides. Many rounded cirques at drainage headwaters are visible. At the west end of the mountains, glaciers almost removed the central ridge. Many lakes are visible on close inspection. Length of view about 100 miles. Photo: U.S. Department of Agriculture.

Lakes are another striking product of glacial action that lingers long after the ice is gone. This is true of mountain as well as continental glaciers. Glacial lakes result from the fact that ice does not always move downhill but may press down and gouge or scrape out depressions as a normal part of its slow forward movement. Glacial lakes may also be formed by the damming action of material piled up at the edges and sides of glaciers and particularly at the lower ends where great embankments are usual. No one has counted all the lakes in the Uinta Mountains and if it were attempted it would generate difficult decisions when the smaller ponds and vegetation-choked bogs and marshes had to be considered. Even so, more than 4,300 bodies of water larger than 50 feet in diameter can be counted on topographic maps of the glaciated portion of the range.

ECONOMIC

Great Salt Lake has been referred to as a liquid ore body. Soluble materials have been accumulating in its water and sediments for thousands of years. Much attention has been paid to materials contained in the water, the clay layers below the lake bed, and in the associated desert flats to the west. This interest has passed from the state of mere academic or scientific curiosity to the construction of great installations set up on the lake margins to extract valuable constituents on a commercial scale. The lake water and associated sediments, including those in the Great Salt Lake Desert, have been studied extensively by the Utah Geological and Mineral Survey. Important contributions include a map of the lake, studies of the Bonneville Salt Flats, electrochemical potential of the lake water, effects of the causeway, disposal of mill tailings, variations in brine composition, and possible geothermal resources of the salt flats.

According to a comprehensive study, the lake brine during the period October, 1959, to September, 1961, had an average volume of 10 million ac/ft and a concentration of 266,000 ppm (26.6 percent by weight) dissolved solids. This amounts to about 4.4 billion tons of dissolved minerals, of which about 91 million tons are K_2O (potash) and 500 million tons are $MgCl_2$ (magnesium chloride). It has been calculated that if the lake water were evaporated entirely, approximately 77 percent of the dissolved material would precipitate as sodium chloride (table salt, fig. 20-30), 9 percent as sodium sulfate, 5 percent as magnesium chloride, 4 percent as magnesium sulfate, 4 percent as potassium chloride, and 1 percent as compounds of lithium, bromine, and other elements. In addition to the major constituents listed above, the following have been detected in trace amounts: iodine, strontium, aluminum, bismuth, cadmium, chromium, cobalt, copper, gallium, germanium,

Figure 20-30. Salt from evaporation of Great Salt Lake water, Leslie Salt Company, Tooele County.

iron, lead, manganese, molybdenum, nickel, titanium, vanadium, and zinc.

The largest installation based on saline resources of the lake is the $70 million magnesium division plant of AMAX Corporation, Inc., on the west side of the lake 50 miles from Salt Lake City. A series of large evaporation ponds occupying 33,000 acres of diked lake bed constitute the heart of the operation; anticipated production is 45,000 tons of magnesium annually.

Although sand and gravel are probably the most unromantic of mineral products, they rank high in commercial importance. Yearly production in Utah is valued at between $10 and $15 million. This places them about fifth or sixth in

Figure 20-31. Gravel bars and terraces at higher levels of Lake Bonneville, northern Terrace Mountains, Box Elder County. Deposits of gravel left by Pleistocene lakes in Utah appear inexhaustible.

rank insofar as value is concerned, well above the more glamorous products such as silver and zinc. Sand and gravel are unconsolidated rock fragments sorted by water so that very fine and very coarse fractions have been eliminated. The product may be used as found or it can be screened and washed for special purposes. Most sand and gravel is a product of the past few thousand or, at most, few million years. Anything older is likely to be more or less consolidated and would, therefore, constitute sandstone or conglomerate. Most of the sand and gravel used today was deposited along the shorelines of the Pleistocene lakes (fig. 20-31). The deposits in western Utah are near or between the Bonneville and Provo levels, 5,090 to 4,740 feet above sea level. By a fortunate combination of circumstances, many fine deposits are found near the centers of population where demand is greatest. The sand and gravel industry is widely dispersed and production is recorded from every county.

Any material used in making concrete that is lighter than gravel and sand is called light-weight aggregate. Pumice, volcanic cinders, perlite, diatomite, and volcanic ash are in this group (fig. 20-32). They occur in great quantities, mainly in connection with the more recent volcanic cones and flows. A chief source has been the cinder cones in Millard, Beaver, and Utah Counties. The only material on the list that is not of volcanic origin is diatomaceous earth. This is fine, white, siliceous, powdery material made up of shells or tests of aquatic algae. Locally such organisms thrived in

Figure 20-32. Pumice mine in Ice Springs volcanic field near Fillmore, Millard County.

the ice age lakes and left extensive deposits along the shorelines. Future potential use of some of these is as insulation and prefabricated building materials.

For additional reading on the topics discussed in Chapter 20, please see the following list of authors:

Antevs, 1948
Atwood, 1909
Baumhoff and Heizer, 1965
Bick, 1966
Bissell, H.J., 1963, 1968
Blackwelder, 1948, 1949
Blagbrough and Breed, 1967
Cohenour, 1966
Cohenour and others, 1963
Crittenden and others, 1967
Currey, 1980, 1981
DeGraf, 1976
Eardley, 1938, 1961, 1970
Eardley and others, 1957
Eardley and others, 1973
Feth, 1955, 1963
Feth and others, 1966
Flint and Denney, 1958
Gilbert, 1890, 1928
Goode, 1975
Goode and Eardley, 1960
Grogger, 1974
Gvosdetsky, 1953
Gwynn, 1977
Hahl and Handy, 1969
Hahl and Mitchell, 1963
Handy, 1967
Handy and Hahl, 1935
Hansen, W.R., 1969a, 1969b
Hardy and Muessig, 1952
Hibbard and others, 1965
Hite, 1964
Hunt, C.B., 1953a, 1953b

Ives, 1951
Jennings, 1957
Lister, 1975
McMillan, 1974
Madison, 1969
Marsell, 1964
Mehringer and Nash, 1971
Miller, 1976
Morrison, 1960, 1961, 1965a, 1965b, 1966, 1968, 1975
Nelson and Madsen, 1980
Nolan, 1943
Osmond, 1960
Richmond, 1962, 1964
Rigby, 1958
Roscoe, 1963
Smith and others, 1968
Spieker and Billings, 1940
Stock and Stokes, 1969
Stokes, 1973
Stokes and Condie, 1961
Talmage, 1902
Tayler and others, 1977
Threet, 1959
Turk, 1973
Van Horn, 1964a, 1964b
Vlam, 1963
Whelan, 1971, 1973, 1975
Whelan and Peterson, 1974, 1976
Williams, J.S., 1958, 1962, 1970
Wimber and Crowford, 1933
Woolley, 1948

For complete bibliographic citations, please see List of References.

Figure 20-33. Dollar Lake, High Uinta Wilderness area. Strata of the Uinta Mountain Group make up the background peaks and ridges. Photo: U.S. Forest Service.

Figure 20-34. Eastern slopes of Mt. Timpanogos showing steep-walled cirques and abundant talus. Cliffs are Pennsylvanian Oquirrh Formation. Famous Timp Trail to the summit crosses the talus, left center. Photo: Arthur C. King.

21 THE FACE OF THE LAND

Utah has a total area of 84,916 square miles. This places it 11th in size among the fifty states and equivalent to Connecticut, Massachusetts, Rhode Island, Vermont, New Hampshire, Maine, New Jersey, and Maryland combined. Within this relatively large area, four major physiographic provinces that meet near the center of the state have been described. In this chapter the major provinces are subdivided into smaller units called physiographic sections. These are shown on the physiographic map in the pocket.

Most of the section names are taken from well-known, topographic features, but where none are available or do not give distinctive mental images, names have been taken from prominent geologic structures or formations. In a few sections there appear to be neither natural geologic nor geographic peculiarities from which a name may be borrowed; for these localities, place names have been used.

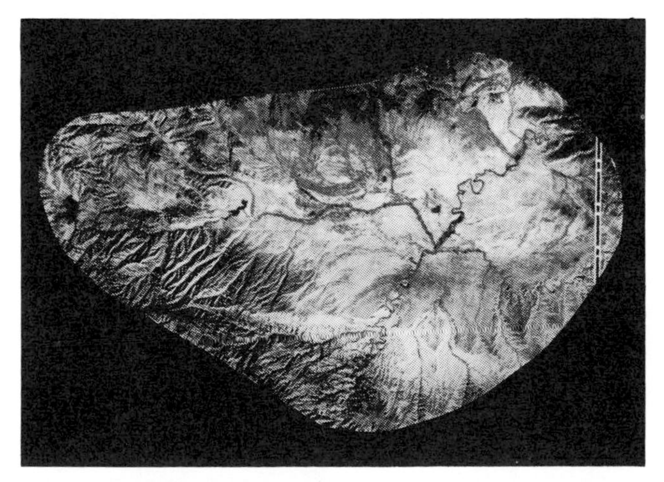

Figure 21-1. Aerial view of the Uinta Basin. Green River crosses view from upper right to lower center and the Duchesne River joins it from the west and the White River from the east. Utah-Colorado boundary is shown as a broad dashed line. Distance across view is about 185 miles. Photo: U. S. Department of Agriculture.

THE COLORADO PLATEAU

Centered roughly at the Four Corners, the Colorado Plateau Province is shared by Utah, Colorado, New Mexico, and Arizona. It is probably the most distinctive province in the United States, being world-famous not only for many scenic attractions but also for the diversity of geologic features displayed with textbook simplicity in its rocky outcrops. The 16 sections into which the Utah portion of the Plateau has been subdivided can be best described under subheads, starting with the Uinta Basin to the north and progressing in a rough clockwise manner around the province.

Uinta Basin Section

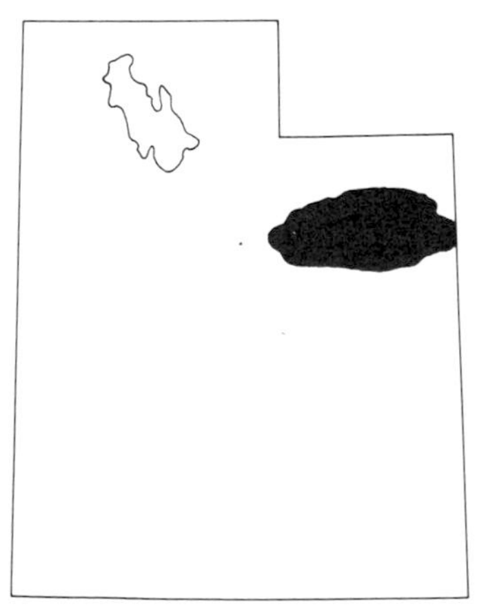

The Uinta Basin is well named; it is distinctly bowl-shaped in both topographic form and geologic structure (fig. 21-1). The topography conforms closely, but not exactly, to the structure. It is a puzzling fact that the Duchesne River, the lowest part of the topographic basin, follows a course about 10 miles south of the structural axis of the basin. In other words, the change in direction of dip of the rocks lies nearer the Uinta Mountains than does the change in direction of surface drainage.

The central part of the Uinta Basin is relatively flat and the many river tributaries that cross it from adjacent highlands flow in relatively wide shallow valleys not more than a few hundred feet below the surrounding country. The course of the Green River can, in no sense, be called a canyon across this section.

The topography, apart from the stream valleys, is best described in terms of sloping surfaces. Those which incline northward are mainly dip slopes on the harder layers of the Green River and Uinta Formations. The sloping surfaces of much of the northern half of the basin are pediments planed by erosion and coated with a veneer of gravel and sand from the Uinta Mountains. Pebbles of quartzite from the core of the Uinta Mountains are very durable and tend to be transported downward level by level so as to coat numerous flat-topped hills at various elevations.

The Book Cliffs-Roan Plateau Section

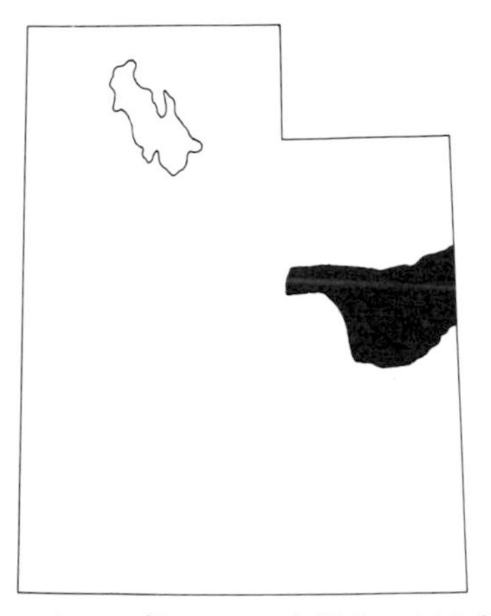

Between the relatively level interior of the Uinta Basin and the valleys cut in the Mancos Shale in Carbon, Emery, and Grand Counties is one of Utah's most rugged areas. The structure is relatively simple; strata of Cretaceous and Tertiary ages rise gradually southward and upward from the center of the Uinta Basin to reach elevations of between 8,000 and 10,000 feet where they are abruptly cut off in great erosional cliffs that descend in giant steps to the valleys of the south where elevations are between 4,000 and 5,500 ft.

The great systems of linear cliffs are impressive. The lower one, most visible and best known, is the Book Cliffs. Above, and separated by a bench or valley as much as 10 miles wide, are the Roan Cliffs (fig. 21-2). For that part of the Uinta rim in Carbon County, there is a third, relatively short system, the Badland Cliffs. The Book Cliffs are carved mainly from marine Cretaceous sandstone, the Roan Cliffs of Paleocene and Eocene river and flood plain deposits, and the Badlands Cliffs of Eocene lake beds (see geologic and physiographic maps).

Figure 21-2. West Tavaputs Plateau, Carbon County. Junction of Price River and Green River, left lower center, eroded Late Cretaceous rocks which make up most of the view with Tertiary strata of the Roan Cliffs in the distance. Photo: Hal Rumel.

The cliffs are retreating from former positions far to the south. The tendency to retreat along a regular front has exercised a much greater influence than the Green River that is confined to a relatively narrow gorge through the formations without interrupting the dominantly east-west sweep of the cliff system. Desolation Canyon traverses the Tertiary section and Gray Canyon the Cretaceous formations. In passing through these two canyons the river drops about 600 feet.

The Mancos Shale Lowlands Section

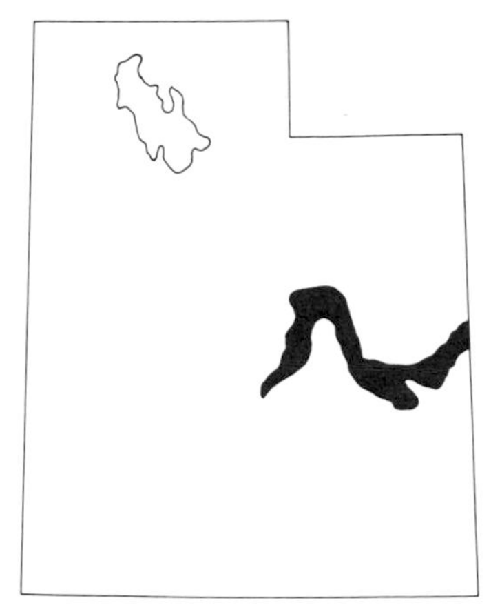

The largest region of fairly level land in eastern Utah has the shape of a huge recumbent "S", extending roughly between the town of Emery, Emery County, and the Colorado line. It includes three so-called valleys: Castle Valley (fig. 21-3), Clark Valley, and Grand Valley, the boundaries of which are not distinctly marked. The Mancos Shale Lowlands form a broad border on the west, north, and northeast sides of the San Rafael Swell and then swing eastward parallel with the Book Cliffs in conformity with the southern contours of the Uinta Basin. The lowland is crossed by a few permanent streams, the largest of which is the Green River, and by a great number of intermittent washes draining higher country to the west or north. Sloping pediments, rugged badlands, and narrow flat-bottomed alluvial valleys are common. Most of the agricultural settlements of Emery, Carbon, and Grand Counties are located in this section.

The Uncompahgre Section

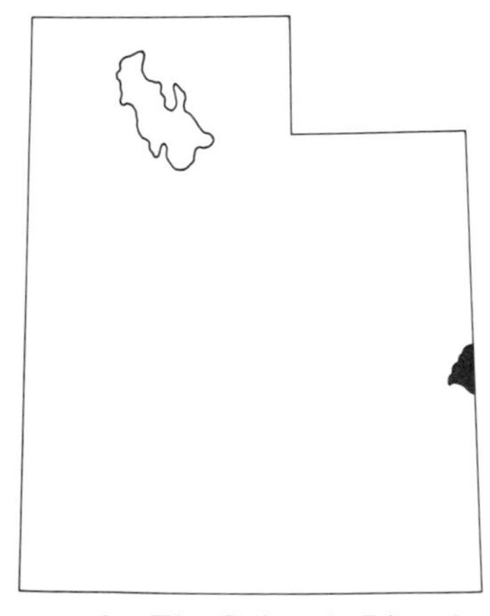

The small section of the Uncompahgre Plateau extending from Colorado into Utah is the downward-plunging end, or nose, of the ancient Uncompahgre Uplift. The formations and structures have an arc-like pattern in conformance with a great buried core of crystalline rock that is basically a smoothed-off, buried mountain of Precambrian rocks. The Colorado River has cut through several hundred feet of these rocks in the Westwater Canyon area (fig. 21-4). On either side are colorful cliffs, buttes, and mesas

Figure 21-3. Typical view of Castle Valley about 10 miles south of Price. Wasatch Plateau forming skyline, sloping, gravel-covered pediment on the left, the badlands on the right, and the shrub-covered valley floor in the foreground are all carved in the soft Mancos Shale of Late Cretaceous age. Photo: Glen Ungerman.

of non-marine Mesozoic strata. The buried range extends farther into Utah but its surface expression is lost at the level of the Dakota Sandstone, the outer outcropping edge of which serves as a boundary to this section.

Figure 21-4. Inner gorge of Colorado River in Westwater Canyon, Grand County. River flows between walls of Precambrian crystalline rock. Soft Chinle Shale (Triassic) has been stripped away to form a bench. Triassic and Jurassic sandstone formations are above. Photo: Joy Okland.

The Salt Anticline-Lisbon Prong Section

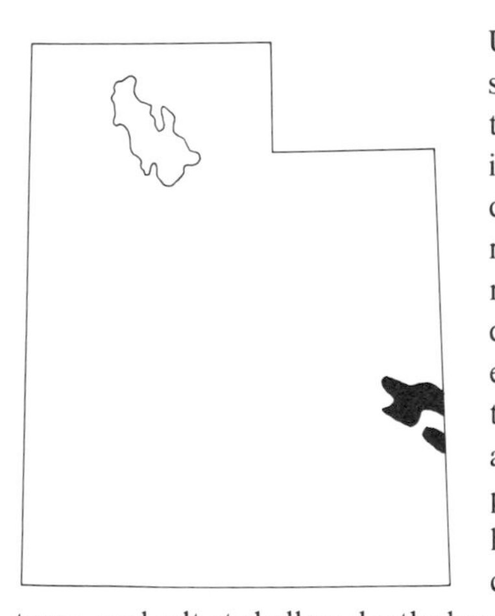

Utah and Colorado share a unique type of topography characterized by great elongate depressions formed by removal of subterranean salt masses. The depressions are mostly elongate oval valleys, trend northwesterly, are collapsed or depressed anticlines, have high surrounding walls, complex marginal structures, and salt at shallow depths beneath the valley bottoms.

The chief salt-related valleys are Spanish (Moab) Valley (fig. 21-5), Lisbon Valley, Salt Valley, and Castle Valley. The LaSal Mountains separate Lisbon Valley from the remainder of the group, but the basic geologic pattern is continuous east of the mountains in Colorado. In referring to Utah only it may be best to designate the southern part of the group as the Lisbon Prong of the Salt Valley Anticline section.

Because of the semi-protected nature of these deep valleys they have received and retained various thicknesses of windblown silt that is good soil where water is available. The drainage is out of harmony with the topography; the Colorado River strikes directly across the Spanish and Salt Valleys. Fisher Valley is drained by Onion Creek and Castle Valley by Salt Creek.

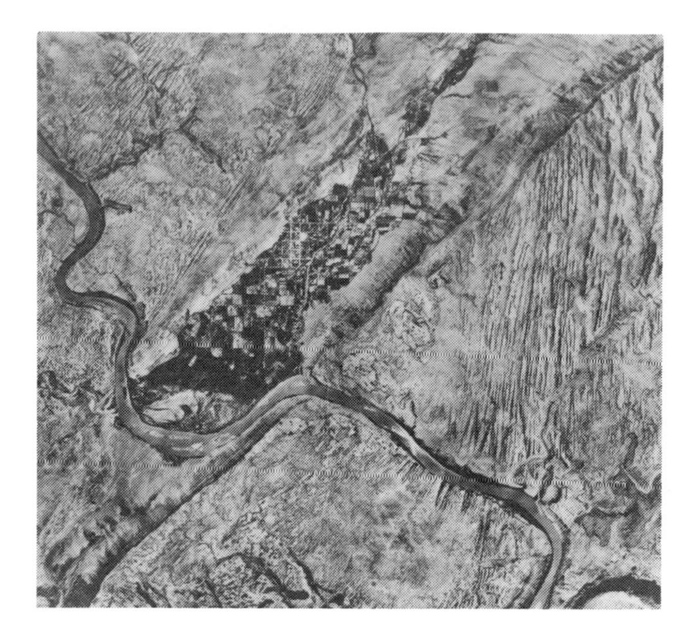

Figure 21-5. Vertical air view of Moab, Grand County, and its geological setting. The collapse structure of Spanish Valley in which the city is located is well shown, joint systems are pronounced in the Entrada and Navajo Sandstones. The Colorado River flows southwesterly from the upper left. Photo: Vincent E. Kelley.

Figure 21-6. Warner Lake, LaSal Mountains, Grand County. The LaSal Mountains were glaciated during the Pleistocene. Photo: Ward Roylance.

Many scenic areas are associated with the collapsed anticlines. Best known is Arches National Park which includes territory on both flanks of the Salt Valley Anticline.

LaSal Mountains Section

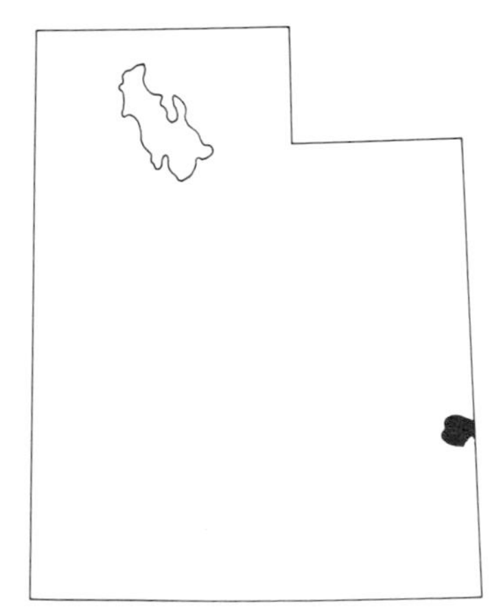

The LaSal Mountains (fig. 21-6, named from Spanish, sal = salt) dominate the landscape of east-central Utah and supply water for Moab and LaSal, Utah, and Paradox, Colorado. Three separate groups of peaks make up the LaSal Mountains, each group representing a center of intrusive igneous rocks that rose from depth and pushed outward into the sediments. Mt. Peale (12,721 feet) is in the middle group and is the highest point.

Material eroded from the mountains has spread out along adjacent drainages and has built a huge fan or pediment to the south. The fringing, debris-coated foothills are included with the mountains to make up the LaSal Mountains Section.

Hatch Syncline Section

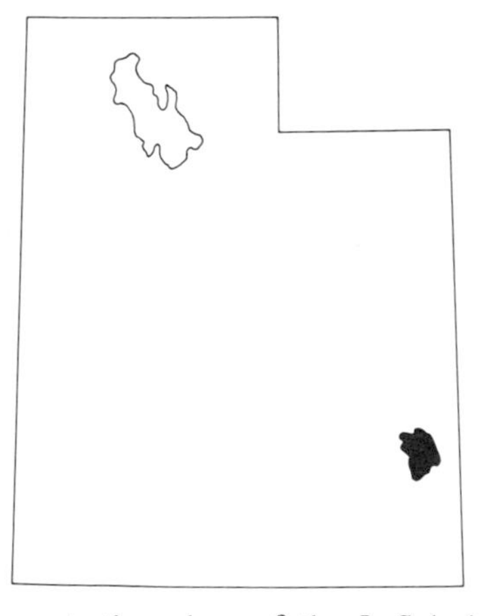

The territory between the LaSal and Abajo Mountains is an eroded lowland that drains northwesterly into the Colorado River. For this area the name Hatch Syncline Section (fig. 21-7) is proposed. Boundaries are determined by the edge of the Great Sage Plains to the south, the escarpment of the inner Canyonlands on the west, the edges of the LaSal slopes in the north and the lower flanks of the Lisbon Valley Anticline to the east.

Most of this territory has been stripped of overlying formations to the top of the Navajo Sandstone. Scattered erosional remnants of Entrada Sandstone, with local cappings of Summerville and Morrison Formations, constitute the chief topographic features. Wind erosion seems to have been effective in removing much material and the surface is veneered with thin, wind-derived soil. Looking-glass Rock and Church Rock are famous landmarks.

Figure 21-7. Hatch syncline, looking north. Remnant of Entrada Sandstone is at the right center. Hatch Wash occupies the shallow depression.

Great Sage Plains Section

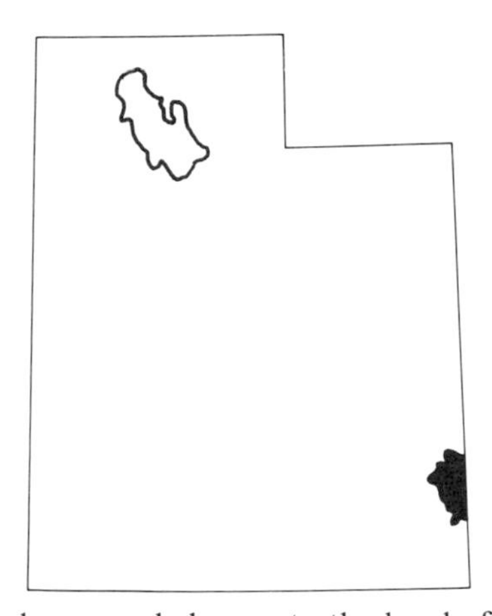

Extending from the base of the Abajo Mountains many miles into Colorado are the Great Sage Plains (fig. 21-8), one of the most extensive flat areas of the Colorado Plateau. This is an excellent example of a stripped plain, a level region that conforms to the top of a resistant rock layer. In this instance the very soft Mancos Shale has been eroded away to the level of the much harder Dakota Formation and Burro Canyon Formation, both difficult to remove except at the margins where they break away under headward erosion by many small tributary streams. The sandstone layers are being undermined by many branches of Montezuma Creek from the south and by tributaries of East Canyon from the north. A thin soil, derived chiefly from wind-blown dust, supports extensive dry-land agriculture between Monticello, Utah, and Cortez, Colorado.

Figure 21-8. The Great Sage Plain looking east from near Monticello, Utah into Colorado.

Abajo or Blue Mountains Section

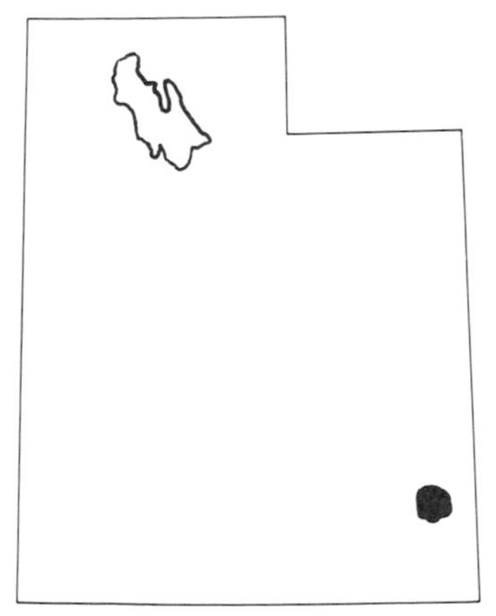

The Abajo, or Blue, Mountains (fig. 21-9) dominate the skyline of southeastern Utah and provide a water supply for the nearby towns of Monticello and Blanding, San Juan County. The highest point is Abajo Peak, elevation 11,345 feet. The mountains owe their existence to the relative hardness of the igneous rock that has intruded upward through several conduits and pushed outward into the surrounding sediments. The group as a whole is nearly circular but there is an offshoot, Shay Mountain, several miles to the north, in which the igneous core is not exposed. The Abajo Mountains give rise to southward-flowing Cottonwood, Recapture, and Montezuma Creeks and to Indian Creek flowing north into Canyonlands National Park.

Figure 21-9. The Abajo Mountains, looking west. Abajo Peak is 11,360 feet with the southernmost peak of the northern mountain group its highest point. Great Sage Plain is in the foreground. Photo: Sherman A. Wengerd.

Blanding Basin Section

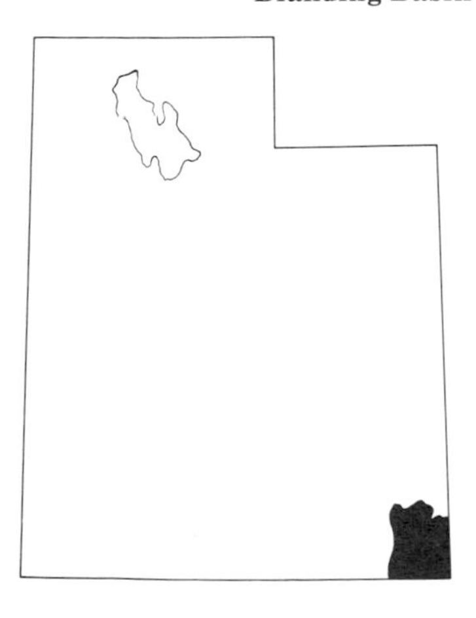

The geologic term Blanding Basin (fig. 21-10) serves best to designate the section making up the southeast corner of Utah. The western boundary is Comb Ridge and a northern boundary may be drawn along the cliffs of the northern tributaries of Montezuma Creek. The San Juan River traverses the central part of the Basin and the entire area drains into it through intermittent washes or by way of McElmo Creek.

This is an area of low mesas, buttes, and finger-like points between relatively shallow drainages such as Cottonwood, Recapture and Montezuma Creeks running south and Gothic Creek running north.

Figure 21-10. Blanding Basin looking southeasterly from a point 10 miles south of Blanding.

Monument Upwarp Section

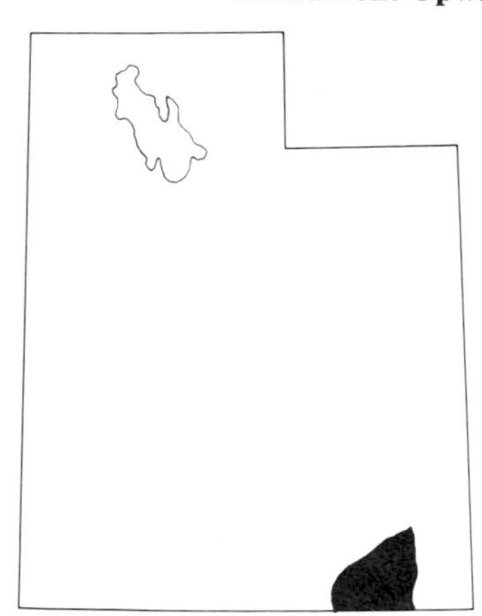

Utah and Arizona share the Monument Upwarp section (fig. 21-11). Except for the northern border the section coincides with the broad anticlinal fold known as the Monument Upwarp. Comparison can be made with the San Rafael Swell and Circle Cliffs. Each has a prominent hogback cut from steeply dipping Jurassic and Triassic strata along the eastern margin. For the Monument Upwarp, it is Comb Ridge. As with the other great folds the central area is late Paleozoic, flanked by Triassic and Jurassic formations. Much of the higher, interior part is relatively flat due to the stripping away of the softer formations to the top of the more resistent limestone strata.

The canyon of the San Juan River displays world-famous examples of incised meanders at the east end and is relatively straight at the west end. Grand Gulch, a spectacular south-flowing tributary that drains much of the interior, is an intermittent stream subject to occasional flash floods.

Figure 21-11. The broad summit area of the Monument Upwarp looking south across the canyon of the San Juan River into Monument Valley, Arizona. Black Mesa (Cretaceous and Jurassic) forms distant skyline. Triassic formations skirt the lowlands around Black Mesa and form caprocks for the monuments. Permian formations form the main body of the mesas and buttes, the level plain beyond the gorge and the upper few hundred feet of the canyon walls. Deeper part of canyon is Pennsylvanian Hermosa Formation. Cedar Mesa Sandstone forms tree-covered white rim above canyon on the right. Photo: Hal Rumel.

Monument Valley Subsection

Also shared by Utah and Arizona is Monument Valley (fig. 21-12), made famous by its scenic assemblage of colorful mesas, buttes, and spires cut from Permian DeChelly Sandstone. In reality the so-called valley is perched on the Monument Upwarp; the strata descend eastward at Comb Ridge and westward at the Red House Cliffs and Nokai Canyon. Like the Slick-Rock Section to the west, the Monument Valley Subsection includes territory north and south of the San Juan River.

Figure 21-12 Buttes and spires of the Permian DeChelly Sandstone characterize Monument Valley. View is toward the north. The Utah-Arizona boundary passes near the base of the most distant flat-topped remnant, Sentinel Mesa. Photo: Hal Rumel.

The rock layers of Monument Valley are such that one formation, the DeChelly Sandstone, readily gives rise to high, isolated remnants while the next lower level, the Organ Rock Formation, produces flat areas almost devoid of deep waterways. There are no permanent streams to disrupt the landscape and a traveler or road builder can easily proceed in almost any direction as long as he skirts the monuments.

Slick-Rock Section

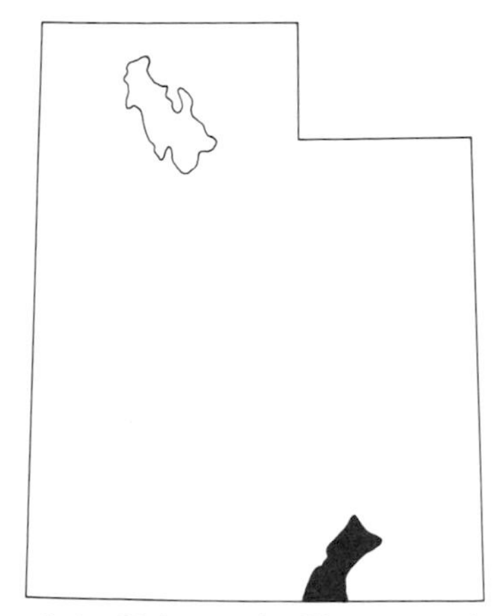

South of and across the Colorado River from the Kaiparowits Plateau is a rugged area of mesas, canyons, and promontories that has been called the Navajo Mountain Section (fig. 21-13) by workers in Arizona. Navajo Mountain (10,388 feet) dominates the scene and its rounded profile stands in striking contrast to the squared-off points of the Kaiparowits Plateau to the north. The surface rock is chiefly the Navajo Sandstone that erodes to deep canyons and slick-rock slopes (see geologic map). The lower foothills including Rainbow Bridge, once remote and difficult to reach, have now been made accessible by boat on Lake Powell.

Chiefly because of the continuity and similarity of surface exposures, the Slick-Rock Section is drawn to include a tract that crosses the San Juan River and extends as far north as Red Canyon (see physiographic map).

Figure 21-13. Slick rock outcrops of the Navajo Sandstone, near Navajo Mountain. Tributaries of the Colorado River partly drowned by water of Lake Powell cross the view. Photo: Robert Q. Oaks, Jr.

The Kaiparowits Plateau and Escalante Bench Section

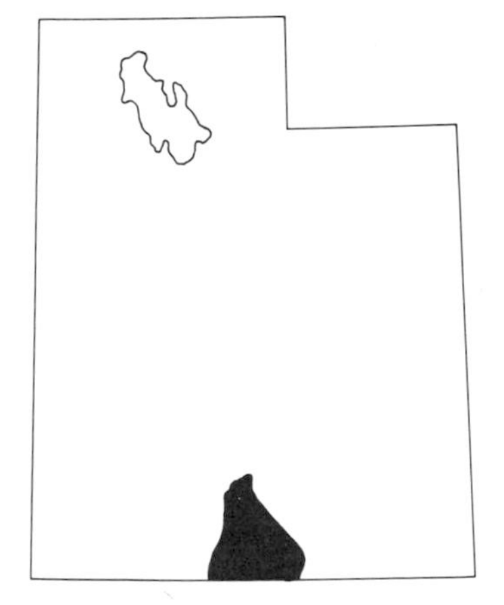

The large, fanlike mass of flat-lying sedimentary rocks extending southeasterly from a narrow connection with the Table Cliffs has been given the name Kaiparowits Plateau from Piute words meaning "the mountain home of these people." The plateau is made up chiefly of non-marine Jurassic and marine Cretaceous formations. The eastern edge is bounded by the Straight Cliffs (fig. 21-14), well named from their remarkably even profile free of both canyons and protruding points. The south edge is a ragged assemblage of terraces, benches, points, and promontories overlooking the Colorado River. The western edge is the East Kaibab Fold, along which older rocks rise to the surface and from which the Cretaceous strata have been eroded.

East of the Straight Cliffs is a flat area cut in Jurassic rocks. Strata equivalent to the nearby cliffs have been stripped away by erosion. The structure and lower formations of this bench or valley are similar to those of nearby Kaiparowits Plateau.

Figure 21-14. The Straight Cliffs south of Escalante, Kane County. Cretaceous rocks make up the higher cliffs and slopes. Jurassic formations appear in the foothills and level bench area. Photo: Ward Roylance.

The Grand Staircase Section

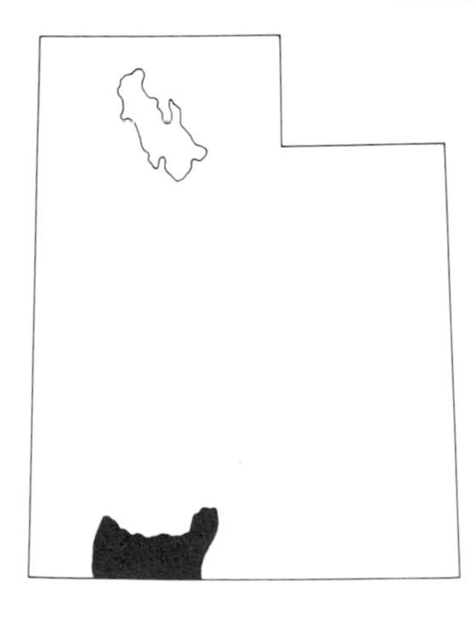

The great series of cliffs and terraces that rises from the Grand Canyon in Arizona to the summit of the High Plateaus in Utah has been called the Grand Staircase of plateau geology (fig. 21-15). Here, in succession upward, are the Vermillion Cliffs (Triassic), White Cliffs (Jurassic), Gray Cliffs (Cretaceous), and Pink Cliffs (Tertiary). Be-

Figure 21-15. The Grand Staircase of Utah geology as seen from space. The four great lines of cliffs are labeled. Utah-Arizona boundary is shown by dashed line. The view is about 40 miles across. Photo: U.S. Department of Agriculture.

tween, like staircase treads, are relatively flat areas like the Skutumpah Terrace cut chiefly in soft Middle Jurassic strata and the Kolob Terrace cut chiefly across Cretaceous formations. Zion Canyon National Park and vicinity embraces gigantic erosional forms in the White Cliffs carved by the Virgin River and there are other areas almost as spectacular. The rocks are predominantly continental deposits and display an array of colors only partly described by the names of the great cliffs.

This section is bounded on the east by the East Kaibab Monocline, on the west by the Hurricane Fault, on the north by the edges of the various high plateaus, and on the south by the Grand Canyon of Arizona.

St. George Basin Section

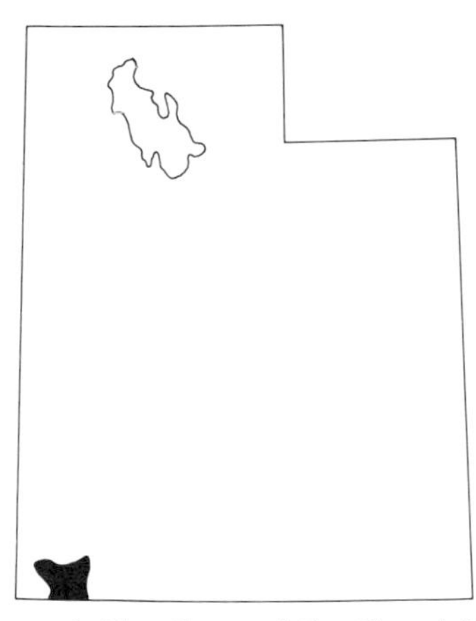

The city of St. George, Washington County, lies near the center of a topographic basin (fig. 21-16) that is bounded by the Hurricane Cliffs on the east, the Pine Valley Mountains on the north, and the Beaver Dam Mountains on the west. To the south it opens into the Shivwits Plateau of Arizona. The structure and rock formations are much like those of the Grand Staircase Section east of the Hurricane Cliffs but the Beaver Dam Mountains on the west are of the Basin and Range type. Between St. George and the highest peaks of the Pine Valley Mountains is an elevational difference of more than 7,000 feet. Because of the relatively low elevation of this section, it has gained the name of "Utah's Dixie." The average growing season is about 2 months longer than at Cedar City, only 40 miles farther north. The geography and geology of this section has been described by E.F. Cook (1960a).

Figure 21-16. St. George Basin from the southeast. The town is situated on Triassic formations. The lava-capped bench is seen in lower right and the slopes of Beaver Dam Range are upper left. Photo: LaRell Nielson.

Circle Cliffs-Teasdale Anticline Section

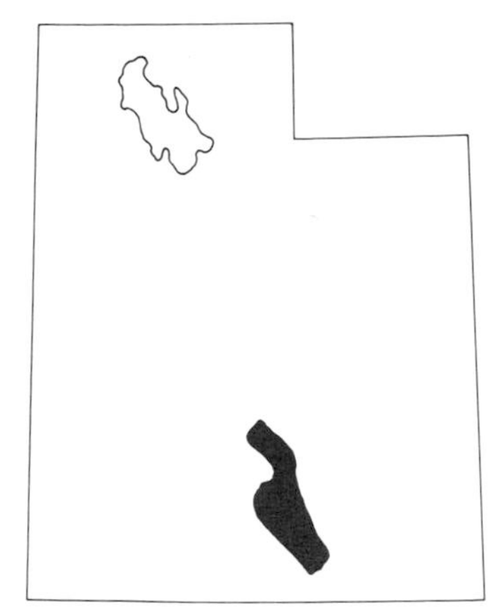

The Circle Cliffs Anticline (fig. 21-17) is much like the Monument Upwarp except that it is shorter, narrower, and has a northwesterly trend. The term Circle Cliffs refers to the high inward-facing Jurassic and Triassic cliffs which ring the central, lower area of Triassic and Permian formations. A spectacular monocline, the Waterpocket Fold, exposes sawtooth edges of the Navajo Sandstone and Wingate Formation and marks the eastern margin of the anticline. The western flank is more gentle, but it is cut into block-like segments by numerous canyons that draining westward into the Escalante River that runs close to the western edge of the fold. Because of its alignment, no drainage-ways cross the fold from east to west.

Figure 21-17. Steeply dipping strata on the east flank of the Circle Cliffs anticline. The prominent sandstone hogbacks constitute Waterpocket Fold. Cretaceous formations make up the valley and mesa on the left. Photo: U.S. National Park Service.

Henry Mountains and Henry Mountains Basin Section

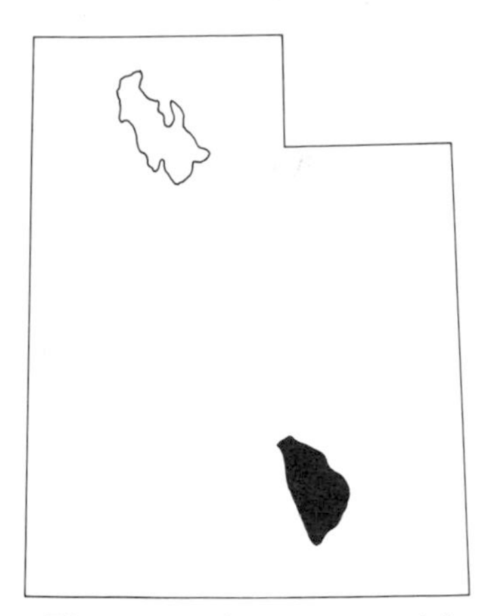

The Henry Mountains Section (fig. 21-18) lies between the Waterpocket Fold to the west and the canyon of the Colorado River to the east. The northern boundary of the section is not clearly marked but, for practical purposes, may be drawn to include badlands and slopes within the Henry Mountains Syncline.

The mountains are carved from complex vertical intrusives of igneous rock that have penetrated from a broad syncline or basin into the surrounding strata. Although the intrusions have domed or elevated the strata in their immediate vicinity, the basic regional structure is synclinal. In other words, the strata rise gently upward from the belt in which the mountains lie. These are the classic laccolithic mountains described by Gilbert in 1877. They consist of several peaks, or closely associated groups of peaks, spread out for 35 miles along a trend of about N. 15° W. From north to south the dominant peaks are Mt. Ellen (11,615 feet), Mt. Pennell (11,371 feet), Mt. Hillers (10,650 feet), Mt. Holmes (7,930 feet), and Mt. Ellsworth (8,235 ft).

The San Rafael Swell Section

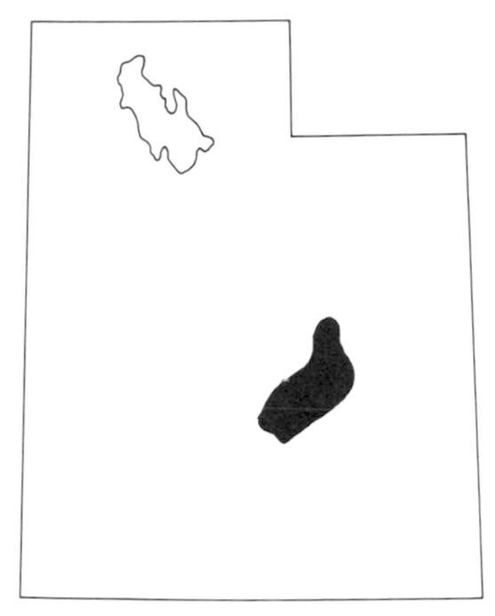

The San Rafael Swell (fig. 21-19) is a name given by Spanish explorers to a great anticlinal, kidney-shaped upwarp lying entirely within Emery County. It is roughly 75 miles long and 30 miles wide but all except the eastern limits must be arbitrarily drawn. Alternating hard and soft formations of Triassic, Jurassic and Cretaceous ages ring a central area of late Paleozoic outcrops. Great cliffs of Jurassic sandstone enclose the central area known as Sinbad. The east side is a spectacular easterly-dipping monocline with almost vertical Triassic and Jurassic sandstone beds. Three permanent rivers—the Muddy, San Rafael, and Price—cut directly across the structure.

Figure 21-18. The southernmost members of the Henry Mountains Group, Mt. Ellsworth (left) and Mt. Holmes (right). Nearly level formations of the Henry Mountains syncline surround the intrusions of diorite porphyry. Rugged exposures of the Navajo Sandstone make up much of the foreground. Photo: U.S. Bureau of Reclamation.

Green River Desert Section

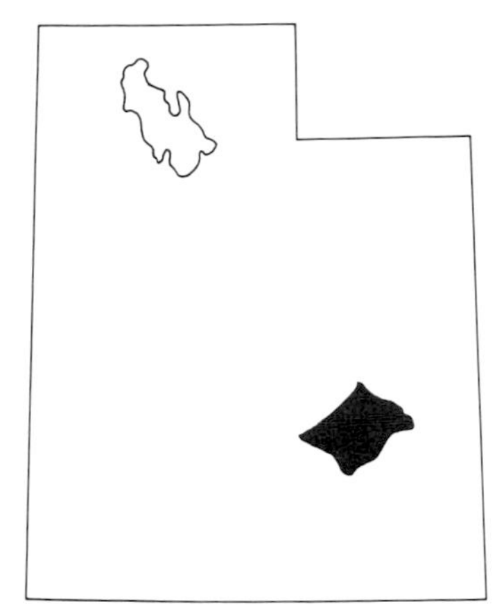

Between the San Rafael Swell in the northwest, the Orange Cliffs to the southeast, the edge of the Mancos Shale Lowlands Section to the northeast, and roughly, the Dirty Devil River to the southwest, is a rectangular area known as the Green River Desert (fig. 21-20). The area is low and relatively flat with many patches of shifting sand that choke and obliterate the drainages. A few mesas and buttes break the monotonous skyline but there is only one deep gorge, Horseshoe Canyon, that descends notably below the general level. Goblin Valley and Cathedral Valley are scenic spots tucked away in the southwestern corner of the section.

Inner Canyonlands Section

In 1931, the physiographer N. M. Fenneman used the very appropriate term Canyon Lands for the area south of the Uinta Basin and between the High Plateaus on the west and the Rocky Mountains on the east. It will be readily apparent that this wide region includes many newly named sections. It is not intended to eliminate the term Canyonlands (it has come to be written as one word), and the name Inner Canyonlands may well be applied to the rugged heart of the region surrounding the junction of the Green and Colorado Rivers (fig. 21-21). The boundaries of this section must, of necessity, be rather irregular, but a useable guide is furnished by the inward-facing cliff of Wingate Sandstone which almost invariably marks a transition from benchlands or flats above to rugged dissected country below. Only to the north is this a really unsatisfactory boundary and it may not be straining the implication of the name to include all territory that remains between the subdivisions already designated. This would essentially include Canyonlands National Park without following the more formally designated legal boundaries.

Inner Canyonlands is dominated by bare rock surfaces arranged in gigantic stair-step configurations. Soil and vegetation are sparse and the scenic attractions clearly outweigh any other human values. The junction of the Colorado and Green Rivers lies near the center of the region. All tributaries, large and small, have such high gradients and, sporadically at least, such tremendous erosive energy that loose material is swept away and all formations are fully exposed.

Figure 21-19. Aerial view looking directly down on the San Rafael Reef. Triassic rocks make up the left part of the view including the inner and higher ridge of the hogback. The light-colored Navajo Sandstone makes up the outer (right) part of the hogback. The marine Carmel Formation appears on the extreme right. Photo: Karl J. Smith.

Figure 21-20. Looking down on the Green River Desert. Flat Top Butte, lower center, is surrounded by drifting sand. Green River - Hanksville Road crosses the view. Photo: Karl J. Smith.

Figure 21-21. Aerial view of the confluence of the Green River, right, and Colorado, left. Light-colored strata on high rims is Cedar Mesa Sandstone. Photo: U.S. Bureau of Reclamation.

THE MIDDLE ROCKY MOUNTAINS

The Rocky Mountains rank with the great mountain systems of the world and are well known to all students of United States history and geography. Two of the many ranges that make up the Rocky Mountain system, the Wasatch Range (fig. 21-22) and the Uinta Mountains, are almost entirely within Utah. Both are members of the Middle Rocky Mountains sub-province that also includes most of Wyoming and part of eastern Idaho. Because of the wide dispersal of the Rocky Mountains system, many extensive basins, plains, and river valleys are included within the province. This explains why tracts that are not really mountainous in character must be described in the following pages as subdivisions of the Middle Rocky Mountains.

By any topographic, geologic, scenic, or economic standard, the Uinta Mountains and the Wasatch Range are of paramount importance. Geologically they have little in common. The Wasatch Range has a northerly trend, the Uinta Mountains an easterly one. The Uinta Mountains are broad and gently arched, the Wasatch Range is mostly narrow and sharp crested. The Uintas are a broadly folded anticline, the Wasatch displays many geologic structures, including major thrust faults. In a geologic sense these two systems meet in the form of a gigantic "T", or geologic crossroads, about midway between Salt Lake City and Provo, Utah County.

In general the boundaries of the Middle Rocky Mountains are easily mapped. The western edge of the Wasatch Range coincides with the Wasatch Fault zone and is remarkable in having few foothills. The Uinta Mountains, in contrast, do have foothills and there is usually a noticeable bench where the softer Mesozoic and Cenozoic sediments have been stripped away from the harder Paleozoic formations. The area between the ranges is complex and mostly covered by a large body of Tertiary volcanic rock (see the geologic map).

Figure 21-22. Crest of the Wasatch Range, looking south from a spot over Little Cottonwood Canyon. Upper Bells Canyon Reservoir surrounded by glaciated outcrops of the Big Cottonwood quartz monzonite. Lone Peak (11,253 feet) on right. American Fork Canyon lies over the ridge, and Provo Canyon is beyond heavily forested slope. Mt. Timpanogos with snow fields is on middle skyline and other high points of southern Wasatch are beyond. Photo: Hal Rumel.

The Wasatch Range Section

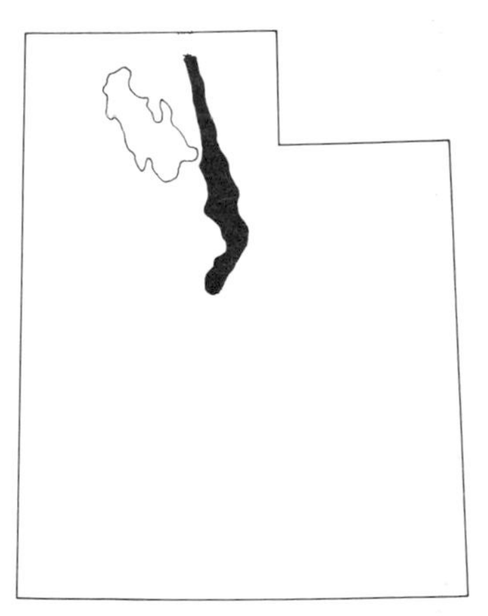

Most physiographers consider the Wasatch Range to terminate where the Bear River leaves Cache Valley. This is mostly a choice of convenience, however, as the structure and typical formations clearly continue beyond that point. Some students regard the Wasatch as dividing at the south end of Cache Valley, one branch constituting Wellsville Mountain, the other the Bear River Range that continues 45 miles north into Idaho. Southward the Wasatch Range clearly terminates at Salt Creek near Nephi, Juab County. The western base of the range is sharply marked by an abrupt decline to adjacent valleys but the eastern boundary must be drawn somewhat arbitrarily in places.

The Wasatch Range is conveniently subdivided into three major segments. The Northern Wasatch extends from the Bear River narrows to the Weber River, the Central Wasatch from the Weber River to the American Fork River, and the Southern Wasatch from the American Fork River to Salt Creek. In general, the northern and southern subdivisions consist of Paleozoic rocks that have been moved eastward to their present position along great thrust faults, while the central Wasatch has remained in place as though buttressed by the Uinta Mountains. Another comparison may be useful, the entire range is roughly spindle-shaped, wide in the central section and narrower toward the ends (see physiographic map). At its intersection with the Uinta Mountains trend, the Wasatch reaches a maximum width of about 15 miles. Much of this width is due to great intrusions of resistant igneous rock that are not found elsewhere in the range. It is this expanded and elevated area near Salt Lake City that gives rise to the seven permanent streams essential to the nearby dense population centers. Where the range is narrow with a knife-edge summit, the run-off is very minor. Important elevations are Willard Peak (9,820 feet), Mt. Ogden (9,572 feet), Twin Peaks (11,319 feet), Timpanogos (11,750 feet), Provo Peak (11,068 feet), and Mt. Nebo (11,877 ft).

Wasatch Hinterlands Section

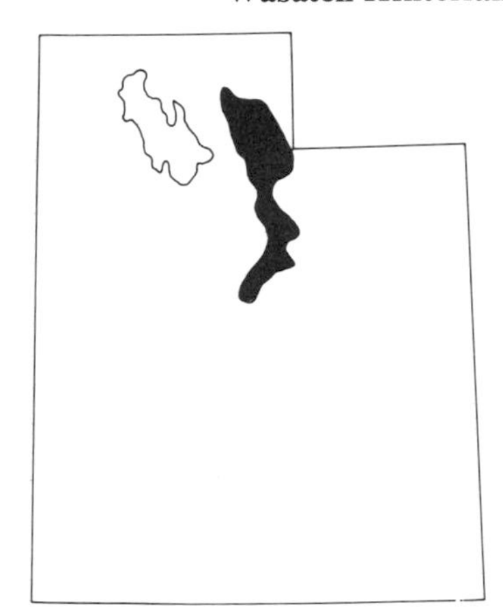

East of the Wasatch Range is a belt of mixed, moderately rugged topography that may be called the Wasatch Hinterlands. It is relatively high but still lower than either the Wasatch or Uinta mountains. The topography is varied and unorganized with hilly areas dominating valley areas. The rainfall is favorable to the development of deep soil and relatively heavy vegetation; actual bedrock outcrops are not common. The region is largely slopes and there are few continuous cliffs or badlands. Streams follow random courses but all drainage is eventually gathered into several major west-flowing rivers that pass directly across the Wasatch Range. As a general rule, the rivers are actively eroding the Hinterlands Section and little deposition is occurring.

A line of discontinuous valleys, sometimes called "back valleys of the Wasatch," lies within a few miles of the eastern base of the Wasatch Range. From north to south they are: Ogden Valley (fig. 21-23), lower Weber (or Morgan) Valley, valley of East Canyon, Parleys Park, Heber Valley, Round Valley, and the valley of Thistle Creek. Farther east and nearer the west end of the Uinta Mountains are Weber Valley, Rhodes Valley, and Strawberry Valley.

Figure 21-23. Ogden Valley, from the north. Slopes of Wasatch Range on the right and Durst Mountain is in the middle distance. The valley is a downfaulted block and was occupied by an arm of Lake Bonneville. Photo: U.S. Forest Service.

Clarkston Mountain Section

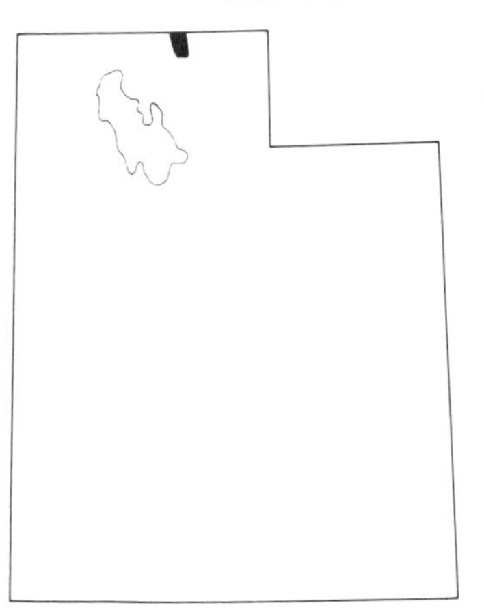

Clarkston Mountain (fig. 21-24) is the southernmost termination of the Malad Range, most of which lies in Idaho. It is narrow and sharp-crested, much like Wellsville Mountain from which it is separated by the pass through which the Bear River flows toward Great Salt Lake. Geologically, the Malad Range and the northern Wasatch are clearly related and the Wasatch Fault continues unbroken between them. Clarkston Mountain consists mainly of much-faulted early Paleozoic formations. Some students would place this mountain in the Basin and Range Province.

Figure 21-24. Clarkston Mountain, partly in shadow, looking northeast. Early Paleozoic rocks, chiefly Cambrian, make up the range.

Cache Valley Section

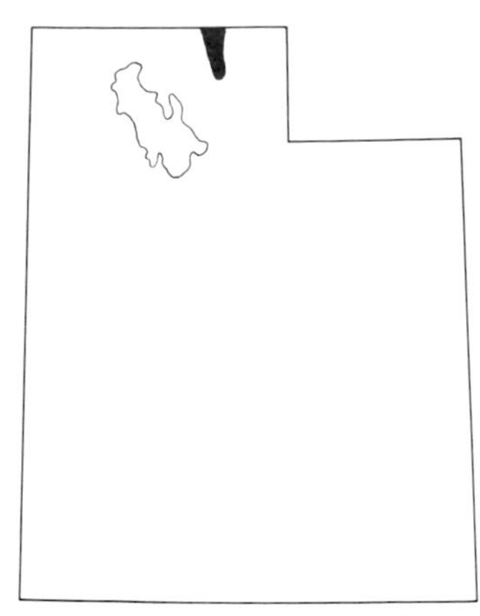

Cache Valley (fig. 21-25) may be defined as the area below the highest level of Lake Bonneville between Wellsville Mountain on the west and the Bear River Range on the east. Thus outlined, the section includes many sloping benches and several hilly tracts such as the Bergeson Hills. The valley is veneered by Lake Bonneville deposits that overlie thick deposits of early Tertiary age (Salt Lake Formation). The valley is well watered and supports intensive agriculture; it has been called the "garden spot of Utah."

Figure 21-25. Cache Valley, looking northwest. Newton Mountain is at right center and Clarkston Mountain is at left. Photo: Robert Q. Oaks, Jr.

Bear River Plateau-Bear Lake Section

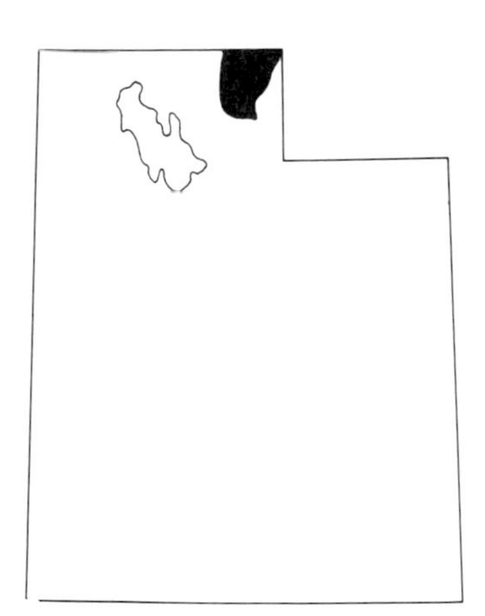

A natural physiographic section is made by combining the Bear River Plateau with Bear Lake (fig. 21-26) and its drainage area. The Bear River Plateau (or Range) is considered by some to be a continuation of the Wasatch Range but it is structurally and physiographically distinct and is not treated here as a part of the Wasatch Range. The southern and eastern borders follow the divide between the Ogden and Bear Rivers, respectively. The western margin is the eastern edge of Cache Valley and the northern termination is the Transverse Canyon of the Bear River southeast of Montpelier, Idaho. At the southwest the line may be drawn between the east and south branches of the Little Bear River. Except for Bear Lake and its immediate vicinity, this section is fairly rugged, mountainous terrain. Elevations range roughly from the Bonneville level (5,230 feet) around Cache Valley to Naomi Peak (9,980 ft).

Tributaries of Bear Lake (elevation 5,524 feet, maximum depth 200 feet) drain about 25 percent of the section; tributaries of the Bear River drain the rest. The Bear Lake Plateau rises abruptly on the east side of Bear Lake and supports only semi-arid vegetation whereas forest growth generally characterizes the rest of the section. There are several small agricultural settlements on the south and west margins of Bear Lake.

Figure 21-26. Bear Lake, Rich County, looking east across level summit of Bear Lake Plateau. Photo: Utah State Historical Society.

Bear River Valley Section

The Bear River (fig. 21-27) rises in the western High Uintas and pursues a winding course out of Utah into Wyoming, back into Utah, again into Wyoming, then into Idaho where it makes a hairpin turn and returns to Utah by way of Cache Valley to empty into Great Salt Lake. In its course through northeastern Utah and southwestern Wyoming it meanders widely across a floodplain bordered by extensive alluvial slopes. The boundaries are drawn along the divides separating its tributaries from those of nearby systems. Many ranches and the towns of Woodruff and Randolph, Rich County, are dependent on the Bear River.

Figure 21-27. Air view of the meandering Bear River, Rich County, showing present and former courses of the stream on its flood plain. The river is flowing toward the top of the view. Photo: U.S. Department of Agriculture.

Crawford Mountains Section

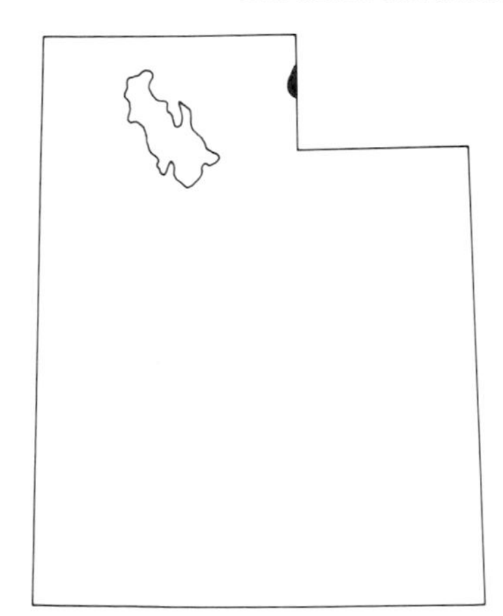

The Crawford Mountains (fig. 21-28) is a small north-trending range, partly in Utah, partly in Wyoming. The western slope descends abruptly to the flood plain of the Bear River. The structure is that of a tightly folded syncline with normal faults along both flanks. Late Paleozoic formations comprise most of the range and important phosphate deposits are being mined in the Park City Formation.

Figure 21-28. Crawford Mountains looking north across the flood plain of Bear River.

Green River Basin Section

A narrow slice of Utah north of the Uinta Mountains is geologically and geographically part of the Green River Basin that lies mostly in southwestern Wyoming. Part of this slice has been included in the Bear River Valley Section just described. The boundary between the two separates the internal and external drainage of the intermountain region.

The boundary between the mountains and the basin is drawn at the known and suspected position of the North Flank Fault. Deep drilling in the Bridger Lake oil field proves that deformed strata characteristic of the mountains have been displayed northward onto rocks of basinlike character.

The entire strip and much of adjacent Wyoming is covered with glacial debris or coarse deposits of the various north-flowing tributaries of Blacks Fork, Smiths Fork, and Henrys Fork Rivers which eventually join the Green River.

Uinta Mountains Section

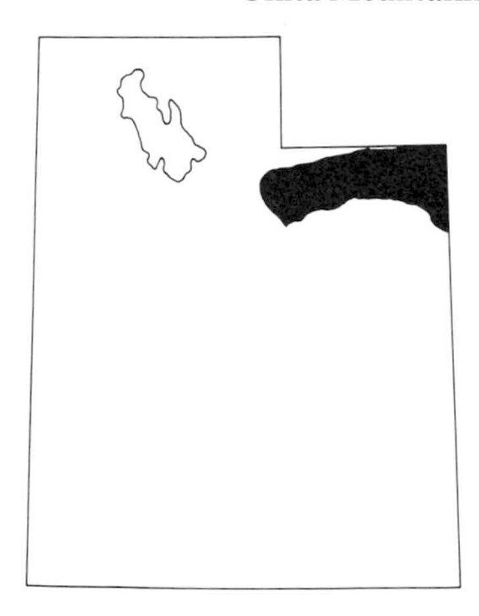

The Uinta Mountains form a distinct topographic unit lying parallel with the southern border of Wyoming. Although essentially the same anticlinal, geologic structure and rock formations extend from Kamas, Summit County, eastward to the Colorado border, it may be best to recognize three significantly different subsections.

The High Uintas Subsection

The crestal portion of the Uinta Mountains, specifically that in the western half roughly between Mirror Lake on the west and Fox Lake on the east, is topographically significantly different not only from the lower territory surrounding it but also from the eastward continuation of the range. The High Uintas include the headwaters of the Provo, Weber, Duschesne, Uinta, and Bear Rivers that gather much of the surface water of Utah. Here are many of the state's high peaks including Kings Peak (13,528 feet), the highest. The area shows a distinctive glacial topography with gently sloping, semi-circular, flat-bottomed cirque valleys separated from each other by steep-walled narrow aretes. Hundreds of rock-rimmed lakes have been left by glaciers. Timberline is currently at about 11,500 feet so most of the High Uintas presents a stark barren appearance, especially striking when covered by snow (fig. 21-29).

Figure 21-29. The High Uintas. The heavily glaciated central area of the range is mostly above timberline and gives rise to the major streams of the region. Bedrock is chiefly Precambrian quartzite. Photo: John A. Burger.

Figure 21-30a. East central Uinta Range, looking southwest, shows rounded, weakly glaciated summit of this part of the range. Photo: U.S. Forest service.

The Eastern Uintas Subsection

When compared with the High Uintas the most distinctive surficial character of the eastern part of the range is the scarcity of glacial features. There are, instead, a number of wide shallow valleys that cross the crest of the range (fig. 21-30a). Lakes are almost absent. The basic anticlinal structure has been disrupted by subsidence of an elongate tract known as Browns Hole, only the western part of which is in Utah. This seems to have lowered the former crest of the range several thousands of feet and to have created the depression into which the Green River began to flow about 20 million years ago. Several other modifications of structure are to be noted, such as the Split Mountain and Blue Mountain Anticlines that enter Utah from Colorado and plunge westward to die out near Vernal, Uintah County.

Figure 21-30b. North-central slopes of the Uinta Range, near Flaming Gorge. This view shows central upland, the flat bench area marking former widespread erosion surface, and deeply incised canyon of more recent origin. Photo: U.S. Forest Service.

The Marginal Benches Subsection

The central, higher portion of the Uinta Mountains, especially the eastern subsection, is ringed by benches (fig. 21-30b) or shoulderlike remnants of old erosion surfaces between about 7,500 and 8,500 feet elevation. On one side they rise and merge with the higher, more rugged central tracts; on the other they descend rather abruptly toward the adjacent lowlands. From the fact that the benches are mostly covered with gravel debris from the core of the range and stand at about the same general level, it is concluded that they are patch-like remnants of once more extensive surfaces. The topography of Diamond Mountain, for example, may be as much as 15 million years old, perhaps the oldest unaltered surface in the state. Present-day streams, including the Green River, are currently cutting away the bench surfaces so as to expose the underlying formations. They have, in a sense, uncovered the cores of such structures as the Split Mountain Anticline.

GREAT BASIN-COLORADO PLATEAU TRANSITION PROVINCE

There is some disagreement as to where the boundary between the Great Basin and the Colorado Plateau should be drawn. Even among physiographers, in whose domain such problems fall, there are differences of opinion. When features of stratigraphy, structure, and tectonics are considered, the problem becomes even more difficult. If, for example, it is decided to include all elements with plateau-like structure in the Colorado Plateau, a problem is created by such features as the Gunnison Plateau, Valley Mountains, and the Pavant Mountains (or Plateau). On the other hand, if structure is taken as a criterion there can be no doubt that the faults of the High Plateaus are quite similar to those of the Basin and Range. The zone of major faults, volcanic centers, and earthquake epicenters is, likewise, quite broad and presents no easily defined common boundaries.

In view of the uncertainties as to where a boundary should be drawn and the possibility of setting up a precedent that others may not wish to follow, it seems best to designate the broad area of possible dispute as a transition belt or zone. This would definitely be in line with growing current usage— several geologic guidebooks to the area have specifically designated it as one of transition. The various sections will be described in order from north to south.

The Wasatch Plateau

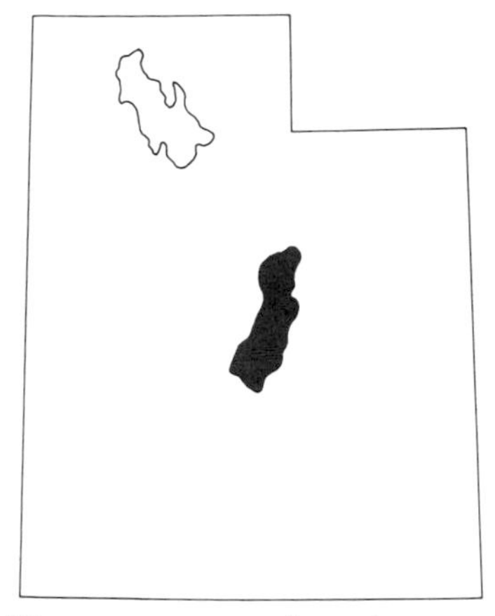

Of the eight elevated tracts known as the High Plateaus, only the Wasatch Plateau (fig. 21-31) is capped entirely by sedimentary rocks. It is, in effect, an erosional remnant undergoing geologically rapid removal along a ragged eastern margin and a summit area protected in places by the thin, resistant Flagstaff Limestone (Paleocene). The steep eastern front is not related to faulting but is an erosional continuation of the Book Cliffs. The western edge coincides with an abrupt descent of beds along the Wasatch Monocline. The remarkably long, straight, and narrow Joes Valley is a down-dropped block (graben) that splits the plateau roughly from its northwest to southeast margins. Elevations reach 11,000 feet and there are a number of permanent streams including Muddy Creek, Ferron Creek, Cottonwood Creek, and Huntington Creek. Salina Canyon, together with Ivy Creek, forms a natural southern border and the Price/Spanish Fork Rivers a northern one.

Figure 21-31. The summit of the Wasatch Plateau looking northwest toward the Wasatch Range on the horizon. The Wasatch Plateau here is capped by the North Horn Formation and Flagstaff Limestone of Paleocene age. Photo: U.S. Forest Service.

Sanpete-Sevier Valleys Section

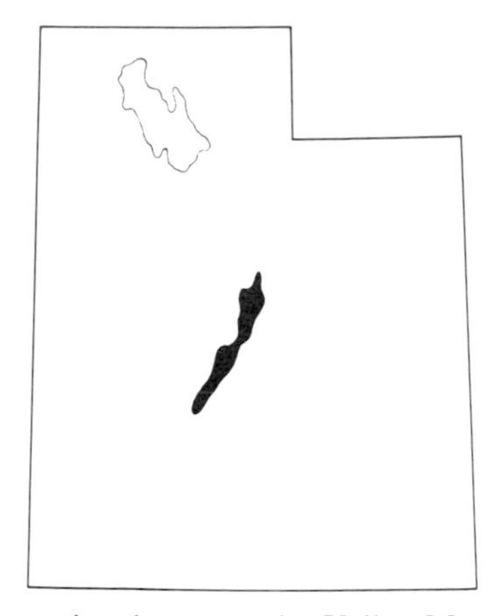

Sanpete-Sevier Valley, a long narrow depression cutting through the geographic center of the state takes its name from the two rivers that traverse it, the Sevier on the south (fig. 21-32) and the San Pitch on the north (the San Pitch River drains Sanpete Valley). The streams join near Gunnison, Sanpete County, and leave the section between the Valley Mountains and Gunnison Plateau. The depression is dominantly of structural origin. Average width of the lowlands along the rivers is 10 to 15 miles. There is relatively intensive agricultural use based on irrigation and abundant marshlands.

The structure of the valley bottom appears deceptively simple; the surficial deposits of soil and alluvial fans mask a complex area of subsidence caused by faulting, folding, and the removal of salt from buried Jurassic formations. The boundaries of the section are drawn fairly easily on the basis of topography.

Figure 21-32. Meander patterns of the Sevier River, immediately east of the Canyon Range, Juab County. Photo: Robert Q. Oaks.

Gunnison Plateau-Valley Mountains Section

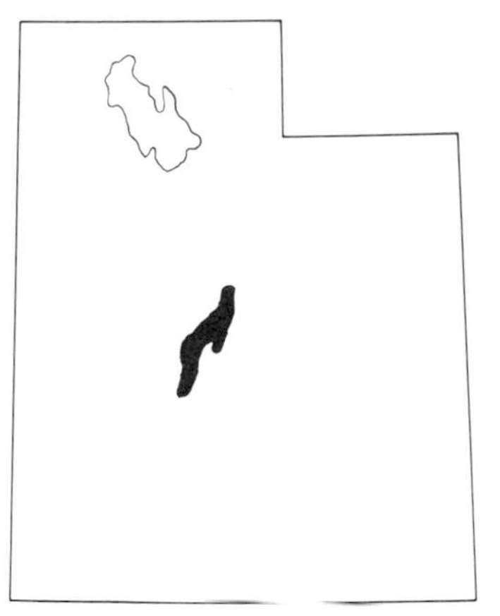

Two distinctly transitional features, the Valley Mountains and Gunnison Plateau (fig. 21-33), show resemblances to the Colorado Plateau in the age of formations and to the Great Basin in their trends, dimensions, and relations to faults. Formations of Tertiary Age make up most of the Valley Mountains while the Gunnison Plateau includes Cretaceous and Jurassic deposits. The structure of both is synclinal. The east face of the Gunnison Plateau is abrupt and cut by several deep and scenic canyons that reveal a complicated history of deposition and deformation. The summit area is fairly flat and ranges between 8,000 and 9,500 feet in elevation.

Figure 21-33. North section of the Gunnison Plateau, San Pitch Mountain, looking southeasterly from the western edge of Lyndall. Jurassic rocks make up the foothills and Cretaceous appears on the upper slopes and skyline.

Pavant Range-Canyon Range Section

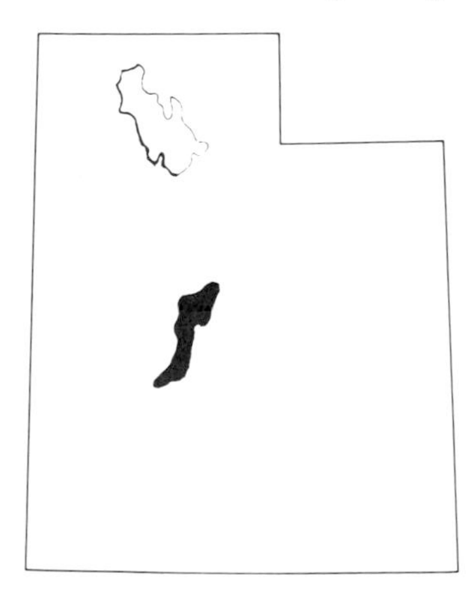

Two important elements transitional from the Great Basin to the Colorado Plateau are the Pavant (fig. 21-34) and Canyon Ranges. Neither is plateau-like in form or structure, but the rocks of which they are composed include formations typical of both provinces that have been brought together by great thrust faults. In both ranges, older rocks from the west have moved eastward across and upon younger rocks to the east. This area is one of the few in which fault relationships can be plainly seen. Elevations are moderate. The highest point of the Pavant Range is White Pine Peak (10,279 feet); Williams Peak (9,238 feet) is highest of several peaks in the Canyon Range. Long Ridge, lying between the Canyon Range and the Gunnison Plateau, is placed in this section chiefly because it, too, contains both Paleozoic and Mesozoic strata and is almost surely underlain by the same thrust-fault system seen in the other mountains.

Figure 21-34. Summit area of Pavant Range, east of Meadow, Millard County. Photo: Walter P. Cottam.

Tushar Volcanic Section

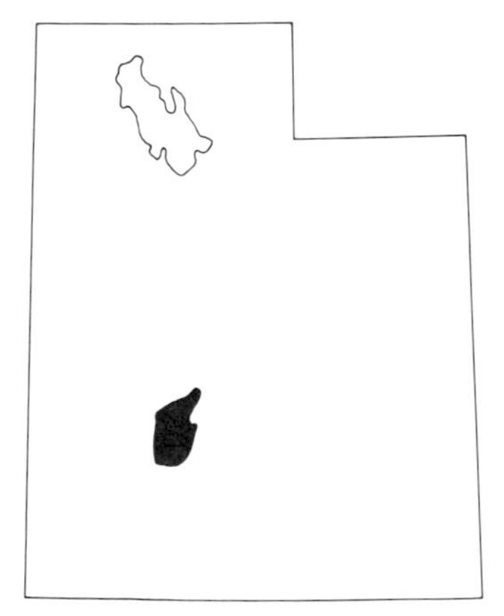

The Tushar Mountains (fig. 21-35) reach a maximum elevation of 12,173 feet at Mt. Delano and are eroded remnants of an ancient volcanic center built between 31 and 20 million years ago. Igneous rock types include breccias, ash-flow tuffs, and lava flows. In terms of composition, the rocks are chiefly latite, dacite, andesite, rhyolite, and basalt. The igneous material was deposited upon a preexisting topography of sedimentary rocks similar to that seen in nearby areas.

The volcanic pile was deeply eroded at various intervals during its accumulation particularly during the past several million years. The Sevier River cuts into and exposes many of the component units. Mineral deposits formed during the volcanic episodes include ores of gold, silver, lead, zinc, uranium, aluminum, and potassium. The last two metals are combined in a complex mineral, called alunite, that is widely distributed throughout the area. A famous landmark is Big Rock Candy Mountain, near Marysvale, Piute County, with colorful alteration effects in volcanic material.

Figure 21-35. Glaciated upper part of Cottonwood Creek, Tushar Mountains, Piute County. Delano Peak (12,173 feet) is at left center. Note lateral moraine at lower right. Photo: Eugene E. Callaghan.

Southern High Plateaus Section

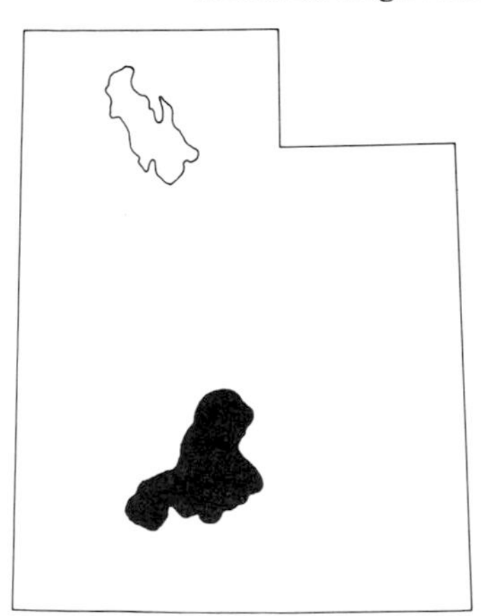

The most extensive, relatively unbroken expanse of extrusive igneous rocks is that capping much of the High Plateaus and making up portions of Iron, Garfield, Wayne, Piute, and Sevier Counties. From the earliest studies by Charles Dutton (1875-77) it has been customary to recognize seven distinct plateaus in this section: the Fish Lake, Awapa, Aquarius, Table Cliffs, Paunsaugunt, Markagunt, and Sevier (fig. 21-36). This division is based on convenient physiographic breaks produced chiefly by external bounding cliffs and by internal alluvium-filled valleys that follow north-trending fault lines or narrow grabens. If the somewhat superficial and recently formed features are disregarded, a fundamental unity of stratigraphy and geologic history becomes evident that justifies combining all the predominantly lava-capped plateaus into one geologic-geographic section. There can be little doubt that the valley areas are underlain at shallow depths by the same igneous rocks seen on nearby uplifted blocks.

Flat-lying flows of andesite, rhyolite, latite, and basalt, together with extensive deposits of volcanic ash and agglomerate, form the latest and highest formations. Thicknesses reach several thousand feet. The Tushar volcanic center, physically continuous with the plateaus insofar as certain rock types are concerned, is not a plateau and has distinctly different overall geologic structure and history. It has been designated as a separate section. On the other hand, Thousand Lake Mountain, a basalt-capped, mesa-like outlier east of Loa, Wayne County, is included with the greater plateaus to the south and west (see physiographic map). The general surface of the plateaus ranges between 8,000 and 11,000 feet in elevation. Representative high points are Lookout Peak (Aquarius Plateau, 11,306 feet), Mt. Marvine (Fish Lake Plateau, 11,600 feet), Monroe Peak (Sevier Plateau, 11,226 feet), and Brian Head (Markagunt Plateau, 11,307 feet). At higher elevations forests of conifers alternate with parks of sage and grass. Many small, permanent streams arise at the higher levels to replenish the Sevier River that drains most of the area. Lower valleys support ranches and small communities where cattle raising is the chief occupation.

Figure 21-36. Upper surface of Sevier Plateau, northwest of Greenwich, Piute County. Photo: Eugene Callaghan.

Limestone-Capped Subsection

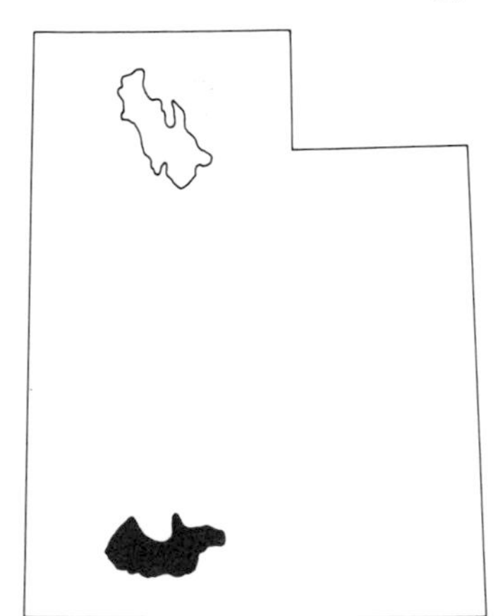

The Table Cliffs Plateau (which some consider a southern prong of the Aquarius Plateau), the southern half of the Paunsaugunt Plateau and the southern rim of the Markagunt Plateau have so much in common that they are here designated a separate physiographic subsection. All are characterized by outcrops of the Wasatch Formation and a mutual sharing of the Pink Cliffs. Cedar Breaks National Monument on the southwest corner of the Markagunt Plateau, and Bryce Canyon National Park (fig. 21-37) on the east margin of the Paunsaugunt Plateau are especially noted for scenic badland exposures of colorful Tertiary formations. The northern boundary of this subsection is the edge of volcanic rocks as exposed or projected under cover.

The elevation of the limestone-capped subsection is between 9,000 and 11,000 feet and the upland topography is rolling and well vegetated. From the edges, the descent onto and across Cretaceous formations is abrupt and the view southward and eastward is world famous. The original continuity of the formations has been broken by the Paunsaugunt Fault between the Table Cliffs and Paunsaugunt Plateaus, and by the Sevier Fault between the Paunsaugunt and Markagunt Plateaus.

Figure 21-37. Famed Bryce Canyon is carved from outcrops of limy sediments at the edge of the Paunsaugunt Plateau. Photo: U.S. Park Service.

The Tonoquints Volcanic Section

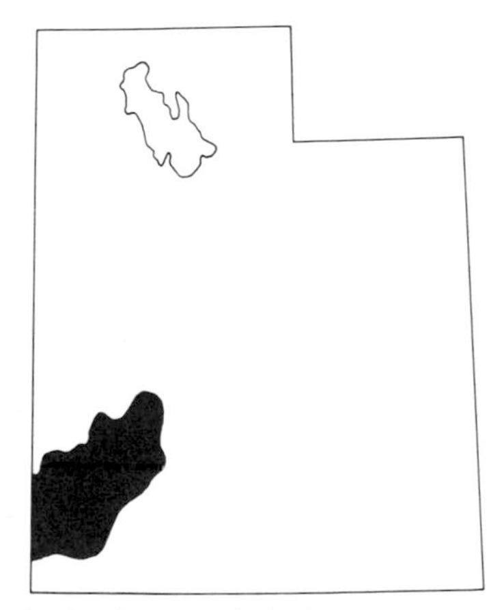

The southeastern part of the Great Basin, including and surrounding the Escalante Desert, is a mixture of very diverse topographic and geologic features, none of which seems to provide a distinctive designation. The name, Tonoquints, is that of the tribe of Piute Indians who once claimed the heart of this area. The one common geologic characteristic is a concentration of related, extrusive, volcanic rocks that were once continuous from near Pioche, Nevada, to Marysvale, Piute County. Some of the volcanic cover has been eroded to expose pre-existing topography of Paleozoic and Mesozoic sedimentary rocks. In other large areas, such as the Escalante Valley, igneous rocks have been lowered by faulting and are covered by alluvium or lake deposits. Nearer the ancient volcanic centers, where production of extrusive material reached a maximum, all traces of the underlying sedimentary section have been submerged in volcanic rocks of great thickness and complexity.

The Pine Valley Mountains (10,238 feet high, fig. 21-38) are eroded remnants of a large intrusive-extrusive body of monzonite porphyry. Many volcanic rocks classified as flows, agglomerates, tuffs, breccias, and ash flows have been identified and mapped in the Tonoquints Section, and the Iron Mountain intrusives are clearly associated with important ore deposits near Cedar City, Iron County. Boundaries are drawn to include middle Tertiary volcanic rocks and do not follow topographic features to the extent that other boundaries do. Although many of the igneous rock units are equivalent to those in the High Plateaus and Tushar Volcanic Sections, there are structural and stratigraphic differences that warrant recognition of this section as a separate division of the volcanic-dominated terrain.

Figure 21-38. Pine Valley Mountains, looking north. Igneous intrusion makes up the main mass of the mountain, Triassic and Jurassic formations, the foothills and foreground. Photo: Walter P. Cottam.

THE GREAT BASIN

Western Utah includes part of the Great Basin defined as the area of internal drainage between the Wasatch Range and the Sierra Nevada. The Great Basin is part of a much larger region, the Basin and Range Province, that extends far south into west Texas and Mexico and north into Oregon and central Idaho. The Basin and Range is characterized by short mountain ranges bounded by normal faults and surrounded by alluvium-filled valleys.

A number of unique subdivisions or sections are easily recognized in the Great Basin of Utah. A good descriptive starting point is Great Salt Lake. Other sections are described in clockwise order around the western part of the state.

Great Salt Lake Section

Great Salt Lake, with its included islands and a narrow belt of surrounding land, constitutes a unique physiographic division. The lake is one of the Earth's great landmarks. It is shown on most world maps and is visible from space hundreds of miles above the Earth. It ranges greatly in areal extent from more than 2,300 square miles to less than 1,000 square miles depending on the balance between inflow and evaporation. The mean elevation of the surface for the period of record is about 4,200 feet and the average depth 13 feet, with a maximum of 35 feet when at the 4,200-foot stage.

Islands and prominent peninsulas include Promontory Point, Fremont Island (fig. 21-39), Antelope Island (often joined to the land), Stansbury Island (usually a peninsula), Carrington Island (generally bound to Stansbury Island), Bird or Hat Island, Gunnison Island, Cub Island, and Dolphin Island. For present purposes the Promontory Peninsula is included with the lake as are most of the low-lying mud flats that would be submerged when and if the water rises to upper historic limits.

Figure 21-39. Fremont Island, looking north. Precambrian rocks make up the island; former lake levels are well marked. Photo: Ward Roylance.

Wasatch Front Valleys Section

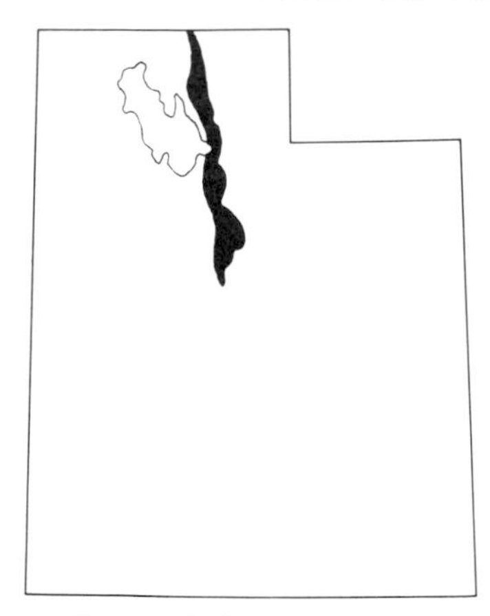

What is usually referred to as the Wasatch Front is not one continuous open valley. A number of spurs, or salients, divide it into distinct geographic segments. Farthest south is Utah Valley (called by some the upper Jordan Valley) that includes Utah Lake (elevation 4,487 feet, greatest depth about 18 feet). Utah Valley is bounded on the north by the Traverse Mountains that separate it from Salt Lake Valley (lower Jordan Valley) to the north. The Salt Lake salient (Becks spur) forms a partial barrier northeast of the Salt Lake Valley and separates it from the much longer and less well defined tract in which Ogden, Weber County (fig. 21-40), is located. This tract appears to have no distinctive name. North of Ogden another projection, the Pleasant View salient, protrudes into the lowlands providing a southern boundary for what may be called the lower Bear River Valley. Still farther north is the Malad River Valley that continues into Idaho. The Malad River is a tributary of the Bear River and joins it near Bear River City, Box Elder County.

In a very real sense the Wasatch Range has no western foothills; the front of the range rises abruptly from the valley floor. Even the short spurs that characterize the mountain front have been cut off or truncated. The steep west-facing front follows the Wasatch Fault zone that is clearly responsible for cutting away large slices of the range. The upward-moving block of the Wasatch Fault is the

Figure 21-40. The Wasatch Front, adjacent to the city of Ogden. Weber River crosses the range and enters the valley in the indentation near the upper left corner of the photograph. Great Salt Lake is visible in upper right. Photo: U. S. Department of Agriculture.

Wasatch Range, so spectacular that it has drawn attention from the down-dropped block, no less remarkable in its own way. The down-dropped block or blocks west of the Wasatch Fault zone are buried under thousands of feet of lake-bed sediments and alluvium worn from the adjacent mountains. If this could be removed a series of great steep-walled trenches, or rifts, would be revealed. Their depths, as estimated from geophysical data, are as great as 7,000 feet.

In spite of very rapid erosion and deposition by active streams, the down-dropped areas are still far from being filled. That deposition has failed to keep up with subsidence is shown by the nearness of Utah Lake and the southeast arm of Great Salt Lake to the front of the range. Normally, bodies of water are crowded away from nearby highlands as sediments accumulate.

The Uinta Extension Section

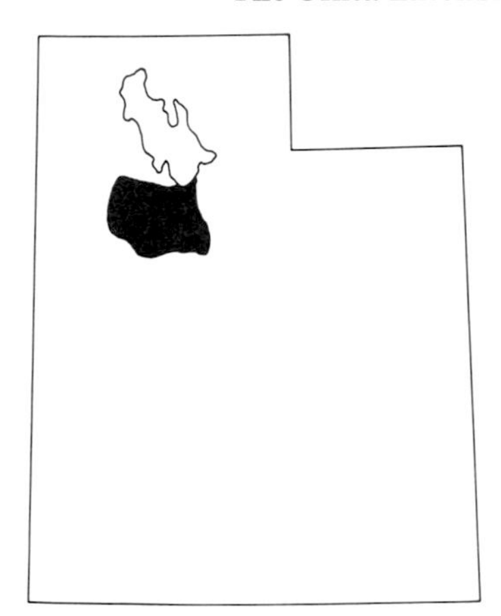

Three prominent ranges, the Oquirrh, Stansbury (fig. 21-41), and Cedar Mountains, are in line with a westward projection of the Uinta Mountains axis and the high central part of the Wasatch Range. It will be noted that the ranges become narrower and lower in average elevation westward and that there is a small isolated remnant in the Salt Lake Desert (Wildcat Knolls) also in line with the projected Uinta axis (see geologic and physiographic maps). This same axis is marked by the Traverse Mountains connecting the Wasatch Range and Oquirrh Mountains, and South Mountain between the Oquirrh and Stansbury Mountains. Recent workers have found geologic anomalies along a projection of the Uinta Mountains far into Nevada; for this, the term Cortez-Uinta Axis is proposed. Reasons for the surface relations are deep seated and not well understood.

The Oquirrh Mountains are relatively broad and made up mainly of the very thick Pennsylvanian-Permian Oquirrh Formation. The great open pit of Kennecott's Bingham Canyon Mine is here. The Stansbury Mountains have representative formations of all Paleozoic periods, but no known major ore deposits. The high point is Deseret Peak (11,031 feet), well above timber line. The Cedar Mountains are much lower and composed chiefly of Pennsylvanian and Permian formations. Wide alluvial valleys between the ranges drain northward into Great Salt Lake. These include Skull Valley between the Cedar Mountains and the Stansbury Mountains, Rush Valley between the southern Stansbury Mountains and the Oquirrh Mountains, and Tooele Valley between the northern Stansbury Mountains and the Oquirrh Mountains. The Jordan, or Salt Lake, Valley is included in the Wasatch Front Valleys Section.

The Thomas Range-Tintic Mountains Section

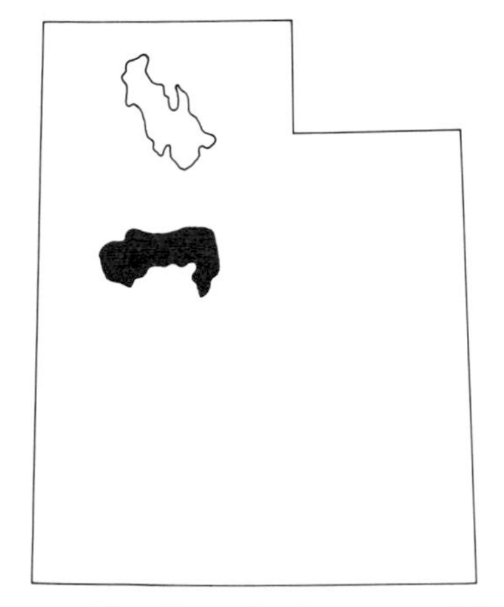

A group of mountain ranges confined almost entirely to Juab County may be considered as a natural unit. Included are the Thomas Range (fig. 21-42), Keg or McDowell Mountain, the Simpson Mountains, the Sheeprock Mountains, West Tintic Mountains, and East Tintic Mountains. Each has a shape that is more equidimensional than is usual for Great Basin ranges. Other common features are a high proportion of igneous rocks and more highly faulted, complex internal structures. Clearly this section has had a different history from that of adjacent sections. In addition to the major ore deposits of the Tintic mining districts there are important deposits in the Thomas Range and much mineralization elsewhere.

Figure 21-41. Crest of Stansbury Range, Tooele County, looking north. Ridge crest is Cambrian quartzite thrust eastward upon younger Paleozoic rocks of the eastern slopes on right. Photo: Arthur C. King.

Figure 21-42. Thomas Range from the north. This mountain is built of a succession of Tertiary lava flows and tuffs. Photo: Arthur C. King.

The Sevier and Black Rock Deserts Section

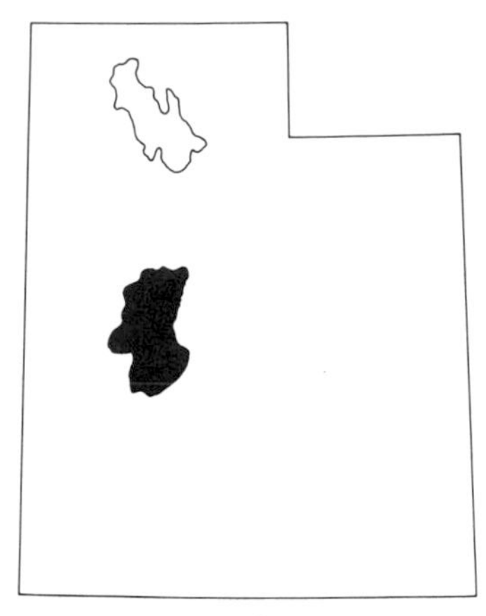

The town of Delta, Millard County, is located near the center of a large level area called the Sevier Desert. The term desert may seem inappropriate in view of the lush irrigated fields around the settlements, but the precipitation is on the order of 8 to 10 in. annually and the native vegetation is of desert-like character. The Sevier River traverses the area from northeast to southwest and enters Sevier Lake (more properly a sink or playa).

An extension of the Sevier Desert south toward Cove Fort, Millard County, is called the Black Rock Desert by some. The outstanding characteristic of this region is the general lack of sedimentary outcrops and the fields of basaltic lava that lie in patches on the surface. At the northeast corner is Utah's largest sand dune field, the Jericho Dunes, set aside as a state park. The sand has been picked up on the desert and is being transported northeasterly by the prevailing winds.

Confusion Basin Section

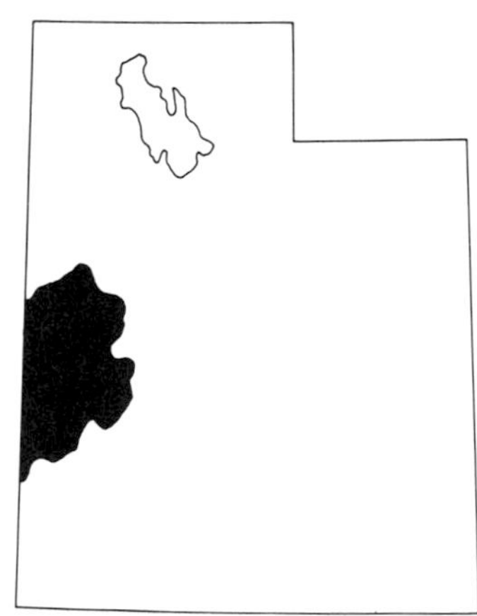

Much of southwestern Utah is occupied by the Confusion Basin. The designation is used mostly by geologists and refers to a Paleozoic center of deposition more than it does to the present configuration. Local residents refer to the area as the West Desert. Mountain ranges of the Confusion Basin are almost exclusively sedimentary rocks; igneous rocks are relatively rare except along the southern margin (see geologic map).

Chief ranges of the Confusion Basin, from north to south, are the Fish Springs Range, the Drum Mountains, the Little Drum Mountains, the House Range (fig. 21-43), the Confusion Range, the Mountain Home or Needle Range, the Wah Wah Mountains, the Cricket Mountains, and the San Francisco Mountains.

In this section of the Great Basin, the valleys are distinct entities and each one is almost surrounded by mountains. White Valley, between the House and the Confusion Ranges, has no external drainage. It might be said that mountains dominate this section while valleys or open flats dominate the Great Salt Lake Desert section to the north.

Figure 21-43. Looking south along Tule Valley in the Confusion Basin. House Range is at left and Confusion Range at right. Photo: Arthur C. King.

Beaver Dam Mountains Section

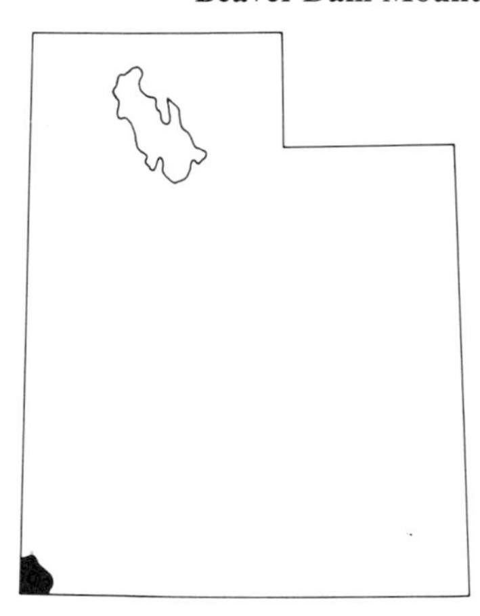

The Beaver Dam Mountains (fig. 21-44), an eroded fault block in the extreme southwestern corner of the state, is one of a cluster of similar rocky ranges in adjacent parts of Utah, Nevada, and Arizona. The group is separated from other sedimentary ranges to the north by the great Tonoquints volcanic field. High points of the Beaver Dam Mountains are slightly more than 6,500 feet. There are no permanent streams and the terrain has the barren aspect common to the arid southwest. Rocks exposed include Precambrian and all Paleozoic systems except the Silurian. A great fan-like alluvial deposit lying west of the range is included. This deposit, called the Overton Fanglomerate, is highly eroded and contains semi-consolidated material of uncertain age.

Deep Creek Range Section

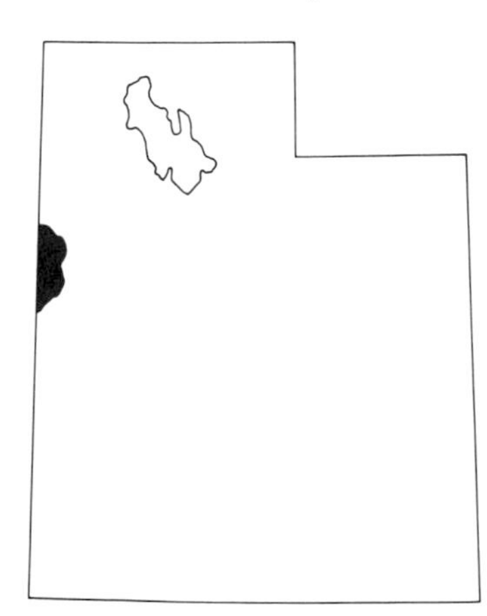

The Deep Creek Range (fig. 21-45) near the Utah-Nevada border in Tooele and Juab Counties is the highest range in the western part of the state. Dutch Mountain and others to the north are geologically and topographically related to the main uplift and are included with it. Also included is Ibapah Valley on the western side of the range, chiefly on the Goshute Indian Reservation.

The highest point is Ibapah Peak (12,109 feet). It is eroded from a large granite stock dated at 18.1 million years old. South of the stock is a thick sequence of metamorphosed Precambrian formations, and to the north a series of about 24 Paleozoic formations forms rugged parallel outcrops trending toward Gold Hill. The lower foothills have the barren aspect of the surrounding desert; higher elevations support groves of pine and aspen. There are a number of mining districts but the important deposits at Gold Hill appear to have been worked out.

Figure 21-44. The Beaver Dam Mountains, looking northeasterly. Light-colored cliff is Mississippian limestone. Photo: LaRell Nielson.

Figure 21-45. Deep Creek Range, Tooele and Juab Counties, from the east. Ibapah Peak (12,109 feet) is the highest point. Bonneville Lake level is in the middle distance. Photo: Ward Roylance.

Great Salt Lake Desert Section

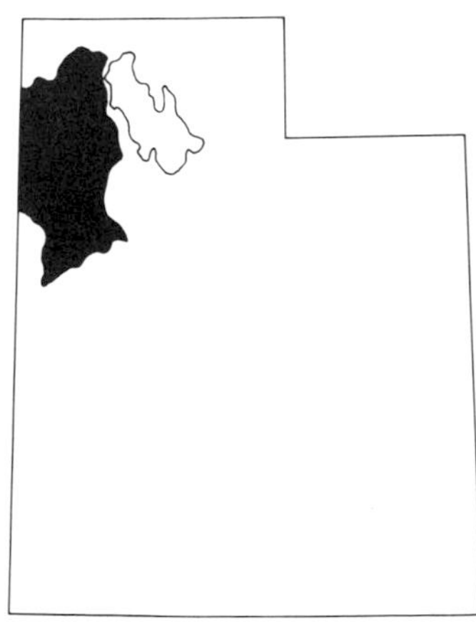

West of Great Salt Lake is an extensive level area coated by sand, mud, and salt known as the Great Salt Lake Desert (fig. 21-46). The chief ranges that rise above the flats are the Newfoundland Mountains, the Desert Range or Silver Island Mountains with a semi-detached outlier called Crater Island, the Pilot Range, and the Granite Mountains. Other lower bedrock ridges that rise above the general level are obviously only the tips of other buried ranges. Two areas, one north-northeast and the other east-northeast of Wendover, Tooele County, have permanent deposits of salt and are the true "salt flats."

In addition to the salt-encrusted tracts, the Great Salt Lake Desert includes much greater areas of silt, mud, and fine sand. Practically the entire area is saturated with water to, or nearly to, the surface. This section, therefore, includes all flat, undrained territory tributary to Great Salt Lake as well as elevated bedrock outcrops surrounded by it. Wide areas are reserved by the U. S. Department of Defense for military purposes.

Figure 21-46. Great Salt Lake Desert and Granite Mountain. Although the soil is very saline, a few hardy plants are able to survive. Photo: U.S. Army.

Lakeside Section

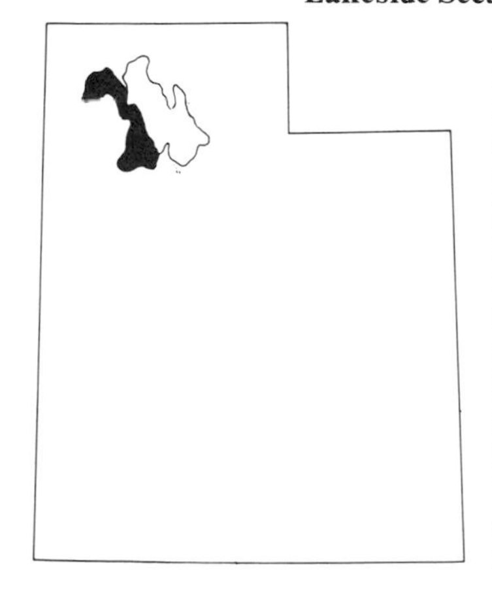

An elevated section made up of several low mountains separates Great Salt Lake from the Great Salt Lake Desert (fig. 21-47). A low pass through which the Southern Pacific Railway runs separates the Hogup-Terrace Mountains to the north from the Lakeside Mountains to the south. The entire section is arid and remote with few known resources.

Figure 21-47. Strongs Knob and the gap between the Great Salt Lake to the east (right) and the Great Salt Lake Desert. A train of the Southern Pacific Railroad is seen in the pass. Photo: Hellmut H. Doelling.

Figure 21-48. West-central Raft River Mountains, Box Elder County. Slopes and cliffs are chiefly Precambrian quartzite. Photo: Hellmut H. Doelling.

Goose Creek Mountains-Raft River Mountains Section

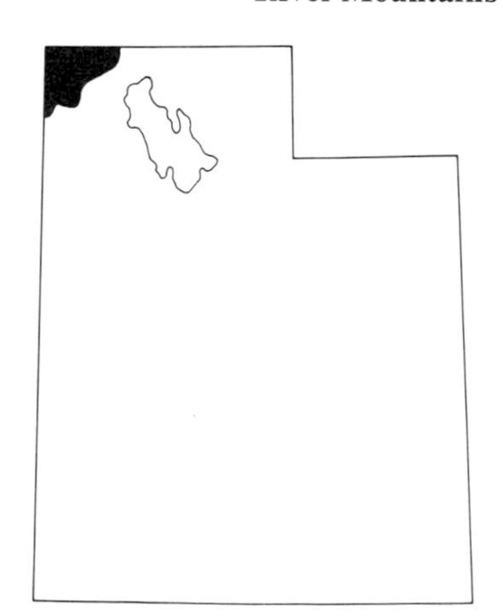

The northwest corner of Utah is occupied by the Goose Creek, Dove Creek, Grouse Creek, and Raft River Mountains (or ranges) (fig. 21-48). The Raft River Mountains, like the Uintas, trend east-west and have a core of resistant, Precambrian, metamorphic rocks. The highest point is 9,092 feet in elevation. The Goose Creek Mountains have a southerly trend along the Utah-Nevada line and display complex internal structure resembling that of nearby ranges of northeastern Nevada. They are separated from the Grouse Creek Mountains, 10 to 15 miles to the east, by Grouse Creek Valley. The Grouse Creek Mountains are chiefly Paleozoic sedimentary rocks with a large granite intrusion dated at 23.3 million years near the south end. The northern slopes of these ranges drain into the Raft River and are technically part of the Snake River Plain rather than the Great Basin. Streams running south into the Great Salt Lake are small but support a number of ranches and small towns.

Curlew Valley Section

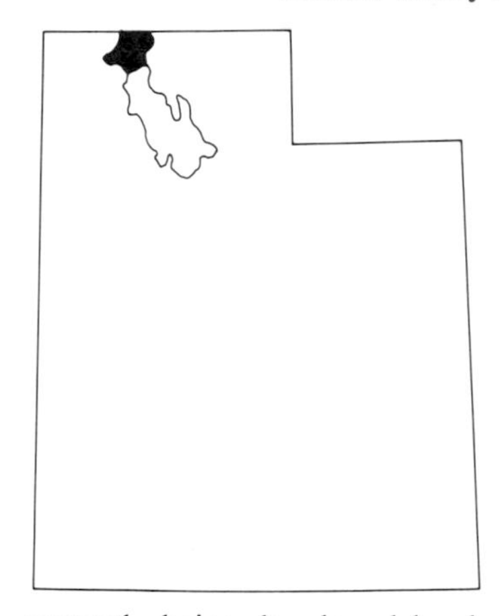

Curlew Valley (fig. 21-49), a wide tract of level land north of Great Salt Lake and between the Raft River and Hansel Mountains, merits a separate listing, being part of a much larger area in Idaho and lacking the soil and vegetation typical of the Great Salt Lake Desert to the south. It is sagebrush land that, with suitable water such as is currently being developed by deep drilling west of Snowville, Box Elder County, supports good crops.

Hansel Mountains-Blue Springs (or West) Hills Section

Between Curlew Valley on the west and the Malad River Valley on the east is an aggregation of low, north-trending ranges and narrow valleys that is significantly different from the surrounding sections. The topography is best described as rolling or rounded and there are few outcrops of bare rock (fig. 21-50). This is typical of the weathering and erosion of the Oquirrh Formation that produces mainly small, blocky fragments. This section also has great accumulations of gravel and sand along Lake Bonneville shorelines. Intermittent streams drain the valleys but the water supply is insufficient for irrigation and dry-land farming is extensive.

Figure 21-49. Looking northwest across Curlew Valley to the Raft River Range in the distance. Photo: Utah State Historical Society.

Figure 21-50. View in the Blue Hills, eastern Box Elder County. The Oquirrh Formation forms the rounded ledge-free hills.

For additional reading about the topics discussed in chapter 21, please see the following list of authors:

Baer and Callaghan, 1972
Baker, A.A.J., 1933, 1936, 1946
Baker, C.H., 1974
Baker, W.H., 1959
Beus, 1963
Bick, 1966
Bissell, H.J., 1959
Bowers, W.E., 1972
Bradley, 1936
Bray and Wilson, 1975
Bruhn, 1952
Bullock, 1970
Burma and Hardy, 1953
Buss, 1962, 1963
Butler and others, 1915, 1920
Byrd, 1967
Callaghan, 1939, 1947, 1973b
Campbell, 1975, 1978
Chapusa, 1969
Christiansen, 1951a, 1952
Clark, E.E., 1977
Cohenour, 1959
Cohenour and Thompson, 1966
Compton, 1977
Condie and Barsky, 1972
Cook, D.R., 1961
Cook, E.F., 1960a, 1960b, 1965
Cook, K.L., and others, 1966
Crampton, 1964
Crittenden and others, 1967
Crosby, 1959
Cross, 1907
Dane, 1935
Davidson, 1967
Doelling, 1964
Dutton, 1875, 1877
Eardley, 1952, 1970
Eardley and Schaack, 1971
Felix, 1956
Fenneman, 1928
Fishman, 1976
Forrester, 1937
Garvin, 1969
Gilbert, 1877, 1928
Gilliland, 1951, 1963
Gilluly, 1929
Gregory, 1938, 1951
Gregory and Moore, 1931
Groff, 1959
Grogger, 1974
Gwynn, 1980
Hagood, 1967
Hamblin, 1963
Hansen, W.R., 1965, 1969a, 1969b
Hanson, A.M., 1953
Hardy and Zeller, 1953
Hickcox, 1971
Hill, 1976
Hilpert, 1971
Hoover, 1973
Hose, 1966
Hose and Repenning, 1959
Hunt, C.B., 1953, 1956, 1958, 1974
James, 1973
Kaliser, 1972
Kelley, 1955, 1960
Kerr, 1957, 1963, 1968
Larson, 1957
Lautenschlager, 1952
Lindsay, 1970
Lohman, 1974, 1975
Mackin, 1947, 1960, 1968
Mallory, 1972a, 1972b, 1972c
Marsell, 1932
Marsell and Threet, 1964
Maurer, 1960, 1970
Maxey, 1946
Meeves and others, 1966
Morris and Lovering, 1962
Muessig, 1951a

Nolan, 1935, 1943
Osmond, 1961, 1965
Paddock, 1956
Palmer, 1970
Peterson and Waldrop, 1965
Picard, 1980
Pratt and Callaghan, 1970
Reber, 1952
Reeside, 1923, 1930
Richardson, 1941
Ridd, 1960
Rigby, 1958b
Ritzma, 1969a
Roberts and others, 1965
Rowley and others, 1975, 1978
Sando and others, 1959
Schaeffer and Anderson, 1960
Sharp and Williams, 1963
Shoemaker and others, 1958
Spieker, 1931a, 1949a, 1954
Staatz, 1960
Staatz and Carr, 1964
Staub, 1975
Steed, 1954
Stifel, 1964
Stokes, 1948, 1961, 1966, 1973, 1979
Stokes and Cohenour, 1956
Talmage, 1896
Thomas, G.H., 1958
Thomson, 1973
Thorpe, 1919
Threet, 1959, 1963
Untermann and Untermann, 1964, 1969b
Waddell and Price, 1972
Weir and Puffett, 1960
Williams, J.S., 1958, 1962a
Winkler, 1970
Witkind, 1958, 1964
Woolley, 1947
Young, J.C., 1953

For complete bibliographic citations, please see List of References.

Figure 21-51. Standing Up Country; the Valley of Standing Men, northwestern section of Canyonlands National Park. Fluted cliffs of the Permian Red Cutler Sandstone combine to create the monuments. Photo: Hal Rumel.

REFERENCES

Abbott, W. O., 1951, Cambrian diabase flow in central Utah: Compass, v. 29, no. 1, p.5-10.

Andersen, D. W., and M. D. Picard, 1973, Stratigraphy of the Duchesne River Formation (Eocene-Oligocene?) northern Uinta Basin, northeastern Utah: Utah Geological and Mineral Survey Bulletin 97, p. 1-29.

Anderson, J. J., and P. D. Rowley, 1975, Cenozoic geology of the southwestern High Plateaus of Utah: Geological Society of America Special Paper 160, 80 p.

Anderson, R. E., and H. H. Mehnert, 1979, Reinterpretation of the history of the Hurricane Fault in Utah: Rocky Mountain Association of Geologists and Utah Geological Association Basin and Range Symposium, p. 145-165.

Anderson, L. W., and D. G. Miller, 1980, Quaternary faulting in Utah: U.S. Geological Survey Open-File Report 80-801, p. 194-226.

Anderson, W. L., 1960a, Economic geology of the northern Silver Island Mountains *in* Geology of the Silver Island Mountains, Box Elder and Tooele Counties, Utah, and Elko County, Nevada: Utah Geological Society Guidebook to the Geology of Utah 15, p. 159-161.

———1960b, Geomorphology of the Silver Island Mountains *in* Geology of the Silver Island Mountains, Box Elder and Tooele Counties, Utah, and Elko County, Nevada: Utah Geological Society Guidebook to the Geology of Utah 15, p. 150-158.

Antevs, E. V., 1948, The Great Basin, with emphasis on glacial and postglacial times; III, Climatic changes and pre-white man: University of Utah Bulletin 38, no. 20, p. 168-191.

Arabaz, W. J., R. B., Smith, and W. D. Richins (eds), 1979, Earthquake studies in Utah, 1850 to 1978: University of Utah Seismograph Stations Special Publication, 552 p.

Arabaz, W. J., R. B Smith and W. D. Richins, 1980, Earthquake studies along the Wasatch Front, Utah—Network monitoring, seismicity and seismic hazards: Seismological Society of America, v. 70, no. 5, p. 1479-1499.

Armstrong, R. L., 1967, The Cordilleran miogeosyncline in Nevada and Utah: Utah Geological and Mineral Survey Bulletin 78, 58 p.

———1968a, Sevier orogenic belt in Nevada and Utah: Geological Society of America Bulletin, v. 79, no. 4, p. 429-458.

———1968b, Mantled gneiss domes in the Albion Range, southern Idaho: Geological Society of America Bulletin, v. 79, no. 10, p. 1295-1314.

———1969, K-Ar dating of laccolithic centers of the Colorado Plateau and vicinity: Geological Society America Bulletin, v. 80, p. 2081-2096.

———1970, Geochronology of Tertiary igneous rocks, eastern Basin and Range Province, western Utah, eastern Nevada and vicinity, U.S.A.: Geochimica et Cosmochimica Acta, v. 34, no. 2, p. 203-232.

———1972, Low-angle (denudation) faults, hinterland of the Sevier orogenic belt, eastern Nevada and western Utah: Geological Society of America Bulletin, v. 83, no. 6, p. 1729-1754.

Armstrong, R. L., and J. Suppe, 1973, Potassium-argon geochronometry of Mesozoic igneous rocks in Nevada, Utah and southern California: Geological Society of America Bulletin, v. 84, no. 4, p. 1375-1392.

Armstrong, R. L., and others, 1969, Space-time relations of Cenozoic silicic volcanism of the Great Basin of the western United States: American Journal of Science, v. 267, p. 478-490.

Arnold, D. E., 1956, Geology of the northern Stansbury Range, Tooele County, Utah: M.S. thesis, University of Utah, Salt Lake City, Utah, 57 p.; *also* Utah Geological and Mineral Survey Bulletin 86, p. 10-11, 1970.

Arnow, Ted, and R. E. Mattick, 1968, Thickness of valley fill in the Jordan Valley east of the Great Salt Lake, Utah *in* Geological Survey research: U.S. Geological Survey Professional Paper 600-B, p. B79-B82.

Ash, S. R., 1975, The Chinle (Upper Triassic) flora of southeastern Utah *in* Canyonlands Country: Four Corners Geological Society Guidebook, 8th Annual Field Conference.

Ash, S. R., and C. B. Read, 1976, North American species of *Tempskya* and their stratigraphic significance: U.S. Geological Survey Professional Paper 874, 42 p.

Astin, G. K., 1977, Geology and hydrocarbon potential of Co-op Creek quadrangle, Wasatch County, Utah *in* Rocky Mountain thrust belt geology and resources: Wyoming Geological Association Guidebook, 29th Annual Field Conference.

Atwater, T., 1970, Implications of plate tectonics for the Cenozoic tectonic evolution of western North America: Geological Society of America Bulletin, v. 81, no. 12, p. 3513-3536.

Atwater, T., and P. Molnar, 1973, Relative motion of the Pacific and North American plates deduced from sea-floor spreading in the Atlantic, Indian and south Pacific Oceans *in* Proceedings of the conference on tectonic problems of the San Andreas Fault system, K. L. Kovach and A. Nur, eds.: Stanford University Publications in Geological Sciences, Stanford, California, v. 13, p. 136-148.

Atwood, W. W., 1909, Glaciation of the Uinta and Wasatch Mountains, Utah: U.S. Geological Survey Professional Paper 61, 96 p.

Averitt, Paul, 1962, Geology and coal resources of the Cedar Mountain quadrangle, Iron County, Utah: U.S. Geological Survey Professional Paper 389, 72 p.

———1964, Table of post-Cretaceous geologic events along the Hurricane Fault near Cedar City, Iron County, Utah: Geological Society of America Bulletin, v. 75, no. 9, p. 901-907.

———1969, Mineral fuels and associated resources—Coal *in* Mineral and water resources of Utah, L. S. Hilpert, ed.: Utah Geological and Mineral Survey Bulletin 73, 275 p.

Baars, D. L., 1958, Cambrian stratigraphy of the Paradox Basin region (Colorado Plateau) *in* Geology of the Paradox Basin: Intermountain Association of Petroleum Geologists Guidebook, 9th Annual Field Conference, p. 93-101.

———1962, Permian system of Colorado Plateau: American Association of Petroleum Geologists Bulletin, v. 46, no. 2, p. 149-218.

———1966, Pre-Pennsylvanian paleotectonics—Key to basin evolution and petroleum occurrences in Paradox Basin, Utah and Colorado: American Association of Petroleum Geologists Bulletin, v. 50, no. 10, p. 2082-2111.

———1971, Permian blanket sandstones of the Colorado Plateau *in* Geometry of sandstone bodies, J. A. Peterson and J. C. Osmond, eds.: American Association of Petroleum Geologists Bulletin, v. 55, no. 2, p. 179-207.

———1972, Red Rock Country: Doubleday, 250 p.

———1973b, Rocks of the inner gorges—The Pennsylvanian system *in* Geology of the canyons of the San Juan River, a river-runner's guide: Four Corners Geological Society, 7th Annual Field Conference, p. 16-26.

———1973c, Permianland—The rocks of Monument Valley *in* Geology of the canyons of the San Juan River, a river-runner's guide: Four Corners Geological Society, 7th Annual Field Conference, p. 27-34.

———1975, The Permian System of Canyonlands country, *in* Canyonlands Country: Four Corners Geological Society Guidebook, 8th Field Conference.

———1981, Tectonic evolution of the Paradox Basin, *in* Wiegand, D. L. (ed), Geology of the Paradox Basin: Rocky Mountain Association of Geologists, p. 23-31.

Baars, D. L., and D. M. Molenaar, 1971, Geology of the Canyonlands and Cataract Canyon: Four Corners Geological Society, 6th Annual Field Conference, 99 p.

Baetcke, G. B., 1969, Stratigraphy of the Star Range and reconnaissance study of three selected mines: Ph.D. dissertation, University of Utah, Salt Lake City, Utah.

Baer, J. L., 1969, Paleoecology of the lower Green River Formation, central Utah: Brigham Young University Geology Studies, v. 16, pl. 3, 63 p.

Baer, J. L., and E. Callighan, (eds), 1973, Plateau-basin range transition zone, central Utah: Utah Geological Association Publication 2, 123 p.

Baer, J. L., R. L. Davis, and S. E. George, 1982, Structure and stratigraphy of the Pavant Range, central Utah: Utah Geological Association Publication 10, p. 31-48.

Bahr, C. W., 1963, Virgin oil field, Washington County, Utah, *in* Geology of southwestern Utah: Intermountain Association of Petroleum Geologists, 12th Annual Field Conference, p. 169-173.

Baker, A. A. J., 1933, Geology and oil possibilities of the Moab district, Grand and San Juan Counties, Utah: U.S. Geological Survey Bulletin 841, 95 p.

———1936, Geology of the Monument Valley-Navajo Mountain region, San Juan County, Utah: U.S. Geological Survey Bulletin 865, 106 p.

———1946, Geology of the Green River Desert-Cataract Canyon region, Emery, Wayne and Garfield Counties, Utah: U.S. Geological Survey Bulletin 951, v, 122 p.

———1947, Stratigraphy of the Wasatch Mountains in the vicinity of Provo, Utah: U.S. Geological Survey Oil and Gas Inv. Prelim. Chart 30.

Baker, A. A. J., and others, 1949, Paleozoic geology of north and west sides of Uinta Basin, Utah: American Association of Petroleum Geologists Bulletin, v. 33, p. 1161-1197.

———1959, Faults in the Wasatch Range near Provo, Utah, *in* Geology of the Wasatch and Uinta Mountains Transition Area: Intermountain Association of Petroleum Geologists Guidebook, 10th Annual Field Conference, p. 153-158.

Baker, A. A. J., C. H. Dane, and J. B. Resside, Jr., 1936, Correlation of the Jurassic formations of portion of Utah, Arizona, New Mexico and Colorado: U.S. Geological Survey Professional Paper 183, v, 66 p.

Baker, A. A. J., J. W. Huddle and D. M. Kinney, 1949, Paleozoic geology of the north and west sides of the Uinta Basin, Utah: American Association of Petroleum Geologists Bulletin, v. 33, no. 7, p. 1161-1197.

Baker, A. A. J., and others, 1947, Stratigraphy of the Wasatch Mountains in the vicinity of Provo, Utah: U.S. Geological Survey Oil and Gas Investigations Preliminary Chart no. 30.

Baker, C. H., Jr., 1974, Water Resources of the Curlew Valley drainage basin, Utah and Idaho: State of Utah Department of Natural Resources, Division of Water Rights, Technical Publication 45.

Baker, W. H., 1959, Geologic setting and origin of the Grouse Creek pluton, Box Elder County, Utah: Ph.D. dissertation, University of Utah, Salt Lake City, Utah, 175 p.; *also* Utah Geological and Mineral Survey Bulletin 86, p. 14.

Balsley, J. K., 198?, Cretaceous wave-dominated delta systems; Book Cliffs, east central Utah: Field Guide, Amoco Production Company, Denver, Colorado, 163 p.

Barker, F., 1969, Precambrian geology of the Needle Mountains, southwestern Colorado: U.S. Geological Survey Professional Paper 644-A, 35 p.

Barnes, M. P., and J. C. Simos, 1968, Ore deposits of the Park City district with a contribution on the Mayflower lode: *in* Ore deposits of the United States, 1933-1967, AIME, Graton Sales, v. 2, New York, p. 1102-1126.

Barosh, P. J., 1960, Beaver Lake Mountains, Beaver County, Utah—Their geology and ore deposits: Utah Geological and Mineral Survey Bulletin 68, 89 p.

Baumhoff, J. A., and R. F. Heizer, 1965, Post-glacial climate and archaeology in the desert west *in* The Quaternary of the United States, Wright and Frey, eds., Princeton University Press, Princeton, New Jersey.

Bayley, R. W., 1963, A preliminary report on the Precambrian iron deposits near Atlantic City, Wyoming: U.S. Geological Survey Bulletin 1142-C, 23 p.

Beeson, J. J., 1927, Mining districts and their relation to structural geology (with discussion): American Institute of Mining Engineers Transactions 75, p. 757-796.

Behnken, F. H., 1975, Leonardian and Guadalupian (Permian) conodont biostratigraphy in the western and southwestern United States: Journal of Paleontology, v. 49, p. 284-315.

Bell, G. L., 1952, Geology of the northern Farmington Mountains, Utah *in* Geology of the central Wasatch Mountains, R. E. Marsell, ed.: Utah Geological Society Guidebook to the Geology of Utah 8, p. 38-51.

Berg, J. S., Jr., and K. L. Cook, 1961, Energies, magnitudes and amplitudes of seismic blasts at Promontory and Lakeside Utah: Seismological Society America Bulletin, v. 5, no. 3, p. 389-399.

Best, M. G., 1969, Late Cenozoic basalts on the western margin of the Colorado Plateaus, Utah and Arizona: Brigham Young University Geology Studies, Provo, Utah, v. 16, pt. 1, p. 39.

Best, M. G., and W. H. Brimhall, 1970, Late Cenozoic basalt types in the western Grand Canyon region *in* The western Grand Canyon district: Utah Geological Society Guidebook to the Geology of Utah 23, p. 57-74.

———1974, Late Cenozoic alkalic basaltic magmas in the western Colorado Plateaus and the Basin and Range transition zone, U. S. A., and their bearing on mantle dynamics: Geological Society of America Bulletin, v. 85, no. 11, p. 1677-1690.

Best, M. G., and W. K. Hamblin, 1978, Origin of the Basin and Range—Implications from the geology of the eastern boundary: Geological Science of America Memoir 152, p. 111-141.

———1980, Origin of the northern Basin and Range Province—Implications from the geology of its eastern boundary *in* Cenozoic tectonics and regional geophysics of the western Cordillera: Geological Society of America Memoir 152, p. 313-340.

Best, M. G., E. H. McKee and P. E. Damon, 1980, Space-time-composition patterns of late Cenozoic mafic volcanism, southwestern Utah and adjoining areas: American Journal of Science, v. 280, p. 1035-1050.

Best, M. G., R. T. Shuey and C. F. Caskey, 1973, Stratigraphic relations of members of the Needles Range Formation at type localities in southwestern Utah: Geological Society of America Bulletin, v. 84, no. 10, p. 3269-3278.

Beus, S. S., 1963, Geology of the central Blue Spring Hills, Utah-Idaho: Ph.D. dissertation, University of California (Los Angeles), Los Angeles, California, 282 p.

Beus, S. S., and R. H. Gelnett, 1958, Geology of Wellsville Mountain, northern Wasatch Range, Utah: M.S. thesis, Utah State University, Logan, Utah, 84 p.

Beus, S. S. and R. W. Rush, 1968, Paleozoic stratigraphy of Samaria Mountain, Idaho-Utah: American Association of Petroleum Geologists Bulletin, v. 52, no. 5, p. 782-808.

Bick, K. F., 1958, Geology of the Deep Creek quadrangle, western Utah: Ph.D. dissertation, Yale University, New Haven, Connecticut.

———1966, Geology of the Deep Creek Mountains, Tooele and Juab Counties, Utah: Utah Geological and Mineral Survey Bulletin 77, 120 p.

Billingsley, Paul, and Augustus Lacke, 1933, Tectonic position of ore districts in the Rocky Mountain region: American Institution Mining Engineers Technical Publication 501, p. 59-68.

Bissell, H. J., 1949, The Cretaceous System of Utah: Utah Geological and Mineral Survey, Oil and Gas possibilities of Utah, pp 90-100.

———1952, Stratigraphy and structure of northeastern Strawberry Valley quadrangle, Utah: American Association of Petroleum Geologists Bulletin, v. 36, no. 4, p. 575-634.

———1962a, Pennsylvanian-Permian Oquirrh Basin of Utah: Brigham Young University Geology Studies, Provo, Utah, v. 9, pt. 1, p. 26-49.

———1962b, Permian rocks of parts of Nevada, Utah and Idaho: Geological Society of America Bulletin, v. 73, no. 9, p. 1083-1110; *also* Geoscience Abstracts, v. 5, no. 4, p. 18.

———1963a, Pennsylvanian and Permian systems of southwestern Utah *in* Geology of southwestern Utah: Intermountain Association of Petroleum Geologists Guidebook, 12th Annual Field Conference, p. 42-58.

———1963b, Lake Bonneville—Geology of southern Utah Valley, Utah: U.S. Geological Survey Professional Paper 257-B, p. B101-B130.

———1964a, Wasatch fault of the south-central Wasatch Mountains *in* The Wasatch Fault zone in north-central Utah, R. E. Marsell, ed.: Utah Geological Society Guidebook to the Geology of Utah 18, p. 15-30.

———1964b, Ely, Arcturus and Park City Groups (Pennsylvanian-Permian) in eastern Nevada and western Utah: American Association of Petroleum Geologists Bulletin, v. 48, no. 5 p. 565-636.

———1964c, Lithology and petrography of the Weber Formation in Utah and Colorado *in* Geology and mineral resources of the Uinta Basin, Utah's hydrocarbon storehouse: Intermountain Association of Petroleum Geologists Guidebook, 13th Annual Field Conference, p. 67-92.

———1967, Pennsylvanian and Permian basins in northwestern Utah, northeastern Nevada and south-central Idaho—Discussion (of paper by R. J. Roberts and others, 1965): American Association of Petroleum Geologists Bulletin, v. 51, no. 5, p. 791-802.

———1968, Bonneville, an ice-age lake: Brigham Young University Geology Studies, Provo, Utah, v. 15, no. 4, 66 p.

———1970, Realms of Permian tectonism and sedimentation in western Utah and eastern Nevada: American Association of Petroleum Geologists Bulletin, v. 54, no. 2, p. 285-312.

Bissell, H. J., and O. E. Childs, 1958, The Weber Formation of Utah and Colorado *in* Symposium on Pennsylvanian rocks of Colorado and adjacent areas: Rocky Mountain Association of Geologists, p. 26-30.

Bissell, H. J., J. K. Rigby and P. D. Proctor, 1959, Geology of the southern Oquirrh Mountains and Fivemile Pass-northern Boulter Mountains area, Tooele and Utah Counties, Utah *in* Geology of the southern Oquirrh Mountains and Fivemile Pass-northern Boulter Mountain area, Tooele and Utah Counties, Utah, H. J. Bissell, ed: Utah Geological Society Guidebook to the Geology of Utah 14, p. 1-8.

Blackwelder, Eliot, 1932, An ancient glacial formation in Utah: Journal of Geology, v. 40, p. 289-304.

———1934, Origin of the Colorado River: Geological Society of America Bulletin, v. 45, no. 3, p. 551-556.

———1949, The Great Basin—The geological background: University of Utah Bulletin 38, no. 20, p. 3-16.

Blagbrough, J. W., and W. J. Breed, 1967, Protalus ramparts on Navajo Mountain, southern Utah: American Journal of Science, v. 265, no. 9, p. 759-772.

Blakey, R. C., 1974, Stratigraphic and depositional analysis of the Moenkopi Formation, southeastern Utah: Utah Geological and Mineral Survey Bulletin 104, 81 p.

———1977, Petroliferous lithosomes in the Moenkopi Formation, southern Utah: Utah Geology, v. 4, no. 2, p. 67-84.

Blue, D. M., 1960, Geology and ore deposits of the Lucin mining district, Box Elder County, Utah, and Elko County, Nevada: M.S. thesis, University of Utah, Salt Lake City, Utah; *also* Utah Geological and Mineral Survey Bulletin 86, p. 23.

Bodell, J. M., 1981, Heat flow in the north-central Colorado Plateau: M.S. thesis, University of Utah, Salt Lake City, Utah.

Bodily, N. M., 1970, An armored dinosaur from the Lower Cretaceous of Utah: Brigham Young University Geology Studies, Provo, Utah, v. 16 pt. 3, p. 35-60.

Boutwell, J. M., 1912, Geology and ore deposits of the Park City district, Utah *with contributions by* L. H. Woolsey: U.S. Geological Survey Professional Paper 77, 231 p.

———1933, Park City mining district *in* The Salt Lake Region, J. M. Boutwell and others: 16th International Geological Congress, U.S., Guidebook 17, p. 69-82; *also* Cottonwood region *in* The Salt Lake Region, J. M. Boutwell and others, p. 82-94.

Bowers, D., 1978, Potassium-argon age dating and petrology of the Mineral Mountains pluton, Utah: M.S. thesis, University of Utah, Salt Lake City, Utah.

Bowers, W. E., 1972, The Canaan Peak, Pine Hollow and Wasatch Formations in the Table Cliff region, Garfield County, Utah: U.S. Geological Survey Bulletin 1331-B, 39 p.

Bradley, W. H., 1929, Algal reefs and oolites of the Green River Formation: U.S. Geological Survey Professional Paper 154, p. 203-223.

———1930, The varves and climate of the Green River Epoch: U.S. Geological Survey Professional Paper 158-E, p. 87-110.

———1931, Origin and microfossils of the oil shale of the Green River Formation of Colorado and Utah: U.S. Geological Survey Professional Paper 168, 58 p.

———1936, Geomorphology of the north flank of the Uinta Mountains (Utah): U.S. Geological Survey Professional Paper 185-I, p. 163-199.

———1964, Geology of the Green River Formation and associated Eocene rocks in southwestern Wyoming and adjacent parts of Colorado and Utah: U.S. Geological Survey Professional Paper 496-A, 86 p.

Braile, L. W., and others, 1974, Crustal structure across the Wasatch Front from detailed seismic refraction studies: Journal of Geophysical Research, v. 79, no. 17, p. 2669-2677.

Braithwaite, L. F., 1976, Graptolites from the Lower Ordovician Pogonip Group of western Utah: Geological Society of America Special Paper 166.

Bray, R. E., and J. C. Wilson, eds., 1975, Guidebook to the Bingham mining district: Society of Economic Geologists, Kennecott Copper Corporation Geology Department, Utah Copper Division and Anaconda Company, 156 p.

Breed, C. S., 1969, A century of conjecture on the Colorado River in the Grand Canyon *in* Geology and natural history of the Grand Canyon region: Four Corners Geological Society Guidebook, 5th Annual Field Trip.

———1971, Two hypotheses of the origin and geologic history of the Colorado River *in* Eastern Basin and Range, Colorado Plateau and southern Rocky Mountains: National Association of Geology Teachers, Field Conference Guidebook.

Breed, C. S., and Breed, W. J., eds., 1972, Investigations in the Triassic Chinle Formation: Museum of Northern Arizona Bulletin 47, p. 103.

Breed, W. J., and E. Road, eds., 1976, Geology of the Grand Canyon: Museum of Northern Arizona and Grand Canyon Natural History Association.

Bright, R. D., and others, 1965, Lake Bonneville: Nebraska Academy of Sciences Proceedings, Lincoln Nebraska, p. 104-117.

Bromfield, C. S., 1968, General geology of the Park City region, Utah *in* Park City district: Utah Geological Society Guidebook no. 22, p. 10-29.

Brophy, G. P., and others, 1957, Marysvale, Utah uranium area: Geological Society of America Special Paper 63.

Brown, H. H., 1973, The Dakota Formation in the Plateau area, southwest Utah, *in* Cretaceous and Tertiary rocks of the southern Colorado Plateau: Four Corners Geological Society, Durango, Colorado, p. 52-56.

Brown, R. W., 1949, Pliocene plants from Cache Valley, Utah: Washington Academy Science Journal, v. 39, no. 7, p. 224-229.

Brox, G. S., 1961, The geology and erosional development of northern Bryce Canyon National Park, Garfield County, Utah: M.S. thesis, University of Utah, Salt Lake City, Utah, 77 p.; *also* Utah Geological and Mineral Survey Bulletin 86, p. 29, 1970.

Bruhn, A. F., 1952, Your guide to southern Utah's land of color: Salt Lake City, Utah, 61 p.

Bruhn, R. L., M. D. Picard, and S. L. Beck, Mesozoic and early Tertiary structure and sedimentology of the central Wasatch Mountains, Uinta Mountains and Uinta Basin, Special Study Utah Geological and Mineral Survey Bulletin 59, p. 83-105.

Budge, D. R., 1966, Stratigraphy of the Laketown Dolostone, north-central Utah: M.S. thesis, Utah State University, Logan, Utah, 86 p.; *also* Utah Geological and Mineral Survey Bulletin 86, p. 29, 1970.

———1972, Paleontology and stratigraphic significance of Late Ordovician and Silurian corals from the eastern Great Basin: Ph.D. dissertation, University of California, Berkeley, Berkeley, California.

Bullock, K.C., 1953, Timpanogos Cave National Monument: National Parks and National Monuments of Utah, p. 28-40.

———1970, Iron deposits of Utah: Utah Geological and Mineral Survey Bulletin 88, 101 p.

———1973, Geology and iron deposits of Iron Springs district, Iron County, Utah: Brigham Young University Geology Studies, Provo, Utah, v. 20, pt. 1, p. 26-63.

———1981, Minerals and mineral localities of Utah: Utah Geological and Mineral Survey Bulletin 117, 117 p.

Bullock, K. D., and P. D. Procter, 1949, Igneous rocks of Utah, intrusive *in* The Oil and Gas Possibilities of Utah, a symposium volume: Utah Geological and Mineral Survey, p. 119-126.

Burchell, P. W., 1974, Historical development of oil and gas production from Utah's greater Altamont-Bluebell field *in* Energy resources of the Uinta Basin: Utah Geological Association Publication 4.

Burchfiel, B. C., and C. W. Hickcox, 1972, Structural development of central Utah, *in* Plateau — Basin and Range transition zone central Utah: Utah Geological Association Publication 2, p. 55-66.

Burchfiel, B. C., and G. A. Davis, 1975, Structural framework and evolution of the southern part of the Cordilleron orogeny, western United States: American Journal of Science, v. 272, p. 97-118.

Buss, W. R., 1963, The physiography of Utah *in* Oil and gas possibilities of Utah, re-evaluated: Utah Geological and Mineral Survey Bulletin 54, p. 13-18.

Buss, W. R., and D. O. Peterson, 1964, The Wasatch Fault in Weber and Davis Counties, Utah *in* The Wasatch Fault zone in north-central Utah, R. E. Marsell, ed.: Utah Geological Society Guidebook to the Geology of Utah 18, p. 51-52.

Butkus, T. A., 1975, Sedimentology and depositional environments of the Great Blue Limestone (Late Mississippian), north-central Utah: M.S. thesis, University of Utah, Salt Lake City, Utah.

Butler, B. S., 1913, Geology and ore deposits of the San Francisco and adjacent districts, Utah: U.S. Geological Survey Professional Paper 80, 212 p.

Butler, B. S., and others, 1920, The ore deposits of Utah: U.S. Geological Survey Professional Paper 111, 672 p.

Byrd, W. D., III, 1967, Phosphate lands in the Crawford Mountains, Rich County, Utah: Utah Geological and Mineral Survey Reports of Investigations 31, 7 p.

———1970, P. R. Springs oil-impregnated sandstone deposit, Uinta and Grand Counties, Utah: Utah Geological and Mineral Survey Special Studies 31, 34 p.

Cadigan, R. A., 1971, Petrology of the Triassic Moenkopi Formation and related strata in the Colorado Plateau region, with a section on stratigraphy by J. H. Stewart: U.S. Geological Survey Professional Paper 692.

Calkins, F. C., and B. S. Butler, 1943, Geology and ore deposits of the Cottonwood-American Fork area, Utah: U.S. Geological Survey Professional Paper 201, 152 p.

Calkins, F. C., and others, 1943, Geology and ore deposits of the Cottonwood-American Fork area, Utah: U.S. Geological Survey Professional Paper 201.

Callaghan, Eugene, 1939, Volcanic sequence in the Marysvale region in southwest central Utah: Eos, American Geophysical Union Transactions, 20th Annual Meeting, Washington, D.C., pt. 3, p. 438-452.

———1947, Geological features *in* Utilization of surface-water resources of Sevier Lake Basin, Utah by R. R. Woolley: U.S. Geological Survey Water-Supply Paper 920, 393 p.

———1973a, Mineral resource potential of Piute County, Utah, and adjoining area: Utah Geological and Mineral Survey Bulletin 102, 135 p.

———1973b, Geologic map of the Marysvale region, Piute County and parts of adjoining counties, Utah: Utah Geological and Mineral Survey Map 34.

Campbell, G. S., 1962, Bloomington Dome, Washington County, Utah: Utah Geological Society Guidebook to the Geology of Utah, no. 7, p. 86-89.

Campbell, D. P., 1974, Biostratigraphy of the *Albertella* and *Glossopleura* zones (lower Middle Cambrian) of northern Utah and southern Idaho: M.S. thesis, University of Utah, Salt Lake City, Utah.

Campbell, J. A., 1969, Upper Valley oil field, Garfield County, Utah, *in* Geology and natural history of the Grand Canyon region—Powell Centennial: Four Corners Geological Society, 5th Annual Field Conference, p. 195-200.

———1975a, Oil-impregnated sandstone deposits of Utah: Mining Engineering, v. 27, no. 5, p. 47-51, 53.

———1975b, Structural geology and petroleum potential of the south flank of the Uinta Mountains uplift, northeastern Utah: Utah Geology, v. 2, no. 2, p. 129-132.

———1978, Cenozoic structural and geomorphic evolution of the Canyon Range, central Utah: Ph.D. dissertation, University of Utah, Salt Lake City, Utah.

Campbell, J. A., and R. S. Bacon, 1976, Penetration chart of Utah oil and gas fields: Utah Geological and Mineral Survey Oil and Gas Fields Studies no. 14.

Campbell, J. A., and H. R. Ritzma, 1979, Geology and petroleum resources of the major oil-impregnated sandstone deposits of Utah: Utah Geological and Mineral Survey Special Studies, no. 50, 24 p.

Campbell, J. A., J. W. Gwynn and L. I. Perry, 1980, Geology and mineral resources of Box Elder County, Utah: Utah Geological and Mineral Survey Bulletin 115, pt. 2, Economic geology, p. 85-251.

Campbell, R. H., and R. Q. Lewis, Sr., 1961, Distribution of uranium ore deposits in the Elk Ridge area, San Juan County, Utah: Economic Geology, v. 56, no. 1, p. 111-131.

Carrier, D. L. and D. S. Chapman, 1981, Gravity and thermal models for the Twin Peaks silicic volcanic center, southwestern Utah: Journal of Geophysical Research, v. 86, no. B11, p. 10287-10302.

Carter, W. D., and J. L. Gvaltieri, 1965, Geology and uranium-vanadium deposits of the LaSal quadrangle, San Juan County, Utah and Montrose County, Colorado: U.S. Geological Survey Professional Paper 508, p. 82.

Cashion, W. B., 1961, Potential oil-shale reserves of the Green River Formation in the southeastern Uinta Basin, Utah and Colorado *in* Short papers in the geologic and hydrolgic sciences: U.S. Geological Survey Professional Paper 424-C, p. C22-C24.

———1964, Distribution and quality of oil shale in the Green River Formation of the Uinta Basin *in* Geology and mineral resources of the Uinta Basin, Utah's hydrocarbon storehouse: Intermountain Association of Petroleum Geologists Guidebook, 13th Annual Field Conference, p. 209-212; *also* U.S. Geological Survey Professional Paper 501-D, p. D86-D89.

———1967, Geology and fuel resources of the Green River Formation, southeastern Uinta Basin, Utah and Colorado: U.S. Geological Survey Professional Paper 548, 48 p.

———1973, Geologic and structure map of the Grand Junction Quadrangle, Colorado and Utah: U.S. Geological Survey Map I-736.

———1974, Revision of nomenclature of the upper part of the Green River Formation, Piceance Creek basin, Colorado and E. Utah: U.S. Geological Survey Bulletin.

Cater, F. W., and D. P. Elston, Structural development of salt anticlines of Colorado - Utah: American Association Petroleum Geologists Memoir 2, p. 152-159.

Chamberlain, C. K., 1969, Carboniferous trilobites—Utah species and evolution in North America: Journal of Paleontology, v. 43, no. 1, p. 41-67.

Chamberlain, K. C., and D. L. Clark, 1973, Trace fossils and conodonts as evidence for deep water deposits in the Oquirrh basin of central Utah: Journal of Paleontology, v. 47, no. 4., p. 663-682.

Chandler, M. E. J., 1966, Fruiting organs from the Morrsion Formation of Utah, USA: British Museum (Natural History) Bulletin, Geology, v. 12, no. 4, p. 138-172.

Chapman, D. S., and others, 1979, Regional heat flow and geochemical studies in southwestern Utah: U.S. Geological Survey contract 14-08-001-G-341, final report, v. 2, 119 p.

Chapusa, F. W. P., 1969, Geology and structure of Stansbury Island: M.S. thesis, University of Utah, Salt Lake City, Utah.

Chatfield, J., 1972, Case history of Red Wash field, Uintah County, Utah *in* Stratigraphic oil and gas fields—Classification, exploration methods and case histories: American Association of Petroleum Geologists Memoir 16, p. 342-353; *also* Society for Exploration Geophysicists, Special Publication 10, 1972.

Cheney, T. M., 1957a, Phosphate deposits in the Uinta Mountains, Utah *in* Geology of the Uinta Basin: Intermountain Association of Petroleum Geologists Guidebook, 8th Annual Field Conference, p. 144-148.

———1957b, Phosphate in Utah and an analysis of the stratigraphy of the Park City and the Phosphoria Formations, Utah—A preliminary report: Utah Geological and Mineral Survey Bulletin 59, 54 p.

Cheney, T. M., and others, 1953, Stratigraphic sections of the Phosphoria Formation in Utah, 1949-51: U.S. Geological Survey Circular 306, 40 p.

Chen-Yen, Teng, 1954, Nonmarine mollusks of Late Cretaceous age from Wyoming, Utah and Colorado: U.S. Geological Survey Professional Paper 254-B, p. 45-66.

Childs, O. E., 1950, Geologic history of the Uinta Basin: Intermountain Association of Petroleum Geologists Guidebook to the Geology of Utah, no. 5., p. 49-60.

Christiansen, F. W., 1951, A summary of the structure and stratigraphy of the Canyon Range *in* Geology of the Canyon, House and Confusion Ranges, Millard County, Utah, W. L. Stokes, ed.: Utah Geological Society Guidebook to the Geology of Utah 6, p. 5-18.

———1951b, Structure and stratigraphy of the Canyon Range, central Utah: Geological Society of America Bulletin, v. 63, no. 7, p. 717-740.

———1952, Structure and stratigraphy of the Canyon Range, central Utah: Geological Society of America Bulletin, v. 63, p. 717-740.

Christiansen, R. L., and E. H. McKee, 1978, Late Cenozoic volcanic and tectonic evolution of the Great Basin and Columbia intermountain region *in* Cenozoic tectonics and the regional geophysics of the western Cordillera: Geological Society of America Memoir 152.

Christiansen, W. J., 1977, Geology of the Fish Springs Mining district, Juab County, Utah: M.S. thesis, University of Utah.

Christiansen, R. L., and P. W. Lipman, 1972, Cenozoic volcanism and plate tectonic evolution of the western United States, II. Late Cenozoic: Royal Society of London Philosophical Transactions, ser. A., v. 271, p. 249-284.

Church, Victor, 1942, Origin and development of Logan Cave, Utah: Utah Academy of Sciences Proceedings, vols. 19-20, 1941-43, p. 111-120.

Clark, D. L., 1957, Marine Triassic stratigraphy in Eastern Great Basin (Nevada, Utah): American Association Petroleum Geologists Bulletin, v. 41, no. 10, p. 2192-2222.

———1959, Conodonts from the Triassic of Nevada and Utah: Journal of Paleontology, v. 33, no. 2, p. 305-312.

———1967, Conodonts as indicators of diachronism in Devonian rocks of the Great Basin *in* U.S. International Symposium on the Devonian System: Alberta Society of Petroleum Geologists, Calgary, Alberta, 1967, Proceedings, v. 2, p. 673-677.

Clark, D. L., and J. H. Becker, 1960, Upper Devonian correlations in western Utah and eastern Nevada: Geological Society of America Bulletin, v. 71, no. 11, p. 1661-1674.

Clark, D. L., and R. L. Ethington, 1966, Conodonts and biostratigraphy of the Lower and Middle Devonian of Nevada and Utah: Journal of Paleontology, v. 40, no. 3, p. 659-689.

———1967, Conodonts and zonation of the Upper Devonian in the Great Basin: Geological Society of America Memoir 103, 94 p.

Clark, D. L., and W. L. Stokes, 1957, Marine Triassic stratigraphy in the eastern Great Basin (Nevada-Utah): American Association of Petroleum Geologists Bulletin, v. 41, no. 10, p. 2192-2222.

Clark. D. L., and others, 1977, Permian-Triassic sequence in northwest Utah: Geology, v. 5, no. 11, p. 655-658.

Clark, E. E., 1977, Late Cenozoic volcanic and tectonic activity along the eastern margin of the Great Basin, in the proximity of Cove Fort, Utah: Brigham Young University Studies, Provo, Utah, v. 24, pt. 1, p. 87-114.

Clark, F. R., 1918, Geology of the Lost Creek coal field, Morgan County, Utah: U.S. Geological Survey Bulletin 691-L, p. 311-322.

———1928, Economic Geology of the Castlegate, Wellington and Sunnyside quadrangles, Carbon County, Utah: U.S. Geological Survey Bulletin 793.

Cluff, L. S., A. S. Palwardhan, and K. J. Coppersmith, 1980, Estimating the probability of occurrences of surface faulting earthquakes on the Wasatch Fault Zone: Bulletin of the Seismological Society of America, v. 70, no. 5, p. 1463-1478.

Cobban, W. A., 1951, Scaphitoid cephalopods of the Colorado Group: U.S. Geological Survey Professional Paper 239, 42 p.

———1976, Ammonite record from Mancos Shale of the Castle Valley-Price-Woodside area, east-central Utah: Brighan Young University Geology Studies, Provo, Utah, v. 22, pt. 3, p. 117-126.

Cobban, W. A., and J. B. Reeside, Jr., 1952, Correlation of the Cretaceous formations of the western interior of the United States: Geological Society of America Bulletin, v. 63, no. 10, p. 1011-1044.

Coffin, Clare, 1954, History of radium-uranium mining in the Plateau Province *in* Uranium deposits and general geology of southeastern Utah, W. L. Stokes, ed.: Utah Geological Society Guidebook to the Geology of Utah 9, p. 1-7.

Cohenhour, R. E., 1959, Geology of the Sheeprock Mountains, Tooele and Juab Counties, Utah: Utah Geological and Mineral Survey Bulletin 63, 201 p.

———1963a, Beryllium belt of western Utah *in* Beryllium and uranium mineralization in western Juab County, Utah. B. J. Sharp and N. C. Williams, eds.: Utah Geological Society Guidebook to the Geology of Utah 17, p. 4-7.

———1963b, Beryllium and associated mineralization in the Sheeprock Mountains, Utah *in* Beryllium and uranium mineralization in western Juab County, B. J. Sharp and N. C. Williams, eds.: Utah Geological Society Guidebook to the Geology of Utah 17, p. 8-13.

———1966, Industrial development and potential of Great Salt Lake with notes on engineering geology and operation problems *in* The Great Salt Lake, W. L. Stokes, ed.: Utah Geological Society Guidebook to the Geology of Utah 20, p. 153-163.

———1967a, Selected references and papers pertinent to uranium exploration *in* Uranium districts of southeastern Utah, L. F. Hintze, ed.: Utah Geological Society Guidebook to the Geology of Utah 21, p. 106-108.

———1967b, History of uranium and development of Colorado Plateau ores with notes on uranium production in Utah *in* Uranium districts of southeastern Utah, L. F. Hinte, ed.: Utah Geological Society Guidebook to the Geology of Utah 21, p. 12-22.

———1969, Uranium in Utah, *in* Guidebook of northern Utah: Utah Geological and Mineral Survey, Bulletin 82, p. 231-249.

Cohenour, R. E., and M. P. Erickson, 1963, Beryllium minerals *in* Beryllium and uranium mineralization in western Juab County, Utah, B. J. Sharp and N. C. Williams, eds.: Utah Geological Society Guidebook to the Geology of Utah 17, p. 1-3.

Cohenour, R. E.., and K. C. Thomson, 1966, Geologic setting of the Great Salt Lake *in* The Great Salt Lake, W. L. Stokes, ed.: Utah Geological Society Guidebook to the Geology of Utah 20, p. 35-56.

Collinson, J. W., and W. A. Hesenmueller, 1978, Early Triassic paleogeography and biostratigraphy of the Cordilleran miogeosyncline *in* Mesozoic paleogeography of the western United States: Society of Economic Paleontologists and Mineralogists.

Compton, R. R., 1972, Geologic map of the Yost quadrangle, Box Elder County, Utah, and Cassia County, Idaho: U.S. Geological Survey Miscellaneous Investigations Map I-672.

Compton, R. R., and others, 1977, Oligocene and Miocene metamorphism, folding and low-angle faulting in northwestern Utah: Geological Society of America Bulletin, v. 88, no. 9, p. 1237-1250.

Coney, P. J., 1980, Cordilleran metamorphic core complexes; An overview, *in* Geological Society of America Memoir 153, p. 7-34.

Condie, K. C., 1960, Petrogenesis of the Mineral Range pluton, southwestern Utah: M.S. thesis, University of Utah, Salt Lake City, Utah.

———1967, Petrology of the late Precambrian tillite(?) association in northern Utah: Geological Society of America Bulletin, v. 78, no. 11, p. 1317-1344.

———1969, Geologic evolution of the Precambrian rocks in northern Utah and adjacent areas *in* Guidebook of northern Utah, M. L. Jensen, ed.: Utah Geological and Mineral Survey Bulletin 82, p. 71-90.

Condie, K. C.,and C. K. Barsky, 1972, Origin of Quaternary basalts from the Black Rock Desert region, Utah: Geological Society of America Bulletin 83, no. 2, p. 333-352; *also* Applied Science Technical Index, v. 60, no. 8, p. 171.

Condra, G. E., and M. K. Elias, 1944, Study and revision of *Archidedes* (Hall): Geological Society of America Special Paper 53, viii, 243 p.

Coney, P. J., 1972, Cordilleran tectonics and North American plate motion: American Journal of Science, v. 272, p. 603-628.

———1978, Mesozoic-Cenozoic Cordilleran plate tectonics: Geological Society of America Special Paper 152.

Cook, D. R., 1957, Ore deposits of the Main Tintic mining district *in* Geology of the East Tintic Mountains and ore deposits of the Tintic mining districts: Utah Geological Society Guidebook to the Geology of Utah 12, p. 57-79.

Cook, E. F., 1957, Geology of the Pine Valley Mountains, Utah: Utah Geological and Mineral Survey Bulletin 58, 11 p.

———1960a, Geologic atlas of Utah-Washington County: Utah Geological and Mineral Survey Bulletin 70, 115 p.

———1960b, Great Basin ignimbrites (Nevada-Utah) *in* Geology of east-central Nevada: Intermountain Association of Petroleum Geologists Guidebook, 11th Annual Field Conference, p. 134-141.

———1963, Ignimbrites of the Great Basin, U. S. A.: Bulletin of Volcanologique, v. 25, p. 89-96.

———1965, Stratigraphy of Tertiary volcanic rocks in eastern Nevada: Nevada Bureau of Mines Report 11, 61 p.

Cook, H. J., 1960, New concepts of late Tertiary major crustal deformations in the Rocky Mountain region of North America—Part 12, Regional paleogeography: International Geological Congress, 21st, Copenhagen, Denmark, p. 198-212.

Cook, K. L., 1950, Magnetic surveys in the Iron Springs district, Utah: U.S. Bureau of Mines Report of Investigations 4586, 78 p.

———1966, Rift system in the Basin and Range Province in The world rift system—International Upper Mantle Committee Symposium, Ottawa, Canada, 1965: Canada Geological Survey Paper 66-14, p. 246-279.

———1967, Geophysics, mineral exploration tool: Utah Geological and Mineral Survey Quarterly Review, v. 1, no. 11, p. 3-4, 12.

———1969, Active rift system in the Basin and Range Province *in* The world rift system—International Upper Mantle Committee, Upper Mantle Project Scientific Report 19: Tectonophysics, v. 8, nos. 4-6, p. 469-511.

———1970, Earthquake hazards in Utah *in* Governor's conference on geologic hazards in Utah, December 14, 1967: Utah Geological and Mineral Survey Special Studies 32, p. 22-27.

———1972, Earthquakes along the Wasatch Front, Utah—The record and the outlook *in* eds. Hilpert, L.S., Environmental Geology of the Wasatch Front, 1971: Utah Geological Association Publication 1 H, p. H1-H29.

Cook, K. L., and J. W. Berg, Jr., 1961, Regional gravity survey along the central and southern Wasatch Front, Utah: U.S. Geological Survey Professional Paper 316-E, p. 75-89.

Cook, K. L., and Elwood Hardman, 1967, Regional gravity survey of the Hurricane fault area and Iron Springs district, Utah: Geological Society of America Bulletin, v. 78, no. 9, p. 1063-1076; *also* Geological Society of America Special Paper 101, p. 298, 1968.

Cook, K. L., and R. B. Smith, 1967, Seismicity in Utah 1850 through June, 1965: Seismological Society of America Bulletin, v. 57, no. 4, p. 689-718.

Cook, K. L., and others, 1964, Regional gravity survey of the northern Great Salt Lake Desert and adjacent areas in Utah, Nevada and Idaho: Geological Society of America Bulletin, v. 75, no. 8, p. 715-740.

Cook, K. L., and others, 1966, Some Cenozoic structural basins in the Great Salt Lake area, Utah, indicated by regional studies *in* The Great Salt Lake: Utah Geological Society Guidebook to the Geology of Utah 20, p. 57-75.

Cook, K. L., and others, 1975, Simple Bouguer gravity anomaly map of Utah: Utah Geological and Mineral Survey Map 37.

Cope, E. D., 1880, The Manti beds of Utah: American Naturalist, v. 14, p. 303-304.

Covington, R. E., 1957, The bituminous sandstones of the Asphalt Ridge area, northeastern Utah *in* Geology of the Uinta Basin: Intermountain Association of Petroleum Geologists Guidebook, 8th Annual Field Conference, p. 172-175.

———1963, Bituminous sandstones and limestone deposits of Utah *in* Oil and gas possibilities of Utah, reevaluated: Utah Geological and Mineral Survey Bulletin 54, p. 225-247.

———1964, Bituminous sandstones in the Uinta Basin *in* Geology and mineral resources of the Uinta Basin, Utah's hydrocarbon storehouse: Intermountain Association of Petroleu Geologists Guidebook, 13th Annual Field Conference, p. 227-242.

Craig, L. C., 1972, Mississippian system, *in* Geologic Atlas of the Rocky Mountain Region, United States of America: Rocky Mountain Association of Geologists, p. 100-110.

Craig, L. C., and others, 1955, Stratigraphy of Morrison and related formations, Colorado Plateau region—A preliminary report: U.S. Geological Survey Bulletin 1009-E, p. 125-168.

Cramer, H. R., 1954, Coral zones in the Mississippian of the Great Basin area: Ph.D. disseration Northwestern University, Chicago, Illinois.

Crampton, C. G., 1964, Standing-up country—The canyonlands of Utah and Arizona: Alfred A. Knopf, New York, New York, 191 p.

Crawford, A. L., 1963, Oil and gas possibilities of Utah re-evaluated: Utah Geological and Mineral Survey Bulletin 54, 565 p.

Crawford, A. L., and R. G. Pruitt, Jr., 1963, Gilsonite and other bituminous resources of central Uintah County, Utah *in* Oil and gas possibilities of Utah, reevaluated: Utah Geological and Mineral Survey Bulletin 54, p. 215-224.

Crawford, A. L., and C. F. Tuttle, 1964, Nonmetallic mining and processing in Salt Lake County *in* Geology of Salt Lake County: Utah Geological and Mineral Survey Bulletin 69, sec. 8, p. 125-139.

Crecraft, H. R., W. P. Nash, and S. H. Evans, Jr., 1980, Chemical and thermal evolution of the Twin Peaks magma system, west-central Utah: Geothermal Resources Council Transactions 4, p. 117-120.

———1981, Late Cenozoic volcanism at Twin Peaks, Utah, 1, Geology and Petrology: Journal of Geophysical Research, v. 86, no. B11, p. 10303-10320.

Crittenden, M. D., Jr., 1959, Mississippian stratigraphy of the central Wasatch and western Uinta Mountains, Utah *in* Geology of the Wasatch and Uinta Mountains transition area: Intermountain Association of Petroleum Geologists Guidebook, 10th Annual Field Conference, p. 63-74.

———1961, Magnitude of thrust faulting in northern Utah: U.S. Geological Survey Professional Paper 424-D, p. 128-131.

———1963a, New data on the isostatic deformation of Lake Bonneville: U.S. Geological Survey Professional Paper 454-E, p. E1-E31.

———1963b, Emendation of the Kelvin Formation and Morrison(?) Formation near Salt Lake City, Utah: U.S. Geological Survey Professional Paper 475-B, p. B95-B98.

———1963c, Effective viscosity of the Earth derived from isostatic loading of Pleistocene Lake Bonneville: Journal of Geophysical Research, v. 68, no. 19, p. 5517-5530.

———1964a, General geology of Salt Lake County *in* Geology of Salt Lake County: Utah Geological and Mineral Survey Bulletin 69, p. 11-48.

———1964b, Metallic mineral resources—Manganese *in* Mineral and water resources of Utah: U.S. Congress 88th, 2nd Session, Comm. Print, p. 103-108; *also* Utah Geological and Mineral Survey Bulletin 73, reprinted, 1969.

———1964c, Nonmetallic and industrial minerals and materials resources—Geology/structure *in* Mineral and water resources of Utah: U.S. Congress 88th, 2nd Session, Comm. Print., p. 25-28; *also* Utah Geological and Mineral Survey Bulletin 73, reprinted, 1969.

———1965, Geology of the Draper quadrangle, Utah: U.S. Geological Survey Map GQ-377.

———1972a, Willard thrust and the Cache allochthon, Utah: Geological Society of America Bulletin, v. 83, no. 9 p. 2871-2880.

———1972b, Geologic map of the Browns Hole quadrangle, Utah: U.S. Geological Survey Map GQ-968.

Crittenden, M. D., Jr., and Z. E. Peterman, 1975, Provisional Rb/Sr age of the Precambrian Uinta Mountain Group, northeastern Utah: Utah Geology, v. 2, no. 1, p. 75-77.

Crittenden, M. D., Jr., and C. A. Wallace, 1973, Possible equivalents of the Belt Supergroup in Utah: Belt Symposium, University of Idaho, Moscow, Idaho, p. 116-138.

Crittenden, M. D., Jr., B. J. Sharp, and F. D. Calkins, 1952, Geology of the Wasatch Mountains east of Salt Lake City *in* Geology of the central Wasatch Mountains: Utah Geological Society Guidebook to the Geology of Utah 8, p. 1-37.

Crittenden, M. D., Jr., J. H. Stewart, and C. A. Wallace, 1972, Regional correlation of upper Precambrian strata in western North America: 24th International Geological Congress, Montreal, Quebec, Sec. 1, Precambrian Geology, p. 334-341.

Crittenden, M. D., Jr., C. A. Wallace, and M. J. Sheridan, 1967, Mineral resources of the High Uintas primitive area, Utah: U.S. Geological Survey Bulletin 1230-I, p. I1-I27.

Crittenden, M. D., Jr., and others, 1971, Nomenclature and correlation of some upper Precambrian and basal Cambrian sequences in western Utah and southeastern Idaho: Geological Society of America Bulletin, v. 82, no. 3, p. 581-601.

Crittenden, M. D. Jr., and others, 1973, Radiometric dating of intrusive rocxks in the Cottonwood area, Utah: Journal of Research, U.S. Geological Survey, V. 1, no. 2, p. 173-178.

Crosby, G. W., 1959, Geology of the south Pavant Range, Millard and Sevier Counties, Utah: Brigham Young University Geology Studies, Provo, Utah, v. 6, no. 3, 59 p.

———1972, Dual origin of Basin and Range faults *in* Plateau—Basin and Range transition zone, central Utah: Utah Geological Association Publication 2, p. 67-73.

———1973, Regional structure in southwestern Utah *in* Geology of the Milford area: Utah Geological Association Publication 3, p. 27-32.

———1976, Tectonic evolution in Utah's miogeosyncline-shelf boundary zone *in* Symposium on the geology of the Cordilleran Hingeline: Rocky Mountain Association of Geologists Proceedings, p. 27-35.

Cross, A. T. and E. B. Maxfield, eds., 1975, Field guide and road log to the western Book Cliffs, Castle Valley and parts of the Wasatch Plateau: Brigham Young University Geology Studies, Provo, Utah, v. 22, pt. 2, 132 p.

———1976, Aspects of coal geology, northwestern Colorado Plateau: Brigham Young University Geology Studies, Provo, Utah, v. 22, pt. 3, 173 p.

Cross, Whitman, 1886, On the occurrence of topaz and garnet in lithophysae of rhyolite, Thomas Range, Utah: American Journal of Science 131 (3s 31), p. 432.

———1907, Stratigraphic results of a reconnaissance in western Colorado and eastern Utah: Journal of Geology, v. 15, p. 634-679.

Cummings, Byron, 1910, The great natural bridges of Utah: University of Utah Bulletin 3, no. 3, pt. 1, p. 1-24.

Cunningham, C. G., T. A. Steven and C. W. Naeser, 1973, Preliminary structural and mineralogical analysis of the Deer Trail Mountain-Alunite Ridge mining area, Utah: U.S. Geological Survey open-file report 78-314.

Curfman, R. L., 1975, Solution mining project *in* Mining Congress Journal, March, 1974.

Currey, H. D., 1957. Fossil tracks of Eocene vertebrates, southwestern Uinta Basin, Utah, *in* Geology of the Uinta Basin: Intermountain Association Petroleum Geologists Guidebook, 8th Annual Field Conference, p. 42-47.

Currey, D. R., 1980, Coastal geomorphology of Great Salt Lake and vicinity *in* Great Salt Lake, a Scientific, historical and economic overview: Geological and Mineral Survey Bulletin 116, p. 69-82.

Dane, C. H., 1935, Geology of the Salt Valley anticline and adjacent areas, Grand County, Utah: U.S. Geological Survey Bulletin 863, v, (1936), 184 p..

———1955, Stratigraphic and facies relationships of the upper part of the Green River Formation and the lower part of the Uinta Formation in Duchesne, Uintah and Wasatch Counties, Utah: American Association of Petroleum Geologists Bulletin, v. 38, no. 3, p. 405-425.

———1955, Stratigraphic and facies relationships of the upper part of the Green River Formatin and the lower part of the Uinta Formation in Duchesne, Uintah and Wasatch Counties, Utah: U.S. Geological Survey Chart OC-52.

Dasch, M. D., 1964, Nonmetallic and industrial and materials resources—Gem materials *in* Mineral and water resources of Utah: U.S. Congress, 88th, 2nd Sess., Comm. Print, p. 169-177; *also* Utah Geological and Mineral Survey Bulletin 73, reprinted 1969.

Davidson, E. S., 1959, Geology of the Rainy Day uranium mine, Garfield County, Utah: Economic Geology, v. 54, no. 3, p. 436-448.

———1967, Geology of the Circle Cliffs area, Garfield and Kane Counties, Utah: U.S. Geological Survey Bulletin 1229, 140 p.

Davies, S. F., 1980, Geology of the Grayback Hills, north-central Tooele County, Utah: M.S. thesis University of Utah, Salt Lake City, Utah.

Davis, D. E., 1956, A taxonomic study of the Mississippian corals of central Utah: Brigham Young University Geology Studies, Provo, Utah, v. 3, no. 5, 49 p.; *also* Utah Geological and Mineral Survey Bulletin 86, p. 45, 1970.

Davis, F.D. and P. A. Moyer, 1971, Sand and gravel versus urban development, *in* Environmental geology of the Wasatch Front: Utah Geological Association Publication 1, sec. Q, Q1-Q9.

Davis, G. H., 1978, Monocline fold pattern of the Colorado Plateau: Geological Society of America Memoir 151, p. 215-233.

Davis, William Morris, 1933, Geomorphology of the Salt Lake Region: 16th International Geological Congress Guidebook 17, p. 6-14.

DeGraf, J. V., 1976, Relict patterned ground, Bear River Range, north-central Utah: Utah Geology, v. 3, no. 2, p. 111-116.

Deiss, C. F., 1938, Cambrian formations and sections in part of the Cordilleran trough: Geological Society of America Bulletin 49, p. 1069-1168.

———1941, Cambrian geography and sedimentation in the central Cordilleran region: Geological Society of America Bulletin 52, p. 1085-1115.

Dellenbaugh, F. S., 1962, A Canyon Voyage: New Haven Conn., Yale University Press, 277 p., originally published 1908.

Demars, L. C., 1956, Geology of the northern part of Dry Mountain, southern Wasatch Mountains, Utah: Brigham Young University Geology Studies, v. 3, no. 2, 49 p.

Denison, R. H., 1952, Early Devonian fishes from Utah, pt. 1, Osteostraci: Chicago Museum of Natural History, Fieldiana Geol., v. 11, no. 6, p. 265-287. (see also papers on related subjects, 1953, 1958 and 1968, same author and journal.)

Dickinson, W. R. and W. S. Snyder, 1978, Plate tectonics of the Laramide orogeny: Geological Society of America Memoir 151, p. 355-366.

Dickey, D. D., and J. C. Wright, 1958, San Rafael (Entrada) studies: U.S. Atomic Energy Commission TEI 750, p. 59-65.

Dix, G. P. Jr., 1953, Reconnaissance of the uranium deposits of the Lockhart Canyon-Indian Creek area, San Juan County, Utah: U.S. Atomic Energy Commission, RME-4038.

Doelling, H. H., 1964, Geology of the northern Lakeside Mountains and the Grassy Mountains and vicinity, Tooele and Box Elder Counties, Utah: Ph.D. dissertation, University of Utah, Salt Lake City, Utah.

———1972, Tertiary strata, Sevier-Sanpete region, *in* Plateau — Basin and Range transition zone, Central Utah: Utah Geological Association Publication 2, p. 41-53.

———1975, Geology and Mineral Resources of Garfield County: Utah Geological and Mineral Survey Bulletin 107, 175 p.

———1980, Geology and Mineral Resources of Box Elder County, Utah: Utah Geological and Mineral Survey Bulletin 115, 225p.

———1983, Observations on Paradox Basin Salt Anticlines: Grand Junction Geological Society Guidebook to the Northern Paradox Basin - Uncompahgre Uplift, p. 81-90.

Doelling, H. H., and R. L. Graham, 1972a, Southwestern Utah coal fields—Alton, Kaiparowits Plateau and Kolob-Harmony: Utah Geological and Mineral Survey Monograph Series, no. 1, 333 p.

———1972b, Eastern and northern Utah coal fields—Vernal, Henry Mountains, Sego, LaSal-San Juan, Tabby Mountain, Coalville, Henrys Fork, Goose Creek and Lost Creek: Utah Geological and Mineral Survey Monograph Series, no. 2, 409 p.

Doelling, H. H., and others, 1972, Central Utah coal fields—Sevier-Sanpete, Wasatch Plateau, Book Cliffs, and Emery and three other papers: Utah Geological and Mineral Survey Monograph Series, no. 3, 507 p.

Dowler, B. D., and W. L. Dowler, 1978, Lake Powell; Rainbow Bridge boat and tour guide: Welsh Graphics, Pasadena, CA.

Duncan, D. C., 1944, Mt. Pleasant coal field, Sanpete County, Utah: U.S.. Geological Survey Preliminary Coal Map.

Duncan, H. M., 1956, Ordovician and Silurian coral fauna of the western United States: U.S. Geological Survey Bulletin 1021-F, p. 209-236.

Dutton, C. E., 1880, Report on the geology of the High Plateaus of Utah: U.S. Geological Survey of the Rocky Mountain Region, (Powell).

Dyer, R. J., J. H. Hawley, and L. C. Craig, 1983, Upper Tertiary sedimentary rocks of the Salt Valley anticline, south-eastern Utah (abstract): Geological Society of America, Abstracts with Programs, v. 15, no. 5, p. 332.

Eardley, A. J., 1933a, Stratigraphy of the southern Wasatch Mountains, Utah: Michigan Academy of Science Paper 18, p. 307-344.

———1933b, Strong relief before block faulting in the vicinity of the Wasatch Mountains, Utah: Journal of Geology, v. 41, p. 243-267.

———1934, Structure and physiography of the southern Wasatch Mountains, Utah: Michigan Academy of Science Paper 19, p. 377-400; (abs.) 1933, Geological Society of American Bulletin 44, p. 83-84.

———1938, Sediments of Great Salt Lake, Utah: American Association of Petroleum Geologists Bulletin 22, p. 1305-1411; *also* 1939, Comments, American Association of Petroleum Geologists Bulletin 23, p. 1089-1090.

———1939, Structure of the Wasatch Great Basin region. Geological Society of America Bulletin, v. 50, p. 1277-1350.

———1944, Geology of the north-central Wasatch Mountains, Utah: Geological Society of America Bulletin 55, p. 819-894.

———1949, Structural evolution of Utah *in* Oil and gas possibilities of Utah, a symposium volume: Utah Geological and Mineral Survey, p. 10-23.

———1952, Wasatch hinterland *in* Geology of the central Wasatch Mountains: Utah Geological Society Guidebook No. 8, p. 52-60.

———1961, Map of the Great Salt Lake, Utah: Utah Geological and Mineral Survey Miscellaneous Publication, MP5.

———1963, Relation of uplifts to thrusts in the Rocky Mountains *in* Backbone of the Americas, O. E. Childs and B. W. Beebe, eds.: American Association of Petroleum Geologists Memoir 2, p. 209-219.

———1966, Rates of denudation in the High Plateaus of southwestern Utah: Geological Society of America Bulletin, v. 77, no. 7, p. 777-780.

———1967, Bonneville chronology—Correlation between the exposed stratigraphic record and the subsurface sedimentary succession: Geological Society of America Bulletin, v. 78, no. 7, p. 907-909.

———1968, Major structures of the Rocky Mountains of Colorado and Utah *in* A coast-to-coast tectonic study of the United States: UMR Journal, no. 1, ser., 1, p. 79-99.

———1969b, Charting the Laramide structures of western Utah *in* Guidebook of northern Utah: Utah geological and Mineral Survey Bulletin 82, 266 p.

———1969c, Willard thrust and the Cache uplift: Geological Society of America Bulletin, v. 80, no. 4, p. 669-680.

———1970, Salt economy of the Great Salt Lake, Utah *in* Symposium on salt, 3rd: Northern Ohio Geological Society, v. 1, p. 78-105.

———1972, Willard thrust and the Cache allochthon, Utah—Discussion: Geological Society of America Bulletin, v. 83, no. 9, p. 2871-2880.

Eardley, A. J., and R. A. Hatch, 1940, Precambrian crystalline rocks of north-central Utah: Journal of Geology, v. 48, p. 58-72.

Eardley, A. J., and J. W. Schaak, 1971, Zion, The story behind the scenery: K. C. Publications.

Eardley, A. J., V. Gvosdetsky, and R. E. Marsell, 1957, Hydrology of Lake Bonneville and sediments and soils of its basin, Utah: Geological Society of America Bulletin, v. 68, no. 9, p. 1141-1201.

Eardley, A. J., and others, 1973, Lake cycles in the Bonneville Basin, Utah: Geological Society of America Bulletin, v. 84, no. 1, p. 211-215.

Eaton, G. P., 1980, The Basin and Range province: Origin and tectonic significance: Annual review Earth and Planetary Science, no. 8, p. 409-440.

East, E. A., 1966, Structure and stratigraphy of San Francisco Mountains, western Utah: American Association of Petroleum Geology Bulletin, v. 50, no. 5, p. 901-920.

Eaton, G. P., and others, 1978, Regional gravity and tectonic patterns—Their relation to late Cenozoic epeirogeny and lateral spreading in the western Cordillera: Geological Society of America Special Paper 152.

Elison, J. H., 1952, Geology of the Keigley quarries and Genola Hills area, Utah: M.S. thesis, Brigham Young University, Provo, Utah, 76 p.

Ellingson, J. A., 1973, Mule Ear diatreme *in* Geology of the canyons of the San Juan River: Four Corners Geological Society, p. 43-50.

Elston, D. P., and others, 1962, Uncompahgre front and Salt Anticline region of the Paradox Basin, Colorado and Utah: American Association of Petroleum Geologists Bulletin, v. 46, no. 10, p. 1857-1878.

El-Shatoury, H. M., and Whelan, J. A., 1970, Mineralization in the Gold Hill mining district, Tooele County, Utah: Utah Geological and Mineral Survey Bulletin 83, 37 p.

Elston, D. P., and E. M. Shoemaker, 1963, Salt anticlines of Paradox Basin, Colorado and Utah, *in* Symposium on Salt: North Ohio Geological Society, Cleveland, Ohio, p. 131-145.

Erickson, A. J., Jr., 1968, Ontario Mine, east flank ore bodies *in* Park City district: Utah Geological Association Guidebook to the Geology of Utah 22, p. 56-65.

Erickson, M. P., 1963, Volcanic geology of western Juab County, Utah *in* Beryllium and uranium mineralization in western Juab County, Utah: Utah Geological Society Guidebook to the Geology of Utah 17, p. 23-35.

———1973, Volcanic rocks of the Milford area, Beaver County, Utah *in* Geology of the Milford area: Utah Geological Association Publication 3, p. 13-22.

Ethington, R. L., and D. L. Clark, 1971, Lower and Middle Ordovician conodonts from the Ibex area, western Millard County, Utah: Brigham Young University Geology Studies, v. 28, pt. 2, 155 p.

Evans, S. H., Jr., H. R. Crecraft and W. P. Nash, 1980, Potassium-argon ages of silicic volcanism in the Twin Peaks/Cove Creek Dome area, southwestern Utah: Isochron West.

Evans, S. H., Jr. and W. P. Nash, 1979, Quaternary rhyolite from the Mineral Mountains, U.S.A.: University of Utah, Final volume, 77-10, 59 p.

Everden, J. F., and G. T. James, 1964, Potassium-argon dates and the Tertiary floras of North America: American Journal of Science, v. 262, no. 8, p. 945-974.

Everden, J. F., and others, 1964, Potassium-argon dates and the Cenozoic mammalian chronology of North America: American Journal of Science, v. 262, no. 2, p. 145-198.

Everett, F. D., 1961, Tungsten deposits in Utah: U.S. Bureau of Mines Information Circular 8014, 44 p.

Felix, C. E., 1956, Geology of the eastern part of the Raft River Range, Box Elder County, Utah *in* Geology of parts of northwestern Utah: Utah Geological Society Guidebook to the Geology of Utah 11, p. 76-97.

Fenneman, N. M., 1931, Physiography of Western United States: McGraw-Hill Book Company, Inc., New York, 534 p.

Feth, J. H., 1955, Sedimentary features in the Lake Bonneville Group in the East Shore area, near Ogden, Utah *in* Tertiary and Quaternary geology of the eastern Bonneville Basin: Utah Geological Society Guidebook to the Geology of Utah 10, p. 45-69.

———1963, Tertiary lake deposits in western coterminous United States: Science, v. 139, no. 3550, p. 107-110.

Feth, J. H., and others, 1966, Lake Bonneville—Geology and hydrology of the Weber delta district, including Ogden, Utah: U.S. Geological Survey Professional Paper 518, 76 p.

Fetzner, R. W., 1960, Pennsylvanian paleotectonics of the Colorado Plateau: American Association of Petroleum Geologists Bulletin, v. 44, no. 8, p. 1371-1413.

Finch, W. I., 1959, Geology of uranium deposits in Triassic rock of the Colorado Plateau region: U.S. Geological Survey Bulletin 1074-D.

———1967, Geology of epigenetic uranium deposits in sandstone in the United States: U.S. Geological Survey Professional Paper 538, 121 p.

Finnell, T. L., P. C. Frank and H. A. Hubbard, 1963, Geology, ore deposits and exploratory drilling in the Deer Flat area, White Canyon district, San Juan County, Utah: U.S. Geological Survey Bulletin 1132, 114 p.

Fischer, R. P., 1942, Vanadium deposits of Colorado and Utah, a preliminary report: U.S. Geological Survey Bulletin 936-P, p. 363-394.

———1944, Simplified geologic map of the vanadium region of southwestern Colorado and southeastern Utah: U.S. Geological Survey Stratified Minerals Investigations Preliminary Map 1944; 2nd ed. issued as Stratified Minerals Investigations Preliminary Map 3-226, 1949.

———1950, Uranium-bearing sandstone deposits of the Colorado Plateau: Economic Geology, v. 45, p. 1-11.

———1959, Vanadium and uranium in rocks and ore deposits *in* R. M. Garrels and E. S. Larsen, III, (compilers), Geochemistry and mineralogy of the Colorado Plateau uranium ores: U.S. Geological Survey Professional Paper 320, p. 219-230.

Fischer, R. P., and J. D. Vine, 1964, Metallic mineral resources—Vanadium *in* Mineral and water resources of Utah: U.S. Cong., 88th 2nd sess., Comm. Print. p. 133-135; *also* Utah Geological and Mineral Survey Bulletin 73, reprinted 1969.

Fisher, D. J., 1936, The Book Cliffs coal field in Emery and Grand Counties, Utah: U.S. Geological Survey Bulletin 852.

Fisher, D. J., C. E. Erdmann, and J. B. Reeside, 1960, Cretaceous and tertiary formations of the Book Cliffs, Carbon, Emery and Grand counties, Utah and Garfield and Mesa counties, Colorado. U.S. Geological Survey, Professional Paper 332, 80 p.

Fishman, H. S., 1976, Geologic structure and regional gravity of a portion of the High Plateaus of Utah: M.S. thesis, University of Utah, Salt Lake City, Utah.

Flint, R. F., and C. S. Denny, 1958, Quaternary geology of Boulder Mountain, Aquarius Plateau, Utah: U.S. Geological Survey Bulletin 1061-D, p. 103-164.

Forrester, J. D., 1937, Structure of the Uinta Mountains: Geological Society of America Bulletin 48, p. 631-666.

Foster, J. M., 1959, Geology of the Bismark Peak area, North Tintic District, Utah County, Utah: Brigham Young University Research Studies, Geology Series, v. 6, no. 4, 95 p.

Foutz, D. R., 1966, Stratigraphy of the Mississippian System in northeastern Utah and adjacent states: Ph.D. dissertation, Washington State University, 218. p.

Francis, C. G., 1972, Stratigraphy and environmental analysis of the Swan Peak Formation and Eureka Quartzite, northern Utah: M. S. Thesis, Utah State University, 125 p.

Freeman, W. E., and G. S. Visher, 1975, Stratigraphic analysis of the Navajo Sandstone: Journal of the Society of Petrology, v. 45, no. 3, p. 651-668; *also* Journal of Sedimentary Petrology, v. 47, no. 1, p. 491-497.

Gale, Hoyt S., 1910, Coal fields of northwestern Colorado and northeastern Utah: U.S. Geological Survey Bulletin 415.

Garmoe, W. J., and A. J. Erickson, Jr., 1968, Ore deposits of the Park City district *in* Park City district: Utah Geological Society Guidebook to the Geology of Utah 22, p. 30-39.

Garvin, R. F., 1967, Stratigraphy of the Currant Creek Formation (Cretaceous-Tertiary), Wasatch and Duchesne Counties, Utah: M.S. thesis, University of Utah, Salt Lake City, Utah.

———1969, Bridger Lake field, Summit County, Utah *in* Uinta Mountains—Utah's maverick range: Intermountain Association of Petroleum Geologists (and Utah Geological Society) Guidebook, 16th Annual Field Conference, p. 109-115.

Gazin, C. L., 1941, The mammalian faunas of the Paleocene of central Utah, with notes on the geology: U.S. National Museum Proceedings 91, no. 3121, p. 1-53.

Gehman, H. M., 1958, Notch Peak intrusive, Millard County, Utah—Geology, petrogenesis and economic deposits: Utah Geological and Mineral Survey Bulletin 62, 50 p.

Gere, W. C., 1964, Nonmetallic and industrial minerals and material resources—Phosphate *in* Mineral and water resources of Utah: U.S. Congress 88th 2nd. Sess., Comm. Print. p. 195-205; *also* Utah Geological and Mineral Survey Bulletin 73, reprinted 1969.

———1967, Phosphate deposits in Utah and Nevada *in* Industrial seminar, western phosphate region, 1966, Proc.: Montana Bureau of Mines and Geology Special Publication 42, p. 21-29.

Gilbert, G. K., 1877, Report on the geology of the Henry Mountains: U.S. Geographical and Geological Survey Rocky Mountain Region (Powell), 1877.

———1880, The outlet of Lake Bonneville: American Journal of Science 119 (3s, 19), p. 341-349.

———1890, Lake Bonneville: U.S. Geological Survey Monograph 1, 402 p.

———1928, Studies of Basin/Range structure: U.S. Geological Survey Professional Paper 153.

Gilliland, W. N., 1951, Geology of the Gunnison quadrangle, Utah: University of Nebraska Studies, new ser., no. 8, Lincoln, Nebraska, 101 p.

———1963, Sanpete-Sevier Valley Anticline of central Utah: Geological Society of America Bulletin, v. 74, no. 2, p. 115-123.

Gilluly, James, 1929, Geology and oil and gas prospects of part of the San Rafael Swell, Utah: U.S. Geological Survey Bulletin 806, p. 69-130.

———1932, Geology and ore deposits of the Stockton and Fairfield quadrangles, Utah: U.S. Geological Survey Professional Paper 173.

———1949, Distribution of mountain-building in geologic time: Geological Society of America Bulletin, v. 60, no. 4, p. 561-590.

———1963, The tectonic evolution of the western United States—17th William Smith lecture: Quarterly Journal of the Geological Society of London, v. 119, no. 2, p. 133-174.

———1965, Volcanism, tectonism and plutonism in the western United States: Geological Society of America Special Paper, no. 80, 69 p.

Gilmore, Charles W., 1943, Osteology of Upper Cretaceous lizards from Utah, with a description of a new species: U.S. Ntional Museum Proceedings 93, no. 3163, p. 209-214.

———1946a, Reptilian fauna of the North Horn Formation of central Utah: U.S. Geological Survey Professional Paper, 210-C, p. 29-53.

Girty, G. H., 1910, The fauna of the phosphate beds of the Park City Formation in Idaho, Wyoming and Utah: U.S. Geological Survey Bulletin 436; *also* Abstracts of Washington Academy of Science Journal 1, p. 39, 1911.

Good, J. M., T. M. White, and G. F. Stucker, 1961, The dinosaur quarry, Dinosaur National Monument, Colorado-Utah: U.S. National Park Service, Washington, D. C., 47 p.

Goode, Harry D., 1975, Great Salt Lake and deposits of Lake Bonneville at Little Valley, Utah, October 23, 1975: Field trip guide, Geological Society of America Annual Meeting Field Trip.

———1979, Hot waters of western Utah: Rocky Mountain Association of Geologists (and Utah Geological Association) Symposium, 1979, p. 371-380.

Gordon, Mckenzie Jr., and H. M. Duncan, 1970, Biostratigraphy and correlation of the Oquirrh Group and related rocks in the Oquirrh Mountains, Utah, *in* Upper Paleozoic rocks in the Oquirrh Mtns. and Bingham mining district: U.S. Geological Survey Professional Paper 629-A, p. A38-A57.

Gordon, Mackenzie Jr., and J. Pojeta, Jr., 1975, Pelecypoda and Rostroconchia of the Amsden Formation (Mississippian and Pennsylvanian) of Wyoming: U. S. Geological Survey Professional Paper 848-E, p. E1-E24.

Gordon, Mackenzie Jr., and E. L. Yochelson, 1975, Gastropoda, cephalopoda, and trilobita of the Amsden Formation (Mississippian and Pennsylvanian) of Wyoming: U.S. Geological Survey Professional Paper 848-F, p. F1-F30.

Gould, W. J., 1959, Geology of the northern Needle Range, Millard County, Utah: Brigham Young University Geology Studies, Provo, Utah, v. 6, no. 5, 47 p.

Granger, A. E., 1953, Stratigraphy of the Wasatch Range near Salt Lake City, Utah: U.S. Geological Survey Circular 296.

———1963, The iron province of southwestern Utah *in* Geology of southwestern Utah: Intermountain Association of Petroleum Geologists Guidebook, 12th Annual Field Conference, p. 146-150.

Granger, A. E., and B. J. Sharp, 1952, Geology of the Wasatch Mountains east of Salt Lake City—City Creek to Parleys Canyon *in* Geology of the central Wasatch Mountains: Utah Geological Society Guidebook to the Geology of Utah 8, p. 1-37.

Grant, T. C., and J. J. Anderson, 1979, Geology of the Spry intrusion, Garfield County, Utah: Utah Geology, v. 6, no. 2, p. 5-24.

Green, D. J., and W. R. Halliday, 1958, America's deepest cave: National Speleological Society Bulletin, no. 20, p. 31-37.

Greer, Deon C., and others, 1981. Atlas of Utah, Weber State College and Brigham Young University Press, 300 p.

Gregory, H. E., 1917, Geology of the Navajo country, a reconnaissance of parts of Arizona, New Mexico and Utah: U.S. Geological Survey Professional Paper 93; *also* (abs. by R. W. Stone) Washington Academy of Science Journal 8, p. 64-65, 1918.

———1938, The San Juan country: A geographic and geological reconnaissance of southeastern Utah: U.S. Geological Survey Professional Paperf188, 123 p.

———1940, A geologic and geographic sketch of Bryce Canyon National Park: Zion-Bryce Museum Bulletin 4.

———1949, Geologic and geographic reconnaissance of the eastern Markagunt Plateau, Utah: Geological Society of America Bulletin, v. 60, p. 969-998.

———1950a, Geology of eastern Iron County, Utah: Utah Geological and Mineral Survey Bulletin 37, 153 p.

———1950b (1952), Geology and geography of the Zion Park region, Utah and Arizona: U.S. Geological Survey Professional Paper 220, 220 p.

———1951, The geology and geography of the Paunsaugunt region, Utah: U.S. Geological Survey Professional Paper 226, 16 p.

Gregory, H. E., and R. C. Moore, 1931, The Kaiparowits region, a geographic and geologic reconnaissance of parts of Utah and Arizona: U.S. Geological Survey Professional Paper 164.

Gregory, H. E., and others, 1938, The San Juan country, a geographic and geologic reconnaissance of southeastern Utah: U.S. Geological Survey Professional Paper 188, 123 p.

Gregory, H. E. and J. C. Anderson, 1939, Geographic and geologic sketch of the Capitol Reef region, Utah: Geological Society of America Bulletin, v. 50, p. 1827-1850.

Gregory, H. E., and N. C. Williams, 1947, Zion National Monument, Utah: Geological Society America Bulletin 58, p. 211-244.

Griffitts, W. R., 1964, Nonmetallic and industrial minerals and materials resources—Beryllium *in* Mineral and water resources of Utah: U.S. Cong., 88th 2nd Sess., Comm. Print., p. 71-75.

Griffitts, W. R., and L. F. Rader, Jr., 1963, Beryllium and fluorine in mineralized tuff, Spor Mountain, Juab County, Utah: U.S. Geological Survey Professional Paper 475-B, p. 16-17.

Groenwald, B. C., 1961, Subsurface geology of the Mesozoic formations overlying the Uncompahgre Uplift in Grand County, Utah: M.S. thesis, University of Utah, Salt Lake City, Utah, 194 p.

Groff, S. L., 1959, Geology of the West Tintic Range and vicinity, Tooele and Juab Counties, Utah: Ph.D. dissertation, University of Utah, Salt Lake City, Utah, 183 p.

Grogger, P., 1974, Glaciation of the High Uintas primitive area, Utah, with emphasis on the northern slope: Ph.D. disseration, University of Utah, Salt Lake City, Utah.

Gross, E. B., 1955, Mineralogy and paragenesis of the uranium ore, Mi Vida Mine, San Juan County, Utah: Economic Geology, v. 51, no. 7, p. 632-648.

Gvosdetsky, V., 1953, Reappraisal of the history of Lake Bonneville, Utah: University of Utah Engineering Experiment Station Bulletin 60.

Gwynn, J. W., 1977, A preliminary investigation into the electrochemical potential of the Great Salt Lake, Utah: Utah Geological and Mineral Survey Report of Investigations 115, 8 p.

Gwynn, J. W., ed., 1980, Great Salt Lake—A scientific, historical and economic overview: Utah Geological and Mineral Survey Bulletin 116, 400 p.

Hackman R. J., and D. G. Wyant, 1973, Geology, structure, and uranium deposits of the Escalante Quadrangle, Utah and Arizona: U.S. Geological Survey Miscellaneous Geologic Investigation, Map 1-744.

Hague, Arnold and S. F. Emmons, 1877, Descriptive geology: U.S. Geological Exploration 40th Parallel (King Survey), 2, p. 191-468.

Hagood, A., 1967, This is Zion—An interpretation of a colorful landscape in pictures and story: Zion Natural History Association, Springdale, Utah, 72 p.

Hahl, D. C., and A. H. Handy, 1969, Great Salt Lake, Utah—Chemical and physical variations of the brine, 1963-1966: Utah Geological and Mineral Survey Water Resources Bulletin 12, 33 p.

Hahl, D. C., and C. G. Mitchell, 1963, Dissolved-mineral inflow to Great Salt Lake and chemical characteristics of the brine, Pt. 1—Selected hydrologic data: Utah Geological and Mineral Survey Water Resources Bulletin 3.

Hale, L. A., and T. R. Van de Graaff, 1964, Cretaceous stratigraphy and facies patterns - northeastern Utah and adjacent areas, *in* Geology and mineral resources of the Uinta Basin: Intermountain Association Petroleum Geologists Guidebook, 13th Annual Field Conference, p. 115-138.

Hallgarth, W. E., 1962, Upper Paleozoic rocks exposed in Straight Wash Canyon, San Rafael Swell, Utah: American Association of Petroleum Geologists Bulletin, v. 46, no. 8, p. 1494-1501.

Hamblin, W. K., 1963, Late Cenozoic basalts of the St. George Basin, Utah *in* Geology of southwestern Utah: Intermountain Association of Petroleum Geologists Guidebook, 12th Annual Field Conference, p. 84-89.

———1970a, Structure of the western Grand Canyon region *in* The western Grand Canyon Region: Utah Geological Society Guidebook to the Geology of Utah 23, p. 3-20.

———1970b, Late Cenozoic basalt flow of the western Grand Canyon *in* The western Grand Canyon district, W. K. Hamblin and M. G. Best, eds.: Utah Geological Society Guidebook to the Geology of Utah 23, p. 21-37.

———1976, Patterns of displacement along the Wasatch fault: Geology, v. 40, no. 10, p. 619-622.

Hamilton, H. V., 1960, A descriptive list of minerals from Utah - type localities: Mineralogical Society of Utah Bulletin, v. 9, no. 2, p. 24-36.

Hamilton, W., and W. B. Myers, 1966, Cenozoic tectonics of the western United States: Review of Geophysics, v. 4, no. 4.

Hammond, E. D., 1961, History and mining in the Bingham district, ch 17 Utah: Utah Geolo. Soc. Guidebook no. 16, p 120-130.

Handy, A. H., 1967, Distinctive brines in Great Salt Lake, Utah *in* Geological Survey Research: U.S. Geological Survey Professional Paper 575-B, p. B225-B-227.

Handy, A. H., and D. C. Hahl, 1966, Great Salt Lake, chemistry of the water *in* the Great Salt Lake: Utah Geological Society Guidebook to the Geology of Utah 20, p. 135-151.

Hanks, K. L., 1962, Geology of the central House Range areas, Millard County, Utah: Brigham Young University Geology Studies, v. 9, pt. 2, p. 115-136.

Hanley, J. B., E. W. Heinrich and L. R. Page, 1950, Pegmatite investigations in Colorado, Wyoming and Utah: U.S. Geological Survey Professional Paper 277, 125 p.

Hansen, G. H., and M. M. Bell, 1949, The oil and gas possibilites of Utah: Utah Geological and Mineral Survey, 341 p.

Hansen, A. R., 1963, The Uinta Basin—Structure, stratigraphy and tectonic setting *in* Oil and gas possibilities of Utah, re-evaluated: Utah Geological and Mineral Survey Bulletin 54, p. 175-176.

Hansen, W. R., 1961, Geologic map of the Dutch John Mountain and Goslin Mountains quadrangles, Utah-Wyoming: U.S. Geological Survey Map I-324.

———1965, Geology of the Flaming Gorge area, Utah-Colorado-Wyoming: U.S. Geological Survey Professional Paper 490, 196 p.

———1969a, The geologic story of the Uinta Mountains: U.S. Geological Survey Bulletin 1291, 144 p.

———1969b, Nonmetallic and industrial minerals and materials resources—Stone, *in* Mineral and water resources of Utah: U.S. Cong., 88th, 2nd sess., Comm. Print.; *also* Utah Geological and Mineral Survey Bulletin 73, reprinted 1969.

———1969c, Development of the Green River drainage system across the Uinta Mountains *in* Geology of the Uinta Mountains, Utah's maverick range: Intermountain Association of Petroleum Geologists (and Utah Geological Society) Guidebook, 16th Annual Field Conference, p. 93-100.

———1976, Jurassic salts of the hingeline area, southern Rocky Mountains *in* Geology of the Cordilleran Hingeline: Rocky Mountain Association of Geologists, 1976 Symposium.

Hanson, A. M., 1953, Upper Cambrian formations in northern Utah and southeastern Idaho *in* Geology of northern Utah and southeastern Idaho: Intermountain Association of Petroleum Geologists Guidebook, 4th Annual Field Conference, p. 19-21.

Hardy, C. T., 1952, Eastern Sevier Valley, Sevier and Sanpete Counties, Utah: Utah Geological and Mineral Survey Bulletin 43, 98 p.

Hardy, C. T., and H. D. Zeller, 1953, Geology of the west-central part of the Gunnison Plateau, Utah: Geological Society of America Bulletin, v. 64, no. 11, p. 1261-1278.

Harris, H. D., 1958, A late Mesozoic positive area in western Utah-Nevada: American Association of Petroleum Geologists, Rocky Mountain Section, Geology Record, p. 89-102; *also* American Association of Petroleum Geologists Bulletin, v. 43, no. 11, p. 2636-2652 (slightly revised).

———1959, A late Mesozoic positive area in western Utah-Nevada: American Association of Petroleum Geologists Bulletin, v. 43, no. 11, p. 2636-2652.

Harshbarger, J. W., C. A. Repenning, and J. H. Irwin, 1957, Stratigraphy of the uppermost Triassic and the Jurassic rocks of the Navajo country: U.S. Geological Survey Professional Paper 291, p. 1-74.

Hausel, W. D., and W. P. Nash, 1977, Petrology of Tertiary and Quaternary volcanic rocks, Washington County, southwestern Utah: Geological Society of America Bulletin, v. 88, no. 12, p. 1831-1842.

Hawley, C. C., D. G. Wyant and D. B. Brooks, 1965, Geology and uranium deposits of the Temple Mountain district, Emery County, Utah: U.S. Geological Survey Bulletin 1192, 154 p.

Heisey, E. L., and others (eds.), 1977, Rocky Mountain thrust belt, geology and resources: Wyoming Geological Association Guidebook, 29th Annual Field Conference, 787 p.

Herman, G., and C. A. Barkell, 1957, Pennsylvanian stratigraphy and productive zones, Paradox Salt Basin: American Association of Petroleum Geologists Bulletin, v. 41, no. 5, p. 861-881.

Herman, G., and S. L. Sharps, 1956, Pennsylvanian and Permian stratigraphy of the Paradox salt embayment *in* Geology and economic deposits of east-central Utah: Intermountain Association of Petroleum Geologists Guidebook, 7th Annual Field Conference, p. 77-84.

Hewitt, W. P., 1968, Western Utah, eastern and central Nevada *in* Ore deposits of the United States, 1933-1967: American Institute of Mining Engineers, Graton-Sales, v. 1, New York, p. 857-885.

Heylmun, E. B., 1959, The ancestral Rocky Mountain system in northern Utah *in* Geology of the Wasatch and Uinta Mountains transition area: Intermountain Association of Petroleum Geologists Buidebook, 10th Annual Field Conference, p. 172-174.

———1958, Paleozoic stratigraphy and oil possibilites of the Kaiparowits region, Utah: American Association Petroleum Geologists Bulletin, v. 42, no. 8, p. 1781-1811.

———1965, Reconnaissance of the tertiary sedimentary rocks in western Utah: Utah Geological and Mineral Survey Bulletin, 75, 38 p.

Heylmun, E. B., R. E. Cohenour, and R. B. Keyser, 1965, Drlling records for oil and gas in Utah, January 1, 1954 to December 31, 1963: Utah Geological and Mineral Survey Bulletin 74, 518 p.

Hill, G. R., 1966, Economic aspects of coal in Utah—The present status of investigations of western coal utilization *in* Central Utah coals: Utah Geological and Mineral Survey Bulletin 80, p. 121-129.

Hill, G. R. (ed.), 1977, Geology of the Cordilleran Hingeline: Symposium of Rocky Mountain Association of Geologists, 1976.

Hilpert, L. S., (ed.), 1971, Environmental geology of the Wasatch Front: Utah Geological Assocation, publication 1, secs. A to S.

Hilpert, L. S., and Roberts, P. J., 1964, Economic geology in Mineral and water resources of Utah: Utah Geological and Mineral Survey Bulletin 73, p. 28-37.

Hilpert, L. S., and M. D. Dasch, 1964, Metallic mineral resources—Uranium *in* Mineral and water resources of Utah: U.S. Cong., 88th 2nd Sess., Comm. Print., p. 124-143; *also* Utah Geological and Mineral Survey Bulletin 73, reprinted in 1969.

Hinds, R. W., 1970, Ordovician bryozoa from the Pogonip Group of Millard County, Utah: Brigham Young University Geology Studies, Provo, Utah, v. 17, pt. 1, p. 19-40.

Hintze, F. F. Jr., 1913, A contribution to the geology of the Wasatch Mountains, Utah: New York Academy of Science Annals, v. 23, p. 85-143; *also*, M.S. thesis, Columbia University, New York, New York, 1913.

Hintze, L. F., 1949a, The Ordovician, Silurian, and Devonian Systems of Utah *in* Oil and gas possibilities of Utah: Utah Geological and Mineral Survey, p. 38, 55-66.

———1949, Ordovician system of Utah *in* Oil and gas possibilities of Utah: Utah Geological and Mineral Survey, p. 38-54.

———1951, Lower Ordovician detailed stratigraphic sections for western Utah: Utah Geological and Mineral Survey Bulletin 39, 100 p.

———1952, Lower Ordovician trilobites from western Utah and eastern Nevada: Utah Geological and Mineral Survey Bulletin 48, 249 p.

———1959, Ordovician regional relationships in north-central Utah and adjacent areas *in* Geology of the Wasatch and Uinta Mountains transition area: Intermountain Association of Petroleum Geologists Guidebook, 10th Annual Field Conference, p. 46-53.

———1960, Ordovician of the Utah-Nevada Great Basin *in* Geology of east-central Nevada: Intermountain Association of Petroleum Geologists Guidebook, 11th Annual Field Conference, p. 59-62.

———1962, Structure of the southern Wasatch Mountains and vicinity, Utah: Brigham Young University Geology Studies, v. 9, no. 1, p. 70-79.

———1963b, Summary of Ordovician stratigraphy of Utah *in* Oil and gas possibilities of Utah, re-evaluated: Utah Geological and Mineral Survey Bulletin 54, p. 51-61.

———1973a, Geologic road logs of western Utah and eastern Nevada: Brigham Young University Geology Studies, Provo, Utah, v. 20, pt. 2, 66 p.

———1973b, Geologic history of Utah: Brigham Young University Geology Studies, Provo, Utah, v. 20, pt. 3, 181 p.

———1973c, Lower and middle Ordovician stratigraphic sections in the Ibex area, Millard County, Utah: Brigham Young University Geologic Studies, Provo, Utah, v. 20, pt. 4, p. 3-36.

———1980, (compiler) Geologic map of Utah, 1/500,000, colored with cross sections and stratigraphic columns.

Hintze, L. F., and R. A. Robison, 1975, Middle Cambrian stratigraphy of the House, Wah Wah and adjacent ranges in western Utah: Geological Society of America Bulletin, v. 86, no. 7, p. 881-891.

Hintze, L. F., and J. A. Whelan, 1973, Geologic road logs in the Star Range, Rocky Range and San Francisco Mountains, Beaver County, Utah *in* Geology of the Milford area: Utah Geological Association Publication 3, p. 75-94.

Hintze, L. F., and others, 1969, A fossiliferous Lower Ordovician reference section from the western United States *in* the Ordovician symposium: El Paso Geological Society, 3rd Annual Field Trip, p. 8-90.

Hite, R. J., 1960, Stratigraphy of the saline facies of the Paradox Member of the Hermosa Formation of southeastern Utah and southwestern Colorado *in* Geology of the Paradox fold and fault belt: Four Corners Geological Society Guidebook, 3rd Annual Field Conference, p. 86-89; *also* U. S. Geological Survey open-file report.

———1961, Potash-bearing evaporite cycles in the salt anticlines of the Paradox Basin, Colorado and Utah: U.S. Geological Survey Professional Paper 424-D, p. 135-138.

———1964, Nonmetallic and industrial minerals and material resources—Salines *in* Mineral and water resources of Utah: U.S. Cong., 88th, 2nd Sess., Comm. Print., p. 206-215.

———1968, Salt deposits of the Paradox Basin, southeast Utah and southwest Colorado *in* Saline deposits: Geological Society of American Special Paper 88, p. 319-330.

Hite, R. J., F. W. Cater and J. A. Liming, 1972, Pennsylvanian rocks and salt anticlines, Paradox Basin, Utah and Colorado *in* Geologic Atlas of the Rocky Mountain Region: Rocky Mountain Association of Geologists, p. 133-142.

Hodge, C. E., and others, 1968, Precambrian geochronology of the northwestern Uncompahgre Plateau, Utah and Colorado *in* Geological Survey Research, 1968: U.S. Geological Survey Professional Paper 660-C.

Holland, F. D., Jr., 1953, Mississippian stratigraphy in the Utah-Idaho-Wyoming area *in* Geology of northern Utah and southeastern Idaho: Intermountain Association of Petroleum Geologists Guidebook, 4th Annual Field Conference, p. 32-37.

Holmes, C. N., 1956, Tectonic history of the ancestral Uncompahgre Range in Colorado *in* Geology and economic deposits of east-central Utah: Intermountain Association of Petroleum Geologists Guidebook, 7th Annual Field Conference.

Holmes, C. N. and others, 1948. Geology of the bituminious sandstone deposits near Sunnyside, Carbon County, Utah: U.S. Geological Survey Oil and Gas Investigations Preliminary Map no. 86.

Hooper, W. G., 1951, Geology of the Smith and Morehouse-South Fork area, Utah: M.S. thesis, University of Utah, Salt Lake City, Utah, 55 p.

Hoover, J. D., 1973, Periodic Quaternary volcanism in the Black Rock Desert, Utah: Brigham Young University Geology Studies, Provo, Utah, v. 21, pt. 1, p. 3-72.

———1966, Devonian stratigraphy of the Confusion Range, west-central Utah: U.S. Geological Survey Professional Paper 550-B, p. B36-B-41.

Hose, R. K., and C. A. Repenning, 1959, Stratigraphy of Pennsylvanian, Permian and Lower Triassic rocks of Confusion Range, west-central Utah: American Association of Petroleum Geologists Bulletin, v. 43, no. 9, p. 2167-2196.

Hose, R. K., 1977, Structured geology of the Confusion Range, west-central Utah: U.S. Geological Survey Professional Paper 971.

Huddle, J. W., W. J. Mapel, and F. T. McCann, 1951, Geology of the Moon Lake area, Duchesne County, Utah: U.S. Geological Survey Map OM-115.

Huddle, J. W., and F. T. McCann, 1947, Geologic Map of Duchesne River area, Wasatch and Duchesne Counties, Utah: U.S. Geological Oil and Gas Investigations Preliminary Map no. 75.

Huff, L. C. and F. G. Lesure, 1962, Geology and uranium deposits of Montezuma Canyon area, San Juan County, Utah: U.S. Geological Survey Bulletin 1190, 102 p.

Hummel, J. M., 1969, Anatomy of a gas field—Clay Basin, Daggett County, Utah *in* Geology of the Uinta Mountains, Utah's maverick range: Intermountain Association of Petroleum Geologists (and Utah Geological Society) Guidebook, 16th Annual Field Conference, p. 117-126.

Hunt, C. B.,1956, Conozoic geology of the Colorado Plateau: U.S. Geological Survey Professional Paper 279, 99 p.

———1969, Geologic history of the Colorado River *in* The Colorado River region and John Wesley Powell: U.S. Geological Survey Professional Paper 669-C, p. 59-130.

———1974, Natural regions of the United States and Canada: W. H. Freeman and Company, San Francisco, 725 p.

Hunt, C. B., P. Averitt and R. L. Miller, 1953, Geology and geography of the Henry Mountains region, Utah: U.S. Geological Survey Professional Paper 228, 234 p.

Hunt, C. B., and R. B. Morrison, 1957, Geology of Danger and Juke Box Caves near Wendover, Utah, ap. A *in* Danger Cave by J. D. Jennings: University of Utah Anthropological Papers, no. 27, p. 298-301; *also* American Antiquities, v. 23, no. 2, pt. 2, p. 298-301.

Hunt, C. B., H. D. Varnes and H. E. Thomas, 1953, Lake Bonneville—Geology of northern Utah Valley, Utah: U.S. Geological Survey Professional Paper 257-A, v, p. 1-99.

Hunt, C. B., *with collaboration by* A. C. Waters, 1958, Structural and igneous geology of the La Sal Mountains, Utah: U.S. Geological Survey Professional Paper 294-I, p. 305-364.

Hunt, J. M., 1963, Composition and origins of the Uinta Basin bitumens *in* Oil and gas possibilities of Utah re-evaluated: Utah Geological and Mineral Survey Bulletin 54, p. 249-273.

Hunt, J. M., F. Stewart and P. A. Dickey, 1954, Origin of hydrocarbons of the Uinta Basin, Utah: American Association of Petroleum Geologists Bulletin, v. 38, no. 8, p. 1671-1698.

Hunt, R. E., 1954, South Flat Formation, new upper Cretaceous formation of central Utah: American Association of Petroleum Geologists Bulletin, v. 38, p. 118-128.

Imlay, R. W., 1948, Characteristic marine Jurassic fossils from the western interior of the United States: U.S. Geological Survey Professional Paper 214-B, iii, p. 13-33.

———1949, Paleoecology of Jurassic seas in the western interior of the U. S.: National Resource Council Committee on Marine Ecology Report for 1948 to 1949, p. 72-104.

———1953a, Callovian (Jurassic) ammonites from the United States and Alaska, Part 1, western interior United States: U.S. Geological Survey Professional Paper 249-A, iii, p. 1-39; *also* Professional Paper 249 B, iii, p. 41-108.

———1953b, Characteristics of the Jurassic Twin Creek Limestone in Idaho, Wyoming and Utah, *in* Geology of Northern Utah and Southeast Idaho: Intermountain Association Petroleum Geologists Guidebook, 4th Annual Field Conference, p.54-62.

———1957, Paleoecology of Jurassic seas in the western interior of the United States *in* Paleoecology, H. S. Ladd, ed., chap. 17: Geological Society of America Memoir 67, v. 2, p. 469-504.

———1964, Marine Jurassic pelecypods from central and southern Utah: U.S. Geological Survey Professional Paper 483-C, 43 p.

———1967, Twin Creek Limestone (Jurassic) in the western interior of the United States: U.S. Geological Survey Professional Paper 540, 105 p.

Irwin, C. D., Jr., 1971, Stratigraphic analysis of Upper Permian and Lower Triassic strata in southern Utah: American Association of Petroleum Geologists Bulletin, v. 55, no. 11, p. 1976-2007.

Isachsen, Y. W., 1954, Ore deposits of the Big Indian Wash-Lisbon Valley area *in* Uranium deposits and general geology of southeastern Utah: Utah Geological Society Guidebook to the Geology of Utah 9, p. 95-106.

Ives, R. L., 1946, Glaciation in the desert ranges, Utah: Journal of Geology 54, 335 p.

———1951, Pleistocene valley sediments of the Dugway area, Utah: Geological Society of America Bulletin, v. 62, no. 7, p. 781-797.

Jaffe, F. C., 1962a, Oil shale, pt. 1, Nomenclature, uses, reserves and production: Colorado School of Mines, Mineral Industries Bulletin, v. 5, no. 2, 11 p.

———1962b, Oil shale, pt., 2, Geology and mineralogy of the oil shales of the Green River Formation, Colorado, Utah and Wyoming: Colorado School of Mines, Mineral Industries Bulletin, v. 5, no. 3, 16 p.

James, A. H., W. H. Smith, and J. E. Welsh, 1961, General geology and structure of the Bingham district, Utah, *in* Geology of the Bingham mining district and northern Oquirrh Mountains: Utah Geological Society Guidebook, no. 16, p. 49-69.

James, A. H., 1973, Lead and zinc resources in Utah: Utah Geological and Mineral Survey Special Studies 44, 66 p.

James, A. H., W. H. Smith and R. E. Bray, 1969, Bingham district—A zoned porphyry ore deposit *in* Geology of the Bingham mining district and the northern Oquirrh Mountains: Utah Geological Society Guidebook to the Geology of Utah 16, p. 81-100; *also* Utah Geological and Mineral Survey Bulletin 82, Guidebook of northern Utah, p. 200-212.

James, H. L., (ed.), 1973, Guidebook of Monument Valley and vicinity: New Mexico Geological Society, 24th Annual Field Conference.

James, L. P., 1978, Geology of Big Cottonwood Mining District: Utah Geological and Mineral Survey Bulletin 114, 39.

Jennings, J. D., 1957, Geological considerations in Danger Cave: University of Utah Anthropological Papers, no. 27, p. 85-98; *also* American Antiquities, v. 23, no. 2, pt. 2, p. 85-98.

Jensen, J. A., Jr., 1966, Dinosaur eggs from the Upper Cretaceous North Horn Formation of central Utah: Brigham Young University Geology Studies, Provo, Utah, v. 13, p. 55-67.

———1970, Fossil eggs in the Lower Cretaceous of Utah: Brigham Young University Geology Studies, Provo, Utah, v. 17, pt. 1, p. 51-66.

Jensen, M. L., 1958, Sulfur isotopes and the origin of sandstone-type uranium deposits: Economic Geology v. 53, no. 5, p. 599-616.

Jensen, R. G., 1967, Ordovician brachiopods from the Pogonip Group of Millard County, western Utah: Brigham Young University Geology Studies, Provo, Utah, v. 14, p. 67-100.

Joesting, H. R., J. E. Case, and D. Plouff, 1966, Regional geophysical investigations of the Moab-Needles area, Utah; U.S. Geological Survey Professional Paper 516-C, 21 p.

Johnson, J. B., Jr., and K. L. Cook, 1957, Regional gravity survey of parts of Tooele, Juab and Millrd Counties, Utah: Geophysics, v. 22, no. 1, p. 48-61.

Johnson, H. S., Jr., 1957, Uranium resources of the Cedar Mountain area, Emery County, Utah—A regional synthesis: U.S. Geological Survey Bulletin 1087-B, iv, p. 23-58.

———1959, Uranium resources of the Green River and Henry Mountains districts, Utah - a regional synthesis: U.S. Geological Survey Bulletin 1987-C, p. 59-104.

Johnson, H. S., Jr. and W. Thordorson, 1966, Uranium deposits of the Moab, Monticello, White Canyon and Monument Valley districts, Utah and Arizona: U.S. Geological Survey Bulletin 1222-H, p. 41-53.

Johnson, K. D., 1959, Structure and stratigraphy of the Mount Nebo-Salt Creek area, southern Wasatch Mountains, Utah: Brigham Young University Geology Studies, Provo, Utah, v. 6, no. 6, 49 p.

Johnson, M. G., 1973, Placer gold deposits of Utah: U.S. Geological Survey Bulletin 1357, 26 p.

Jones, D. J., ed. 1953, Microfossils of the Upper Cretaceous of northeastern Utah and southwestern Wyoming: Utah Geological and Mineral Survey Bulletin 47, 158 p.

Kaliser, B. N., 1972, Environmental geology of Bear Lake area, Rich County, Utah: Utah Geological and Mineral Survey Bulletin 96, 32 p.

Kauffman, E. G., 1977a, Illustrated guide to biostratigraphically important Cretaceous microfossils, western interior basin, United States: Mountain Geologist, v. 14, no. 3, p. 225-274.

———1977b, Geological and biological overview—western interior Cretaceous Basin: Mountain Geologist, v. 14, no. 4, p. 75-99.

Kay, G. M., 1951, North American geosynclines: Geological Society of America Memoir 48, 143 p.

Kay, J. L., 1953, Faunal list of vertebrates from the Uinta Basin, Utah: Society of Vertebrate Paleontologists Guidebook, 6th Annual Field Conference, p. 20-24.

———1957, The Eocene vertebrates of the Uinta Basin, Utah *in* Geology of the Uinta Basin: Intermountain Association of Petroleum Geologists Guidebook, 8th Annual Field Conference, p. 110-114.

Kayser, R. B., 1967, Bituminous sandstone deposits, Asphalt Ridge, Uintah County, Utah: Utah Geological and Mineral Survey Special Studies 19, 62 p.

Keller, G. R., R. B. Smith, and L. W. Braile, 1975, Crustal structure along the Great Basin - Colorado Plateau transition from seismic retraction profiling: Journal Geophysical Research v. 80, p. 1093-1098.

Kelley, V. C., 1955a, Tectonics of the Four Corners region: Four Corners Geological Society Field Conference, p. 108-117.

———1955b, Regional tectonics of the Colorado Plateau and relationship to the origin and distribution of uranium: New Mexico University Publications in Geology, Albuquerque, New Mexico, no. 5, 120 p.

Kelley, V. C., and N. J. Clinton, 1960, Fracture systems and tectonic elements of the Colorado Plateau: New Mexico University Publications in Geology, Albuquerque, New Mexico, no. 6, 104 p.

Kennedy, R. R., 1963, Sedimentary stratigraphy of the Tusher Range, Piute County, Utah *in* Geology of southwestern Utah: Intermountain Association Petroleum Geologists Guidebook, 12th Annual Field Conference, p. 118-124.

Kepper, J. C., 1960, Stratigraphy and structure of the southern half of the Fish Springs Range, Juab County, Utah: M.S. thesis, University of Washington, Seattle, Washington, 92 p.

———1966, Primary dolostone patterns in the Utah-Nevada middle Cambrian: Journal of Sedimentary Petrology, v. 36, no. 2, p. 548 562.

———1972, Paleoenvironmental patterns in middle to lower Upper Cambrian interval in eastern Great Basin: American Association of Petroleum Geologists Bulletin, v. 56, no. 3, p. 503-527.

Kerr, P. F., 1963, Geologic features of the Marysvale uranium area, Utah *in* Geology of southwestern Utah: Intermountain Association of Petroleum Geologists Guidebook, 12th Annual Field Conferences, p. 125-135.

———1968, The Marysvale, Utah, uranium deposits *in* Ore deposits of the United States, 1933-1967: American Institute of Mining Engineers, v. 2, Graton Sales, New York, p. 1020-1042.

Kerr, P. F., and others, 1957, Marysvale, Utah, uranium area (geology, volcanic relations and hydrothermal alteration)—Geology, volcanic relations and hydrothermal alteration: Geological Society of American Special Paper 64, 212 p.

Ketner, K. B., 1968, Origin of Ordovician quartzite in the Cordilleran miogeosyncline: U.S. Geological Survey Professional Paper 600-B.

———1969, Refractory minerals, *in* Mineral and water resources of Utah: Utah Geological and Mineral Survey Bulletin 73, p. 205-206.

King, Clarence, 1878, U.S. Geological Explorations 40th Parallel Report, v. 1, Systematic Geology, 494 p.

King, P. B., 1977, Precambrian geology of the United States—An explanatory text to accompany the geologic map of the United States: U.S. Geological Survey Professional Paper 902, 85 p.

Kinney, D. M., and J. F. Rominger, 1947, Geology of the Whiterocks River - Ashley Creek area, Uinta County, Utah; U.S. Geological Survey Oil and Gas Investigation Preliminary Map no. 82 with text.

Kinney, D. M., 1956, Geology of the Uinta River-Brush Creek area, Duchesne and Uintah Counties, Utah: U.S. Geological Survey Bulletin 1007, 185 p.

Knight, R. L., and J. C. Cooper, 1955, Suggested changes in Devonian terminology *in* Geology of parts of Paradox, Black Mesa and San Juan Basins: Four Corners Geological Society, 1st Annual Field Conference, p. 56-58.

Knowlton, F. H., 1923, Revision of the flora of the Green River Formation with descriptions of new species: U.S. Geological Survey Professional Paper 131-F, p. 133-136.

Kummel, Bernard, 1954, Triassic stratigraphy of southeastern Idaho and adjacent areas: U.S. Geological Survey Professional Paper 254-H, p. 165-194.

Kunkel, R. P., 1960, Permian stratigraphy in the salt anticline region of western Colorado and eastern Utah *in* Geology of the Paradox Basin fold and fault belt: Four Corners Geological Society Guidebook, 3rd Annual Field Conference, p. 91-97.

Kunkel, R. P., and R. B. Schick, 1963, Geology of the Lisbon oil and gas field, San Juan County, Utah *in* Oil and gas possibilities of Utah re-evaluated: Utah Geological and Mineral Survey Bulletin 54, p. 429-446.

Lachenbruch, A. H., and J. H. Sass, 1979, Models of an extending lithosphere and heat flow in the Basin and Range Province *in* Cenozoic tectonics and regional geophysics of the western Cordillera: Geological Society of America Memoir 152, p. 209-250.

Lane, B. O., 1962, Fauna of the Ely Group in the Illipah area of Nevada: Journal of Paleontology, v. 36, no. 5.

———1960, Molluscan faunas of the Flagstaff Formation of central Utah: Geological Society of America Memoir 78, 100 p.; *also* GeoScience Abs., v. 2, no. 4, p. 19 (2-882).

Larsen, Willard, 1957, Petrology and structure of Antelope Island, Davis County, Utah: Ph.D. dissertation, University of Utah, Salt Lake City, Utah, 185 p.

Larson, E. E., W. C. Bradley and M. Ozima, 1975, Development of the Colorado River system in northwestern Colorado during the late Cenozoic *in* Canyonlands Country: Four Corners Geological Society Guidebook, 8th Annual Field Conference, p. 97-102.

Lautenschlager, H. K., 1952, The geology of the central part of the Pavant Range, Utah: Ph.D. disseration, Ohio State University, Columbus, Ohio, 188 p.

Lawrence, J. C., 1965, Stratigraphy of the Dakota and Tropic formations of Crecaceous age in southern Utah: Utah Geological Society Guidebook to the Geology of Utah no. 19, p. 71-91.

Lawson, A. C., 1913, The gold of the Shinarump at Paria: Economic Geology, v. 8, p. 434-448.

Lee, W. T., 1907, The Iron County coal field, Utah: U.S. Geological Survey Bulletin 316-E, p. 359-375.

Leith, C. K., and E. C. Harder, 1908, Iron ores of the Iron Springs district, southern Utah: U.S. Geological Survey Bulletin 338.

Lessard, R. H., 1973, Micropaleontology and paleoecology of the Tununk Member of the Mancos Shale: Utah Geological and Mineral Survey, Special Studies 45, 28 p.

Lemmon, D. M., M. L. Silberman and R. W. Kistler, 1973, Some K-Ar ages of extrusive and intrusive rocks of the San Francisco and Wah Wah Mountains, Utah *in* Geology of the Milford area: Utah Geological Association Publication 3, p. 23-26.

Lewis, G. E., 1966, The Dinosaurs: "Terrible Lizards," *in* (??), W. R., Dinosau National Monument (topographic map with text): UnitedStates Geological Survey.

Lewis, G. E. and others, 1961, Age of the Glen Canyon Group (Triassic and Jurassic) on the Colorado Plateau: Geological Society America Bulletin, vol 72, no. 9, p. 1437-1440.

Lewis, R. Q., Sr., and R. H. Campbell, 1965, Geology and uranium deposits of Elk Ridge and vicinity, San Juan County, Utah: U.S. Geological Survey Professional Paper 474-B, 69 p.

Lindgren, Waldemar, 1915, Processes of mineralization and enrichment in the Tintic mining district: Economic Geology 10, p. 225-240.

Lindgren, Waldemar, and G. F. Loughlin, 1919, Geology and ore deposits of the Tintic mining district, Utah: U.S. Geological Survey Professional Paper 107, 282 p.

Lindquist, R. C., 1980, Slope processes and forms at Bryce Canyon National Park: Ph.D. dissertation, University of Utah, Salt Lake City, Utah, 134 p.

Lindsay, J. B., (ed.), 1970, Geology of the Uinta Mountains, Utah's maverick range: Intermountain Association of Petroleum Geologists (and Utah Geological Society) Guidebook, 16th Annual Field Conference, 237 p.

Lindquist, R. C., 1980, Slope forms at Bryce Canyon National Park: Ph..D. dissertation, University of Utah, 122 p.

Lindsey, D. A., C. W. Naeser, and D. R. Shawe, 1975, Age of volcanism, intrusion, and mineralization in the Thomas Range, Keg Mountains, and Desert Mountains, western Utah: Journal of Research, U.S. Geological Survey, v. 3, no. 5, p. 597-604.

Lipman, P. W., H. J. Prostka and R. L. Christiansen, 1972, Cenozoic volcanism and plate-tectonic evolution of the western United States, I, Early and Middle Cenozoic: Philosophical Transactions, Royal Society of London, Series A, v. 271, no. 1213, p. 217-248.

Lipman, P. W. and others, 1978, Pleistocene rhyolite of the Mineral Mountains, Utah,—Geothermal and archeological significance *with sections by* G. A. Izatt, C. W. Naeser and I. Friedman: U.S. Geological Survey Journal of Research, v. 6, no. 1, p. 133-147.

Lister, K. H., 1975, Paleoecology of ostracoda from Quaternary sediments of the Great Salt Lake Basin, Utah: The University of Kansas Paleontological Contributions Paper 78, 33 p.

Livingston, V. E., Jr., 1955, Sedimentation and stratigraphy of the (Mississippian) Humbug Formation in central Utah: Brigham Young University Geology Studies, Provo, Utah, v. 2, no. 6, 60 p.

Lochman-Balk, Christina, 1955, Cambrian stratigraphy of the south and west margins of the Green River Basin (Utah-Wyoming) *in* the Green River Basin: Wyoming Geological Association Guidebook, 10th Annual Field Conference, p. 29-37.

———1956a, Cambrian stratigraphy of eastern Utah *in* Geology and economic deposits of east-central Utah: Intermountain Association of Petroleum Geologists Guidebook, 7th Annual Field Conference, p. 58-64.

———1956b, The Cambrian of the Rocky Mountains and southwest deserts of the U. S. and adjoining Sonora Province, Mexico: Symposium El Sistema Cambrico *see* Paleogeografia y el problemas de su base, v. 2, Congressio Geologico Internacional, p. 529-656.

———1959, The Cambrian section in the central and southern Wasatch Mountains (Utah) *in* Geology of the Wasatch and Uinta Mountains transition zone: Intermountain Association of Petroleum Geologists Guidebook, 10th Annual Field Conference, p. 40-45.

———1972, Cambrian system *in* Geologic Atlas of the Rocky Mountains: Rocky Mountain Association of Geologists, p.60-75.

Lofgren, B. E., 1955, Resume of the Tertiary and Quarternary stratigraphy of Ogden Velley, Utah, *in* Tertiary and Quaternary geology of the eastern Bonneville Basin: Utah Geological Society Guidebook no. 10, p. 70-84.

Lohman, S. W., 1974, The geologic story of Canyonlands National Park: U.S. Geological Survey Bulletin 1327, 127 p.

———1975, The geologic story of Arches National Park: U.S. Geological Survey Bulletin 1393.

Longwell, C. R., 1950, Tectonic theory viewed from the Basin ranges: Geological Society of America Bulletin 61, p. 413-434.

Loring, A. K., 1976, Distribution in time and space of late Phanerozoic normal faulting in Nevada and Utah: Utah Geology, v. 3, no. 2, p. 97-109.

Lovering. T. S., 1949, Rock alteration as a guide to ore, East Tintic district, Utah: Economic Geology Monograph 1, 65 p.

Lovejoy, E. M. P., 1973, Major Cenozoic deformation along Hurricane fault zone, Utah and Arizona: American Association Petroleum Geology Bulletin, v. 56, no. 3, p. 510-519.

Lovering, T. S., and H. T. Morris, 1960, The Chief Oxide-Burgin area discoveries, East Tintic district, Utah—A case history, pt. 1, U.S. Geological Survey Studies and Exploration: Economic Geology, v. 55, no. 6, p. 1116-1147.

Lowder, G. G., 1973, Late Cenozoic transitional alkali olivine-tholeiite basalt and andesite from the margin of the Great Basin, southwest Utah: Geological Society of America Bulletin, v. 84, no. 9, p. 2993-3012.

Lucchitta, I., 1972, Early history of the Colorado River in the Basin and Range province: Geological Society of America Bulletin, v. 83, p. 1933-1948.

Ludlum, J. C., 1943, Structure and stratigraphy of part of the Bannock Range, Idaho: Geological Society of America Bulletin, v. 54, no. 7, p. 973-986.

Lupton, C. T., 1912, The Blacktail (Tabby) Mountain coal field, Wasatch County, Utah: U.S. Geological Survey Bulletin 471, p. 595-628.

———1913, Gypsum along the west flank of the San Rafael Swell, Utah: U.S. Geological Survey Bulletin 530, p. 221-231; *also* U.S. Geological Survey Bulletin 607, 1920, p. 272-282, 1920.

———1916, Geology and coal resources of Castle Valley in Carbon, Emery and Sevier Counties, Utah: U.S. Geological Survey Bulletin 628; *also* Washington Academy of Science Journal 6, abs., p. 504-505.

McCormick, C. D., and M. D. Picard, 1969, Petrology of Gartra Formation (Triassic), Uinta Mountain area, Utah and Colorado: Journal of Sedimentary Petrology, v. 39, no. 4, p. 1484-1508.

McDonald, R. E., 1972, Eocene and Paleocene rocks of the southern and central basins *in* Geologic atlas of the Rocky Mountain region: Rocky Mountain Association of Geologists, p. 243-256.

———1976, Tertiary tectonics and sedimentary rocks along the transition: Basin and Range Province to Plateau and Thrust Belt Province, Utah *in* Syposium on Geology of the Cordilleran Hingeline, Rocky Mountain Association of Geologists, p. 281-317.

McFall, C. C., 1955, Geology of the Escalante - Boulder area, Garfield County, Utah: Ph. D. dissertation, Yale University, 180 p.

McGill, G. E., and A. W. Stromquist, 1975, Origin of graben in the Needles district, Canyonlands National Park *in* Canyonlands Country: Four Corners Geological Society Guidebook, 8th Annual Field Conference, p. 235-243.

McGookey, D. P., 1960, Early Tertiary stratigraphy of part of central Utah: American Association of Petroleum Geologists Bulletin, v. 44, no. 5, p. 589-615.

———(coordinator), 1972, Cretaceous system *in* Geologic atlas of the Rocky Mountain region: Rocky Mountain Asociation of Geologists, p. 190-228.

McKee, E. D., 1938, The environment and history of the Toroweap and Kaibab Formations of northern Arizona and southern Utah: Carnegie Institute of Washington Publication 492.

———1954, Stratigraphy and history of the Moenkopi Formation of Triassic age: Geological Society of America Memoir 61, 133 p.

McKee, E. D., and E. J. Crosby, 1975, Paleotectonic investigations of the Pennsylvanian System in the United States; Part I: Introduction and regional analysis of the Pennsylvanian System: U.S. Geological Survey Professional Paper 853, Chap. A-R.

McKee, E. D., and others, 1956, Paleotectonic maps of the Jurassic system: U.S. Geological Survey Miscellaneous Geologic Investigations Map I-175, 6 p.

McKee, E. D., and others, 1960, Paleotectonic maps, Triassic system: U.S. Geological Survey Map I-300.

———1967, Evolution of the Colorado River in Arizona: Museum of Northern Arizona Bulletin 44.

McKee, E. H., 1971, Tertiary igneous chronology of the Great Basin of the western United States—Implications for tectonic models: Geological Society of America Bulletin, v. 82, no. 12, p. 3497-3501.

McKelvey, V. E., and others, 1956, Summary description of Phosphoria, Park City and Shedhorn Formations in the western phosphate field: American Association of Petroleum Geologists Bulletin, v. 40, no. 12, p. 2826-2863.

———1959, The Phosphoria, Park City and Shedhorn Formations in the western phosphate field: U.S. Geological Survey Professional Paper 313-A, p. 1-47.

McMillan, D. T., 1974, Bonneville salt Flats—A comparison of salt thickness in July, 1960, and October, 1974: Utah Geological and Mineral Survey Report of Investigations 91, 6 p.

McKnight, E. T., 1940, Geology of area between Green and Colorado Rivers, Grand and San Juan Counties, Utah: United States Geological Survey Bulletin 908.

Mackin, J. H., 1947, Some structural features of the intrusions in the Iron Springs district, Utah: Utah Geological Society Guidebook to the Geology of Utah 2 63 p., *also* Utah Geological Association Reprint 98, 1974.

———1960a, Structural significance of Tertiary volcanic rocks in southwestern Utah: American Journal of Science, v. 258, no. 2, p. 81-131.

———1963, Reconnaissance stratigraphy of the Needles Range Formation in southwestern Utah *in* Geology of southwestern Utah: Intermountain Association of Petroleum Geologists Guidebook, 12th Annual Field Conference, p. 71-78.

———1968, Iron-ore deposits of the Iron Springs district, southwestern Utah *in* Ore deposits of the United States, 1933-1967, American Institute of Mining Engineers, Graton-Sales, New York, v. 2, p. 922-1010.

MacGintie, H. D., 1969, The Eocene Green River flora of northwestern Colorado and northeastern Utah: California University Publications in the Geological Sciences, v. 83, 203 p.

MacLachlan, M. E. H., 1957, Triassic stratigraphy in parts of Utah and Colorado *in* Geology of the Uinta Basin: Intermountain Association of Petroleum Geologists Guidebook, 8th Annual Field Conference, p. 82-91.

———(compiler), 1972, The Triassic system *in* Geologic atlas of the Rocky Mountains: Rocky Mountain Association of Petroleum Geologists.

Madison, R. J., 1969, Hydrology and chemistry of Great Salt Lake *in* Guidebook of northern Utah: Utah Geological and Mineral Survey Bulletin 82, p. 140-157.

Madsen, J. H., Jr., 1959, Geology of the Lost Creek-Echo Canyon area, Morgan and Summit Counties, Utah: M.S. thesis, University of Utah, Salt Lake City, Utah, 60 p..

———1974, A new theropod dinosaur from the Upper Jurassic of Utah: Journal of Paleontology, v. 48, no. 1, p. 27-31.

———1976a, A second new theropod dinosaur from the later Jurassic of east-central Utah: Utah Geology, v. 3, no. 1.

———1976b, Allosaurus fragilis—A revised osteology: Utah Geological and Mineral Survey Bulletin 109, 163 p.

Madsen, J. H., Jr., and W. E. Miller, 1979, The fossil vertebrates of Utah, an annotated bibliography: Brigham Young University Geology Studies, v. 26, pt. 4, 147 p.

Maher, P. D., 1976, The geology of the Pineview field area, Summit County, Utah *in* New concepts of exploration in Rockies, Geology of the Cordilleran Hingeline symposium: Rocky Mountain Association of Geologists; *also* American Association of Petroleum Geologists Bulletin, v. 60, no. 8, p. 1402-1403.

Malan, R. C., 1968, The uranium mining industry and geology of the Monument Valley and White Canyon districts, Arizona and Utah *in* Ore deposits of the United States, 1933-1967: American Institute of Mining Engineers, Graton-Sales, v. 1, New York, p. 790-804.

Mallory, W. M., 1972a, Continental setting of the region (Rocky Mountains) *in* Geologic atlas of the Rocky Mountains: Rocky Mountain Association of Geologists, p. 32-34.

Mallory, W. M., 1972b, Pennsylvanian arkose and the ancestral Rocky Mountains *in* Geologic atlas of the Rocky Mountains: Rocky Mountain Association of Geologists.

———1972c, Regional synthesis of the Pennsylvanian system *in* Geologic atlas of the Rocky Mountain region: Rocky Mountain Association of Geologists.

Mann, D. C., 1974, Wasatch hinterland, northeastern Utah: M.S. thesis, University of Utah, Salt Lake City, Utah.

Mapel, W. J., and W. J. Hail, Jr., 1959, Tertiary geology of the Goose Creek district, (??) County, Idaho, Box Elder County, Utah, and Elko County, Nevada, *in* Uranium in coal in Western United States: U.S. Geological Survey Bulletin 1055, p. 217-254.

Marcantel, E. L., 1975, Conodont biostratigraphy and sedimentary petrology of the Gerster Formation (Guadalupian) in east-central Nevada and west-central Utah: Ph.D. dissertation, Ohio State University, Columbus, Ohio.

Mardirosian, C. A., (compiler), 1966, Mining districts and mineral deposits of Utah, with production and gross value of the larger metal mining districts (excluding uranium districts): Salt Lake City, privately printed.

Marsell, R. E., 1932, Geology of the Jordan Narrows region, Traverse Mountains, Utah: M.S. thesis, University of Utah, Salt Lake City, Utah.

———1964a, The Wasatch fault zone in north-central Utah—Introduction: Utah Geological Society Guidebook to the Geology of Utah 18, p. 1-14.

———1964b, The Wasatch fault zone in Salt Lake County *in* The Wasatch fault zone in north-central Utah: Utah Geological Society Guidebook to the Geology of Utah 18, p. 31-50.

———1964c, Glaciation (Salt Lake County) *in* Geology of Salt Lake County, A. L. Crawford, ed.: Utah Geological and Mineral Survey Bulletin 69, p. 55-68.

Marsell, R. E., and R. L. Threet, 1964, Geologic map of Salt Lake County, Utah *in* Geology of Salt Lake County, A. L. Crawford, ed.: Utah Geological and Mineral Survey Bulletin 69 and Reprint 83.

Marzolf, J. E., 1970, Evidence of changing deposition environments in the Navajo Sandstone, Utah: Ph.D. dissertation, University of California at Los Angeles, Los Angeles, Califrnia.

Mathews, Asa A. L., 1929, The Lower Triassic cephalopod fauna of the Fort Douglas area, Utah: Walker Museum Memoir 1, no. 1, University of Chicago Press.

———1931, Mesozoic stratigraphy of the central Wasatch mountains: Oberlin College Laboratory Bulletin, n. s, no.1, 50 p.

Mattick, R. E., 1970, Thickness of unconsolidated to semiconsolidated sediments in Jordan Valley, Utah: U.S. Geological Survey Professional Paper 700-C, p. C119-C124.

Maurer, R. E., 1960, Geology of the Cedar Mountains, Tooele County, Utah: Ph.D. dissertation, University of Utah, Salt Lake City, Utah.

Maxey, G. B., 1946, Geology of part of the Pavant Range, Millard County, Utah: American Journal of Science, v. 244, no. 5, p. 324-356.

———1958, Lower and Middle Cambrian stratigraphy in northern Utah and southeastern Idaho: Geological Society of America Bulletin, v. 69, no. 6, p. 647-687.

Maxfield, E. B., 1975, Foraminifera(??) from the Mancos Shale of east central Utah: Brigham Young University Geology Studies, v. 23, pt. 3, p 67-162.

May, F. E., 1972, A survey of palynomorphs from several coal-bearing horizons of Utah: Utah Geological and Mineral Survey, Monography Series no. 3, p. 497-542.

Meeves, H. C., and others, 1966, Reconnaissance of beryllium-bearing pegmatite deposits in six western states—Arizona, Colorado, New Mexico, South Dakota, Utah and Wyoming: U.S. Bureau of Mines Information Circular 8298.

Mehringer, P. J., and W. P. Nash, 1971, A Holocene(??) ash from northwestern Utah: Proceedings Utah Academy Sciences, Arts, and Letters, v. 48, pt. 1.

Menard, H. W., Jr., 1960, The east Pacific rise: Science, v. 132, no. 3441.

Menhart, H. H., P. D. Rowley and P. W. Lipman, 1978, Potassium-argon ages and geothermal implications of young rhyolites in west-central Utah: Isochron West, no. 21, p. 3-7.

Miller, A. K., W. L. Youngquist, and M. L. Nielsen, 1952, Mississippian cephalopods from western Utah: Journal of Paleontology, v. 26, no. 2, p. 148-161.

Miller, G. M., 1966, Structure and stratigraphy of the southern part of the Wah Wah Mountains, southewest Utah: American Association of Petroleum Geologists Bulletin, v. 50, no. 5, p. 858-900.

Miller, J. F., 1969, Conodont faunas of the Notch Peak Limestone (Cambro-Ordovician), House Range, Utah: Journal of Paleontology, v. 43, no. 2, p. 413-439.

———1978, Upper Cambrian and lowest Ordovician conodont faunas of the House Range, Utah: Southwest Missouri State University, Geoscience Series no. 5, p. 1-33.

Miller, L. J., 1955, Uranium ore controls of the Happy Jack deposit, White Canyon, San Juan County, Utah: Economic Geology, v. 50, no. 2, p. 156-169.

Miller, W. E., 1976, Late Pleistocene vertebrates of the Silver Creek local fauna from north-central Utah: Great Basin Naturalist, v. 36, no. 4.

Misch, P. H., and J. C. Hazzard, 1962, Stratigraphy and metamorphism of late Precambrian rocks in central northeastern Nevada and adjacent Utah: American Association of Petroleum Geologists Bulletin, v. 46, no. 3, p. 289-343.

Molloy, M. W. and P. F. Kerr, 1962, Tusher uranium area, Marysvale, Utah: Geological Society America Bulletin v. 73, no. 2, p. 211-235.

Moore, W. J., 1973, A summary of radiometric ages of igneous rocks in the Oquirrh Mountains, north-central Utah: Economic Geology, v. 68, no. 1, p. 97-101.

———1973b, Igneous rocks of the Bingham mining district, Utah: U.S. Geological Survey Professional Paper 697-B, 42 p.

Moore, W. J., and M. A. Lanphere, 1971, The age of porphyry-type copper mineralization in the Bingham mining district, Utah—A refined estimate: Economic Geology, v. 66, no. 2, p. 331-334.

Morisawa, Marie, 1971, The Wasatch fault zone—General aspects *in* Environmental Geology of the Wasatch Front: Utah Geological Association Publication 1, sec. D, p. D1-D17.

Morris, H. T., 1964a, Geology of the Tintic Junction quadrangle, Tooele, Juab and Utah Counties, Utah: U.S. Geological Survey Bulletin 1142-L, p. L1-L23.

———1964b, Geology of the Eureka quadrangle, Utah and Juab Counties, Utah: U.S. Geological Survey Bulletin 1142-K, p. K1-K29.

———1964c, Nonmetallic and industrial minerals and materials resources—Limestone and dolomite *in* Mineral and water resources of Utah: U.S. Congress, 88th, 2nd Sess., Comm. Print., p. 188-194.

———1968, The Main Tintic mining district, Utah *in* Ore deposits of the United States, 1933-1967: American Institute of Mining Engineers, Graton-Sales, New York, v. 2, p. 1043-1073..

Morris, H. T., and T. S. Lovering, 1962, Stratigraphy of the East Tintic Mountains, Utah, *with a section on* Quaternary deposits by H. D. Goode: U.S. Geological Survey Professional Paper 361, 145 p.

———1979, General geology and mines of the east Tintic mining district, Utah and Juab Counties, Utah: U.S. Geological Survey Professional Paper 1024, 203 p.

Morris, H. T. and W. M. Shepard, 1964, Evidence for a concealed tear fault with large displacement in the central East Tintic Mountains: U.S. Geological Survey Professional Paper 501-C, p. C19-C21.

Morris, H. T., R. C. Douglass, and R. W. Kopf, 1977, Stratigraphy and micro faunas of the Oquirrh Group in the southern East Tintic Mountains, Utah: U.S. Geological Survey Professional Paper 1025, 22 p.

Morrison, R. B.,, 1965a, Quaternary stratigraphy of the eastern Jordan Valley, south of Salt Lake City, Utah: U.S. Geological Survey Professional Paper 477, 80 p.

———1965b, New evidence on Lake Bonneville stratigraphy and history from southern Promontory Point, Utah: U.S. Geological Survey Professional Paper 525-C, p. C110-C119.

———1965c, Quaternary geology of the Great Basin *in* The Quaternary of the United States: Princeton University Press, Princeton, New Jersey, p. 265-285.

———1966, Predecessors of the Great Salt Lake *in* Guidebook to the geology of Utah: Utah Geological Society Guidebook, no. 20, p. 77-104.

———1975, Predecessors of Great Salt Lake (abs.): Geological Society of America Abstracts with Programs, 1975 Annual Meeting, p. 1206.

Moulton, F. C., 1975, Lower Mesozoic and upper Paleozoic petroleum potential of the Hingeline area *in* Deep drilling frontiers in the central Rocky Mountains: Rocky Mountain Association of Geologists Symposium, p. 87-97.

Moussa, M. M. T., 1965, Geology of the Soldier Summit quadrangle, Utah: Ph. D. dissertation, University of Utah, 192 p.

———1968, Fossil tracks from the Green River Formation (Eocene) near Soldier Summit, Utah: Journal of Paleontology, v. 42, no. 6, p. 1433-1438.

———1969, Green River Formation (Eocene) in the Soldier Summit area, Utah: Geological Society of America Bulletin, v. 80, p 1737-1748.

Moyle, R. W., 1958, Paleoecology of the Manning Canyon Shale in central Utah: Brigham Young University Geology Studies, v. 5, no. 7, 86 p.

Muessig, S. J., 1951a, Geology of a part of Long Ridge, Utah: Ph.D. dissertation, Ohio State University, Columbus, Ohio, 213 p.

———1951b, Eocene volcanism in central Utah: Science, v. 114, no. 2957, p. 234.

Mullens, T. E., 1960, Geology of the Clay Hills area, San Juan County, Utah: U.S. Geological Survey Bulletin 1087-H, p. 259-336.

———1971, Reconnaissance study of the Wasatch, Evanston and Echo Canyon formations in part of northern Utah: U.S. Geological survey Bulletin 1311-D, 31 p.

Mullens, T. E., and V. L. Freeman, 1957, Lithofacies of the Salt Wash Member of the Morrison Formation, Colorado Plateau: Geological Society of America Bulletin, v. 68, no. 4, p. 505-526.

Mundorff, J. C., 1970, Major thermal springs of Utah: Utah Geological and Mineral Survey Water Resources Bulletin 13, 60 p.

———1971, Non-thermal springs of Utah: Utah Geological and Mineral Survey Water Resources Bulletin 16, 70 p.

Nackowski, M. P., Donald Fisher, and Lawrence Beer, 1963, Mineral resources of Duchesne County: Utah University Engineering Experiment Station Bulletin v. 54, no. 20, 97 p.

Nash, W. P. and R. P. Smith, 1977, Pleistocene ash deposits in Utah: Utah Geology, v. 4, no. 1, p. 35-42.

Nash, W. P., H. R. Crecraft and S. H. Evans, Jr., 1980, Geothermal systems in central Utah: Geothermal Resources Council Annual Meeting, Field Trip 7.

Nash, W. P., J. B. Peterson, and C. H. Turley, 1980, Studies in late Cenozoic volcanism in west-central Utah: Utah Geological and Mineral Survey Special Studies 52, 58 p.

Neff, A. W., and S. C. Brown, 1958, Ordovician-Mississippian rocks of the Paradox Basin *in* Geology of the Paradox Basin: Intermountain Association of Petroleum Geologists Guidebook, 9th Annual Field Conference, p. 102-108.

Neff, T. R., 1963, Petrology and structure of the Little Willow Series, Wasatch Mountains, Utah: M.S. thesis, University of Utah, Salt Lake City, Utah, 83 p.

Nelson, M. E., 1971, Stratigraphy and paleontology of the Norwood Tuff and Fowkes Formation, north western Utah and southwestern Wyoming: Ph. D. dissertation, University of Utah, 168 p.

Nelson, M. E., and J. H. Madsen, Jr., 1980, A summary of Pleistocene, fossil vertebrate localities in the northern Bonneville Basin of Utah *in* Great Salt Lake, Utah—A scientific, historical and economic review: Geological and Mineral Survey Bulletin 116, p. 97-113.

Newberry, J. S., 1876, Geological report *in* Report of the exploring expedition from Santa Fe, New Mexico, to the junction of the Grand and Green Rivers of the great Colorado of the west in 1859, J. N. Macomb, : U.S. Army Engineering Department, p. 9-118, 135-148.

Nichols, D. J. and M. A. Warner, 1978, Palynology, age, and correlation of the Wanship Formation and their implications for the tectonic history of northeastern Utah: Geology, v. 6, no. 7, p. 430-433.

Nielson, D. L., and others, 1979, Geology and structural control of geothermal system at Roosevelt hot springs KGRA, Beaver County, Utah (abs.): American Association of Petroleum Geologists Bulletin, v. 63, no. 5, p. 836.

Nielson, R. L., 1981, Depositional environment of the Toroweap(??) and Kaibab Formations of southwestern Utah: Ph. D. dissertation, University of Utah, 1129 p.

Nolan, T. B., 1927, Potash brines in the Great Salt Lake Desert, Utah: U.S. Geological Survey Bulletin 795, p. 25-44.

———1935, The Gold Hill mining district, Utah: U.S. Geological Survey Proessional Paper 177, 172 p.

———1943, The Basin and Range Province in Utah, Nevada and California: U.S. Geological Survey Professional Paper 197-D, p. 141-196.

Nygreen, P. W., 1955, Stratigraphy of the lower Oquirrh Formation in the type area and near Logan, Utah: Utah Geological and Mineral Survey Bulletin 61, 67 p.

Oaks, R. Q., Jr., and others, Summary of Middle Ordovician stratigraphy and tectonics, northern Utah, southern and central Idaho: Wyoming Geological Association Guidebook 29th Annual Field Confernece, p. 101-118.

Ojakangas, R. W.., and C. L. Matsch, 1980, Upper Precambrian (Eocambrain) Mineral Fork Tillite of Utah—A continental glacial and glaciomarine sequence: Geological Society of America Bulletin, v. 91, no. 8, p. 495-501.

O'Sullivan, R. B., and M. E. MacLachlan, 1975, Triassic rocks of the Moab-White Canyon Area, southeastern Utah: Four Corners Geological Survey Bulletin 1395-I, 12 p.

Oldroyd, J. D., 1973, Biostratigraphy of the Cambrian *Glossopleura* zone, west-central Utah: M.S. thesis, University of Utah, Salt Lake City, Utah.

Oliveira, M. E., 1975, Geology of the Fish Springs mining district, Fish Springs Range, Utah: Brigham Young University Geology Studies, Provo, Utah, v. 22, pt. 1, p. 69-104.

Olle, J. M., 1969, Molluscan fauna and lacustrine sediments in Sanpete Valley near Manti, Sanpete County, Utah: Sterkiana,(??) no. 35, p. 5-14.

Olson, R. H., 1956, Geology of Promontory Range *in* Geology of parts of northwestern Utah: Utah Geological Society Guidebook to the Geology of Utah 11, p. 41-75.

Orlansky, R., 1971, Palynology of the Upper Cretaceous straight Cliffs Sandstone, Garfield County, Utah: Utah Geological and Mineral Survey Bulletin 89, 57 p.

Osmond, J. C., 1954, Dolomites in Silurian and Devonian of east-central Nevada: American Association of Petroleum Geologists Bulletin, v. 38, no. 9, p. 1911-1956.

———1961, Tectonic history of the Basin and Range Province in Utah and Nevada (abs.): Mining Engineering, v. 10, no. 12, 11 p.

——1962, Stratigraphy of Devonian Sery(??) Dolomite in Utah and Nevada: American Association of Petroleum Geologists Bulletin v. 45, no. 11, p. 2033-2056.

———1964, Tectonic history of the Uinta Basin, Utah *in* Geology and mineral deposits of the Uinta Basin, Utah's hydrocarbon storehouse: Intermountain Association of Petroleum Geologists Guidebook, 13th Annual Field Conference, p. 47-58.

———1965, Geologic history of site of Uinta Basin, Utah: American Association of Petroleum Geologists Bulletin, v. 49, no. 11, p. 1957-1973.

O'Sullivan, R. B. 1965, Geology of the Cedar Mesa-Boundary Butte area, San Juan County Utah: U.S. Geological Survey, Bulletin 186, 128 p.

O'Toole, W. L., 1951, Geology of the Keetley-Kamas volcanic area: M.S. thesis, University of Utah, Salt Lake City, Utah.

Otto, E. P., 1973, Sedimentology of the Entrada Sandstone (Jurassic) northeastern Utah and northwestern Colorado: M.S. thesis, University of Utah, Salt Lake City, Utah.

Paddock, R. E., 1956, Geology of the Newfoundland Mountains, Box Elder County, Utah: M.S. thesis, University of Utah, Salt Lake City, Utah, 101 p.

Palmer, A. R., 1955, An appraisal of the Great Basin middle Cambrian trilobites described before 1900: U.S. Geological Survey Professional Paper 264-D, p. 55-86.

———1971, The Cambrian of the Great Basin and adjacent areas, western United States *in* Holland, C. H. (ed.), Cambrian of the New World: John Wiley Interscience series, p. 1-78.

Palmer, D. E., 1970, Geology of Stansbury Island, Tooele County, Utah: Brigham Young University Geology Studies, Provo, Utah, v. 17, pt. 2, p. 3-30.

Park, G. M., 1967, Granite Mountain *in* Radioactive and isotopic age determinations of Utah rocks: Utah Geological and Mineral Survey Bulletin 81, p. 21.

———1970, Volcanics, Thomas Range *in* Radioactive and isotopic age determinations of Utah rocks: Utah Geological and Mineral Survey Bulletin 81, J. A. Whelan, compiler, 23 p.

Parker, J. M., 1961, The McIntyre Canyon and Lisbon oil and gas fields, San Miguel County, Colorado, and San Juan County, Utah *in* Symposium on lower and middle Paleozoic rocks of Colorado: Rocky Mountain Association of Geologists, 12th Annual Field Conference, p. 163-173.

Parker, J. W., 1960, Big Flat field, Utah *in* Geology of the Paradox Basin fold and fault belt: Four Corners Geological Society Guidebook, 3rd Annual Field Conference, p. 127-132.

Parker, J. W., and J. W. Roberts, 1963, Devonian and Mississippian stratigraphy of the central part of the Colorado Plateau *in* A Symposium—Shelf carbonates of the Paradox Basin: Four Corners Geological Society, p. 31-60.

Parker, L. R., 1976, The paleoecology of the fluvial coal-forming swamps and associated flood plain environments in the Blackhawk Formation of central Utah: Brigham Young University Geology Studies, v. 22, pt. 3, p. 99-116.

Parks, J. M., Jr., 1951, Corals from the Brazer Formation (Mississippian) of northern Utah: Journal of Paleontology, v. 25, no. 2, p. 171-186.

Parry, W. T., and others, 1977, Geology and geochemistry of the Roosevelt hot springs thermal area, Utah—A summary: Department of Geology and Geophysics, University of Utah, Salt Lake City, Utah.

Patterson, S. H., 1969, Nonmetallic and industrial minerals and materials resources—Clays *in* Mineral and water resources of Utah: U.S. Cong., 88th, 2nd sess., Comm. Print., p. 157-162; *also* Utah Geological and Mineral Survey Bulletin 73, reprinted 1969.

Patton, H. B., 1908, Topaz-bearing rhyolite of the Thomas Range, Utah: Geological Society of America Bulletin, v. 19, p. 177-192.

Peabody, F. E., 1948, Reptile-amphibian trackways from the Lower Triassic Moenkopi Formation of Arizona and Utah: California University Department of Geological Sciences Bulletin, v. 27, no. 8, p. 295-467.

———1956, *Ichnites* from the Triassic Moenkopi Formation of Arizona and Utah: Journal of Paleontology, v. 30, no. 3, p. 731-740.

Peck, R. E., 1941, Lower Cretaceous Rocky Mountain nonmarine microfossils: Journal of Paleontology, v. 15, p. 285-304.

Petersen, C. A., 1973, Roosevelt and Thermal hot springs, Beaver County, Utah, *in* Geology of the Milford area: Utah Geological Association Publication 3, p. 73-74.

———1974, Summary of stratigraphy in the Mineral Range, Beaver and Millard Counties, Utah: Utah Geology, v. 1, no. 1, p. 45-50.

Petersen, D. W., 1976, Geochemistry and geology of the North Peak tungsten deposits, Millard County, Utah: M.S. thesis, University of Utah, Salt Lake City, Utah.

Peterson, F., and R. T. Ryder, 1975, Cretaceous rocks in the Henry Mountains region, Utah, and their relation to neighboring regions *in* Canyonlands Country: Four Corners Geological Society Guidebook. 8th Annual Field Conference, p. 167-189.

Peterson, F., and H. A. Waldrop, 1965, Jurassic and Cretaceous stratigraphy of south-central Kaiparowits Plateau, Utah, *in* Geology and resources of south-central Utah—Resources for power: Utah Geological Society Guidebook to the Geology of Utah 19, p. 47-69.

Peterson, J. A., 1954, Jurassic ostracoda from the "Lower Sundance" and Rierdon Formations, western interior, United States: Journal of Paleontology, v. 28, no. 2, p. 153-176.

———1957, Marine Jurassic of the northern Rocky Mountains and Williston Basin: American Association of Petroleum Geologists Bulletin, v. 41, no. 3, p. 399-440.

———1966, Stratigraphic *vs.* structural controls on carbonate mound hydrocarbon accumulation, Aneth area, Paradox Basin: American Association of Petroleum Geologists Bulletin, v. 50, no. 10, p. 2068-2081.

———1972, Jurrassic system *in* Geologic Atlas of the Rocky Mountain Region, United States of America: Rocky Mountain Association of Geologists, p. 177-189.

Peterson, J. A., and R. H. Hite, 1969, Pennsylvanian evaporite-carbonate cycles and their relation to petroleum occurrence, southern Rocky Mountains *in* Evaporites and petroleum: American Association of Petroleum Geologists Bulletin, v. 53, no. 4, p. 884-908.

Peterson, J. A. and H. R. Ohlen, 1963, Pennsylvanian shelf carbonates, Paradox Basin *in* A symposium—Shelf carbonates of the Paradox Basin: Four Corners Geological Society, p. 65-79.

Peterson, J. B., and W. P. Nash, 1980, Studies in late Cenozoic volcanism in west-central Utah *in* Part II, Geology and petrology of the Fumarole Butte volcanic complex, Utah: Utah Geological and Mineral Survey Special Studies 52, p. 35-55.

Peterson, O. A., and J. L. Kay, 1931, The upper Uinta Formation of northeastern Utah: Carnegie Museum Annals 20, p. 293-306.

Peterson, P. R., 1973a, Bridger Lake field (unitized): Utah Geological and Mineral Survey Oil and Gas Field Studies, no. 5.

———1973b, Bluebell field: Utah Geological and Mineral Survey Oil and Gas Field Studies, no. 12.

Peterson, R. H., D. J. Gauge and R. R. Lankford, 1953, Microfossils of the Upper Cretaceous of northeastern Utah and southwestern Wyoming: Utah Geological and Mineral Survey Bulletin 47, 158 p.

Peterson, V. E., 1942, A study of the geology and ore deposits of the Ashbrook silver mining district, Utah: Economic Geology 37, p. 466-502.

———1957, The Ashley Valley oil field (revised) *in* Geology of the Uinta Basin: Intermountain Association of Petroleum Geologists Guidebook, 8th Annual Field Conference, p. 191-192.

Peterson, William, 1924, Dinosaur tracks in the roofs of coal mines—A strange phenomenon noted in Utah and Colorado: Natural History, American Museum of Natural History Journal, v. 24, p. 388-391.

Phillips, J. D., and D. Forsyth, 1972, Plate tectonics, paleomagnetism and the opening of the Atlantic: Geological Society of America Bulletin, v. 83, no. 6, p. 1579-1600.

Phoenix, D. A., 1963, Geology of the Lees Ferry area, Coconino County, Arizona: U.S. Geological Survey Bulletin 1137, 86 p.

Picard, M. D., 1957a, Criteria used for distinguishing lacustrine and fluvial sediments in Tertiary beds of the Uinta Basin, Utah: Journal of Sedimentary Petrology, v. 27, no. 4, p. 373-377.

———1957b, Red Wash-Walker Hollow field, stratigraphic trap, eastern Uinta Basin, Utah *in* Symposium on stratigraphic-type oil accumulations in the Rocky Mountains: American Association of Petroleum Geologists Bulletin, v. 41, no. 5, Rocky Mountain Section, p. 923-236.

———1958, Subsurface structure, Aneth and adjacent areas, San Juan County, Utah *in* Geology of the Paradox Basin: Intermountain Association of Petroleum Geologists Guidebook, 9th Annual Field Conference, p. 226-230.

———1959, Green River and lower Uinta Formation subsurface stratigraphy in the western Uinta Basin, Utah *in* Geology of the Wasatch and Uinta Mountains transition area: Intermountain Association of Petroleum Geologists Guidebook, 10th Annual Field Conference, p. 139-149.

———1960, Lithologic zone boundaries in the Pennsylvanian Paradox Member, Paradox Basin: American Association of Petroleum Geologist Bulletin, v. 44, p. 1574-1578.

———1962, Source beds in Red Wash-Walker Hollow field, eastern Uinta Basin, Utah: American Association of Petroleum Geologists Bulletin, v. 46, no. 5, p. 690-694.

———1980, Henry Mountains Symposium: Utah Geological Association Publication 8, 389 p.

Picard, M. D. and others, 1960, Geology of Pennsylvanian gas in Four Corners region: American Association of Petroleum Geologists Bulletin, v. 44, no. 9, p. 1541-1569.

Pitman, W. C., III, and Manik Talwani, 1972, Sea-floor spreading in the North Atlantic: Geological Society of America Bulletin, v. 83, no. 3, p. 619-646.

Poborski, S. J., 1954, Virgin Formation (Triassic) of the St. George, Utah, area: Geological Society of America Bulletin, v. 65, p. 971-1606.

Podreborac, T. J., 1976, Trace fossils of the Brigham Quartzite (Lower and Middle Cambrian) in northern Utah and southeastern Idaho: M.S. thesis, University of Utah, Salt Lake City, Utah.

Pojeta, John Jr., 1971, Review of Ordovician pelecypods: U.S. Geological Survey Professional Paper 695, 46 p.

Poole, F. G., 1962, Wind directions in late Paleozoic to middle Mesozoic time on the Colorado Plateau: U.S. Geological Survey Professional Paper 450-D, p. D147-D151.

Poole, F. G., and Stewart, J. H., 1964, Chinle Formation and Glen Canyon Sandstone in northeast Utah and northwest Colorado *in* Geology and mineral resources of the Uinta Basin, Utah's hydrocarbon storehouse: Intermountain Association of Petroleum Geologists Guidebook, 13th Annual Field Conference, p. 93-104; *also* U.S. Geological Survey Professional Paper 501-D, p. D30-D39.

Powell, J. W., 1876, Report on the geology of the eastern portion of the Uinta Mountains and a region of country adjacent thereto: U.S. Geological and Geographical Survey of the Territories (Rocky Mountain region).

Pratt, A. R., and Eugene Callaghan, 1970, Land and mineral resources of Sanpete County, Utah: Utah Geological and Mineral Survey Bulletin 85, 72 p.

Pratt, A. R., E. B. Heylmun, Jr., and R. E. Cohenour, 1966, Salt deposits of Sevier Valley, Utah *in* Symposium on salt: North Ohio Geological Society, 2nd, v. 1, p. 48-58.

Preston, D. A., 1961, A symposium of the Oil and gas fields of Utah: Intermountain Association of Petroleum Geologists, 250 p.

Proctor, P. D., 1953, Geology of the Sevier Reef (Harrisburg) mining district, Washington County, Utah: Utah Geological and Mineral Survey Bulletin 44, 169 p.

———1959, Igneous rocks of the Mercur-Ophir area *in* Geology of the southern Oquirrh Mountains and Fivemile Pass-northern Boulter Mountains area, Tooele and Utah Counties, Utah: Utah Geological Society Guidebook to the Geology of Utah 14, p. 183-187.

Proctor, P. D., and K. C. Bullock, 1963, Igneous rocks of Utah *in* Oil and gas possibilities of Utah, re-evaluated: Utah Geological and MIneral Survey Bulletin 54, p. 155-169.

Pruitt, R. G., JR., 1961, The mineral resources of Uintah County: Utah Geological and Mineral Survey Bulletin 71, 101 p.

Quigley, M. D., and J. R. Price, 1963, Green River oil-shale potential in Utah *in* Oil and gas possibilities of Utah, re-evaluated: Utah Geological and Mineral Survey Bulletin 54, p. 207-213.

Randolph, R. L., 1972, Paleontology of the Swasey Limestone, Drum Mountains, west-central Utah: M.S. thesis, University of Utah, Salt Lake City, Utah.

Rascoe, Bailey, and D. L. Baars, 1972, Permian system *in* Geological atlas of the Rocky Mountains region: Rocky Mountain Association of Geologists.

Reber, S. J., 1952, Stratigraphy and structure of the south-central and northern Beaver Dam Mountains, Washington County, Utah *in* Cedar City, Utah, to Las Vegas, Nevada: Utah Geological Society Guidebook to the Geology of Utah 7, p. 101-108.

Reeside, J.B. Jr., 1923, Notes on the geology of the Green River Valley between Green River, Wyoming, and Green River, Utah: U.S. Geological Survey Professional Paper, 132-C, p. 35-50.

———1930, Descriptive geology of Green River Valley between Green River, Wyoming, and Green River, Utah: U.S. Geological Survey Water Supply Paper 618, p. 56-63.

———1944, Maps showing thickness and general character of Cretaieous(??) deposits of the western interior of the United States: U.S. Geological Survey Oil and Gas Investigations Preliminary Map no. 10.

———1957, Paleoecology of the Cretaceous seas of the western interior of the United States *in* Paleoecology, H. S. Ladd, ed., chap. 18: Geological Society of America Memoir 67, p. 505-541.

Rich, John L., 1935, Origin and evolution of rock fans and pediments: Geological Society of America Bulletin, v. 45, 0. 999-1024.

Rich, M., 1971, Middle Pennsylvanian rocks of eastern Great Basin: American Association Petroleum Geologists Bulletin v. 55, no. 3, p. 432-453.

Rich, T. H., and J. W. Collinson, 1973, First mammalian fossil from the Flagstaff Limestone, central Utah—*Vulpavus Australis* (Carnivora; Miacidae): Journal of Paleon tology, v. 47, no. 5, p. 854-860.

Richardson, G. B., 1913, The Paleozoic section in northern Utah: American Journal of Science 186 (4s, 36), p. 406-416.

———1927, The Upper Cretaceous section in the Colob Plateau, southwest Utah: Washington Academy of Science Journal 17, p. 464-475.

———1941, Geology and mineral resources of the Randolph quadrangle, Utah-Wyoming: U.S. Geological Survey Bulletin 923.

Richmond, G. M., 1962, Quaternary stratigraphy of the La Sal Mountains, Utah: U.S. Geological Survey Professional Paper 324, 135 p.

———1964, Glaciation of Little Cottonwood and Bells Canyons, Wasatch Mountains, Utah: U.S. Geological Survey Professional Paper 454-D, p. D1-D41.

Ridd, M. K., 1960, Landforms of Utah in proportional relief: Privately printed map.

———1963, The proportional relief landform map: Association of American Geographers' Annuals, v. 53, no. 4, p. 569-576.

Rigby, J. K., 1952, Geology of the Selma Hills, Utah County, Utah: Utah Geological and Mineral Survey Bulletin 45, 107 p.

———1958a, Lower Ordovician graptolite faunas of western Utah: Journal of Paleontology, v. 32, no. 5, p. 907-917.

———(ed.), 1958b, Geology of the Stansbury Mountains, Tooele County, Utah: Utah Geological Society Guidebook to the Geology of Utah 13.

———1959a, Late Devonian erosional surface exposed in the Wasatch and Uinta Mountains (Utah) *in* Geology of the Wasatch and Uinta Mountains transition area: Intermountain Association of Petroleum Geologists Guidebook, 10th Annual Field Conference, p. 60-62.

———1959b, Stratigraphy of the southern Oquirrh Mountains - lower Paleozoic succession, *in* Utah Geological Society Guidebook no. 14, p. 225-229.

———1963, Devonian system of Utah *in* Oil and gas possibilities of Utah re-evaluated: Utah Geological and Mineral Survey Bulletin 54, p. 75-88.

———1967, Sponges from the Silurian Laketown Dolomite, Confusion Range, western Utah: Brigham Young University Geology Studies, Provo, Utah, v. 14, p. 241-244.

Rigby, J. K., and D. L. Clark, 1962, Devonian and Mississippian systems in central Utah *in* Geology of the southern Wasatch Mountains and vicinity, Utah: Brigham Young University Geology Studies, v. 9, pt. 1, p. 17-25.

Rigby, J. K., and L. F. Hintze, 1977, Early Middle Ordovician corals from western Utah: Utah Geology, v. 4, no. 2, p. 105-111.

Rigby, J. K., and others, 1971, Guidebook to the Colorado River (pt. 3), Moab to Hite, Utah, through Canyonlands National Park: Brigham Young University Geology Studies, Provo, Utah, v. 18, pt. 2, 91 p.

Ritzma, H. R., 1959, Geologic atlas of Utah, Daggett County: Utah Geological and Mineral Survey Bulletin 66, 111 p.

Ritzma, H. R., 1969a, Tectonic resume, Uinta Mountains *in* Geology of the Uinta Mountains, Utah's maverick range: Intermountain Association of Petroleum Geologists Guidebook, 16th Annual Field Conference, p. 57-64.

———compiler, 1969b, Preliminary location map, oil-impregnated rock deposists of Utah: Utah Geological and Mineral Survey Map 25.

———1971, Faulting on the northern flank of the Uinta Mountains, Utah and Colorado *in* Symposium on Wyoming tectonics and their economic significance: Wyoming Geological Association Guidebook, no. 23, p. 145-150.

———1972, Petroleum and natural gas—The Uinta Basin *in* Geologic atlas of the Rocky Mountain region: Rocky Mountain Association of Geologists, p. 276-278.

———1973, Oil-impregnated rock deposits of Utah; Utah Geological and Mineral Survey Map 33.

———1974, Dating of igneous dike, eastern Uinta Mountains: Utah Geology, v. 1, no. 1, p. 95.

Ritzma, H. R., and D. K. Seeley, Jr., 1969, Determination of oil-shale potential, Green River Formation, Uinta Basin, northeastern Utah: Utah Geological and Mineral Survey Special Studies 26, 15 p.

Robeck, R. C., 1954, Uranium deposits of Temple Mountain (Utah) *in* Geology of the High Plateaus, central and south-central Utah: Intermountain Association of Petroleum Geologists, 5th Annual Field Conference, p. 110-111.

Roberts, R. J., and others, 1965, Pennsylvanian and Permian basins in northwestern Utah, northeastern Nevada and south-central Idaho: American Association of Petroleum Geologists Bulletin, v. 49, no. 11, p. 1926-1956.

Robison, R. A., 1960a, Some Dresbachian and Franconian trilobites of western Utah: Brigham Young University Geology Studies, v. 7, no. 3, 59 p.

———1960b, Lower and middle Cambrian stratigraphy of the eastern Great Basin *in* Geology of east-central Nevada: Intermountain Association of Petroleum Geologists Guidebook, 11th Annual Field Conference, p. 43-52.

———1963a, A reconnaissance survey of the coal resources of southwestern Utah: Utah Geological and Mineral Survey Special studies 3, 34 p.

———1963b, Coal resources of southwestern Utah *in* Geology of southwestern Utah: Intermountain Association of Petroleum Geologists Guidebook, 12th Annual Field Conference, p. 151-156.

———1964a, Late middle Cambrian faunas from western Utah: Journal of Paleontology, v. 38, no. 3, p. 510-566.

———1964b, Upper middle Cambrian stratigraphy of western Utah: Geological Society of America Bulletin, v. 75, no. 10, p. 995-1010.

———1964c, Cambrian of the Uinta Mountains *in* Geology and mineral resources of the Uinta Basin, Utah's hydrocarbon storehouse: Intermountain Association of Petroleum Geologists Guidebook, 13th Annual Field Conference, p. 63-66.

———1965, Middle Cambrian eocrinoids from western North America: Journal of Paleontology, v. 39, no. 3, p. 355-364.

———1966, Geology and coal resources of the Tropic area, Garfield County, Utah: Utah Geological and Mineral Survey Special Studies 18, 47 p.

———1969, Annelids from the middle Cambrian Spence Shale of Utah: Journal of Paleontology, v. 43, no. 5, p. 1169-1173.

———1971, Additional middle Cambrian trilobites from the Wheeler Shale of Utah: Journal of Paleontology, v. 45, no. 5, p. 796-804, illus.

Robison, R. A.., and L. F. Hintze, 1972, An Early Cambrian trilobite faunule from Utah: Brigham Young University Geology Studies, v. 19, pt. 1, p. 3-13.

Robison, R. A., and A. J. Rowell (eds.), 1976, Paleontology and depositional environments, Cambrian of western North America: Brigham Young University Geology Studies, v. 23, pt. 2, 227 p.

Roscoe, E. J., 1963, Stratigraphic summary of Quaternary Bonneville Basin mollusca: Sterkiana, no. 9, p. 19-23.

Rose, P. R., 1976, Mississippian carbonate shelf margins, western United States *in* Geology of the Cordilleran hingeline: U. S. Geological Survey Journal of Research, v. 4, no. 4, p. 449-466.

Ross, R. J., Jr., 1951, Stratigraphy of the Garden City Formation in northeastern Utah and its trilobite faunas: Peabody Museum of Natural History Bulletin 6, Yale University, Cambridge, Massachusetts, 161 p.

———1953a, Additional Garden City (Early Ordovician) trilobites (Utah): Journal of Paleontology, v. 27, no. 5, p. 633-646.

———1953b, The Ordovician system in northeastern Utah and southeastern Idaho *in* Geology of northern Utah and southeastern Idaho: Intermountain Association of Petroleum Geologists Guidebook, 4th Annual Field Conference, p. 22-26.

———1961, Distribution of Ordovician graptolites in eogeosynclinal facies in western North America and its paleogeographic implications: American Association of Petroleum Geologists Bulletin, v. 45, no. 3, p. 330-341.

———1976, Ordovician sedimentation in the western United States *in* Geology of the Cordilleran Hingeline: Rocky Mountain Association of Geologists Symposium, 1976.

Rowley, P. D., J. J. Anderson and P. L. Williams, 1975, A summary of Tertiary volcanic stratigraphy of the southwestern High Plateaus and adjacent Great Basin, Utah: U.S. Geological Survey Bulletin 1405-B, 20 p.

Rowley, P. D., and others, 1978, Age of structural differentiation between the Colorado Plateau and the Basin and Range Provinces: Geology, v. 6, no. 1, p. 51-55.

Rowley, P. D., and others, 1979, Cenozoic stratigraphic and structural framework of southwestern Utah: U.S. Geological Survey Professional Paper 1149, 22 p.

Rush, R. W., 1963, Silurian strata in Utah *in* Oil and gas possibilities of Utah, re-evaluated: Utah Geological and Mineral Survey Bulletin 54, p. 63-73.

Ryder, R. T., T. D. Fouch and J. H. Elison, 1976, Early Tertiary sedimentation in the western Uinta Basin, Utah: Geological Society of America Bulletin, v. 87, p. 496-512.

Sabatka, E. F., ed., 1964, Geology and mineral resources of the Uinta Basin, Utah's hydrocarbon storehouse: Intermountain Association of Petroleum Geologists Guidebook, 13th Annual Field Conference, 277 p.

Sadlick, Walter, 1965, Biostratigraphy of the Chainman Formation (Carboniferous) eastern Nevada and western Utah: Ph.D. dissertation, University of Utah, Salt Lake City, Utah, 227 p.

Sando, W. J., 1965, Revision of some Paleozoic coral species from the western United States: U.S. Geological Survey Professional Paper 503-E, p. E1-E38.

Sando, W. J., J. T. Dutro, Jr., and W. C. Gere, 1959, Brazer Dolomite (Mississippian), Randolph quadrangle, northeastern Utah: American Association of Petroleum Geologists Bulletin, v. 43, no. 12, p. 2741-2769.

Sando, W. J., and others, 1969, Carboniferous megafaunal and microfaunal zonation in the northern Cordillera of the United States: U.S. Geological Survey Professional Paper 613-E, p. E1-E29.

Schaeffer, B., 1950, A semiontoid fish from the Chinle Formation, with considerations of its relationships: American Museum of Natural History Novitiates, no. 1457, 29 p.

Schaeffer, F. E., Jr., and W. L. Anderson (eds.), 1960, Geology of the Silver Island Mountains, Box Elder and Tooele Counties, Utah, and Elko County, Nevada: Utah Geological Society Guidebook to the Geology of Utah 15, 175 p.

Schick, R. B., 1955, Geology of the Morgan-Henefer area, Morgan and Summit Counties, Utah: M.S. thesis, University of Utah, Salt Lake City, Utah, 54 p.

Schneider, M. C., 1967, Early Tertiary continental sediments of central and south-central Utah: Brigham Young University Geology Studies, Provo, Utah, v. 14, p. 143-194.

Shoemaker, E. M., J. E. Case, and D. P. Elston, 1958, Salt anticlines of the Paradox Basin: Intermountain Association of Petroleum Geologists, Ninth Field Conference Guidebook, p. 39-59.

Schoff, S. L., 1951, Geology of the Cedar Hills, Utah: Geological Society of America Bulletin, v. 62, no. 6 p. 619-646.

Schreiber, J. F., Jr., 1958, Sedimentary record in the Great Salt Lake, Utah: Ph. D. dissertation, University of Utah, 99 p.

Scott, W. E., 1980, New interpretations of Lake Bonneville stratigraphy and their significance for studies of earthquake-hazard assessment along the Wasatch Front: U.S. Geological Survey, Open-file report 80-801, p. 548-576.

Scudder, S. H., 1890, Tertiary insects of North America: U.S. Geological and Geographical Survey of the Territories Report, v. 13.

Seeland, D. A., 1968, Paleocurrents of the late Precambrian to early Ordovician (Basal Sauk) transgressive clastics of the western and northern United States with a review of the stratigraphy: Ph.D. dissertation, University of Utah, Salt Lake City, Utah.

Sharp, B. J., and N. C. Williams (eds.), 1963, Uranium in fluorite, Spor Mountain, Utah *in* Beryllium and uranium mineralization in western Juab County, Utah: Utah Geological Society Guidebook to the Geology of Utah 17, p. 14.

Sharp, G. C., 1976, Reservoir variations at Upper Valley field, Garfield County, Utah *in* Symposium on geology of the Cordilleran hingeline: Rocky Mountain Association of Geologists, Symposium Proceedings, p. 325-344.

Shawe, D. R., 1972, Reconnaissance geology and mineral potential of Thomas, Keg and Desert calderas, central Juab County, Utah: U.S. Geological Survey Professional Paper 800-B, p. B67-B77.

Sheehan, P. M., 1976, Late Silurian brachiopods from northwestern Utah: Journal of Paleontology, v. 50, no. 4, p. 710-733.

Shepard, W. M., H. T. Morris and D. R. Cook, 1968, Geology and ore deposits of the East Tintic mining district, Utah *in* Ore deposits of the United States, 1933-1967: American Institute of Mining Engineers, Graton-Sales, v. 1, New York, p. 941-965.

Shepardson, J. W., 1973, Western coal: Coal Age, mid-April issue.

Shoemaker, E. M., 1956, Precambrian rocks of the north-central Colorado Plateau *in* Geology and economic deposits of east-central Utah: Intermountain Association of Petroleum Geologists Guidebook, 7th Annual Field Conference, p. 54-57.

Shuey, R. T., and others, 1973, Aeromagnetics and the transition between the Colorado Plateaus and Basin and Range Provinces: Geology, v. 1, no. 3, p. 107-110.

Shuey, R. T., 1974, Aeromagnetic map of Utah: Utah Geological and Mineral Survey, scale 1:250,000.

Slentz, L. W., 1955, Salt Lake Group in lower Jordan Valley, Utah, *in* Tertiary and Quaternary geology of the eastern Bonneville Basin: Utah Geological Society Guidebook, no. 10, p. 23-26.

Smith, G. R., K. F. Horn and W. L. Stokes, 1968, Some late Pleistocene fishes of Lake Bonneville: Copeia, no. 4.

Smith, H. P., 1968, Paleoecological studies of the Lower Triassic series of western Utah: Ph.D. dissertation, University of Utah, Salt Lake City, Utah.

Smith, J. F., and others, 1963, Geology of the Capitol Reef area, Wayne and Garfield Counties, Utah: U.S. Geological Survey Professional Paper 363, 102 p.

Smith, J. P., 1932, Lower Triassic ammonoids of North America: U.S. Geological Survey Professional Paper 167, p. 3, 10.

Smith, R. B., 1974, Seismicity and earthquate hazards of the Wasatch Front, Utah: U.S. Geological Survey Earthquake Information Bulletin, v. 6, no. 4, p. 12-17.

———1978, Seismicity, crustal structure and intraplate tectonics of the interior of the western Cordillera: Geological Society of America Memoir 152, p. 111-144.

Smith, R. B., and M. L. Sbar, 1974, Contemporary tectonics and seismicity of the western United States with emphasis on the Intermountain Seismic belt: Geological Society of America Bulletin, v. 85, no. 8, p. 1205-1218.

Smith, R. B., and others, 1974, Source mechanisms of microearthquakes associated with underground mines in eastern Utah: Seismological Society of America Bulletin, v. 46, no. 4, p. 1295-1317.

Smith, R. B., and R. L. Bruin, 1984 Intraplate extensional tectonics of the eastern Basin-Range: Inferences on structural style from seismic reflection data, regional tectonics, and thermal-mechanical models of brittle-ductile deformation: Journal of Geophysical Research, v. 89, no. B7. p. 5733-5762.

Sohl, N. F., 1965, Marine Jurassic gastropods, central and southern Utah: U.S. Geological Survey Professional Paper 503-D, p. D1-D29.

Solion, M. A., and others, 1979, Structure and stratigraphy of a lower Triassic donodont locality, Salt Lake City, Utah: Brigham young University Studies, v. 26, pt. 3, p. 165-177.

Sperry, S. W., 1980, The Flagstaff Formation: depositional environment and paleoecology of clastic deposits near Salina, Utah, Brigham Young University Geology Studies, v. 27, pt. 2, p. 153-173.

Spieker, E. M., 1931a, Wasatch Plateau coal field, Utah: U.S. Geological Survey Bulletin 819.

———1931b, Bituminous sandstone near Vernal, Utah: U.S. Geological Survey Bulletin 822-C, p. 77-98.

———1946, Late Mesozoic and early Cenozoic history of central Utah: U.S. Geological Survey Professional Paper 205-D, p. 117-160.

———1949a, The transition between the Colorado Plateaus and the Great Basin Provinces in central Utah: Utah Geological Society Guidebook to the Geology of Utah 4, 85 p.

———1949b, Sedimentary facies and associated diastrophism in the Upper Cretaceous of central and eastern Utah: Geological Society of America Memoir 39, p. 55-81.

———1954, Structural history (central and south-central Utah) *in* Geology of the High Plateaus, central and south-central Utah: Intermountain Association of Petroleum Geologists Guidebook, 5th Annual Field Conference, p. 7-14.

Spieker, E. M., and A. A. Baker, 1928, Geology and coal resources of the Salina Canyon district, Sevier County, Utah: U.S. Geological Survey Bulletin 796, p. 125-170.

Spieker, E. M., and M. P. Billings, 1940, Glaciation in the Wasatch Plateau, Utah: Geological Society of America Bulletin 51, p. 1173-1197.

Spreng, W. C., 1979, Upper Devonian and Lower Mississippian strata on the flanks of the western Uinta Mountains, Utah: Brigham Young University Geology Studies, v. 26, pt. 2, p. 67-78.

Sprinkle, James, 1976, Biostratigraphy and paleoecology of Cambrian echinoderms from the Rocky Mountains: Brigham Young University Geology Studies, v. 23, pt. 2.

Staatz, M. H., 1963, Geology of the beryllium deposits in the Thomas Range, Juab County, Utah: U.S. Geological Survey Bulletin 1142-M, 36 p.

Staatz, M. H., and W. J. Carr, 1964, Geology and mineral deposits of the Thomas and Dugway Ranges, Juab and Tooele Counties, Utah: U.S. Geological Survey Professional Paper 415, 188 p.

Staatz, M. H., and W. R. Griffitts, 1961, Beryllium-bearing tuff in the Thomas Range, Juab County, Utah: Economic Geology, v. 56, no. 5, p. 941-950.

Staatz, M. H., and F. W. Osterwald, 1959, Geology of the Thomas Range fluorospar district, Juab County, Utah: U.S. Geological Survey Bulletin 1069, 97 p.

Stacey, J. S., and R. E. Zartman, 1978, A lead and strontium isotopic study of igneous rocks and ores from the Gold Hill mining district, Utah: Utah Geology, v. 5, no. 1, p. 1-15.

Stanley, K. O. and Collinson, J. W., 1979, Depositional history of Paleocene - Eocene Flafstaff Limestone and coeval(??) rocks, central Utah: American Association of Petroleum Geologists Bulletin v. 63, no. 3, p. 311-323.

Stanton, T. W., 1893, The Colorado Formation and its invertebrate faunas: U.S. Geological Survey Bulletin 106, p. 34-36.

Staub, A. M., 1975, Geology of the Picture Rock Hills quadrangle, southwestern Keg Mountains, Juab County, Utah: M.S. thesis, University of Utah, Salt Lake City, Utah.

Steed, R. H., 1954, Geology of the Circle Cliffs Anticline *in* Geology of the High Plateaus, central and south-central Utah: Intermountain Association of Petroleum Geologists Guidebook, No. 5, p. 99-102.

Steele, Grant, 1959, Stratigraphic interpretation of the Pennsylvanian-Permian systems of the eastern Great Basin: Ph. D. dissertation, University of Washington, 294 p.

———1960, Pennsylvanian-Permian stratigraphy of east-central Nevada and adjacent Utah *in* Geology of east-central Nevada: Intermountain Association of Petroleum Geologists Guidebook, 11th Annual Field Conference, p. 91-113.

Stewart, J. H., 1956, Triassic strata of southeastern Utah and southwestern Colorado *in* Geology and economic deposits of east-central Utah: Intermountain Association of Petroleum Geologists Guidebook, 7th Annual Field Conference, p. 85-92.

———1971, Basin and Range structure—A system of horsts and grabens produced by deep-seated extension: Geological Society of America Bulletin, v. 82, no. 4, p. 1019-1043.

———1976, Late Precambrian evolution of North America: Plate tectonic implication: Geology, v. 4, p. 11 15.

———1978, Basin and Range structure in western North America—A review: Geological Society of North America Special Paper 152.

Stewart, J. H., and R. F. Wilson, 1960, Triassic strata of the Salt Anticline region, Utah and Colorado, *in* Geology of the Paradox Basin Fold and Fault Belt: Four Corners Geological Society Third Field Conference Guidebook, p. 98-106.

Stewart, J. H., and others, 1972a, Stratigraphy and origin of the Chinle Formation and related Upper Triassic strata in the Colorado Plateau region: U.S. Geological Survey Professional Paper 690, 336 p..

———1972b, Stratigraphy and origin of the Trissac Moenkopi Formation and related strata in the Colorado Plateau area: U.S. Geological Survey Professional Paper 691, 195 p.

———-1977, East-West patterns of Cenozoic igneous rocks, aeromagnetic, and mineral deposits, Nevada and Utah: Geological Society of America Bulletin v. 88, p. 67-77.

———1978, Basin and Range structure in western North America—A review: Geological Society of North America Special Paper 152.

Stifel, P. B., 1964, Geology of the Terrace and Hogup Mountains, Box Elder County, Utah: Ph.D. dissertation, University of Utah, Salt Lake City, Utah, 173 p.

Stokes, W. L. 1944, Morrison and related deposits in and adjacent to the Colorado Plateau: Geological Society of America Bulletin 55, p. 951-992.

———1945, A new quarry for Jurassic dinosaurs (Emery County), Utah: Science, n.s. 101, p. 115-117.

———1948, Geology of the Utah-Colorado salt dome region, with emphasis on Gypsum Valley, Colorado: Utah Geological Society Guidebook to the Geology of Utah 3, 50 p.

———1952, Lower Cretaceous in Colorado Plateau: American Association of Petroleum Geologists Bulletin, v. 36, no. 9, p. 1766-1776.

———1952, Uranium-vanadium deposits of the Thompson area, Grand County, Utah, with emphasis on the origin of carnotite(??) ores: Utah Geological and Mineral Sruvey Bulletin 45, 51 p.

———1954, Stratigraphy of the southeastern Utah uranium region, *in* Uranium deposits and general geology of southeastern Utah: Utah Geological Society Guidebook, no. 9, p. 78-94.

———1958, Continental sediments of the Colorado Plateau *in* Geology of the Paradox Basin: Intermountain Association of Petroleum Geologists Guidebook, 9th Annual Field Conference, p. 26-30.

———1960, Inferred Mesozoic history of east-central Nevada and vicinity *in* Guidebook to the geology of east-central Nevada: Intermountain Association of Petroleum Geologists and Eastern Nevada Geological Association p. 117-121.

———1961, (Co-compiler with James H. Madsen, Jr.) Geologic Map of Utah, northeast quarter, 1/250,000.

———1961, Fluvial and aeolian sandstone bodies in the Colorado Plateau *in* Geometry of sandstone bodies, J. A. Peterson and J. C. Osmond, eds.: American Association of Petroleum Geologists, p. 151-178.

———1963, Geologic map of Utah, northwest quarter, 1/250,000/

———1963, (Co-compiler with Lehi F. Hitze) Geologic map of Utah, southwest quarter, 1/250,000.

———1964, Incised, wind-aligned stream patterns of the Colorado Plateau: American Journal of Science, v. 202, no. 6, p. 808-816.

———1965, (Co-compiler with Lehi F. Hintze) Geologic map of Utah, southeast quarter, 1/250,000.

———ed., 1966, The Great Salt Lake: Utah Geological Society Guidebook to the Geology of Utah 20, 170 p.

———1967a, Stratigraphy and primary sedimentary features of uranium occurrences of southeastern Utah *in* Uranium districts of southeastern Utah: Utah Geological Society Guidebook to the Geology of Utah 21, p. 32-52.

———1967b, A survey of southeastern Utah uranium districts *in* Uranium districts of southeastern Utah: Utah Geological Society Guidebook to the Geology of Utah 21, p. 1-11.

———1968a, Multiple parallel-truncation planes—A feature of wind-deposited sandstone formations: Journal of Sedimentary Petrology, v.

———1968b, Relation of fault trends and mineralization, eastern Great Basin, Utah: Economic Geology, v. 63, no. 7, p. 751-759.

———1969, Scenes of the Plateau lands and how they came to be: Privately published, Salt Lake City, Utah, 66 p.

———1973, Geologic and climatic inferences from surfacial deposits of the Colorado Plateau and Great Basin: Brigham Young University Geology Studies, Provo, Utah, v. 20, pt. 1, p. 11-26.

———1976, What is the Wasatch Line? *in* Geology of the Cordilleran Hingeline: Rocky Mountain Association of Geologists Symposium, 1976.

———1977, Subdivisions of the major physiographic provinces in Utah: Utah Geology, v. 4, no. 1, p. 1-17.

———1978a, Impressions of lizard scales from the Green River Formation (Eocene), Uinta Basin, Utah: Journal of Paleontology, v. 52, no. 2, p. 407-410.

———1978b, Animal tracks in the Navajo-Nugget Sandstone: Contributions to Geology, v. 16, no. 2, p. 103-107.

———1979a, Stratigraphy of the Great Basin region *in* Basin and Range Symposium, Rocky Mountain Association of Geologists and Utah Geological Association, p. 195-219.

———1980, Geologic setting of Great Salt Lake *in* Great Salt Lake—A scientific, historical and economic overview, J. W. Gwynn, ed.,: Utah Geological and Mineral Survey Bulletin 116, p. 55-68.

———1982, Geologic comparisons and contrasts, Paradox and Arapien Basins: *in* Utah Geological Association Publication 10, Overthrust Belt of Utah, p. 1-11.

Stokes, W. L., J. A. Peterson, and M. D. Picard, 1955, Correlation of Mesozoic formations of Utah: American Association of Petroleum Geologists Bulletin v. 39, no. 10, p. 2003-2019.

Stokes, W. L., and D. E. Arnold, 1958, Northern Stansbury Range and the Stansbury Formation *in* Geology of the Stansbury Mountains, Tooele County, Utah: Utah Geological Society Guidebook to the Geology of Utah 13, p. 135-149.

Stokes, W. L., and R. E. Cŏhenour, 1956, Geologic atlas of Utah—Emery County: Utah Geological and Mineral Survey Bulletin 52, 92 p.

Stokes, W. L., and K. C. Condie, 1961, Pleistocene bighorn sheep from the Great Basin: Journal of Paleontology, v. 35, no. 3, p. 598-609.

Stokes, W. L., and J. H. Madsen, Jr., 1967, Status and contributions of the University of Utah cooperative dinosaur project: Utah Academy of Sciences, Arts and Letters Proceedings, v. 44, pt. 1, p. 385-386.

———1977, Utah, the dinosaur state: Utah Academy of Sciences, Arts and Letters, Encyclia, v. 54, pt. 2, p. 75-78.

Stone, R. W., and C. T. Lupton, 1920, Gypsum deposits of Utah *in* Gypsum deposits of the United States: U.S. Geological Survey Bulletin 697, p. 261-282.

Stowe, Carlton, compiler, 1972, Oil and gas production in Utah to 1970: Utah Geological and Mineral Survey Bulletin 94, 179 p.

———1975, Utah mineral statistics through 1973: Utah Geological and Mineral Survey Bulletin 106, 121 p.

———1979, Rockhound guide to mineral and fossil localities in Utah: Utah Geological and Mineral Survey Circular 63, 79 p.

Stringham, B. F., 1942, Mineralization in the West Tintic mining district, Utah: Geological Society of America Bulletin 53, p. 267-290.

———1944, Bibliography of the geology and mineral resources of Utah to December 31, 1942: Bulletin of the University of Utah v. 34, no. 15, 95 p.

———1953, Granitization and hydrothermal alteration at Bingham, Utah: Geological Society of America Bulletin, v. 64, p. 945-992.

Stuart-Alexander, D. E., E. M. Shoemaker and H. J. Morre, 1972, Geology of Mule Ear diatreme, San Juan County, Utah: U.S. Geological Survey Miscellaneous Investigations Map I-674, with text.

Stugard, Frederick Jr., 1951, Uranium resources in the Silver Reef (Harrisburg) district, Washington County, Utah: U.S. Atomic Energy Commission TEM, Report 214.

Swain, F. M., Jr., 1956, Early Tertiary ostracode zones of the Uinta Basin (Colorado-Utah) *in* Geology and economic deposits of east-central Utah: Intermountain Association of Petroleum Geologists Guidebook, 7th Annual Field Conference, p. 125-139.

———1964a, Tertiary fresh-water ostracoda of the Uinta Basin and related forms from southern Wyoming, western Utah, Idaho and Nevada *in* Geology and mineral resources of the Uinta Basin, Utah's hydrocarbon storehouse: Intermountain Association of Petroleum Geologists Guidebook, 13th Annual Field Conference, p. 173-180.

Swank, W. J., 1978, Structural history of the Canyon Range thrust, central Utah: M.S. thesis, Ohio State University, 46 p.

Sweet, W. C., and others, 1970, North American Middle and Upper Ordovician conodont faunas: Geological Society of America, Memoir 127, p. 163-193.

Swenson, A. J., 1975, Sedimentary and igneous rocks of the Bingham district *in* Guidebook to the Bingham mining district: Society of Economic Geologists, p. 21-39.

Talmage, J. E., 1896, The Great Salt Lake, past and present: University of Utah Quarterly No. 2, p. 73-82, 137-152.

———1902, Lake Bonneville, predecessor of Great Salt Lake: Scottish Geographic Magazine, 18, p. 449-471.

Tanner, W. F., 1965, Upper Jurassic paleogeography of the Four Corners region: Journal of Sedimentary Petrology, v. 35, p. 564-574.

Tayler, P. L., L. A. Hutchinson and M. K. Muir, 1977, Heavy metals in the Great Salt Lake, Utah: Utah Geology, v. 4, no. 1, p. 19-28.

Terrell, F. M., 1972, Lateral facies and paleoecology of Permian Elephant Canyon Formation, Grand Canyon, Utah: Brigham Young University Geology Studies, v. 19 pt. 2, p. 3-44.

Taylor, M. E., 1963, The Lower Devonian Water Canyon Formation in northeastern Utah: M.S. thesis, Utah State University, 63 p.

Thaden, R. E., and others, 1964, Geology and ore deposits of the White Canyon area, San Juan and Garfield counties, Utah: U.S. Geological Survey Bulletin 1125, 166 p.

Thomas, G. H., 1958, Geology of Indian Springs quadrangle, Tooele and Juab Counties, Utah: Brigham Young University Geology Studies, Provo, Utah, v. 5, no. 4, 35 p.

Thomas, H. E., and G. H. Taylor, 1946, Geology and ground water resources of Cedar City and Parowan Valleys, Iron County, Utah: U.S. Geological Survey Water Supply Paper 993.

Thompson, A. E., and W. L. Stokes, 1970, Stratigraphy of the San Rafael Group, southwest and south-central Utah: Utah Geological and Mineral Survey Bulletin 87, 54 p.

Thompson, G. A., and M. L. Zoback, 1979, Regional geophysics of the Colorado Plateau: Tectonophysics, v. 61.

Thompson, M. L. and others, 1950, Pennsylvanian fusulinids(??) of the south-central Wasatch Mountains, Utah: Journal of Paleontology, v. 24, p. 430-465.

Thomson, K. C., 1973, Mineral deposits of the Deep Creek Mountains, Tooele and Juab Counties, Utah: Utah Geological and Mineral Survey Bulletin 99, 76 p.

Thorpe, M. R., 1919, Strutural features of the Abajo Mountains, Utah: American Journal of Science 198 (4s, 48), p. 379-389.

———1938, Wyoming Eocene fishes in the Marsh collection: American Journal of Science, 5th ser., v. 36, no. 214, p. 279-295.

Threet, R. L., 1959, Geomorphology of the Wasatch-Uinta Mountains junction (Utah-Wyoming) *in* Geology of the Wasatch and Uinta Mountain transition area: Intermountain Association of Petroleum Geologists Guidebook, 10th Annual Field Conferences, p. 24-33.

———1963, Structure of the Colorado Plateau margin near Cedar City, Utah *in* Geology of southwestern Utah: Intermountain Association of Petroleum Geologists Guidebook, 12th Annual Field Conference, p. 104-117.

Tidwell, W. D., 1962, An early Pennsylvanian flora from the Manning Canyon Shale, Utah: Brigham Young University Geology Studies, Provo, Utah, v. 9, pt. 2, p. 83-101.

———1966, Cretaceous paleobotany(??) of eastern Utah and western Colorado: Utah Geological and Mineral Survey Bulletin, v. 80, p. 87-95.

———1967, Flora of the Manning Canyon Shale—A lowermost Pennsylvanian flora from the Manning Canyon Shale, Utah, and its stratigraphic significance: Brigham Young University Geology Studies, Provo, Utah, v. 14, no. 1, p. 3-66.

———1975, Common fossil plants of western North America: Brigham Young University Press, Provo, Utah, 197 p.

Tidwell, W. D., G. F. Thayne, and J. L. Roth, 1976, Cretaceous and early Tertiary floras of the Intermountain area: Brigham Young University Geology Studies, Provo, Utah, v. 22, pt. 3, no. 6, p. 77-98.

Tomida, Y. and R. F. Butler, 1980, Drogonian mammals and Paleocene magnetic polarity stratigraphy, North Horn Formation, central Utah: American Journal of Science, v. 280, no. 8, p. 787-811.

Tooker, E. W., and R. J. Roberts, 1970, Upper Paleozoic rocks in the Oquirrh Mountains and Bingham mining district, Utah, *with a section on* biostratigraphy and correlation: U.S. Geological Survey Professional Paper 629-A, p. A1-A76.

Traver, W. M., 1949, Investigation of Coyote Creek antimony deposits, Garfield County, Utah: U.S. Bureau of Mines Report of Investigations 4470, 18 p.

Trexler, D. W., 1966, The stratigraphy and structure of the Coalville area, northeastern Utah: Colorado School of Mines Professional contribution no. 2, 69 p.

Turk, L. J., 1973, Hydrogeology of the Bonneville Salt Flats, Utah: Utah Geological and Mineral Survey Water Resources Bulletin 19, 81 p.

Turley, C. H., and W. P. Nash, 1980, Studies in late Cenozoic volcanism in west-central Utah, Part I, Petrology of late Tertiary and Quaternary volcanism in western Juab and Millard Counties, Utah: Utah Geological and Mineral Survey Special Studies 52, p. 1-33.

Tynan, M.C., 1977, Conodont biostratigraphy of the Mississippian Chanman Formation, western Millard County, Utah: Journal of Paleontology, v. 54, no. 6, p. 1282-1309.

Untermann, G. E., and B. R. Untermann, 1949, Geology of Green and Yampa River Canyons and vicinity, Dinosaur National Monument, Utah and Colorado: American Association Petroleum Geologists Bulletin 33, p. 683-694.

———1969, Geology of the Uinta Mountains area, Utah-Colorado *in* Geology of the Uinta Mountains, Utah's maverick range: Intermountain Association of Petroleum Geologists (and Utah Geological Society) Guidebook, 16th Annual Field Conference, p. 79-86.

Untermann, G. E., and B. R. Untermann, 1950, Stratigraphy of the Split Mountain area: Intermountain Association of Petroleum Geologists Guidebook, no. 5, p. 121-126.

———1954, Geology of Dinosaur National Monument and vicinity, Utah-Colorado: Utah Geological and Mineral Survey Bulletin 42, 228 p.

———1955, Geology of the eastern end of the Uinta Mountains, Utah-Colorado *in* Geology of northwestern Colorado: Intermountain Association of Petroleum Geologists Guidebook, 6th Annual Field Conference, p. 18-20.

———1964, Geology of Uintah County: Utah Geological and Mineral Survey Bulletin 72, 112 p., reprinted 1968.

———1969a, Popular guide to the geology of Dinosaur National Monument: Utah Dinosaur Nature Association, 126 p.

———1969b, Geology of the Uinta Mountains area, Utah-Colorado, *in* Geology of the Uinta Mountains, Utah's Maverick Range: Intermountain Association Petroleum Geologists Guidebook 16th Annual Field Conference, p. 79-86.

Utah Geological Association, 1974, Energy resources of the Uinta Basin, Utah: Utah Geological Association Publication 4, 73 p.

Utah Geological and Mineral Survey, 1966, Central Utah Coals—A guidebook prepared for the Geological Society of America and associated societies: Utah Geological and Mineral Survey Bulletin 80, 164 p.

———1974, Seismograph network expanded: Quarterly Review, v. 8, no. 2, p. 2.

Utah Mining Association, 1959, Utah's Mining Industry, An Historical, Operational, and Economic review of Utah's Mining Industry: Salt Lake City, Utah, 133 p.

Utah State Historical Society, 1963, Utah, treasure house of the nation—Century of mining, 1863-1963: Utah Historical Assocation Quarterly, v. 31, no. 3, p. 178-311.

Van Horn, Richard, 1964a, Nonmetallic and industrial minerals and materials resources—Sand and gravel *in* Mineral and water resources of Utah: U.S. Congress, 88th, 2nd Sess., Comm. Print., p. 215-218; *also* Utah Geological and Mineral Survey Bulletin 73, reprinted, 1969.

———1964b, Nonmetallic and industrial minerals and material resources—Lightweight aggregate *in* Mineral and water resources of Utah: U.S. Congress, 88th, 2nd Sess., Comm. Print., pp 185-188; *also* Utah Geological and Mineral Survey Bulletin 73, reprinted, 1969.

Van Sant, J. N., 1964, Refractory clay deposits of Utah: U.S. Bureau of Mines Information Circular 8213, 176 p.

Varney, P. J., 1972, Depositional environment of the Mineral Fork Formation (Precambrian) Wasatch Mountains, Utah: M.S. thesis, University of Utah, Salt Lake City, Utah.

Vaughn, P. P., 1973, Vertebrates from the Cutler Group of Monument Valley and vicinity *in* Guidebook of Monument Valley and vicinity, Arizona and Utah: New Mexico Geological Society Guidebook, 24th Annual Field Conference, p. 99-105.

Visher, G. S., 1971, Depositional processes and the Navajo Sandstone: Geological Society of America Bulletin, v. 82, no. 5, p. 1421-1423.

Visher, G. S., and W. E. Freeman, 1975, Stratigraphic analysis of the Navajo Sandstone—Reply: Journal of Sedimentary Petrology, v. 47, p. 492-497.

Vlam, H. A. A., 1963, Petrology of Lake Bonneville gravels, Salt Lake County, Utah: M.S. thesis, University of Utah, Salt Lake City, Utah, 58 p.

Von Dorston, P. L., 1970, Environmental analysis of the Swan Peak Formation in the Bear River Range, north-central Utah and southeastern Idaho: American Association of Petroleum Geologists Bulletin, v. 54, no. 7, p. 1140-1154.

Waddell, K. M., and Don Price, 1972, Quality of surface water in the Bear River Basin, Utah, Wyoming and Idaho: U.S. Geological Survey (and Utah Department of Natural Resources) Hydrologic Investigations Atlas HA-417.

Walcott, C. D., 1908a, Cambrian trilobites: Smithsonian Misc. Coll. 53, no. 2, p. 13-52.

———1908b, Cambrian sections of the Cordilleran area: Smithsonian Misc. Coll. 53, no. 5, p. 167-185, 189-200.

Walker, T. R., 1967, Formation of red beds in modern and ancient deserts: Geological Society of America Bulletin, v. 78, no. 3, p. 353-368.

Wallace, C. A. and M. D. Crittenden, Jr., 1969, The stratigraphy, depositional environment and correlation of the Precambrian Uinta Mountain Group, Utah *in* Geology of the Uinta Mountains, Utah's maverick range: Intermountain Association of Petroleum Geologists (and Utah Geological Society) Guidebook, 16th Annual Field Conference, p. 127-141.

Walton, P. T., 1964, Late Cretaceous and early Paleocene conglomerates along the margin of the Uinta Basin *in* Geology and mineral resources of the Uinta Basin, Utah's hydrocarbon storehouse: Intermountain Association of Petroleum Geologists Guidebook, 13th Annual Field Conference, p. 139-143.

Ward, S. H., 1977, From the heat of the Earth, the 40th annual Frederick William Reynolds lecture: University of Utah Press, Salt Lake City, Utah, 25 p.

Wardlaw, B. R., 1975, The biostratigraphy and paleontology of the Gerster Formation (Upper Permian) in Nevada and Utah: Ph.D. dissertation, Case Western Reserve University, Cleveland, Ohio.

Wardlaw, B. R., and J. W. Collinson, 1977, Biostratigraphic zonation of the Park City Group: U.S. Geological Survey Open-file report 77-853, 15 p.

Warner, L. A., 1978, The Colorado Lineament—A middle Precambrian wrench fault system: Geological Society of America Bulletin, v. 89, no. 2, p. 161-171.

Warner, M. A., 1956, The origin of the Rex Chert: Ph.D. dissertation, University of Wisconsin, Madison, Wisconsin, 493. p.

———1966, Sedimentational analysis of the Duchesne River Formation, Uinta Basin, Utah: Geological Society of America Bulletin, v. 77, no. 9, p. 945-957.

Waters, A. C., and H. C. Granger, 1953, Volcanic debris in uraniferous sandstone and its possible bearing on the origin and precipitation of uranium: U.S. Geological Survey Circular 224, 26 p.

Webb, G. W., 1956, Middle Ordovician detailed stratigraphic sections for western Utah and eastern Nevada: Utah Geological and Mineral Survey Bulletin 57, 78 p.

———1958, Middle Ordovician stratigraphy in eastern Nevada and western Utah: American Association of Petroleum Geologist Bulletin, v. 42, no. 10, p. 2335-2377.

Wegemann, C. H., 1915, The Coalville coal field, Utah: U.S. Geological Survey Bulletin 581, p. 161-184.

Weir, G. W., and W. P. Puffett, 1960, Similarities of uranium-vanadium and copper deposits in the Lisbon Valley area, Utah-Colorado, U.S.A. *in* Genetic problems of uranium and thorium deposits: International Geological Congress, 21st Annual Meeting, Copenhagen, Denmark, pt. 15, p. 133-148.

Wells, F. G., 1938, The origin of the iron-ore deposits in the Bull Valley and Iron Springs districts, Utah: Economic Geology 33, p. 477-507.

Welsh, J. E., 1959, Biostratigraphy of the Pennsylvanian and Permian systems in southern Nevada: Ph.D. dissertation, University of Utah, Salt Lake City, Utah.

———1972, Upper Paleozoic stratigraphy, Plateau-Basin and Range transition zone, central Utah: Utah Geological Association Publication 2, p. 13-20.

———Welsh, J. E., 1976, Relationships of Pennsylvanian and Permian stratigraphy to the Late Mesozoic thrust belt in the eastern Great Basin, Utah: Rocky Mountain Association of Petroleum Geologists Symposium on the Geology of the Cordilleran Hinge Line, p. 153-161.

Wender, L. E., 1976, Chemical and mineralogical evolution of the Cenozoic volcanics of the Marysvale, Utah, area: M.S. thesis, University of Utah, Salt Lake City, Utah.

Wengerd, S. A., 1958, Pennsylvanian stratigraphy, southwestern shelf, Paradox Basin *in* Geology of the Paradox Basin: Intermountain Association of Petroleum Geologists Guidebook, 9th Annual Field Conference, p. 109-134.

———1962, Pennsylvanian sedimentation in the Paradox Basin, Four Corners region *in* Pennsylvanian system in the United States, C. C. Branson, ed.,: American Association of Petroleum Geologists, p. 264-330.

Wengerd, S. A., and M. L. Matheny, 1958, Pennsylvanian system of the Four Corners region: American association of Petroleum Geologists Bulletin, v. 42, no. 9, p. 2048-2106.

Wengerd, S. A., and J. W. Strickland, 1954, Pennsylvanian stratigraphy of Paradox Salt Basin, Four Corners region, Colorado and Utah: American Association of Petroleum Geologists Bulletin, v. 38, no. 10, p. 2157-2199; correction, v. 39, no. 2, p. 259.

Wheeler, H. E. and G. Steele, 1951, Cambrian sequence of the House Range, Utah *in* Geology of the Canyon, House and Confusion Ranges, Millard County, Utah: Utah Geological Society Guidebook to the Geology of Utah 6, p. 29-37.

Whelan, J. A., (compiler), 1970, Rocky Range quartzmonzonite *in* Radioactive and isotopic age determinations of Utah rocks: Utah Geological and Mineral Survey Bulletin 81, p. 25; *also* University of Utah Bulletin, v. 61, no. 18 *and* Utah Engineering Experiment Station Bulletin 135.

———1971, Freshening of the south arm, Great Salt Lake, Utah, 1959-1971+: Utah Geological and Mineral Survey Report of Investigations 60.

———1973, Great Salt Lake, Utah—Chemical and physical variations of the brine, 1966-1972: Utah Geological and Mineral Survey Water Resources Bulletin 17, 24 p.

———1974, Bonneville Salt Flats—A possible geothermal area?: Utah Geology, v. 1, no. 1, p. 71-82.

———1975, Great Salt Lake—An overview of a brine resource: Utah Geology, v. 2, no. 1, p.69-74.

Whelan, J. A., and C. A. Peterson, 1975, Great Salt Lake, Utah—Chemical and physical variations of the brine, water-year 1973: Utah Geological and Mineral Survey Water Resources Bulletin 20, 29 p.

White, D., 1929, Flora of the Hermit Shale, Grand Canyon, Arizona: Carnegie Institution of Washington Publication 405.

White, T. E., 1964, The dinosaur quarry *in* Geology and mineral resources of the Uinta Basin, Utah's hydrocarbon storehouse: Intermountain Association of Petroleum Geologists Guidebook, 13th Annual Field Conference, p. 21-28.

White, T. E., 1968, Dinosaurs at home: Vantage Press, New York, 232 p.

White, W. W., III, 1973, Paleontology and depositional environments of the Cambrian Wheeler Formation, Drum Mountains, west-central Utah: M.S. thesis, University of Utah, Salt Lake City, Utah.

Willard, M. E. and Eugene Callaghan, 1962, Geology of the Marysvale quadrangle: U.S. Geological Survey Map GQ-154.

Williams, J. S., 1943, Carboniferous formations of the Uinta and northern Wasatch Mountains, Utah: Geological Society of America Bulletin 54, p. 591-624.

———1948, Geology of the Paleozoic rocks, Logan quadrangle, Utah: Geological Society of America Bulletin 59, p. 1121-1163.

———1949, Carboniferous and Permian rocks *in* Oil and gas possibilities of Utah: Utah Geological Society of America Bulletin 59, p. 1121-1163.

———1958, Geologic Atlas of Utah, Cache County: Geological and Mineral Survey Bulletin 64, 104 p.

———1962a, Recent history of Bear Lake Valley, Utah: American Journal of Science, v. 260, no. 1, p. 24-36.

———1962b, Lake Bonneville—Geology of southern Cache Valley, Utah: U.S. Geological Survey Professional Paper 257-C, p. 131-152.

———1963, Carboniferous and Permian rocks in Utah *in* Oil and gas possibilities of Utah, re-evaluated: Utah Geological and Mineral Survey Bulletin 54, p. 89-107.

———1970, Patterned ground indicates unstable landscapes: Journal of Soil and Water Conservation, v. 25, p. 194-196.

———1971, The Beirdneau and Hyrum Formations of north-central Utah *in* Paleozoic perspectives—A paleontological tribute to G. Arthur Cooper: Smithsonian Contributions to Paleobiology, no. 3, p. 219-229.

Williams, J. S., and George B. Maxey, 1941, The Cambrian section in the Logan quadrangle, Utah, and vicinity: American Journal of Science 239, p. 276-285.

Williams, J. S., and M. L. Tapper, 1953, Earthquake history of Utah, 1850-1949: Seismological Society of America Bulletin, v. 43, no. 3, p. 191-218.

Williams, N. C., 1955, Laramide history of the Wasatch, western Uinta Mountains area, Utah: Wyoming Geological Association Guidebook, 10th Annual Field Conference, p. 127-129.

———1963, Beryllium deposits, Spor Mountain, Utah *in* Beryllium and uranium mineralization in western Juab County, Utah: Utah Geological Society Guidebook to the Geology of Utah 17, p. 36-59.

Wilson, B. E., and L. Pierson, 1958, Arches and Natural Bridges National Monuments (Utah) *in* Geology of the Paradox Basin: Intermountain Association of Petroleum Geologists Guidebook, 9th Annual Field Conference, p. 16-18.

Wilson, J. R., 1976, Glaciated dolomite karst in the Bear River Range, Utah: Ph.D. dissertation, University of Utah, Salt Lake City, Utah.

Wilson, R. F., and J. H. Stewart, 1967, Correlation of Upper Triassic and Triassic (?) formation between southwestern Utah and southern Nevada: U.S. Geological Survey Bulletin 1244-D, 20 p.

Wilson, Wesley R., 1980, Thermal studies in a geothermal area: Ph. D. dissertation, University of Utah, 145 p.

Wimber, R., and A. L. Crawford, 1933, The occurrence and possible economic value of diatomaceous earth in Utah: Utah Academy of Science Proceedings, v. 10, 61 p.

Winkler, G. R., 1970, Sedimentology and geomorphic significance of the Bishop Conglomerate and the Browns Park Formation, eastern Uinta Mountains, Utah, Colorado and Wyoming: M.S. thesis, University of Utah, Salt Lake City, Utah.

Winkler, G. R., and others, 1970, K-Ar dates from Browns Park Formation tuff on the south flank of the eastern Uinta Mountains, Utah: U.S. Atomic Energy Commission, Annual Progress Report No. C00-89-130.

Withington, C. F., 1964, Nonmetallic and industrial minerals and materials resources—Gypsum and anhydrite *in* Mineral and water resources of Utah: U.S. Cong., 88th, 2nd Sess., Comm. Print., p. 175-185; *also* Utah Geological and Mineral Survey Bulletin 73, reprinted 1969.

Witkind, I. J., 1958, The Abajo Mountains, San Juan County, Utah, *in* Geology of the Paradox Basin: Intermountain Association of Petroleum Geologists Guidebook, 9th Annual Field Conference, p. 60-65.

———1975, The Abajo Mountains, an example of the laccolithic groups of the Colorado Plateau *in* Canyonlands Country: Four Corners Geological Association Guidebook, 8th Annual Field Conference, p. 244-252.

———1964, Geology of the Abajo Mountains area, San Juan County, Utah: U.S. Geological Survey Professional Paper 453, 110 p.

Wong, I. G., 1983, Seismicity of the Paradox Basin and the Colorado Plateau Interior, ONWI-492, prepared by Woodward-Clyde Consultants for Office of Nuclear Waste Isolation, Batelle Memorial Institute, 131 p.

Wood, H. B., 1968, Geology and exploitation of uranium deposits in the Lisbon Valley area, Utah, *in* Ore deposits of the United States, 1933-67: American Institute of Mining Engineers, Greton Sales Volume, p. 770-789.

Wood, J. W., 1976, Characteristics of aquifers in the northern Uinta Basin area, Utah and Colorado: Utah Department of Natural Resources Technical Publication no. 53.

Woodward, L. A., 1965, Late Precambrian stratigraphy of the northern Deep Creek Range, Utah: American Association of Petroleum Geologists Bulletin, v. 49, no. 3, pt. 1, p. 310-316.

———1968, Lower Cambrian and upper Precambrian strata of the Beaver Mountains, Utah: American Association of Petroleum Geologists Bulletin, v. 52, no. 7, p. 1279-1290.

———1972, Upper Precambrian stratigraphy of central Utah in Plateau-Basin and Range transition zone, central Utah: Utah Geological Association Publication 2, p. 1-5.

———1976a, Stratigraphy and correlation of late Precambrian rocks of Pilot Range, Elko County Nevada, and Box Elder County, Utah: American Association of Petroleum Geologists Bulletin, v. 51, no. 2, p. 235-243.

Woodward, L. A., 1976b, Stratigraphy of younger precambrian rocks along the Cordilleran Hingeline, Utah and southern Idaho: Rocky Mountain Association of Geologists Symposium on the Geology of the Cordilleran Hingeline.

Woolley, R. R., 1947, Utilization of surface-water resources of Sevier Lake Basin, Utah: U.S. Geological Survey Water Supply Paper 920.

Wright, J. C., and D. D. Dickey, 1963a, Block diagram of the San Rafael and underlying strata in Utah and part of Colorado: U.S. Geological Survey Map OC-63.

———1963b, Relations of the Navajo and Carmel Formations in southwest Utah and adjoining Arizona: U.S. Geological Survey Professional Paper 450-E, p. 63-67.

Wright, J. C., and others, 1962, Definition of members of Jurassic Entrada Sandstone in east-central Utah and west-central Colorado: American Association of Petroleum Geologists Bulletin, v. 46, no. 11, p. 2057-2070.

Yen, Teng-Chien, 1952, Molluscan fauna of the Morrison Formation: U.S. Geological Survey Professional Paper 233-B, p. 21-51.

———1954, Nonmarine molluscs of Late Cretaceous age from Wyoming, Utah and Colorado: U.S. Geological Survey Professional Paper 254-B, p. 45-66.

Yochelson, E. L., 1963, Paleoecology of the Permian Phosphoria Formation and related rocks: U.S. Geological Survey Professional Paper 475-B, p. 123-124.

———1968, Biostratigraphy of the Phosphoria, Park City and Shedhorn Formations: U.S. Geological Survey Professional Paper 313-D, p. 571-660.

Young, J. C., 1953, Geology of the southern Lakeside Mountains: Utah Geological and Mineral Survey Bulletin 56, 110 p.

Young, R. G., 1955, Sedimentary facies and intertonguing in the Upper Cretaceous of the Book Cliffs, Utah-Colorado: Geological Society of America Bulletin, v. 66, no. 2, p. 177-201.

———1960, Dakota Group of the Colorado Plateau: American Association of Petroleum Geologists Bulletin, v. 44, no. 2, p. 156-194.

———1964, Distribution of uranium deposits in the White Canyon-Monument Valley district, Utah-Arizona: Economic Geology, v. 59, no. 5, p. 850-873.

———1973, Depositional environments of basal Cretaceous rocks of the Colorado Plateau *in* Cretaceous and Tertiary rocks of the southern Colorado Plateau: Four Corners Geological Society, Durango, Colorado, p. 10-27.

Zeller, E. J., 1957, Mississippian endothyroid foraminifera from the Cordilleran geosyncline: Journal of Paleontology, v. 31, no. 4, p. 679-704.

Zietz, I., R. Shuey, and R. Kirby, Jr., 1976, Aeromagnetic map of Utah: U.S. Geological Survey Geophysical Investigations Map GP-907.

Zoback, M. L., 1983, Structure and Cenozoic tectonism along the Wasatch fault zone, Utah: Geological Society of America Memoir 157, p. 3-27.

GLOSSARY

A majority of the definitions are taken from the American Geological Institute's *Glossary of Geology* edited by Robert L. Bates and Julia A. Jackson, 1972

Acmite—A brown or green mineral of the clinopyroxene group; it occurs in certain alkali-rich igneous rocks.

Adobe—A fine-grained, usually calcareous, hard-baked, clayey deposit mixed with silt, usually formed as sheets in the central or lower parts of desert basins, as in the playas of the southwestern United States. It is probably a wind-blown deposit, often reworked and redeposited by running water.

Aegirine—The term is sometimes applied to impure acmite containing calcium, magnesium, or aluminum.

Agglomerate—A term originally used for a chaotic assemblage of coarse, angular, pyroclastic material. The term has been variously defined since then and should be defined in context to avoid confusion.

Albite—A colorless or milky-white triclinic mineral of the feldspar group, a variety of plagioclase. It occurs in all groups of rocks forming a common constituent of granite, and of various acid-to-intermediate igneous rocks; it is widely distributed in low-temperature metamorphic rocks (greenschist facies) and is regularly deposited from hydrothermal solutions in cavities and veins.

Alluvial—Pertaining to or composied of alluvium, or deposited by a stream or running water.

Alluvial fan—A low, outspread, relativley flat to gently sloping mass of loose rock material, shaped like an open fan or a segment of a cone, deposited by a stream wherever a constriction or steep gradient changes.

Alluvial plain—A level or gently sloping tract or a slightly undulating land surface produced by extensive deposition of alluvium, usually adjacent to a river that periodically overflows its banks; it may be situated on a flood plain, a delta, or an alluvial fan.

Alluvium—A general term for clay, silt, sand, gravel, or similar unconsolidated detrital material deposited during comparatively recent geologic time by a stream or other body of running water as a sorted or semisorted sediment in the bed of the stream or on its flood plain or delta, or as a cone or fan at the base of a mountains slope; esp. such a deposit of fine-grained texture (silt or silty clay) deposited during time of flood.

Alunite—A mineral which is isomorphous with natroalunite, sometimes contains appreciable sodium, generally occurs as a hydrothermal alteration product in feldspathic igneous rocks, and is used in the manufacture of alum.

Alteration—Any change in the mineralogic composition of a rock brought about by physical or chemical means, esp. by the action of hydrothermal solutions.

Amethyst—A transparent to translucent, purple to pale violet variety of crystalline quartz, much used as a semiprecious gemstone. The color is due to iron compounds.

Amphibole—A group of dark rock-forming ferromagnesian silicate minerals, closely related in crystal form and composition.

Andesine—A mineral of the plagioclase fledspar group with a composition of albite to anorthoclase ranging from 70:30 to 50:50 percent.

Andesite—A dark-colored, fine-grained extrusive rock that, when porphyritic, contains phenocrysts composed primarily of zoned acid plagioclase and one or more of the mafic minerals, with groundmass composed generally of the same minerals as the phenocrysts, although the plagioclase may be more sodic and quartz is generally present; the extrusive equivalent of diorite. Andesite grades into latite with increasing alkali feldspar content, and into dacite with more alkali feldspar and quartz.

Angiosperm—A plant with true flowers in which the seeds are enclosed in an ovary, comprising the ftuit. Such plants range from the Early Cretaceous or possibly before.

Anorthoclase—A triclinic mineral of the alkali feldspar groups. It is a sodium-rich feldspar that shows deviations from monoclinic symmetry and that contains very fine-grained intergrowths; it is widespread as a groundmass constituent of slightly alkalic lavas.

Antecedent—Said of a stream, valley, or drainage system that maintains its original course or direction despite subsequent deformation or uplift.

Anteposition—A term proposed by C.B. Hunt to combine the concepts of *ante*cedence and super*position.*

Anticline—A fold, generally convex upward, whose core contains the stratigraphically older rocks.

Antimony—A hexagonal mineral, the native metallic element Sb. It is brittle and commonly occurs in silvery or tin-white, granular, lamelar, or shapeless masses.

Apatite—A group of variously colored hexagonal minerals consisting of calcium phosphate together with fluorine, chlorine, hydroxyl, or carbonate in varying amounts.

Aphanitic—Said of the texture of an igneous rock in which the crystalline components are not distinguishable by the unaided eye. Also said of a rock or a groundmass exhibiting such texture.

Aplite—A light-colored hypabyssal igneous rock characterized by a fine-grained xenomorphic-granular texture. Aplites may range in composition from granitic to gabbroic, but the term with no modifier is generally understood to mean granitic aplite, consisting of quartz, potassium feldspar, and acid plagioclase.

Arete—A narrow serrate mountain crest or rock sharp-edged ridge or spur, commonly present above the snowline in rugged mountains sculptured by glaciers and resulting from the continued backward growth of the walls of adjoining cirques.

Asthenosphere—The layer or shell of the Earth below the lithospere, which is weak and in which isostatic adjustments take place, in which magmas may be generated, and in which seismic waves are strongly attenuated. It is equivalent to the upper mantle.

Basalt—A general term for the dark-colored mafic igneous rocks, commonly extrusive but locally intrusive, composed chiefly of calcic plagioclase and clinopyroxene; the fine-grained equivalent of gabbro.

Basanite—A group of basaltic rocks characterized by calcic plagioclase, clinopyroxene, a feldspathoid, and olivine; also, any rock in that group.

Basement—(a) The undifferentiated complex of rocks that underlies the rock of interest in an area. (b) The crust of the Earth below sedimentary deposits, extending downward to the Mohorovicic discontinuity.

Bauxite—An off-white, grayish, brown, yellow, or reddish-brown rock composed of a mixture of various amorphous or crystalline hydrous aluminum oxides and aluminum hydroxides, along with free silica, silt, iron hydroxides, and clay minerals. It is the principal commercial source of aluminum.

Bedrock—A general term for the rock, usually solid, that underlies soil or other unconsolidated, superficial material.

Beryl—A mineral: $Be_3Al_2Si_6O_{18}$. It usually occurs in green or bluish-green, sometimes yellow or pink, rarely white, hexagonal prisms in metamorphic rocks and granitic pegmatites and as an accessory mineral in acid igneous rocks. Beryl is the principal ore of beryllium.

Biotite—A widely distributed and important rock-forming mineral of the mica group, generally black, dark brown, or dark green and is a constituent of crystalline rocks or a detrital constituent of sandstones and other sedimentary rocks.

Bixbyite—A black isometric mineral: $(Mn,Fe)_2O_3$.

Caliche—Gravel, rock, soil, or alluvium cemented with soluble nitrate salts.

Chlorite—A group of platy, monoclinic, usually greenish minerals characterized by prominent ferrous iron and by the absence of calcium and alkalies; chromium and manganese may also be present. Chlorites are associated with and resemble micas (the tabular crystals of chlorite cleave into small, thin flakes or scales that are flexible, but not elastic as those of mica), and are widely distributed, esp. in low-grade metamorphic rocks, or as alteration products of ferromagnesian minerals in igneous rocks.

Cirque—A deep, steep-walled, flat or gently floored, half-bowl-like recess or hollow, variously described as horse-shoe- or crescent-shaped or semicircular in plan, situated high on the side of a mountain commonly at the head of a glacial valley, and produced by the erosive activity (frost action, nivation, ice plucking) of mountain glaciers. It often contains a small round lake, and it may or may not be occupied by ice or snow.

Clinopyroxene—(a) A group name for pyroxenes crystallizing in the monoclinic system and sometimes containing considerable calcium with or without aluminum and the alkalies. (b) Any monoclinic mineral of the pyroxene group, such as a diopside, hedenbergite, clinoenstatite, clinohypersthene, clinoferrosilite, augite, acmite, pigeonite, spodumene, jadeite, and omphacite.

Colluvium—(a) A general term applied to any loose, heterogeneous, and incoherent mass of soil material or rock fragments deposited chiefly by mass-wasting, usually at the base of a steep slope or cliff; e.g. talus, cliff debris, and avalanche material. (b) Alluvium deposited by unconcentrated surface runoff or sheet erosion, usually at the base of a slope.

Continental accretion—A theory, originally proposed by J.D. Dana in the 19th Century, that continents have grown at the expense of the ocean basins by the gradual addition of new continental material around an original nucleus. Most of the new material was believed to have accumulated in concentric geosynclinal belts, each in turn consolidated by orogeny and succeeded by a new belt farther out. There is good evidence along some continental borders, as in western North America, that much new continental crust (now land area) has been added to the continent during phanerozoic time, but most geologists now reject the larger implications of the concept.

Dacite—A fine-grained extrusive rock with the same general composition as andesite but having a less calcic feldspar.

Diabase—In the U.S., an intrusive rock whose main components are labradorite and pyroxene and which is characterized by ophitic texture. As originally applied by Brongniart in 1807, the term corresponded to what is now recognized as diorite.

Diatomite—The dense, chert-like consolidated equivalent of diatomaceous earth.

Diatreme—A breccia-filled volcanic pipe formed by a gaseous explosion.

Dike—A tabular igneous intrusion that cuts across the planar structures of the surrounding rock.

Diopside—An igneous intrusive rock composed almost entirely of diopside, with iron ore, ceylonite, and garnet as common accessories.

Diorite—A group of plutonic rocks intermediate in composition between acidic and basic rocks, characteristically composed of dark-colored amphibole (esp. hornblende), acid plagioclase (oligoclase, andesine), pyroxene, and sometimes a small amount of quartz; also, any rock in that group; the approximate intrusive equivalent of andesite. Diorite grades into monzonite with an increase in the alkali feldspar content. In typical diorite, plagioclase contains less that 50% anorthite, hornblende predominates over pyroxene, and mafic minerals total less than 50% of the rock.

Dip—The angle that a structural surface, e.g., a bedding or fault plane, makes with the horizontal, measured perpendicular to the strike of the structure.

Discontinuity—(a) Any interruption in sedimentation, whatever its cause or length, usually a manifestation of nondeposition and accompanying erision; an unconformity. (b) A surface separating two unrelated groups of rock; e.g., a fault or an unconformity.

Dolomite—A common, rock-forming, rhombohedral mineral. Part of the magnesium may be replaced by ferrous iron and less frequently by manganese. Dolomite is white colorless, or tinged yellow, brown, pink, or gray; it has perfect rhombohedral cleavage and a pearly to vitreous luster, feebly effervesces in cold, dilute hydrochloric acid, and forms curved, saddle-like crystals. Dolomite is found in extensive beds as a compact limestone or dolomite rock; it is also precipitated directly from seawater, possibly under warm, shallow conditions.

Dolomite—A carbonate, sedimentary rock consisting chiefly of dolomite or a variety of limestone or marble rich in magnesium carbonate. Dolomite occurs in crystalline and noncrystalline forms, is clearly associated and often interbedded with limestone, and usually represents a postdepositional replacement of limestone. Pure dolomite (unless finely pulverized) will effervesce very slowly in cold hydrochloric acid.

Epicontinental—Pertaining to the continental shelf.

Extrusion—In volcanology, the igneous process of emitting lava and other ejectamenta onto the Earth's surface; also the rock so formed.

Facies change—A lateral or vertical variation in the lithologic or paleontologic characteristics of contemporaneous sedimentary deposits. It is caused by or relfects, a change in the depositional environments.

Fanglomerate—A sedimentary rock consisting of slightly waterworn, heterogeneous fragments, originally deposited in an alluvial fan and subsequently cemented into a firm rock, and characterized by a considerable persistence parallel to the deposition strike but by a rapid downdip thinning. The term was proposed by Lawson (1913, p. 329) for the coarser, consolidated rock material occurring in the upper part of an alluvial fan.

Fault—A surface or zone of rock fracture along which there has been displacement, from a few centimeters to a few kilometers in scale.

Feldspathoid—A group of comparatively rare rock-forming minerals consisting of aluminosilicates of sodium, potassium, or calcium and having too little silica to form feldspar. Feldspathoids are chemically related to the feldspars, but differ from them in crystal form and physical properties; they take the places of feldspars in igneous rocks that are undersaturated with respect to silica or that contain more alkalies and aluminum than can be accommodated in the feldspars. Feldspathoids may be found in the same rock with feldspars but never with quartz or in the presence of free magmatic silica.

Fluorite—A transparent to translucent mineral found in many different colors (often blue or purple) and has a hardness of 4 on Mohs' scale. Fluorite occurs in veins usually as a gangue mineral associated with lead, tin, and zinc ores, and is commonly found in crystalline cubes with perfect octahedral cleavage. It is the principal ore of fluorine, and is used as a flux in the preparation of glasses and enamels, and the manufacture of hydrofluoric acid, and for carved ornamental objects.

Fluorspar—*fluorite.*

Galena—A bluish-gray to lead-gray mineral, PbS, almost always containing silver. Galena occurs in cubic or octahedral crystals, in masses, or in coarse or fine grains; it is often associated with sphalerite as disseminations in veins in limestones, dolomites, and sandstones. It has a shiny metallic luster, exhibits highly perfect cubic cleavage, and is relatively soft and very heavy. Galena is the most important ore of lead and one of the most important sources of silver

Garnet—Any of the minerals of the garnet group, such as the end members almandine (Fe-Al), andradite (Ca-Fe), grossular (Ca-Al), pyrope (Mg-Al), spessartine (Mn-Al), and uvarovite (Ca-Cr). Garnet is a brittle and transparent to subtransparent mineral, having a vitreous luster, absence of cleavage, and usually red color (but also green, brown, black, and most any other color except possibly blue). It occurs as an accessory mineral in a wide range of igneous rocks, but is most commonly found as distinctive euhedral isometric crystals in metamorphic rocks (gneiss, mica schist, eclogite); it may also be massive or granular. Garnet is used as a semiprecious stone and as an abrasive.

Gastroliths—A polished stone or pebble from the stomach of some vertebrates and thought to have been used in grinding up their food.

Geosyncline—A mobile downwarping of the crust of the Earth, either elongate or basin-like, measured in scores of kilometers, which is subsiding as sedimentary and volcanic rocks accumulate to thicknesses of thousands of meters. A geosyncline may form in part of a tectonic cycle in which orogeny follows. The concept was presented by Hall in 1850, and the term *geosynclinal* was proposed by Dana in 1873. The differing opinions of the origin, mechanics, and essential features of geosynclines are reflected in the various schemes that have been used to define aspects of the term. Some are based on the tectonic relationship of crustal units, some emphasize mountain-building processes, and others are concerned with the relationship of geosynclinal sedimentation to subsidence.

Gilsonite—uintahite.

Glauconite—A dull-green, amorphous, and earthy or granular mineral of the mica group. It has often been regarded as the iron-rich analogue of illite. Glauconite occurs abundantly in greensand, and seems to be forming in the marine environment at the present time; it is the most common sedimentary (diagenetic) iron silicate and is found in marine sedimentary rocks from the Cambrian to the present. Glauconite is an indicator of very slow sedimentation.

Gneiss—A foliated rock formed by regional metamorphism in which bands or lenticles of granular minerals alternate with bands and lenticles in which minerals having flakey or elongate prismatic habits predominate. Although a gneiss is commonly fledspar- and quartz-rich, the mineral composition is not an essential factor in its definition. Varieties are distinguished by texture (e.g., augen gneiss), characteristic minerals (e.g., hornblende gneiss), or general composition and/or origins (e.g., granite gneiss).

Goethite—A yellowish, reddish, or brownish-black mineral; FeO(OH). It is dimorphous with lepidocrocite. Goethite is the commonest constituent of many forms of natural rust or of limonite, and it occurs as a weathering product in the gossans of sulfide-bearing ore deposits.

Graben—An elongate, relatively depressed crustal unit or block that is bounded by faults on its long sides. It is a structural form that may or may not be geomorphologically expressed as a *rift valley.*

Granite—A plutonic rock in which quartz constitutes 10-15 percent of the felsic components and in which the alkali feldspar/total feldspar ration is generally restricted to the range of 65 to 90 percent. Rocks in this range of composition are scarce in nature, and sentiment has been growing to expand the definition to include rocks designated as adamellite or quartz monzonite which are abundant in the U.S. The origin of granite is in dispute, with some petrologists regarding it as igneous, having crystallized from magma, and others considering it as the product of intense metamorphism of pre-existing rocks.

Granodiorite—A group of coarse-grained plutonic rocks intermediate in composition between quartz diorite and quartz monzonite, containing quartz, plagioclase (oligoclase or andesine), and potassium feldspar, with biotite, hornblende, or, more rarely, pyroxene, as the mafic components; also, any member of that group; the approximate intrusive equivalent of *rhyodacite.* The ratio of plagioclase to total feldspar is at least two to one but less than nine to ten. With less alkali feldspar it grades into quartz diorite, and with more alkali feldspar, into granite or quartz monzonite. The term first appeared in print in 1893 in a paper by Lindgren and was applied to all rocks intermediate in composition between granite and diorite. The term has the connotation that the rock is a diorite with granitic charactertistics, i.e. with quartz and a certain amount of orthoclase.

Gymnosperm—A plant whose seeds are not enclosed in an ovary. Examples include cycads, ginkgo, pines, firs, and spruces. Such plants range from the upper Devonian.

Gypsum-A widely distributed mineral consisting of hydrous calcium sulfate. It is the commonest sulfate mineral and is frequently associated with halite and anhydrite in evaporites or forming thick, extensive beds interstratified with limestone, shales, and clays (esp. in rock of Permian and Triassic age). Gypsum is very soft (hardness of 2 on Mohs' scale), and is white or colorless when pure, but can be tinted grayish, reddish, yellowish, bluish, or brownish. It occurs massive (alabaster), fibrous (satin spar), or in monoclinic crystals (selenite). Gypsum is used chiefly as a soil amendment, as a retarder in portland cement, and in making plaster of Paris.

Hawaiite—(mineral) a pale-green, iron-poor gem variety of olivine from the lavas of Hawaii.

Hawaiite—(petrology) an andesite-bearing alkali olivine basalt typically found in the Hawaiin Islands.

Heave—A predominantly upward movement of a surface caused by expansion or displacement, such as due to swelling clay, removal of overburden, seepage pressure, or frost action.

Heave—In a fault, the horizontal component of separation or displacement.

Hematite—A common iron mineral, dimorphous with maghemite. Hematite occurs in splendent, metallic-looking, steel-gray or iron-black rhombohedral crystals, in reniform masses or fibrous aggregates, or in deep-red or red-brown earthy forms, and it has a distinctive cherry-red to reddish-brown streak and a characteristic brick-red color when powdered. It is found in igneous, sedimentary, and metamorphic rocks both as a primary constituent and as an alteration product. Hematite is the principal ore of iron.

Hogan—An earth-covered Navaho dwelling.

Hogback—Any ridge with a sharp summit and steep slopes of nearly equal inclination on both flanks, and resembling in outline the back of a hog.

Hornblende—The commonest mineral of the amphibole group. It has a variable composition, and may contain potassium and appreciable fluorine. Hornblende is commonly black, dark green, or brown, and occurs in distinct monoclinic crystals or in columnal, fibrous, or granular forms. It is a primary constituent in many acid and intermediate igneous rocks (granites, syenites, diorites, andesites) and less commonly in basic igneous rocks, and it is a common metamorphic mineral in gneisses and schists.

Horst—An elongate, relatively uplifted crustal unit or block that is bounded by faults on its long sides. It is a structural form and may or may not be expressed geomorphologically.

Host rock—A body of rock containing other rocks or mineral deposits; e.g., a pluton containing xenoliths, or any rock susceptible to attack by mineralizing solutions and in which ore deposits occur (such as the wall rock of an epigenetic ore deposit).

Hydrothermal—Of or pertaining to heated water, to the action of heated water, or to the products of the action of heated water, such as a minerral deposit precipited from a hot aqueous solution.

Ignimbrite—The rock formed by the deposition and consolidation of ash flows and other pyroclastics.

Intrusion—The process of emplacement of magma in pre-existing rock; magmatic activity; also, the igneous rock mass so formed within the surrounding rock.

Intrusion—A sedimentary structure or rock formed by intrusion on a relatively large scale.

Kerogen—Fossilized, insoluble, organic material found in sedimentary rocks, usually shales, which can be converted by distillation to petroleum products.

Laccolith—A concordant igneous intrusion with a known or assumed flat floor and a postulated dike-like feeder somewhere beneath its thickest point. It is generally lens-like in form and roughly circular in plan, less than five miles in diameter, and from a few feet to several hundred feet in thickness.

Lamprophyre—A group of dark-colored, porphyritic, hypabyssal igneous rocks characterized by euhedral crystals, a high percentage of mafic minerals (esp. biotite, hornblende, and pyroxene) which form the phenocrysts, and a fine-grained groundmass with the same mafic minerals in addition to light-colored minerals (feldspars or feldspathoids). Lamprophyres are frequently highly altered and are commonly associated with carbonatites.

Latite—A porphyritic extrusive rock having plagioclase and potassium feldspar (probably mostly sanidine) present in nearly equal amounts as phenocrysts, little or no quartz, and a finely crystalline to glassy groundmass, which may contain obscure potassium feldspar; the extrusive equivalent of monzonite. Latite grades into trachyte with an increase in the alkali feldspar content, and into andesite or basalt, depending on the presence of acid or calcic plagioclase, as the alkali feldspar content decreases.

Lehiite—A white, fibrous mineral found in layers and crusts. It is a hydrated phosphate of Na, K, Ca, and Al.

Limonite—A general field term for a group of brown, amorphous, naturally occurring hydrous ferric oxides whose real identities are unknown. It consists of any of several iron hydroxides (commonlly goethite), or of a mixture of several minerals (such as hematite, geothite, and lepidocrocite) with or without presumably absorbed additional water. It is a common secondary material formed by oxidation (weathering) of iron or iron-bearing minerals, and it may also be formed as an inorganic or biogenic precipitate, and it represents the coloring material of yellow clays and soils. Limonite is commonly dark brown or yellowish brown, but may be yellow, red, or nearly black; it is a minor ore of iron.

Lithosphere—The solid portion of the Earth, as compared with the atmosphere and the hydrosphere; the crust of the Earth, as compared with the barysphere.

Loess—A widespread, homogeneous, commonly nonstratified, porous, friable, unconsolidated but slightly coherent, usually highly calcareous, fine-grained, blanket deposit (generally less than 30 m thick) of marl or loam, consisting predominantly of silt with subordinate grain sizes ranging from clay to fine sand. It is buff to light yellowish or yellowish brown in color. Loess is generally believed to be windblown dust of the Pleistocene age, carried from desert surfaces, alluvial valleys, and outwash plains lying south of the limits of the ice sheets, or from unconsolidated glacial or galciofluvial deposits uncovered by successive glacial recessions but prior to invasion by a vegatation mat. The mineral grains, composed mostly of silica and associated heavy minerals, are fresh and angular, and are generally held together by calcareous cement.

Magma—Naturally occurring mobile rock material, generated within the Earth and capable of intrusion and extrusion, from which igneous rocks are thought to have been derived through solidification and related processes. It may or may not contain suspended solids (such as crystals and rock fragments) and/or gas phases.

Magma chamber—A reservoir of magma in the shallow part of the lithosphere (to a few thousand meters) from which volcanic materials are derived; the magma has ascended into the crust from an unknown source below.

Mantle—A general term for an outer covering of material of one kind or another, such as a regolith.

Matterhorn—A glacial horn resembling the Matterhorn, a peak in the Pennine Alps.

Meander—One of a series of somewhat regular, freely developing, and sinuous curves, bends, loops, turns, or windings in the course of a stream. It is produced by a mature stream swinging from side to side as it flows across its flood plain or shifts its course laterally toward the convex side of an original curve.

Metamorphism—The mineralogical and structural adjustment of solid rocks to physical and chemical conditions which have been imposed at depth below the surface zones of weathering and cementation, and which differ from the conditions under which the rocks in question originated..

Mohorovicic discontinuity—The boundary surface or sharp seismic-velocity discontinuity that separates the Earth's crust from the subjacent mantle. Its depth varies from about 5-10 km beneath the ocean floor to about 35 km below the continents, although its depth below the geoid may reach 70 km under some mountain ranges. The discontinuity probably represents a chemical change between the basaltic materials above to periodoctitic or dunitic materials below, rather than a phase change (basalt to eclogite); however, the discontinuity should be defined by seismic velocities alone.

Moraine—A mound, ridge, or other distinct accumulation of unsorted, unstratified glacial drift, predominantly till, deposited chiefly by direct action of glacier ice in a variety of topographic landforms that are independent of control by the surface on which the drift lies.

Muscovite—(a) A mineral of the mica group that is usually colorless, whitish, or pale brown, and is a common mineral in metamorphic rocks (gneisses and schists), in most acid igneous rocks (such as granites and pegmatites), and in many sedimentary rocks (esp. sandstone). (b) A term applied in clay mineralogy to illite.

Normal fault—A fault in which the hanging wall appears to have moved downward relative to the footwall. The angle of the fault is usually 45-90°. There is dip separation but there may or may not be dip slip.

Obsidian—A black or dark-colored volcanic glass, usually of rhyolitic composition characterized by conchoidal fracture. It is sometimes banded or has microlites. Obsidian has been used for making arrowheads, other sharp implements, jewelry, and art objects.

Olivine—An olive-green, grayish-green, or brown, orthorhombic mineral. It is a common rock-forming mineral of basic, ultrabasic, and low-silica igneous rocks (gabbaro, basalt, peridotite, dunite); it crystallizes early from a magma, weathers readily at the Earth's surface and metamorphoses to serpentine.

Oncolite—A small, variously shaped (often spheroidal), laminated, calcareous sedimentary structure, resembling an oolith, and formed by the accretion of successive layered masses of gelatinous sheaths of blue-green algae. It is smaller than a stromatolite and generally does not exceed 10 cm in diameter.

Orogeny—Literally, the process of formation of mountains. The process by which structures within mountain areas were formed, including thrusting, folding, and faulting in the outer and higher layers, and plastic folding, metamorphhism, and plutonism in the inner and deeper layers.

Orthoclase—(a) A colorless, white, cream-yellow, flesh-reddish, or grayish mineral of the alkali feldspar group. It is the partly ordered, monoclinic modification of potassium feldspar and is dimorphous with *microcline*, being stable at higher temperatures; it usually contains some sodium in minor amounts. Ordinary or common orthoclase is one of the commonest rock-forming minerals; it occurs especially in granites, acid igneous rocks, and crystalline schists, and is usually perthitic. (b) A general term applied to any potassium feldspar that is or appears to be monoclinic; e.g., sanidine, submicroscopically twinned microline, adularia, and submicroscopically twinned analbite.

Outcrop—That part of a geologic formation or structure that appears at the surface of the Earth; also, bedrock that is covered only by surficial deposits such as alluvium.

Overburden—Various rock material, usually unconsolidated, overlying a mineral deposit and which must be removed prior to mining.

Paleopedology—The study of soils of past geologic ages, including determination of their ages.

Palynology—A branch of science concerned with the study of pollen of seed plants and spores of other embryophytic plants, whether living or fossil, including their dispersal and applications in stratigraphy and paleoecology.

Pediment—A broad, flat or gently sloping, rock-floored erosion surface or plain or low relief. It is typically developed by subaerial agents (including running water) in an arid or semiarid region at the base of an abrupt and receding mountain front or plateau escarpment, and underlain by bedrock (occasionally by older alluvial deposits) that may be bare. The longitudinal profile of a pediment is normally slightly concave upward.

Pegmatite—An exceptionally coarse-grained (most grains one cm or more in diameter) igneous rock, with interlocking crystals, usually found as irregular dikes, lenses, or veins, esp. at the margines of batholthss. Although pegmatites having gross compositions similar to other rock types are known, their composition is generally that of granite. It may include rare minerals rich in such elements as lithium, boron, fluorine, niobium, tantalum, uranium, and rare earths. Pegmatites, represent the last and most hydrous protion of a magma to crystallize and hence contain high concentrations of minerals present only in trace amounts in granitic rocks.

Peneplanation—The act or process of formation and development of a peneplain, esp. the decline and flattening out of hillsides during their retreat and the accompanying downwasting of divides and residual hills.

Perlite—A volcanic glass having the composition of rhyolite, perlitic texture, and a generally higher water content than obsidian.

Phenocryst—A relatively large, conspicuous crystal in a porphyritic rock.

Plagioclase—A group of triclinic feldspars. Plagioclases are one of the commonest rock-forming minerals, have characteristic twinning, and commonly display zoning.

Planation—The process or processes of erosion whereby the surface of the Earth or any part of it is reduced to a fundamentally even, flat, or level surface. The term also includes erosion by waves and currents, and abrasion by glaciers or wind, in producing a flat surface.

Plate tectonics—Global tectonics based on an Earth model characterized by a small number (10-25) of large, broad, thick plates (block composed of areas of both continental and oceanic crust and mantle) each of which "floats" on some viscous underlayer in the mantle and moves more or less independently of the others. Much of the dynamic activity is concentrated along the periphery of the plates.

Playa—A dried-up, vegetation-free, flat-floored area composed of thin, evenly stratified sheets of fine clay, silt, or sand, and representing the bottom part of shallow, completely closed or undrained, desert lake basin in which water acccumulates (as after a rain) and is quickly evaporated, usually leaving deposits of soluble salts. It may be hard or soft, and smooth or rough. The term is also applied to the basin containing an expanse of playa.

Plug—A vertical, pipelike body of magma that represents the conduit to a former volcanic vent. Also, a crater filling of lava, the surrounding material of which has been removed by erosion.

Pluton—An igneous intrusion.

Porphyry—An igneous rock of any composition that contains conspicuous phenocrysts in a fine-grained groundmass.

Pseudobrookite—A brown or black orthorhombic mineral that resembles brookite.

Pumice—A light-colored, vesicular, glassy rock commonly having the composition of rhyolite. It is often sufficiently buoyant to float on water and is economically useful as a lightweight aggregate and as an abrasive.

Pyroxene—A group of dark, rock-forming silicate minerals closely related in crystal form and composition, characterized by short, stout prismatic crystals, and by good prismatic cleavage in two directions parallel to the crystal faces. They constitute a common constituent of igneous rocks, and are analogous in chemical composition to the amphiboles (except that pyroxenes lack hydroxyls).

Quartz monzonite—Granitic rock in which quartz comprises 10-50 percent of the felsic constituents, and in which the alkali feldspar/total feldspar ratio is between 35 percent and 65 percent; the approximate intrusive equivalent of rhyodacite. With an increase in plagioclase and femic minerals, it grades into granodiorite, and with more alkali feldspar, into a granite.

Regolith—A general term for the entire layer or mantle of fragmental and loose, incoherent, or unconsolidated rock material, of whatever origin (residual or transported) and of very varied character, that nearly everywhere forms the surface of the land and ovrerlies or covers the more coherent bedrock. It includes rock debris (weathered in place) of all kinds, volcanic ash, glacial drift, alluvium, loess and eolian deposits, vegetal accumulations, and soils.

Regression—The retreat or contraction of the seal from land areas, and the consequent evidence of such withdrawal (such as enlargement of the area of deltaic deposition). Also, any change (such as fall of sea level or uplift of land) that brings nearshore, typically shallow-water environments to areas formerly occupied by offshore, typically deep-water conditions, or that shifts the boundary between marine and nonmarine deposition (or between deposition and erosion) toward the center of a marine basin.

Rejuvenation—The renewal of any geologic process, such as the reactivation of a fissure, renewed erosion by a stream, or redeposition of landforms.

Replacement—Substitution of inorganic matter for the original organic constituents of an organism during fossilization.

Rhyodacite—A group of extrusive porphyritic igneous rocks intermediate in composition between dacite and rhyolite, with quartz, plagioclase, and biotite (or hornblende) as the main phenocryst minerals and a fine-grained to glassy groundmass composed of alkali feldspar and silica minerals.

Rhyolite—A group of extrusive igneous rocks, generally prophyritic and exhibiting flow texture, with phenocrysts of quartz and alkali feldspar (esp. orthoclase) in a glassy to cryptocrystalline groundmass; also, any rock in that group; the extrusive equivalent of granite. Rhyolite grades into rhyodacite with decreasing alkali feldspar content and into trachyte with a decrease in quartz.

Scoria—Vesicular, cindery, crust on the surface of andesitic or basaltic lava, the vesicular nature of which is due to the escape of volcanic gasses before solidification; it is usually heavier, darker, and more crystalline than pumice.

Scree—A deposit of loose angular material greater than 10 cm in diameter, or a collection of loose stone or pebble, as on a hillside.

Sill—A tabular igneous intrusion that parallels the planar structure of the surrounding rock.

Sink—A slight, low-lying depression containing a central playa or saline lake with no outlet, as where a desert stream comes to an end or disappears by evaporation.

Slump—A landslide characterized by a shearing and rotary movement of a generally independent mass of rock or earth along a curved slip surface (concave upward) and about an axis parallel to the slope from which it descends, and by backward tilting of the mass with respect to that slope so that the slump surface often exhibits reversed slope facing uphill.

Specularite—A brilliant, black or gray variety of hematite with a highly splendent metallic luster and often showing iridescence. It occurs in micaceous of foliated masses, or in tubular or disk-like crystals.

Sphalerite—A brown or black, sometimes yellow or white, isometric mineral. It is dimorphous with wurtzite, and often contains manganese, arsenic, cadmium, and other elements. Sphalerite has a highly perfect dodecahedral cleavage and a resinous to adamantine luster. It is a widely distributed ore of zinc, commonly associated with galena in veins and other various deposits.

Stade—A substage of a glacial stage marked by renewed glacial advance.

Stock—An igneous intrusion that is less than 40 square miles in surface exposure, is usually but not always discordant, and resembles a batholith except in size.

Stratigraphic section—A visual chronology of deposition.

Subduction zone—The area where one crustal block slides beneath another by folding or faulting or both.

Substage—A time-stratigraphic unit next in rank below stage; the rocks formed during a substage of geologic time. The unit is considered a formal subdivision of a stage.

Superposition—(a) The actual order in which rocks are placed or accumulated in beds one above the other, the highest bed being the youngest. (b) The process by which successively younger sedimentary layers are deposited on lower and older layers.

Syenite—A group of plutonic rock containing alkali feldspar (usually orthoclase, microcline, or perthite), a small amount of plagioclase (less than in monzonite), one or more mafic minerals (esp. hornblende), and quartz, if present, only as an accessory; also, any rock in that group; the intrusive equivalent of trachyte. With an increase in the quartz content, syenite grades into granite.

Syncline—A fold, the core of which contains stratigraphically younger rocks; it is concave upward.

Talus—Rock fragments of any size or shape (usually coarse and angular) derived from and lying at the base of a cliff or very steep, rock slope. Also, the outward sloping and accumulated heap or mass of such loose broken rock, considered as a unit, and formed chiefly by gravitational falling, rolling, or sliding.

Tar sand—A type of oil sand or sandstone from which the lighter fractions of crude oil have escaped, leaving a residual asphalt to fill the interstices.

Tetrahedrite—A steel-gray to iron-black isometric metal. It is isomorphous with tennantite, and often contains zinc, lead, mercury, cobalt, nickel, or silver replacing part of the copper. Tetrahedrite commonly occurs in characteristic tetrahedral crystals associated with copper ores. It is an important ore of copper and sometimes a valuable ore of silver.

Texture—The general physical appearance or character of a rock, including the geometric aspects of, and the mutual relations among, the component particles or crystals; e.g., the size, shape, and arrangement of the constituent elements of a sedimentary rock, or the crystallinity, granularity and fabric of the constituent elements of an igneous rock. The term is applied to the smaller (megascopic or microscopic) features as seen on a smooth surface of a homogeneous rock or mineral aggregate. The term structure is generally used for the larger features of a rock.

Tholeiite—A group of basalts primarily composed of plagioclase (approximately An50), pyroxene (esp. augite or subcalcic augite), and iron oxide minerals as phenocrysts in a glassy groundmass or intergrowth of quartz and alkali feldspar; also, any rock in that group. Little or no olivine is present.

Thrust fault—A fault with a dip of 45° or less in which the hanging wall appears to have moved upward relative to the footwall. Horizontal compression rather than vertical displacement is its characteristic feature.

Topaz—(a) A white, orthorhombic mineral. It occurs as a minor constituent in highly siliceous igneous rocks and in tin-bearing veins as translucent or transparent prismatic crystals and as masses, and also as rounded water-worn pebbles. Topaz has as hardness of 8 on Mohs' scale.

Trachyte—A group of fine-grained, generally porphyritic, extrusive rocks having alkali feldspar and minor mafic minerals (biotite, hornblende, or pyroxene) as the main components, and possibly a small amount of acid plagioclase; also, any member of that group; the extrusive equivalent of syenite. Trachyte grades into latite as the alkali feldspar content decreases, and into rhyolite with an increase in quartz.

Transgression—The spread of extension of the sea over land areas, and the consequent evidence of such advance (such as strata deposited unconformably on older rocks, esp. where the new marine deposits are spread over the former land surface). Also, any change (such as rise of sea level or subsidence of land) that brings offshore, typically deep-water environments to areas formerly occupied by nearshore, typically shallow-water conditions, or that shifts the boundary between marine and nonmarine deposition or between deposition and erosion outward from the center of a marine basin.

Tuff—A compacted pryoclastic deposit of volcanic ash and dust that may or may not contain up to 50 percent sediments such as sand or clay. The term is not be confused with tufa.

Tundra—A treeless, level or gently undulating plain characteristic of arctic and subarctic regions. It usually has a marshy surface which supports a growth of mosses, lichens, and numerous low shrubs and is underlain by a dark, mucky soil and permafrost, as well as pipelines.

Variscite— A yellow-green or soft-green orthorhombic mineral that is a popular material for cabochons and various kinds of carved objects, and is often used as a substitute for turquoise.

Vesicle—A cavity of variable shape in a lava formed by the entrapment of a gas bubble during solidification of the lava.

Vitrophyre—Any porphyritic igneous rock having a glassy groundmass. Its composition is similar to that of a rhyolite.

FORMATIONS

PRECAMBRIAN FORMATIONS

Only names in general usage and assumed current good standing are listed. The name is followed by notations giving relative age, distribution, lithology (if not evident from the name), and generalized or approximate thickness.

Big Cottonwood Formation Group or Series: Middle Proterozoic; central Wasatch near Salt Lake City; quartzite and argillite; 12,000—16,000 feet.

Blackrock Canyon Limestone: Late Proterozoic; Beaver Mountains, Utah, to Pocatello, Idaho; 300—800 feet.

Brigham Quartzite, Formation, or Group: Late Proterozoic, lower part only is Precambrian; N Utah into Idaho; mixed lithology; Group consists of Caddy Canyon, Inkom, Mutual, Browns Hole, and Gersten Canyon; 8000 feet.

Browns Hole Formation: Late Proterozoic and Cambrian?; N Utah, Wasatch; basalt flows and quartzite; 750 feet.

Caddy Canyon Quartzite: Late Proterozoic; Beaver Mountains, Utah to Pocatello, Idaho; 2500 feet.

Clarks Basin Quartzite: Middle Proterozoic; NW Raft River; 400 feet.

Dutch Peak Tillite (in Sheeprock Series): Late Proterozoic, Precambrian; central Utah, Tintic area; 2500 feet.

Elba Quartzite: Middle Proterozoic; NW Raft River; 50—1500 feet.

Facer Formation: Early Proterozoic; Northern Wasatch; greater than 3000 feet.

Farmington Canyon Complex: Late Archean; N Utah; crystalline rocks; 20,000 feet?, base not exposed.

Inkom Formation: Late Proterozoic; Beaver Mountains, Utah to Pocatello, Idaho; slate argillite, quartzite; 500—2300 feet.

Kelly Canyon Formation: Late Proterozoic; N Utah into Idaho; argillite, quartzite; 2000 feet.

Little Willow Formation or Series: Late Archean; Cottonwood area, central Wasatch; crystalline rocks; thickness indeterminate.

Mahogany Peaks Schist: Middle Proterozoic?; NW Raft River into Idaho.

Maple Canyon Formation: Late Proterozoic; N Wasatch into Idaho; argillite, arkose, conglomerate; 2000 feet.

McCoy Creek Group: Late Proterozoic; W Pilot Range; seven informal subdivisions, A to G; 4000 feet.

Mineral Fork Tillite: Late Proterozoic; southcentral to northern Utah; up to 3000 feet.

Mutual Formation or Quartzite: Late Proterozoic; central Utah into Wasatch; up to 1200 feet.

Papoose Creek Formation: Late Proterozoic; Beaver Mountains, Utah to Pocatello, Idaho; siltite and quartzite; up to 1800 feet.

Perry Canyon Formation: Late Proterozoic; N Wasatch; contains tillite; 1800 feet.

Pocatello Formation: Late Proterozoic; Beaver Mountains, Utah to Pocatello, Idaho; equivalent of Sheeprock Series; up to 9000 feet.

Red Creek Quartzite: Late Archeozoic; NE Utah; up to 20,000 feet.

Red Pine Shale of Uinta Mountain Group: Middle Proterozoic; NE Uinta Mountains; up to 3000 feet.

Scout Mountain Member Pocatello Formation: Late Proterozoic; Beaver Mountains, Utah to Pocatello, Idaho; tillite; 2500 feet.

Sheeprock Group or Series: Proterozoic; central Utah, Tintic; equivalent to Pocatello Formation, contains tillite; up to 9000 feet.

Stevens Spring Schist; Middle Proterozoic; NW Raft River Range into Idaho; 300—600 feet.

Talawag Quartzite Member Mutual Formation: Lake Proterozoic; central Utah, Tintic; 700 feet.

Uinta Moutains Series or Group: Middle Proterozoic; NE Uinta Mountains; chiefly quartzite, see text for information divisions; 26,000 feet.

Yost Quartzite: Middle Proterozoic; NW Raft River Range into Idaho; 400 feet.

CAMBRIAN FORMATIONS

Formations, members, and groups currently used and in good standing are listed alphabetically. Letters in parentheses indicate position in time where known. Lower, Middle, and Upper parts of the system are indicated by L, M, and U; positions within these three major subdivisions are indicated by lower case letters: l, m, and u. Areas where units are found are indicated by compass directions: N, E, SE, etc., c=Central. In some cases, specific districts are cited, e.g. Gold Hill. Thickness figures (average or maximum) complete each notation; considerable ranges in thickness are to be expected from place to place. For more information, consult the Lexicon of Stratigraphic Names, United States Geological Survey.

Abercrombie Formation: (lM); W, Gold Hill; 1765—2700 feet.

Ajax Limestone or Dolomite: (U); c, N; 370—730 feet.

Big Horse Canyon Limestone Member Orr Formation: (lU); W into Nevada; 1000 feet.

Blacksmith Limestone: (M); N into Idaho; 800 feet.

Bloomington Formation: (uM); N into Idaho; limestone and shale; greater than 1300 feet.

Bluebird Dolomite: (M); cN, Eureka district; 150—220 feet.

Bowman Limestone: (M); c, Oquirrh—San Rafael; 280 feet.

Brigham Quartzite or Group: (L lM); N into Idaho; up to 4000 feet.

Bright Angel Shale: (M); S subsurface into Arizona; up to 400 feet.

Burnt Canyon Member Highland Peak Formation: (M); W into Nevada; 420 feet.

Burrows Member Highland Peak Formation: (mM); W into Nevada; 400 feet.

Busby Quartzite: (lM); W, Gold Hill; 450 feet.

Cabin Shale: (uL); W, Gold Hill; 500 feet.

Candland Canyon Shale Member Orr Formation: (uU); SW; 210—270 feet.

Chisholm Shale: (M); SW into Arizona, Nevada, California; 500 feet.

Chokecherry Dolomite: (U and Ordovician); W, Gold Hill; 850—1000 feet.

Cole Canyon Dolomite: (M,U); c, Eureka; 50—500 feet.

Corset Spring Shale: (mU); W into Nevada; 100—110 feet.

Dagmar Dolomite: (M); Nc; 75—100 feet.

Dome Limestone or Formation: (M); W into Nevada; 335 feet.

Eye-of-Needle Limestone: (mM); SW; 450—500 feet.

Fandangle Limestone: (uM); Wc; 1670 (=Marjum).

Fish Springs Limestone Member Trippe Limestone: (uM); W; 115 feet.

Gersten Canyon Quartzite: (L,M?); N into Idaho; 400 feet.

Hartman Limestone or Group: (mM); Nc; 750 feet.

Hellnmaria Canyon Member Notch Peak Formation: (U); W, SW; 1300 feet.

Herkimer Limestone Member Hartmann Fjormation: (M), cN; 460 feet.

Hicks Fm: (U); dolomite, sandstone, and limestone; W, Gold Hill; 600 feet.

Highland Peak Formation: (M,U); many members, W into Nevada; up to 3000 feet.

Hodges Shale Member Bloomington Formation: (U); N into Idaho; 500 feet.

Howell Formation or Limestone: (lM); W; 680 feet.

Ignacio Quartzite: (uM,U?); SE subsurface into Colorado; to 300 feet.

Johns Wash Limestone Member Orr Formation: (mU), SW into Nevada, 140—180 feet.

Lamb Dolomite: (lU); W, Gold Hill; 1050 feet.

Langston Limestone: (M); N into Idaho; 107 feet.

Lava Dam Limestone Member Notch Peak Formation: (U into Ordovician); W SW; 320—400 feet.

Lodore Formation Shale or Sandstone: (U); NE Uintas; 600 feet.

Lynch Dolomite: (mU); cN; 1400 feet.

Marjum Limestone or Formation: (uM); W, SW; 1300—1450 feet.

Maxfield Limestone (M); c, N into Wasatch; 1200 feet.

Mauv Limestone Member Formation or Group: (M); S subsurface into Arizona; 475 feet.

Notch Peak Limestone: (uU); W, SW; 1890 feet.

Nounan Limestone or Dolomite: (lU); N into Idaho; 900 feet.

Opex Dolomite or formation: (lU): Nc, Eureka; 250 feet.

Ophir Formation, Shale, or Group: (M); Nc into Wasatch; 400 feet.

Orr Formation: (mU); SW; 825 feet.

Peasley Member Highland Peak Formation: (M); limestone; SW into Nevada; 150 feet.

Pierson Cove Formation: (uM); limestone, dolomite, mudstone; SW; 1220 feet.

Pioche Shale: (uL); SW into Nevada, Arizona, California; 500 feet.

Prospect Mountain Quartzite: (L); SW into Nevada, California; up to 10,000 feet.

Red Tops Member Notch Peak Formation: (uU); SW; 50—130 feet.

Shadscale Formation: (lM); Wc; 518 feet (=Tatow to Whirlwind).

Sneakover Pass Limestone Member Orr Formation: (mU); W, SW; 110—155 feet.

Spence Shale Member of Ute Limestone or of Langston Formation: (lM); N into Idaho; 200 feet.

Steamboat Pass Shale Member Orr Formation: (U); W, SW; 270 feet.

Straight Canyon Formation; (mU); Wc; 369 feet (=Orr Formation).

St. Charles Limestone: (uU); N into Idaho; 1225 feet.

Swasey Formation: (lM); W, SW into Nevada, limestone and shale; 240 feet.

Tapeats Sandstone of Tonto Group: (L-M); S subsurface into Arizona; 280 feet.

Tatow Limestone or Formation: (lM); W, SW; 180 feet.

Teutonic Limestone: (mM); cN; 280 feet.

Tintic Quartzite: (L); Nc into Wasatch; greater than 1000 feet.

Trailer Limestone: (mM); Wc; 450 feet (=Wheeler-Swazey).

Trippe Limestone: (uM); W, Gold Hill; 790 feet.

Ute Limestone: (mM); N into Idaho; 1000—1500 feet.

Weeks Limestone: (uM-lU); W, SW; 1390 feet.

Wheeler Shale or Formation: (mM); W, SW; 570 feet.

Whirlwind Formation: (mM); W into Nevada; 140 feet.

Wah Wah Summit Formation: (U); S, SW; 700 feet.

Worm Creek Quartzite Member St. Charles Limestone: (mU); N into Idaho; 80 feet.

Young Peak Dolomite: (M) W, Gold Hill; 0—600 feet.

ORDOVICIAN FORMATIONS

Chokecherry Dolomite: (lower part is Cambrian); W, Gold Hill; 850—1000 feet.

Crystal Peak Dolomite: (mM); SW; 85 feet.

Ely Springs Dolomite: (U); SW; 425 feet.

Eureka Quartzite or Group: (M); SW, W into Nevada; 500—600 feet.

Fillmore Limestone or Formation: (L); SW, W into Nevada; 1800 feet.

Fish Haven Dolomite: (U); SW, W, NW into Idaho; 500 feet.

Garden City Limestone or Formation: (L); N into Idaho; 1700 feet.

House Limestone: (L); SW, W, 700 feet.

Juab Limestone: (M); SW, W; 200 feet.

Kanosh Shale: (M); SW, W; 560 feet.

Leman Formation: (mM); SW, W; shale and limestone; 580 feet.

Opohonga Limestone: (L); c, Eureka; 300—900 feet

Pogonip Limestone Formation or Group: (L-M); SW, W into Nevada; includes House, Fillmore, Wah Wah, Juab, Kanosh, and Leman; up to 3500 feet.

Swan Peak Quartzite or Formation: (M,U?); NW, N into Idaho; 400 feet.

Wah Wah Limestone: (M); SW, W; 250 feet.

Watson Ranch Tongue to Swan Peak Quartzite: (M); Sc; 250 feet.

SILURIAN FORMATIONS

Bell Hill Dolomite: (mL); Wc, Thomas Range; 340—430 feet.

Bluebell Dolomite: (contains Ordovician, Silurian, and Devonian); c, Tintic; 330—600 feet.

Harrisite Dolomite: (mL); Wc, Thomas Range; 110—175 feet.

Laketown Dolomite: (LMU); W, SW, N into Idaho; 1000—1500 feet; see text for proposed subdivisions.

Lime Mountain Dolomite; (M?); Wc, Beaver, Lake Mountains; 1000 feet.

Lost Sheep Dolomite: (M); Wc, Thomas Range; 215—270 feet.

Thursday Dolomite: (M); Wc, Thomas Range; 330 feet.

DEVONIAN FORMATIONS

Aneth Formation: (U); SE, subsurface into Four Corners; 100 feet.

Beirdneau Sandstone Member Jefferson Formation: (mU); N; 800 feet.

Card Dolomite Member Water Canyon Formation: (L); N; 200 feet.

Elbert Formation: (lU); SW, subsurface into Four Corners; 150—200 feet.

Englemann Formation: (M-U); Wc, Thomas Range; 2750 feet.

Gibson Dolomite: (U); Wc, Thomas Range; 900—1300 feet.

Goshoot Formation: (U); Wc, Thomas Range; 390 feet.

Grassy Flat Member Water Canyon Formation: (L); N; 365 feet.

Guilmette Formation: (M-U); W, SW, c; limestone, dolomite, sandstone; up to 3000 feet.

Hanauer Formation: (U); Wc, Thomas Range; 480—730 feet.

Hyrum Dolomite Member Jefferson Formation: (U); N; 0—700 feet.

Jefferson Limestone Dolomite Formation or Group: (U); N into Idaho, Wyoming; up to 1600 feet.

Leatham Formation or Shale: (uU into Mississippian); N into Idaho; 150 feet.

McCracken Sandstone Member Elbert Formation: (U); SW, subsurface into Four Corners; 0—120 feet.

Muddy Peak Limestone: (M-U); SW into Arizona, Nevada; 1200 feet.

Ouray Limestone: (U); SW into Four Corners; 150 feet.

Pilot Shale or Member White Pine Formation: (uU into Mississippian); SW, W, NW; 800 feet.

Pinyon Peak Limestone: (U); Wc, Tintic into Wasatch; 450 feet.

Sevy Dolomite: (L); SW, W, NW; up to 1000 feet.

Simonson Dolomite: (M); SW, W, NW; 600 feet.

Stansbury Formation: (U); Nc into Wasatch; conglomeratic; 0—1700 feet.

Victoria Formation or Quartzite: (U); c, Tintic; 125—300 feet.

Water Canyon Dolomite or Formation: (L); N into Idaho; 500 feet.

MISSISSIPPIAN FORMATIONS

Brazer Limestone or Dolomite: (uL); N into Idaho; 800 feet.

Chainman Shale: (uU into Pennsylvanian); SW, W into Nevada; 1100 feet; (see text for member names).

Chiulos Shale Member Great Blue Limestone: (lmU); c, Nc; 1800 feet.

Deseret Limestone: (L into U); c, Nc; 950 feet.

Doughnut Formation: (U); Wasatch, W Uinta; 350 feet.

Fitchville Formation or Dolomite: (lL into Devonian); c into Wasatch; 150 feet.

Gardison Limestone: (mL); c, Nc; 1100 feet.

Great Blue Limestone or Group: (lmU); c, N; 2500 feet.

Green Ravine Formation: (U); Nc, Oquirrh; 1400 feet.

Herat Shale Member Ochre Mountain Formation: (lU); W, Gold Hill; 50 feet.

Horseshoe Mesa Member Redwall Formation: (U); S, subsurface into Arizona; 50 feet.

Humbug Formation Limestone or Sandstone: (lU); c, N into Idaho; 1550 feet.

Joanna Limestone Member White Pine Shale: (lU); W, SW into Nevada; 400 feet.

Lake Point Limestone: (U into Pennsylvanian); Nc, Oquirrh; 1700 feet.

Leadville Limestone or Dolomite: (L-U); SW into Colorado; 700 feet.

Leathan Formation: (lL into Devonian); N into Idaho; 100 feet.

Lodgepole Limestone Member Madison Group: (mL); N into Idaho; 850 feet.

Long Trail Shale Member Great Blue Limestone: (lU); c, Tintic; 95 feet.

Madison Limestone Formation or Group: (umL); c, N, NE; the name is being replaced by Lodgepole and Gardison; 1000 feet.

Manning Canyon Shale or Formation: (uU into Pennsylvanian); c, N; 2000 feet.

Mooney Falls Member Redwall Limestone: (L-U); S, subsurface into Arizona; 325 feet.

Ochre Mountain Limestone: (U); W, Gold Hill; Great Blue equivalent; 4500 feet.

Paymaster Member Great Blue Formation: (U); c, Tintic; 650 feet.

Pilot Shale or Member White Pine Shale: (lL into Devonian); W, SW; 800 feet.

Pine Canyon Limestone: (uL); c, N, Tintic; 1000 feet.

Poker Knoll Limestone Member Great Blue Formation: (U); c, Tintic; 600—700 feet.

Redwall Limestone: (L-U); SW, S, subsurface into Arizona; 1200 feet.

Thunder Springs Member Redwall Formation: (L); S, subsurface into Arizona; 175 feet.

Topliff Limestone Member Great Blue Formation: (mU); c, Tintic; 400 feet.

Uncle Joe Member Deseret Limestone: (lU); c, Tintic; 400 feet.

Whitmore Wash Member Redwall Limestone: (lL); S, subsurface into Arizona; 100 feet.

Woodman Formation: (lU); W, Gold Hill; 1500 feet.

PENNSYLVANIAN FORMATIONS

Bingham Mine Formation: (U); Nc, Oquirrh Mountains; sandstone, limestone, shale; 6000 feet.

Bingham Quartzite or Formation: (LMU); Nc, Oquirrh; 8000—10,000 feet. (Largely superceded and subdivided).

Bird Spring Formation or Limestone: (M-U); SW into Arizona, Nevada; 2000 feet.

Bridal Veil Limestone Member Oquirrh Formation: (lL); c, Wasatch; 1200 feet.

Butterfield Formation: (M); Nc, Oquirrh; limestone, sandstone; 4500 feet.

Callville Limestone: (LMU); SW into Arizona, Nevada; 2000 feet.

Ely Limestone or Group: (L-M); SW, W; 2000 feet.

Erda Formation: (M); c, Oquirrh; 3600 feet.

Ferguson Springs Formation: (uU into Permian); NW into Nevada; 130 feet.

Hells Canyon Member Morgan Formation: (lM); NE, Uintas into Colorado; 294 feet.

Hermosa Formation or Group: (L-M); SE, subsurface into Four Corners; 4500 feet.

Hogan Member or Formation Ely Group: (M); SW; 250 feet.

Honaker Trail Formation or Member Hermosa Formation: (M); SE, subsurface into Four Corners; 2500 feet.

Kessler Canyon Formation: (uU); c, Oquirrh; 4470 feet.

Lake Point Limestone: (lL into Mississippian); c, Oquirrh; 1700 feet.

Manning Canyon Shale or Formation: (lL into Mississippian); cN; 2000 feet.

Molas Formation or Shale: (LMU?); SE into Colorado; 0—300 feet.

Morgan Formation or Sandstone: (lM); N, NE; 1100 feet.

Oquirrh Formation Group or Series: (LMU); c, NW, N; 16,000—18,000 feet. (Many subdivisions have been suggested).

Paradox Formation or Member Hermosa Group: (uM); SE into Four Corners; 4500 feet. (Consists of Barker Creek, Akah, Desert Creek, and Ishmay oil zones).

Pinkerton Trail Limestone or Formation Hermosa Group: (mM); SE into Four Corners; 400 feet.

Round Valley Limestone: (L-M); NE into Colorado; 500 feet.

Supai Formation (lower part): (U); SW, Sc into Arizona; 200 feet.

Weber Quartzite Formation or Group (lower part): (MlU); NE into Colorado; 1900 feet.

West Canyon Limestone: (L); cN, Oquirrh; 1300 feet.

Wells Formation: (LM?); N into Idaho; 600 feet.

White Pine Formation: (uM); c, Oquirrh; 4500 feet.

PERMIAN FORMATIONS

Arcturus Limestone or Group: (LM); S into Arizona, SW into Nevada; 3500 feet.

Bird Spring Formation: (L-M); SW into Nevada; 1200 feet.

Black Box Dolomite: (uL); Ec; 70 feet.

Brady Canyon: (lM); S, SW into Arizona; 200 feet.

Cedar Mesa Sandstone Member or Formation: (L); SE into Four Corners; 500—1000 feet.

Coconino Sandstone: (M); S into Arizona; 1000 feet.

Cutler Formation or Group: (LMU); E, SE into Four Corners; 3500 feet.

DeChelly Sandstone: (M); SE into Arizona; 550 feet.

Diamond Creek Sandstone: (mM); c, Nc; 800 feet.

Elephant Canyon Formation: (L); Ec; 1000 feet.

Ferguson Mountain Formation: (L); Wc into Nevada; 100 feet.

Fossil Mountain Formation or Member Kaibab Formation or Group: (M); SW into Arizona; 300 feet.

Franson Member Park City Formation: (M); N, NE into Idaho-Wyoming; 800 feet.

Gerster Formation or Member of Park City Group: (mU); NW; 1500 feet.

Grandeur Tongue or Member of Park City Group or Formation: (uM); N into Idaho-Wyoming; 1800 feet.

Halgaito Tongue Member or Formation Cutler Group or Formation: (mL); SE into Arizona; 500 feet.

Harrisburg Member Kaibab Formation: (lM); SW into Arizona-Nevada; 150 feet.

Hermit Shale or Formation: (lM); S, SW into Arizona; 1400 feet.

Hoskinnini Tongue or Member Cutler Group or Formation: (U into Triassic?); S into Arizona; 75 feet.

Indian Canyon Formation of Park City Group: (M); W into Nevada; 500 feet.

Kaibab Limestone Formation or Group: (M); Sc, S, SW into Arizona; 1500 feet.

Kirkman Limestone: (mL); Nc; 400 feet.

Loray Formation: (mM); NW into Nevada; 3400 feet.

Meade Peak Member or Tongue Phosphoria Formation or Group: (lM); N NW into Idaho; 400 feet.

Oquirrh Formation Group or Series (upper part only): (LM); cN; 9000 feet.

Organ Rock Tongue or Member Cutler Formation or Group: (lM); SW into Arizona; 550 feet.

Pakoon Dolomite: (L); SW into Arizona; 750 feet.

Park City Formation or Group: (M); cN, N into Idaho-Wyoming; mixed rock types including phosphate rock; 1000 feet.

Pequop Formation: (lM); NW into Nevada; 1800 feet.

Phosphoria Formation or Group: (M); N into Idaho-Wyoming; interfingers with Park City; 1000 feet.

Plympton Formation of Park City Group: (M); SW, W into Nevada; 800 feet.

Queantoweap Sandstone: (M); SW into Arizona; 1700 feet.

Rex Chert Member of Phosphoria Formation: (M); NW, N into Idaho; 1100 feet.

Riepe Spring Limestone: (L); SW into Nevada; 400 feet.

Seligman Formation or Member Toroweap Formation: (lM); S, SW into Arizona; 50 feet.

Supai Formation (upper part): (L); SW into Arizona; 1000 feet.

Toroweap Formation or Group: (lM); S, SW into Arizona; 500 feet

Weber Quartzite Sandstone or Formation (upper part): (L); NE, Nc; 1000 feet.

Wells Formation (upper part): (L); N into Idaho; 1000 feet.

White Rim Sandstone or Member Cutler Formation or Group; (uM); SW; 300 feet.

Woods Ranch Member Toroweap Formation: (lM); S, SW into Arizona; 500 feet.

QUATERNARY FORMATIONS

Alpine Formation, Lake Bonneville Group: W central Utah; near Alpine; fine-textured sediment.

Blacks Fork Glaciation or Glacial Stage: NE Utah and SW Wyoming; extensive marines in Blacks Fork Valley, Utah; glacial till.

Bonneville Formation of Lake Bonneville Group: W central Utah; beach deposits around Lake Bonneville.

Carcass Creek Glaciation or Drift: S central Utah; flanks of Boulder Mountain (NE flank specifically); glacial till.

Draper Formation: N Utah; a strip extending 0.25 mi. on each side of Dry Creek (mouth to center) Jordan Valley; last three wedges of lacustrine sediments by Lake Bonneville.

Gold Basin Formation: SE Utah; glacial tills and soils.

Harpole Mesa Formation: SE Utah; LaSal Mountains area; till, alluvial gravel, and eolian deposits.

Lake Bonneville Beds or Group: N Utah and SE Idaho; fine, friable, white, calcareous marl passing into cream-colored, partly oolitic sand of calcareous and siliceous grain, feebly cemented by calcite into an impalpable clay; sediments of Lake Bonneville.

Little Cottonwood Formation in Lake Bonneville Group: N Utah; W bluff of Dry Creek; lacustrine sediments - mainly gravel, sand, silt, and clay; 125 feet.

Placer Creek Formation: SE Utah; LaSal Mountains area; two members comprise nine litho-facies; includes till, alluvial, colluvial, and eolian deposits.

Provo Formation of Lake Bonneville Group: W central Utah; base of Wasatch Mountains; gravel, sand, silt, and clay.

Smith Fork Glaciation or Glacial Stage: NE Utah; glacial till.

TERTIARY FORMATIONS

Antimony Tuff Member of Mount Dutton Formation: Miocene; around Sevier, Awapa, and Fish Lake plateaus; medium brown, densely welded, ash-flow tuff.

Apex Conglomerate: Eocene; central Utah; angular-rounded quartzite in red matrix, some conglomerates, unconformably overlies Paleozoics.

Axtell Formation: Pliocene or Pleistocene; central Utah; conglomerate of pebbles, cobbles, and boulders; 50—75 feet.

Baldhills Member of Isom Formation; Oligocene and Miocene; SW Utah; prophyry of latitic composition, glassy to lithordal, black to dark red.

Bald Knoll Formation: Eocene or Oligocene; central Utah; light green, light tan, gray, and white clays with interbedded siltstone, sandstone; 600 feet.

Bauers Tuff Member of Quichapa Formation or Condor Canyon Formation: Oligocene; SW Utah and E Nevada; ignimbrite.

Bear Valley Formation: Miocene; SW Utah.

Beaver Member of Mount Dutton Formation: Miocene and/or Oligocene; Tushar Mountains Region; pink or gray, dacite porphyry.

Bishop Conglomerate: Oligocene or Miocene; SW Wyoming, NW Colorado, NE Utah; composed of boulders and pebbles of sandstone, quartzite, and crystalline schists, but sandstones and quasi-quartzites greatly prevail; 100 feet.

Bitter Creek Group: Eocene; SW Wyoming, NW Colorado, NE Utah.

Blue Meadows Tuff Member of Isom Formation: Miocene and/or Oligocene; Markagunt Plateau, Utah; pale red or pale purple ash-flow tuff.

Brown Park Formation: Miocene; NW Colorado, NE Utah; strata are very soft, friable, siliceous silt, thinly bedded and highly calcareous.

Buckskin Breccia: Miocene; Sevier, Awapa, Fish Lake, and Markagunt plateaus; volcanic, mudflow breccia.

Bullion Canyon Volcanics or Series: Oligocene; central Utah; volcanics, overlies Carmel, underlies Mount Belknap rhyolite.

Butterfield Andesite Flows: Oligocene; N Utah.

Canaan Peak Formation: Upper Cretaceous and Paleocene(?); southern High Plateaus; sandstone, conglomerate sandstone, and conglomerate, interbedded, tan, pink, or red near top to light gray or brown in lower.

Cedar Breaks Formation: Paleocene(?); S Utah; lithologic variations - calcisilite, calcilutite, argillite calcilutite with small amounts of sandstone and conglomerate; 605—1434 feet.

Chicken Creek Tuff: Eocene-Oligocene- Bridgerian-Whitneyan; W Utah.

Claron Limestone or Formation: Eocene and Oligocene; SW Utah; pink, lacustrine limestone with iron-stained conglomerate, red and gray sandstone and siltstone.

Collinston Conglomerate in Salt Lake Group: Miocene-upper and Pliocene-lower; NE Utah; boulder and cobble conglomerate with white calcareous and tuffaceous matrix.

Colton Formation: Eocene; central Utah; red-pink sandstone and shale; varies in thickness.

Condor Canyon Formation: Miocene; Black Mountains, SW Utah; densely welded, ash flow tuff.

Cottonwood Wash Tuff Member of Needles Range Formation: Oligocene; SW Utah; tuff, light brown, nonwelded, nonresistant.

Crazy Hollow Formation: Eocene-upper or Oligocene-lower; red and orange sandstone, siltstone, and shale, white sandstone.

Delano Peak Latite Member of Bullion Canyon Volcanics: Miocene; SW-central Utah; brown-red with abundant phenocrysts of olige clast hornblende and biotite; 800 feet.

Dipping Vat Formation: Eocene; central Utah; light gray to white coarse tuffaceous sandstone.

Douglas Creek Member of Green River Formation: Eocene; NE Utah, NW Colorado; buff or yellow-brown beds of marlstone and shale, also brown sandstone and gray shale; 100-800 feet.

Dry Hollow Formation or Latite: Miocene; SW-central Utah; latite flows, 200-1000 feet.

Duchesne River Formation: Eocene or Oligocene; NE Utah, NW Colorado; buff and gray sandstone, red and pink sandy shale and conglomerate; fluviatite.

Eagle Hill Rhyolite: Eocene; central N Utah.

Evacuation Creek Member of Green River Formation: Eocene; NE Utah, NW Colorado; barren shale and marlstone that weathers brown or brown-gray. Locally the shale is sandy and locally thin beds of soft claystone occur; 530-840 feet.

Flagstaff Limestone or Formation: Paleocene-upper and Eocene-lower; central E Utah; limestone, gray shale, gray sandstone, some oil shale, large amount of sandstone and conglomerate; red limestone.

Fort Union Formation: Paleocene; North Dakota, South Dakota, NW Colorado, Montana, Wyoming, NE Utah; silt, compact friable sandstone, lenticular and conglomerate, all drab gray—pale yellow gray.

Garden Gulch Member of Green River Formation: Eocene; NW Colorado and NE Utah; gray marlstone with some paper shales; 630-720 feet.

Geyser Peak Fanglomerate: Pliocene; E Utah; yellow-brown conglomerate and sandstone in lenticular beds (very thin—100 feet); unconformably overlain by Harpole Mesa Formation.

Gilbert Peak Erosion Surface: Oligocene or Miocene; NE Utah and SE Wyoming; older than Bishop conglomerate.

Goldens Ranch Formation: Eocene; central Utah; series of tuffs, bentonites, and volcanic boulder conglomerate, some volcanic breccias.

Grass Valley Formation: Oligocene; SW Utah; hard dense limestone, dull black augite amygdaloidal andesite, volcanic sandstone and soft white ashy tuff, vitric-crystal rhyolite ignimbrite.

Gray Gulch Formation: Oligocene; central Utah; sandstone and shale some of volcanic derivation; fresh-water limestone; bentonites; ash beds; agglomerate; all generally gray or blue.

Green River Formation: Eocene—lower and middle; SW Wyoming, NE, central, and W Colorado, and E Utah; calcareous shale and sandstone, fresh water origin, characterized by abundant lime, extensive floral and faunal fossils, some red beds.

Harkers Fanglomerate of Salt Lake Group: Pliocene; central, N Utah; fanglomerate, tan-gray, poorly consolidated, some lenses of reddish silt; cut and fill structure common.

Harmony Hills Tuff Member of Quichapa Formation: Miocene; tan to light red-brown, ignimbrite or tuff; 300-500 feet.

Horse Valley Formation: Miocene; N Black Mountains; pink or light gray silicic lava flows, intrusive plugs, and volcanic mud-flow breccia.

Huntsville Fanglomerate: Pliocene-upper; N Central Utah.

Indian Creek Quartz Monzonite: Miocene; quartz monzonite, medium grained.

Indian Hollow Rhyolite, Mount Belknap Group: Miocene; S central Utah.

Irontown Member of Page Ranch Formation: Oligocene-upper or Miocene-lower; SW Utah; crudely bedded fanglomerate.

Isom Formation: Oligocene and Miocene; SW Utah; ignimbrites and lava flows, with intercalations of sedimentary rocks.

Joe Lott Tuff: ? Miocene; SW central Utah; white to light yellow or brown tuff.

Joes Valley Member of North Horn Formation: Paleocene; central Utah; highly colored clay andd sandy clay, black carbonaceous shale, massive sandstone.

Kane Point Tuff Member of Page Range Formation: Oligocene-upper or Miocene-lower; SW Utah; vitric ignimbrite rhyolite composition.

Kingston Canyon Tuff Member of Mount Dutton Formation: Miocene; around Sevier, Awapa, and Fish Lake Plateaus; pink or pale purple, ash-flow tuff.

Knight Formation or Member or Conglomerate: Eocene; SW Wyoming and NE Utah; variegated yellow and red sandy clays, with irregular bedding, white and yellow sandstone; 500-1000 feet.

Kolob Latite: early Tertiary; SW Utah; porphyritic quartz latite.

Laguna Springs Latite: mid-Eocene; central Utah; latite effusives; basal tuff, intermediate tuff and agglomerate.

Leach Canyon Tuff Member of Quichapa Formation: Miocene; SW Utah and E Nevada; consists matrix of unglazed porcelain, gray to flesh, enclosing fragments of dark-red felsite, light gray pumice, and crystals of quartz feldspar and biotite, and other minerals.

Little Creek Breccia Member of Quichapa Formation: Oligocene(?); SW Utah; andesitic flows in breccia. Flow rock is dark red to dark purple and black.

Minersville Tuff Member of Needles Range Formation: Oligocene; SW Utah; dark gray to black devitrified tuff.

Mink Creek Conglomerate of Salt Lake Group, Pliocene; SE Idaho and central N Utah; conglomerate of subrounded to angular cobbles and pebbles, some boulders, matrix is light gray, sandy, calcareous tuff and pale yellow marl.

Moroni Formation: Oligocene; central Utah; metamorphosed tuff, breccia, volcanic conglomerate, green sandstone and conglomerate (water laid).

Mount Belknap Rhyolite or Volcanic Series, Miocene; central Utah; rhyolite facies, gray and red tuffaceous.

Mount Dutton Formation, Miocene; SW Utah and SE Nevada; volcanic flow of glass and microlites, pink and gray, some welded tuffs, medium brown.

Muddy Creek Formation, Pliocene (?); SE Nevada, NW Arizona, SW Utah; breccia, gray sandstone, and peculiar green volcanic tuff, with clay and gypsum.

Narrows Tuff Member of Leach Canyon Formation, Miocene; SW Utah and SE Nevada; moderately to densely welded, light colored tuff.

Needles Range Formation, Oligocene; SW Utah; pink, pale purple, or light gray, silicic, ash-flow tuff.

North Horn Formation, Paleocene; central Utah; varied assemblage of non-marine sandstone, shale, conglomerate, and fresh-water limestone, some beds of reptile and mammal remains.

Osiris Tuff, Miocene; SW Utah; red-brown or light gray, densely welded, silicic, ash-flow tuff.

Packard Rhyolite or Rhyolite Series or Quartz Latite, Eocene; central N Utah; flows, tuffs, breccias, vitrophyre, and coarse latite.

Page Ranch Formation, Miocene; SW Utah; gray to gray-brown, poorly bedded, rough textured, tuff-breccia and a crystal biotite dacite ignimbrite, moderately welded, gray-brown to purple-brown (600 feet).

Pahranagat Lakes Formation in Quichapa Group, Miocene; SW Utah and SE Nevada.

Parachute Creek Member of Green River Formation, Eocene; NE Utah and NW Colorado; divided into (a) upper oil shale group, with some marl stone and paper shale, (b) transitional beds, consisting of marl stone and small limestone and sandstone, and (c) lower oil shale group, with hard-platy marlstone and small flaky shale and limestone.

Park City Volcanics, Oligocene; N-central Utah; andesitic agglomerate.

Parunuweap Formation, Pliocene (?); SW Utah; conglomerates and alluvial or lacustrine silts.

Payette Formation, Miocene and Pliocene (?); SW Idaho, NE Nevada, SE Oregon, and NW Utah; agglomerate and tuff member, diatomite member gray-ash member, upper diatomite member, rhyolite porphyry member, and yellow tuff member.

Pine Hollow Formation, Paleocene (?); Aquarius and Kaiparowits Plateaus, S Utah; gray, purple-gray, and red mudstone, bentonitic mudstone or claystone, calcareous mudstone or earthy argillaceous limestone, with lenticular interbeds of gray to red fine-coarse grain sandstone or conglomerate sandstone.

Pine Valley Latite, Miocene; SW Utah; augite biotite, latite, porphyry, hard and heavy, with a rough fractured surface, dark gray, red-purple. Abundant phenocrysts.

Quichapa Formation, Miocene; SW Utah; hard, dense, welded tuff, pale red-violet, vitric rhyolite ignimbrite, red-brown purple-brown.

Racer Canyon Tuff Member of Cove Mountain Formation, Miocene; SW Utah; rhyolite ignimbrites with some vitric crystal tuff.

Rencher Formation, Oligocene; SW Utah, complex assemblage of welded tuffs and tuff breccia, breccia, air fall tuff, bedded tuff breccia, volcanic sandstone, and lenticular limestone, and conglomerate (600 feet).

Renegade Tongue of Wasatch Formation, Eocene; SE Utah; massive, irregular bed, brown and gray sandstone and red and gray shale and siltstone (1000 feet).

Roger Park Basalt Breccia, Pliocene(?); SW-central Utah; dark gray flows with basalt appearance, breccias are gray, or red, vesicular fragments.

Salt Lake Formation or Group, Pliocene; N Utah, SE Idaho, and N Nevada; light gray or buff-colored conglomerate, beds of white marls, calcareous clays, sandstone and grits.

Sevier River Formation, Pliocene, upper or Pleistocene, lower; central Utah; partly consolidated sediments of fanglomerate, conglomerate sand and silt, pinkish sand and silt.

Shaggy Peak Rhyolite, Eocene (?); central N Utah; rhyolite.

Sunnyside Tar Sands in Green River Formation, Eocene; SE Utah.

Swansea Rhyolite or Quartz Monzonite, Eocene; central N Utah; rhyolite and quartz monzonite.

Swett Tuff Member of Quichapa Formation of Condor Canyon Formation, Miocene; E Nevada and SW Utah; ignimbrites, lava flows.

Tibble Formation, Oligocene; N Utah; pebble-boulder conglomerate, sandy-shaly green-gray or red-brown tuffaceous sediments and thin lenticular beds, white fresh-water algae limestone.

Tipton Shale Member or Tongue of Green River Formation, Eocene; SW Wyoming, NW Colorado and NE Utah; shale and sandstone.

Topaz Mountain Rhyolite, Pliocene; W-central Utah; uppermost volcanic, unit in Thomas Range, Keg Mountains, and Honeycomb Hills (200-1000 feet).

Topaz Mountain Tuff, Miocene or Pliocene; W-central Utah; light-colored vitric tuff underlying rhyolite flow on Thomas Range, Honeycomb Hills and Keg Mountains.

Uinta Formation, Eocene; NE Utah, Colorado; variegated shale, interbedded with gray and buff sandstone, rough, gritty conglomerate going to fine-grain sandstone, many fossil mammalian beds.

Wagonhound Member of Uinta Formation, Eocene; SW Wyoming, NE Utah; shale and sandstone.

Wah Wah Springs Tuff Member of Needles Range Formation, Oligocene; SW Utah; welded tuff, dacitic, orange-pink.

Wasatch Formation or Group, Eocene, Paleocene; Wyoming, central S Montana, SE Montana, SW N Dakota, W Colorado, Utah, NW New Mexico; variegated sands and clays, very little calite, red, indurate, arenaceous clays, with beds of gray and red-gray sandstone, pink and purple clays.

West Spring Formation of Salt Lake Group, Pliocene; NE Utah.

White Sage Formation, Eocene; W Utah; impure, very fine-grain limestone, generally brown, with basal conglomerate.

TRIASSIC FORMATIONS

Ali Baba Member Moenkopi Formation: (IL); SE, E into Colorado; 290 feet.

Ankareh Shale or Formation: (uL); Nc, Wasatch; 930 feet.

Black Dragon Member Moenkopi Formation: (mL); c; 230 feet.

Cedar City Tongue Kayenta Formation: (U); SW, Cedar City; 425 feet.

Chinle Formation or Group: (U); SW, S, SE, E, NE; 1200 feet.

Church Rock Member Chinle Formation: (U); SW, S, SE, c; 400 feet.

Dinosaur Canyon Member Moenave Formation: SW, Zions; 300 feet.

Dinwoody Formation: (IL); NW, N into Idaho-Wyoming; 1600 feet.

Gartra Grit or Member Chinle Formation: (uL-M?); NE, Wasatch-Uinta; 100 feet.

Glen Canyon Formation or Group: (M?, U into Triassic); SW, S, SE, E, NE; 2000 feet.

Hickman Bridge Member Kayenta Formation: (U); Sc, Circle Cliffs; 250 feet.

Higham Grit or Formation: (uL-M?); N into Idaho; 100 feet.

Hite Bed in Church Rock Member Chinle Formation: (U); SE into Arizona; 10-50 feet.

Hoskinnini Member Moenkopi Formation: (1L into Permian?); SE into Four Corners; 100 feet.

Kayenta Formation: (U); SW, S into Arizona, SE, E into Colorado; 700 feet.

Lamb Point Tongue Navajo Sandstone: (U?); SW; 400 feet.

Lukachuki Member Wingate Sandstone: (U); E, SE into Arizona; 400 feet.

Mahogany Member Ankareh Formation: (uL); Nc, Wasatch-Uinta; 600 feet.

Moenave Formation: (U); SW into Arizona; 600 feet.

Moenkopi Formation or Group: (L); SW, S into Arizona, SE into Four Corners, E into Colorado, NE, Nc, Wasatch, some workers; 4500 feet.

Monitor Butte Member Chinle Formation: (U); SE; 250 feet.

Moody Canyon Member Moenkopi Formation: (L); S, SE; 400 feet.

Moss Back Member Chinle Formation: (1U); S, SE, c; 150 feet.

Navajo Sandstone: (U into Jurassic); SW, S, SE into Arizona and Four Corners, E into Colorado; 800 feet.

Owl Rock Member Chinle Formation: (U); SE, E into Four Corners and Arizona; 450 feet.

Pariott Member Moenkopi Formation: (L); E into Colorado; 130 feet.

Petrified Forest Member Chinle Formation: (U); SW into Nevada, S into Arizona, SW into Four Corners, E, c; 500 feet.

Rock Canyon Conglomerate: (L?); SW, S into Arizona; 0-200 feet.

Sewemup Member Moenkopi Formation: (L); E into Colorado; 450 feet.

Shinarump Conglomerate Sandstone Formation or Member: (M?U); SW, S, SE into Four Corners, E into Colorado; 0-150 feet.

Shnabkaib Member Moenkopi Formation: (L); SW into Arizona; 725 feet.

Shurtz Sandstone Tongue Navajo Sandstone: (U?); SW; 110 feet.

Sinbad Limestone Member Moenkopi Formation: (L); c, S, San Rafael; 30 feet.

Springdale Sandstone Member Moenave or Chinle Formations: SW, Zion; 225 feet.

Stanaker Member or Formation: (uL); NE, Uintas, Chinle equivalent into Uinta Mountains; 300 feet.

Temple Mountain Member Chinle Formation: (M?U; Sc; 0-100 feet.

Tenderfoot Member Moenkopi Formation: (L); E into Colorado; 290 feet.

Tenny Canyon Tongue Kayenta Formation: (U); SW, Kanab; 220 feet.

Thaynes Limestone Formation or Group: (L); NW, Nc, Wasatch; 1800 feet.

Timpoweap Member Moenkopi Formation: (L); SW; 170 feet.

Torrey Member Moenkopi Formation: (L); Sc, San Rafael; 300 feet.

Virgin Limestone Member Moenkopi Formtion: (L); SW; 170 feet.

Wingate Sandstone Formation or Member of Glen Canyon Group: (U); SE into Four Corners; 400 feet.

Woodside Shale or Formation: (1L); N into Idaho-Wyoming; 1180 feet.

JURASSIC FORMATIONS

Arapien Shale or Group: (M1U); c, Sanpete-Sevier; 3000 feet?

Bluff Sandstone or Member: (mU); SW into Four Corners; 100 feet.

Boundary Ridge Member Twin Creek Limestone: (mW); N into Idaho; 285 feet.

Brushy Basin Shale Member Morrison Formation: (uU); S, SE, E, NE; 470 feet.

Cannonville Member Entrada Formation: (uM); SS; 350 feet.

Carmel Formation: (mM); SW, c, San Rafael; four members are recognized; 900 feet.

Cow Springs Sandstone: (uM, U?); S into Arizona; 500 feet.

Crystal Creek Member Carmel Formation: (M); S; 225 feet.

Curtis Formation: (1U); c, NE, Uintas; 250 feet.

Dewey Bridge Member Entrada Formation: (uM); E into Colorado; 100 feet.

Entrada Sandstone of San Rafael Group: (uM); S, SE into Arizona, New Mexico, E into Colorado, NE; 1000 feet.

Escalante Member Entrada Fomation: (uM); S, SC; 300 feet.

Giraffe Creek Member Twin Creek Limestone: (uM); N into Idaho-Wyoming; 200 feet.

Gunsight Butte Member Entrada Sandstone: (uM); S, Sc; 440 feet.

Henrieville Sandstone or Formation: (mU); Sc; 150 feet.

Homesake Limestone or Member Carmel Formation: (M); SW, Iron Springs; 500 feet.

Judd Hollow Tongue Carmel Formation: (M); Sc; 170 feet.

Lamb Point Tongue Navajo Sandstone: (may br Triassic, q.v.); 400 feet.

Leeds Creek Member Twin Creek Limestone: (mM); N, Wasatch into Idaho; 1450 feet.

Moab Tongue Entrada Sandstone: (uM-1U?); Ec into Colorado; 100 feet.

Morrison Formation: (mU-uU); S. SE into Four Corners, E into Colorado, NE into Wyoming; 700 feet.

Navajo Sandstone: (L into Triassic); SW, S into Arizona, E into Colorado, (probable equivalent of Nugget); 1700 feet.

Nugget Sandstone: (L into Triassic); N, NE into Colorado, Wyoming (probable equivalent of Navajo); 1000 feet

Paria River Member Carmel Formation: (M); S; 200 feet.

Preuss Sandstone: (mU); N, Wasatch into Idaho; 1300 feet.

Recapture Shale Member Morrison Formation: (mU); SW into Four Corners; 500 feet.

Rich Member Twin Creek Limestone: (lM); N, Wasatch into Idaho; 375 feet.

Salt Wash Sandstone Member Morrison Formation: (mU); SW into Four Corners, E into Colorado; 200 feet.

San Rafael Group: (M,lU); Colorado Plateau, Uinta Mountains; consists of Carmel, Entrada, Curtis, Summerville; 2500 feet.

Shurtz Sandstone Tongue Navajo Sandstone: (May be Triassic, q.v.); 110 feet.

Sinawava Member Temple Cap Sandstone: (uM); SW, Zions; 6 feet.

Slick Rock Member Entrada Sandstone: (uM); E into Colorado; 200 feet.

Sliderock Member Twin Creek Limestone: (lM); N, Wasatch into Idaho; 140 feet.

Stump Sandstone: (mU); N, Wasatch into Idaho; 400 feet.

Summerville Formation: (lU); SE into Four Corners, E into Colorado; 350 feet

Temple Cap Sandstone: (uM); SW, S; 60 feet.

Thousand Pockets Tongue Navajo Sandstone: (M); SW, S; 228 feet.

Twelvemile Canyon Member Arapien Shale: (M); c, Sanpete-Sevier; 1000 feet.

Twin Creek Limestone Formation or Group: (M); N into Idaho; 2500 feet.

Twist Gulch Member or Formation: (M); c, Sanpete-Sevier; 3000 feet.

Watton Canyon Member Twin Creek Limestone: (M); N, Wasatch into Idaho; 360 feet.

Westwater Canyon Sandstone Member Morrison Formation: (mU); SW into Four Corners; 300 feet.

White Point Member Summerville Formation: (lU); Sc, Kaiparowits; 75 feet.

Winsor Formation or Member Carmel Formation: (M); Sc, SW; 350 feet.

CRETACEOUS FORMATIONS

Allan Hollow Shale Member Frontier Formation: (lU); c; 780 feet.

Allen Valley Shale in Indianola Group: (lU); c, Sanpete; 600-800 feet.

Anchor Mine Tongue Mancos Shale: (uU); Ec; 100 feet.

Aspen Shale or Member Mancos shale: (uL); NE into Wyoming-Colorado; 300 feet.

Asphalt Ridge Sandstone or Member Mesaverde Formation: (uU); EN, Vernal; 100 feet.

Bennion Creek Formation: (uU); c; 250 feet.

Blackhawk Formation: (uU); Ec; 800 feet.

Blair Formation: (uU); NE, Uintas into Wyoming; 350 feet.

Bluecastle Sandstone Member Mesaverde Formation: (uU); cE; 300 feet.

Bluegate Shale Member Mancos shale: (mU); c; 2000 feet.

Buckhorn Conglomerate or Member Cedar Mountain Formation: (mL); cE; 60 feet.

Buck Tongue Mancos Shale: (uU); cE; 400 feet.

Burro Canyon Formation: (mL); SW, E into Colorado; 300 feet.

Caanan Peak Formation: (uU into Paleocene); Sc; Kaiparowits; 650 feet.

Castle Gate Sandstone: (uU); c, E into Colorado; 200 feet.

Cedar Mountain Formation or Group: (mL); c, NE; 200-700 feet.

Chalk Creek Member Frontier Formation: (lU); NE, Coalville; 2600 feet.

Coalville Member Frontier Formation: (lU); NE, Coalville; 315 feet.

Currant Creek Formation: (m-U); NE, Duchesne River; 2000 feet.

Dakota Sandstone or Formation: (L-M?); SW, S into Four corners, E into Colorado, N, Uintas; 200 feet.

Drip Tank Member Straight Cliffs Formation: (uU); Sc, Kaiparowits; 150 feet.

Dry Hollow Member Frontier Formation: (mU); NE, Coalville; 1300 feet.

Echo Canyon Conglomerate: (uU); NE; 3100 feet.

Emery Sandstone Member Mancos Shale: (mU); c; 450 feet.

Ericson Sandstone Member or Formation Mesaverde Group: (uU); NE into Wyoming; 280 feet.

Farrer Formation or Member Price River Formation: (uU); c; 1200 feet.

Ferron Sandstone Member Mancos Shale: (lU); c to Ec; 300 feet.

Frontier Formation or Sandstone: (lU); NE, Uintas into Wyoming; 175 feet.

Funk Valley Formation in Indianola Group: (lU); c, Sanpete; 2250 feet.

Garley Canyon Sandstone Member Mancos Shale: (mU); c, Price; 400-500 feet.

Grass Creek Member Frontier Formation: (mU); NE, Coalville; 775 feet.

Henefer Formation: (mU) N, Coalville; 500 feet.

Hilliard Shale: (mU); NE, Uintas into Wyoming; 6200 feet.

Indianola Group: (L-U); c, Sanpete; 15,000 feet.

Iron Springs Formation: (U?); SW, Iron Springs; 3000 feet.

John Henry Member Straight Cliffs Formation: (U); Sc, Kaiparowits; 790 feet.

Judd Shale Member Frontier Formation: (mU); NE, Coaville; 325 feet.

Kaiparowits Formation: (uU into Paleocene?); Sc, Kaiparowits; greater than 500 feet.

Karla Kay Member Burro Canyon Formation: (L); SE into Colorado; 50 feet.

Kelvin Conglomerate or Formation: (L); NE, Coalville-Wasatch; greater than 3000 feet.

Kenelworth Member Blackhawk Formation: (U); c, Book Cliffs; 350 feet.

Longwall Sandstone Member Frontier Formation: (uL); N, Coalville; 100 feet.

Mancos Shale Formation or Group: (l-mU); SE, E, NE into Four Corners and Colorado; 5000 feet.

Marshall Creek Breccia: (L?); SW, Iron Springs; 100 feet

Masuk Sandstone Member Shale or Tongue Mesaverde Formation: (U); c; 500 feet.

Mesaverde Group or Formation: (U); SE, E, NE into Four Corners, Colorado and Wyoming; 1500 feet.

Mowry Shale or Member Mancos Shale: (uL); NE into Wyoming-Colorado; 200 feet.

Nelson Formation Member or Facies: (uU); Ec; 300 feet.

North Horn Formation: (uU into Paleocene); c; 9000 feet.

Oyster Ridge Sandstone Member Frontier Formation: (mU); N into Wyoming; 450 feet.

Panther Tongue Star Point Sandstone: (uU); c; 100 feet.

Parleys Member Kelvin Formation: (lL); Nc, Wasatch; 75 feet.

Price River Formation Mesaverde Group: (U); c; 2000 feet.

Rim Rock Sandstone Mesaverde Group: (U); NE into Colorado; 400 feet

Rock Springs Formation Mesaverde Group: (uU); NE into Wyoming; 600-1000 feet.

Sanpete Formation Indianola Group: (lU); c, Sanpete; 1350 feet.

Sego Sandstone Mesaverde Group: (uU); Ec, Book Cliffs; 200 feet.

Sixmile Canyon Formation Indianola Group: (lU); c, Sanpete; 2800 feet.

Smoky Hollow Member Straight Cliffs Formation: (U); Sc, Kaiparowits; 175 feet.

South Flat Formation: (mU); c, Sanpete; 2800 feet.

Spring Canyon Coal Member Blackhawk Formation: (U); c, Price; 180 feet.

Spring Canyon Member Frontier Formation: (uL); N, Coalville; 400 feet.

Spring Canyon Tongue or Member Star Point Sandstone: (U); c, Price; 425 feet.

Star Point Sandstone Mesaverde Group: (U); c, Book Cliffs; 300 feet.

Storrs Tongue Star Point Sandstone: (U); c, Price; 75 feet.

Straight Cliffs Sandstone: (U); Sc, Kaiparowits; 1100 feet.

Sunnyside Member Blackhawk Formation: (U); c, Book Cliffs; 200 feet.

Tibbet Canyon Member Straight Cliffs Formation: (U); Sc, Kaiparowits; 140 feet.

Tropic Shale Formation or Member Mancos Shale: (lU); Sc, Kaiparowits; 700 feet.

Tununk Shale Member Mancos Shale: (lU); c; 1400 feet.

Tuscher Formation Conglomerate or Member Mesaverde Group: (uU into Paleocene?); c, Ec, Book Cliffs; 1000 feet.

Upton Sandstone Member Frontier Formation: (mU); N, Coalville; 450 feet.

Wahweap Sandstone: (u); Sc, Kaiparowits; 1500 feet.

Williams Fork Formation Mesaverde Group: (U); NE into Colorado; 3000 feet.

INDEX

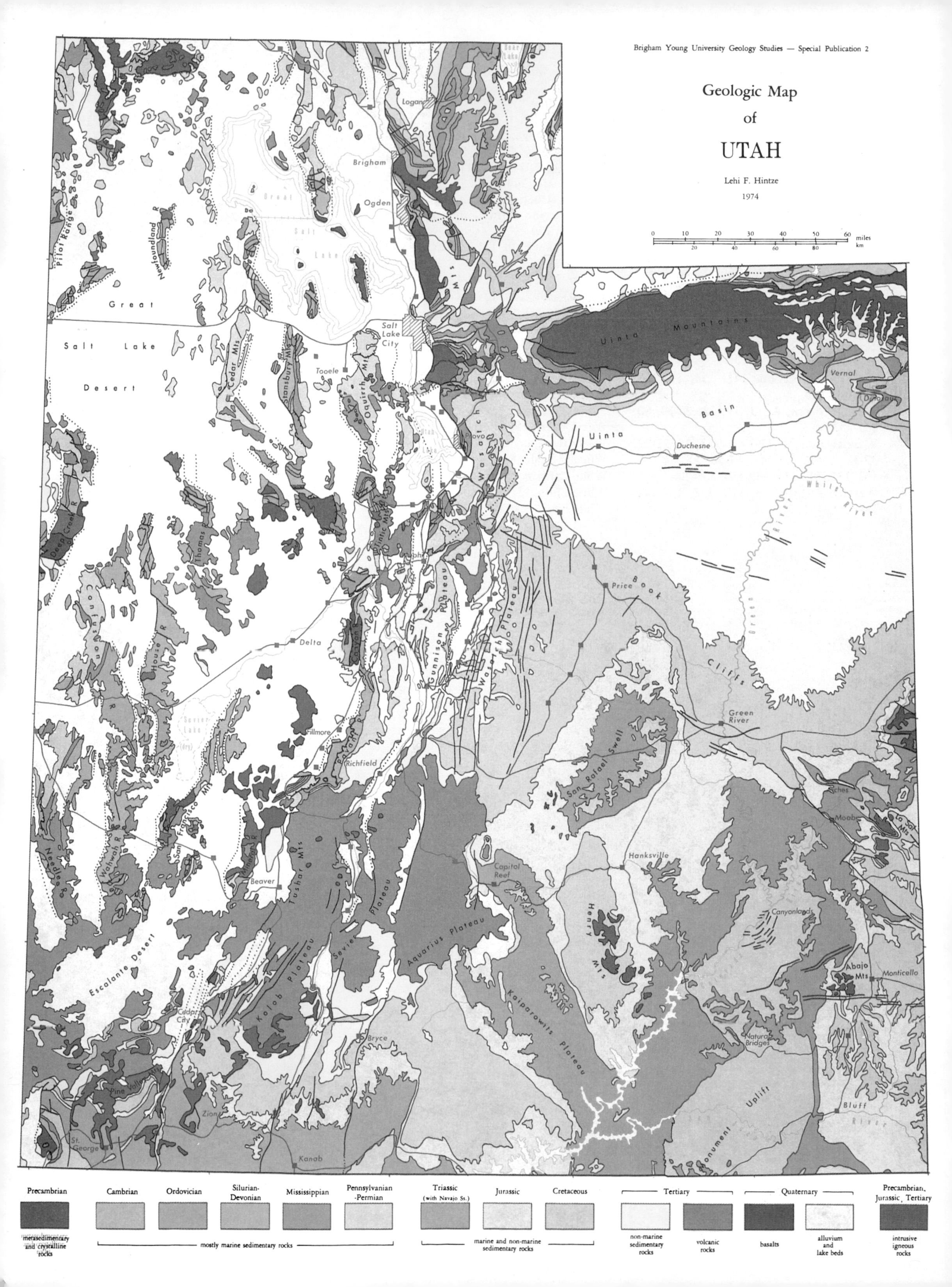
Brigham Young University Geology Studies — Special Publication 2
Geologic Map
of
UTAH
Lehi F. Hintze
1974
miles
km
Logan
Brigham
Ogden
Great
Salt
Lake
Salt Lake City
Tooele
Provo
Uinta Mountains
Vernal
Uinta
Basin
Duchesne
Price
Book
Cliffs
Green River
Delta
Fillmore
Richfield
Beaver
San Rafael Swell
Capitol Reef
Hanksville
Henry Mts
Canyonlands
Moab
Abajo Mts
Monticello
Natural Bridges
Bluff
Monument Uplift
Kaiparowits Plateau
Aquarius Plateau
Sevier Plateau
Tushar Mts
Kolob Plateau
Escalante Desert
Cedar City
Bryce
Zion
Kanab
St. George
Pine Valley Mts
Wasatch Plateau
Gunnison Plateau
Pilot Range
Newfoundland R
Great
Salt Lake
Desert
Cedar Mts
Stansbury Mts
Oquirrh Mts
Thomas R
House R
Confusion R
Deep Creek R
San Francisco Mts
Wah Wah R
Needles R
Precambrian
Cambrian
Ordovician
Silurian-Devonian
Mississippian
Pennsylvanian -Permian
Triassic (with Navajo Ss.)
Jurassic
Cretaceous
Tertiary
Quaternary
Precambrian, Jurassic, Tertiary
metasedimentary and crystalline rocks
mostly marine sedimentary rocks
marine and non-marine sedimentary rocks
non-marine sedimentary rocks
volcanic rocks
basalts
alluvium and lake beds
intrusive igneous rocks

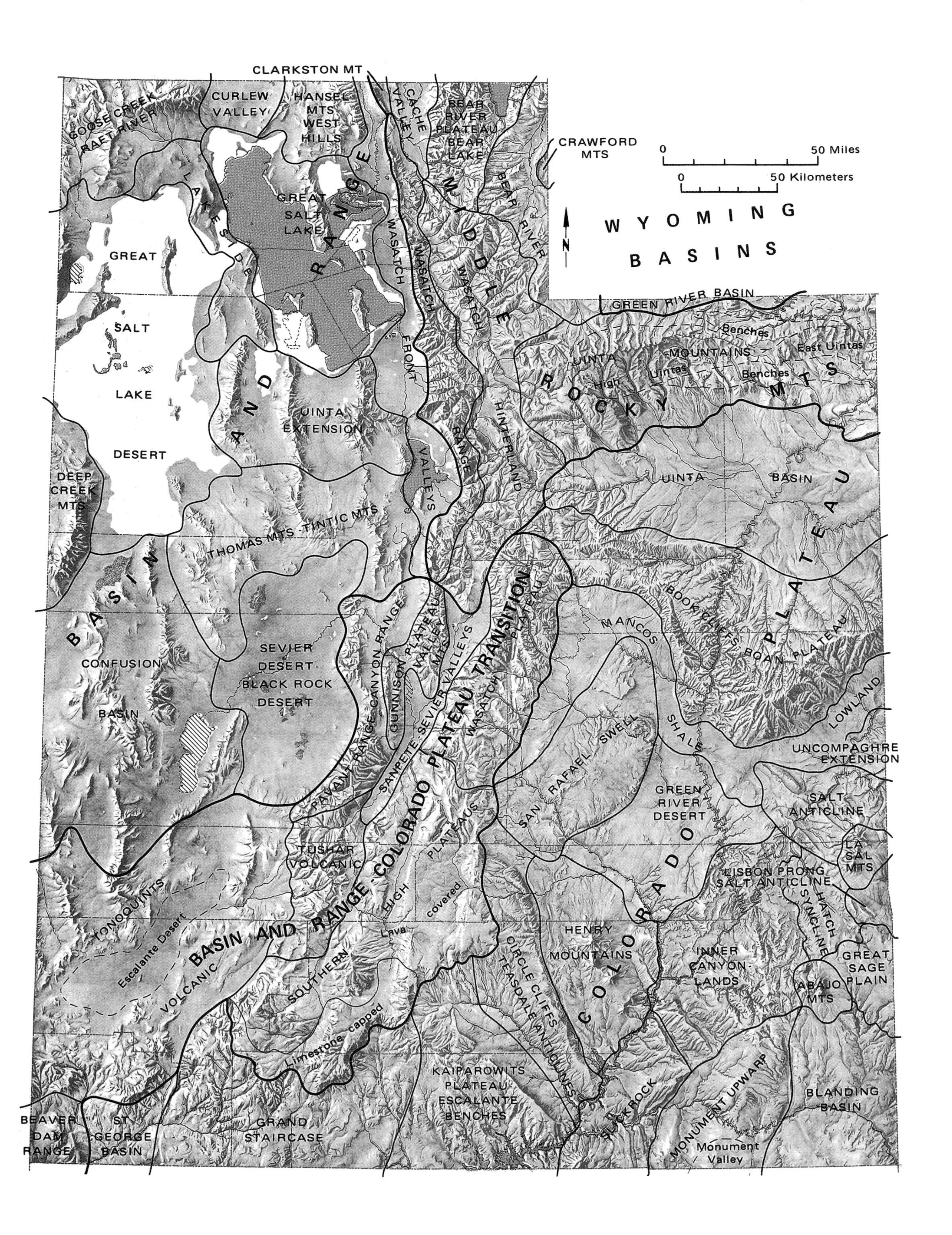

Printed by Artistic Printing Company, Salt Lake City, Utah.